MINERAL PROCESSING

VOLUME II

Concentration, Flotation, Separation
Backup processes

BY

GUSZTÁV TARJÁN

AKADÉMIAI KIADÓ, BUDAPEST 1986

Translated by

B. BALKAY

ISBN 963 05 2243 8 (Vols I—II.)
ISBN 963 05 4143 2 (Vol. II.)

Printed in Hungary

CONTENTS

1. CONCENTRATION BY GRAVITY

1.1. FUNDAMENTALS

Processes of concentration by gravity include
— dense-medium ("heavy-media") separation,
— jigging,
— tabling and
— sluicing.

In each of these processes, the position and progress of a particle in the concentrating device is determined conjointly by particle weight, buoyancy and fluid drag. Buoyancy plays an essential role. Provided the density of the medium is the same, the bouyant force acting upon a particle is also the same regardless of whether the medium is a pure liquid or a pulp or slimes whose average gravity, solids and fluid taken together, equals that of the pure liquid, irrespective of whether the solids in the medium are fine, as in dense-medium separation, or coarse, as in a jig. In the dry (pneumatic) dressing of particulate aggregates, a similar phenomenon can be produced if the density of particles suspended in air can be kept high enough. A measure of separability of particles of s.g. (specific gravity) δ_1 and δ_2, respectively, is the hindered-settling ratio,

$$r' = \frac{(\delta_1 - \gamma')}{(\delta_2 - \gamma')} \; ;$$

it is the greater, the higher the density γ' of the medium (more precisely, of the medium immediately surrounding the particles).

In a process of concentration by gravity, then, it is an advantage if the "bed", the aggregate of solid particles contained in the medium, is rather dense. It should not, on the other hand, be too dense, as in that case the particles lose their mobility in the bed and do not get rearranged. The output of a concentrator varies as the mobility of the particles; mobility in turn varies inversely as bed density. In a medium whose density is below a certain threshold, however, the particles cease to interact, and the system falls apart: particle behaviour, governed by the dynamic action of the medium in motion, results in classification by settling velocity or a similar process.

A certain compromise, then, must be reached between increasing bed density to improve the sharpness of separation and decreasing it to provide mobility and improved output performance. In order to satisfy both conditions simultaneously, certain processes of concentration by gravity (jigging and tabling above all, but certain sluices and classifiers as well) resort to some method of varying bed density by means of rhythmic pulsation. The goal to be attained in each instance is to achieve a rearrangement of particles among them in a medium whose density is as great as is still consistent with sufficient mobility.

The process of stratification by gravity in a bed can be derived most simply from the law of free energy. If the particles of different s.g. making up a system are free to move about relative to one another, then the system will spontaneously proceed from a disordered state into a state of stratification by gravity, provided the free energy of the stratified state is less. Free energy, which in this case is potential energy in the gravity field, will be reduced if the particles of greater s.g. move into the deeper layers.

If the respective volumetric solids contents of particles of s.g. δ_1 and δ_2 are σ_1 and σ_2 in one volume element and σ_1' and σ_2' in the adjoining one, and the interstices of the particles are filled with a medium of density γ, then the first volume element will strive to move downward relative to the second (yielding to Earth gravity), provided its weight is greater:

$$\sigma_1\delta_1 + \sigma_2\delta_2 + (1 - \sigma_1 - \sigma_2)\gamma > \sigma_1'\delta_1 + \sigma_2'\delta_2 + (1 - \sigma_1' - \sigma_2')\gamma,$$

whence

$$\frac{\delta_1 - \gamma}{\delta_2 - \gamma} > \frac{\sigma_2' - \sigma_2}{\sigma_1 - \sigma_1'},$$

or, if $\gamma = 1$,

$$\frac{\delta_1 - 1}{\delta_2 - 1} > \frac{\sigma_2' - \sigma_2}{\sigma_1 - \sigma_2'}.$$

Example 1. A powder ("medium solid") of what s.g. is to be used in the preparation of a dense medium if the volumetric solids content of the suspension is to be $\sigma = 40\%$, with 30% contributed by the powder and 10% by the pulp of the light mineral to be separated?

Let one particle of the light mineral, expected to float up in the dense medium, have s.g. δ_2 and volume σ_2'. The volume of pulp made up of solids of the same s.g., δ_2, contained in an equal volume of suspension, is

$$\sigma_2 = 0.1\sigma_2'$$

and the volume of the dense medium of s.g. δ_1 is

$$\sigma_1 = 0.3\sigma_2'.$$

Hence,

$$\frac{\sigma_2' - 0.1\sigma_2'}{0.3\sigma_2' - 0} = \frac{0.9}{0.3} = 3.0.$$

The limiting gravity of the powder that can be used in the preparation of a dense medium of density $\gamma' \geq \delta_2$ is provided by

$$\frac{\delta_1 - 1}{\delta_2 - 1} > 3.0 .$$

For example, if $\delta_2 = 2.65$, then

$$\delta_1 > 3.0 \cdot 1.65 + 1 = 5.95 ;$$

or, if $\delta_2 = 1.6$, then

$$\delta_1 > 3.0 \cdot 0.6 + 1 = 2.8 .$$

Example 2. In a jig bed, a large lump of coal of s.g. $\delta_2 = 1.4$ is surrounded by particles of waste and middling whose average s.g. is $\delta_1 = 1.8$. What volumetric solids content σ is needed for the lump of coal to float up out of the aggregate of waste and middling?

Here,

$$\sigma_2 = 0, \ \sigma_1' = 0, \ \sigma_1 = \sigma\sigma_2' ,$$

that is,

$$\frac{\sigma_2' - 0}{\sigma\sigma_2' - 0} = \frac{1}{\sigma} \leq \left(\frac{\delta_1 - \gamma}{\delta_2 - \gamma} \right) = \frac{0.8}{0.4} = 2.0 ,$$

and the required volumetric solids content is found to be

$$\sigma \geq 0.5 .$$

In a general way, the condition for a rock particle (liberated or intergrown) of s.g. δ_2 to float up out of an aggregate of particles of average s.g. δ_1 is

$$\delta_2 \leq \gamma' = \sigma\delta_1 + (1 - \sigma)\gamma ,$$

whence

$$\frac{1}{\sigma} > r = \frac{\delta_1 - \gamma}{\delta_2 - \gamma} ,$$

or

$$\sigma \geq \frac{1}{r} .$$

For example, in a pneumatic jig, where $\gamma \simeq 0$, a lump of coal of s.g. 1.4 will float up out of a bed of particles of average s.g. 2.0 if

$$\sigma \geq \frac{1}{r} = \frac{(1.4 - 0)}{(2.0 - 0)} = 0.70 .$$

In a less dense bed of average s.g. δ_1, $\sigma < 1/r$, even a lump of rock of s.g. δ_2 will strive downward, together with every other particle in the layer. Since, however, the force driving the heavier particles downward is greater per unit volume than the force driving the lighter ones, stratification by gravity will come about even though density is less than the $\sigma = 1/r$ corresponding to a state of "floating". At any density $\sigma > 1/r$, a lighter particle will float up from among the heavier ones, regardless of its size. In that case, the phenomenon which arises in dense-medium separation will act upon the coarse particles also, provided the mobility of the particles relative to one another is not arrested by bed friction. (Bed friction is a function of the state of dispersion of the bed, of its "relevant density" γ' and of the size of the particle moving relative to it.)

Finer particles have less mass and, hence, also less potential energy: their separation by gravity is accordingly more sluggish than that of the coarser particles. The concentration by gravity of finer-grained feeds accordingly takes more time: concentrator output decreases as grain size decreases. The stratification by gravity of a fine-grained feed may be accelerated by applying a centrifugal force much exceeding the force of gravity. This is the idea underlying the dense-medium hydrocyclone in which the difference in potential energy between the random and the stratified aggregate is increased by the same factor by which the centrifugal force exceeds the force of gravity; hence, the aggregate is quicker to attain a stable stratified final state (Tarján 1955).

A phenomenon that hinders the stratification by gravity of finer particles as compared with coarser ones and prevents it from becoming complete is the buoyant (gravity-reducing) effect of the water film adhering to the particles' surfaces and moving together with them. On a coarse grain, the volume of this film is negligible against the bulk of the particle; however, if the particle is small enough, the joint (average) s.g. of particle + fluid film will be significantly less than the s.g. of the particle alone. If the volume of the particle is V, its surface area is F, and the thickness of the fluid film adhering to it is y, then the s.g. Δ of the system made up of a solid particle of s.g. δ and a fluid of density γ is implied by the relationship

$$V\delta + Fy\gamma = (V + Fy)\Delta$$

to be

$$\Delta = \frac{\delta\left(V + \dfrac{Fy\gamma}{\delta}\right)}{V + Fy} = \frac{\delta + \dfrac{Fy\gamma}{V}}{1 + \dfrac{Fy}{V}}. \tag{A}$$

For spherical or cubic particles,

$$\frac{F}{V} = \frac{6}{x};$$

for any other particles,

$$\frac{F}{V} = \frac{6k}{x}, \tag{B}$$

10

where $k > 1$ and x is particle size. The substitution of (B) and $y = mx$ brings (A) to the final form

$$\Delta = \frac{\delta + \dfrac{6\gamma k}{m}}{1 + \dfrac{6k}{m}} \cdot$$

The values of Δ at $\gamma = 1$ are stated in Table 1.1 for various values of $m = y/x$, for mineral aggregates of s.g. δ and of cubic or spherical grain shape ($k = 1$).

Table 1.1. Effective s.g. Δ of particles of different s.g. δ at different values of m

$m = y/x$	$\delta =$ 1.50	2.70	5.00	7.50
0.01	1.47	2.60	4.78	7.14
0.025	1.43	2.48	4.48	6.65
0.05	1.38	2.31	4.08	6.00
0.10	1.31	2.06	3.31	5.06

Of the processes of concentration by gravity, dense-medium concentration employs a suspensoid medium resembling a quicksand, whereas jigs, sluices and shaking tables employ more or less closed beds and simple tables employ pure water as the medium of separation.

1.2. PHENOMENA IN CONCENTRATION BY GRAVITY

A solid particle moving in a medium having the consistency of a bed (a compact aggregate) or of a quicksand overcomes the resistance of the medium to its motion (or to its penetration of the medium) by a force proportional to its weight measured in the medium which, in turn, is proportional to its mass, provided the density of the medium is uniform. Hence, of two particles of equal s.g., it is the larger one that will progress faster in a given medium; of two particles of equal weight, that one will progress faster whose s.g. differs more from the density of the medium. This "rule" can be affected by particle shape: flattish particles tend to move slower relative to the medium.

At the bottom of a near-horizontal flow of water, small, flat, heavy particles tend to face a higher resistance to rolling and sliding along the bottom than large, equiaxed, light ones. Of a number of particles of the same shape, the lighter ones are more easily picked up and taken into suspension by the flow than the heavier ones, and the flatter ones more readily than those of any other shape.

In the more or less closed bed of a shaking table or sluice, the separation by gravity of the par-interstitial particles (the particle size class slightly larger than the average interstice size) is less sharp than that of either the finer or the coarser sizes. In an unexpanded bed (i.e. one not loosened up by any vertical motion of the medium), or in a bed where the surge of the medium is not strong enough to move the finer particles upward in the interstices of the coarser ones, a long-range feed (one of a broad particle-size spectrum) will be classified in reverse as compared to classification by joint settling: the fine heavy grains will get to the bottom, the large light ones to the top, and all the others will come to lie in between. (Such reverse sorting is an advantage in screening because the small grains, on attaining the bottom of the layer, are readily presented to and passed by the screen apertures.)

1.3. CONCENTRATION BY HEAVY LIQUIDS AND DENSE MEDIA

1.3.1. Fundamentals. A solid immersed in a fluid will, regardless of its size and shape, float up to and on the fluid surface if it is lighter than the fluid and sink down in it if it is heavier.

(A) This simple principle is resorted to in gravity analysis by heavy liquids, used e.g. to separate a coal feed into gravity classes with a view to predicting its washing behaviour (plotting its washing curve). The heavy liquid employed is a mixture of organic liquids or the aqueous solution of some inorganic salt. Separation using such true liquids is sometimes encountered also in commercial-scale plants. A heavy liquid made relatively cheaply out of the brines of the Dead Sea is tetrabromoethane (TBE, acetylene tetrabromide, $C_2H_2Br_4$, of gravity 2.96): in future, it may find more widespread use. The DuPont process employs for a separating medium a mixture of pentachlorethane (C_2HCl_5, gravity 1.70) and other halogenated hydrocarbons (ethylene bromide, $C_2H_4Br_2$, gravity 2.2; trichlorethylene, C_2HCl_3, gravity 1.46, etc.) and of petroleum: the Lessing and the Bertrand processes employ aqueous solutions of calcium chloride, $CaCl_2$. The great advantage of true liquids is their low viscosity as compared to dense media; this permits them to be used also in the separation of fine-grained feeds (Baniel und Mitzmager 1960).

The DuPont process uses surfactants to ensure that the solid particles are wetted by water rather than by the heavy organic liquid. This reduces the heavy-liquid loss. In coal separation, e.g., the surfactants used are starch acetate, tannic acid, etc. In the Lessing process, the products are washed with water in order to recover the calcium chloride solution adhering to them; excess water from the dilute solution is evaporated by heating sufficiently to restore the original density. In the Bertrand process, the feed is passed through a series of circulating liquid streams whose density increases from that of pure water to that of the separating liquid; the products are made to move in the opposite direction, from the heavier towards the lighter liquids. This permits to avoid the costly evaporation but the flowsheet of the concentrating circuit is rendered overly complicated thereby.

(B) The use of a "suspensoid" separating medium (an aqueous suspension of a finely ground solid or solids) is cheaper and hence more widespread than the use of true liquids. These heavy suspensions (dense media) behave as anomalous (non-Newtonian, most often pseudo-plastic) fluids whose structural viscosity η' or apparent viscosity (consistency) η and flow resistance τ_1 are not independent of the velocity gradient dv/dl. If the concentration of the fine solids of s.g. δ (the volumetric solids content σ) is increased, then the density γ' of the medium varies as the concentration:

$$\gamma' = \sigma\delta + (1 - \sigma)\gamma,$$

whereas its viscosities η' and η and its flow resistance τ_1 rise linearly at first but much more abruptly later on, and its velocity of clarification v' decreases as those increase. For homodisperse suspensions (where all the suspended particles are of the same size),

$$v' = v_0(1 - \sigma)^n,$$

where the power n is a function of the Reynolds number $Re = v_0 x/v$ (cf. also Vol. 1, Section 2.10.3):

$Re =$	$\longrightarrow$ 0.2 $\longleftarrow$	$\longrightarrow$ 1 $\longleftarrow$	$\longrightarrow$ 500 $\longleftarrow$
$n =$	4.7	4.4/Re$^{0.03}$	4.45/Re$^{0.1}$	2.4

A measure of suspension stability is

$$S = \frac{(v_0 - v')}{v_0} = 1 - (1 - \sigma)^n.$$

Another measure of stability may be defined e.g. as the solids remaining suspended in the top one-third, one-half or two-thirds of a settling column after settling for a given space of time (say, one minute), referred to the original, pre-settling solids content or suspension density.

The variables v', γ', η' (η and τ_1) are plotted against σ in Fig. 1.1 (the ordinate scale is different for each variable). The curve of η' (structural viscosity) is near-linear and gently sloping below σ_1 but very steep above σ_2. The volumetric solids content σ of the dense media used in industrial concentrators lies as a rule between these two "critical" values. Above σ_2, viscosity increases fast; below σ_1, on the other hand, the velocity of clarification v' is too great; hence, keeping the dense-medium suspension stable would require strong agitation (or an upward flow faster than v'), which would already impair the sharpness

13

of separation. Given the usual particle size range of the medium solid (minus-65 to minus-100 mesh), the lower critical point, σ_1, tends to lie between 0.2 and 0.3; the upper critical point, σ_2, between 0.4 and 0.45. For a given value of σ, a dense-medium suspension made up of finer and/or less rounded (more angular) particles has a greater viscosity and smaller velocity of clarification, and vice

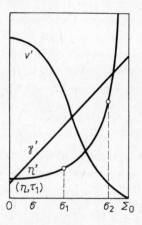

Fig. 1.1. Variation of v', γ', η', η and τ_1 vs. σ in dense media

versa. Suspension viscosity may be reduced by the addition of suitable chemicals (e.g. sodium hexametaphosphate, potassium silicate, etc.) (Klassen et al. 1964). The presence (or deliberate addition) of small doses of clay (3 to 6 per cent) decreases v' substantially, at the price of a simultaneous increase in η'.

Figure 1.2 shows the behaviour of a dense medium of s.g. $\delta = 5.76$, made up half-and-half of magnetite and ferrosilicon of granulometry

| $s_F =$ | 95 | 77 | 48 | 41 weight % |
| at | 208 | 104 | 52 | 44 μm. |

The medium contains clay minerals in different concentrations. Part A of the figure is a plot of apparent viscosity η (full lines) and of stability

$$S = \frac{(v_0 - v')}{v_0}$$

(dashed lines) vs. suspension density γ'. The parameters written beside the curves state weight percent contaminant. Volumetric solids content σ is 29.4 at $\gamma' = 2.4$ and 34.6 at $\gamma' = 2.65$.

Part B of the figure shows plots of η, S, γ' and $\varDelta\gamma'$ vs. weight percent clay mineral content. $\varDelta\gamma'$, a measure of segregation of the dense medium, is the difference between the densities of the suspensions respectively accompanying the sink and the float fraction, as obtained in a cone separator. The viscosity and stability of the suspension increase, its tendency to segregate decreases as the clay mineral content increases.

The apparent viscosity η and the structural viscosity η' of this particular suspension were found to be related by

$$\eta' \cong 6.25(\eta - 3.5)$$

or

$$\eta \cong 0.16\eta' + 3.5 .$$

In other terms, there is the correspondence

apparent viscosity, $\eta =$ 6.7 13.1 19.5 cP;
structural viscosity, $\eta' =$ 20 60 100 cP.

Instead of clay minerals, the stability of a dense medium can be increased also by adding to it small amounts (less than 0.1%) of a suitable polymer (e.g. Kelsan XC). True, η' (and hence, η and τ_1) also increase as a result, but this effect is slight enough not to impair a fair separation performance.

In this manner, the dense-medium suspension can be made more coarse-grained, with a lower viscosity yet a satisfactory stability; the regeneration of such suspensions involves a smaller loss of medium solid (Valentik 1972).

The lower limiting grain size of feeds amenable to treatment in a dense-medium separator is determined by viscosity above all because, in a dense, high-viscosity medium, fine mineral particles are incapable of independent motion: they get "locked in" (keyed to) the suspension, moving together with

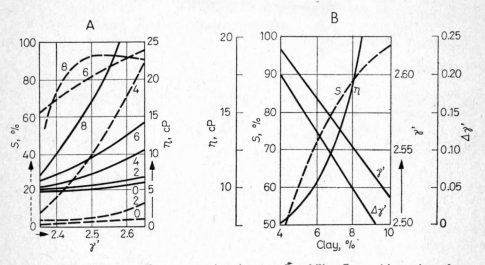

Fig. 1.2. A — variation of apparent viscosity η and stability S vs. γ' in a given dense medium. The parameter is percent clay contaminant. B — η, S, γ' and segregation, $\varDelta\gamma'$, vs. percent contaminant

15

it, so that no separation by gravity can take place. Integrated into the suspension, they cause an avalanche surge of its σ, η and η' if the medium is not reconditioned (Ziemer 1958). The small particles — especially if their s.g. is close to that of the dense medium — move (rise or subside) very sluggishly: therefore, even weak vertical currents and a slight vorticity can prevent their separation by gravity. The velocity of separation is the velocity of vertical displacement relative to the medium. It determines the output of the process per unit volume of dense medium or per unit of separating-tank bottom area and, hence, in the final reckoning, also the cost of the process.

If a static dense-medium concentrator is to be fed a finer feed, one with a lower limiting grain size of 1 to 2 mm, then increasing unit output (decreasing unit cost) requires a lower-viscosity dense medium: the volumetric solids content of the process medium should be as low as possible; the medium-solid particles should be rounded and comparatively coarse, and the continuous reconditioning of the medium should encompass a major part of total volume. The coarser the lower particle size limit of the feed (e.g. 6, 10, 15 mm ...), the more viscous may the process medium be, the less stringent are the requirements as to reconditioning (the higher the permissible percentage of alien contaminants), and the less objection there is to operating in the vicinity of the upper critical limit σ_2. The maximum operating value of σ can be 0.36 to 0.38 for a fine-ground medium solid and 0.45 to 0.48 for a coarser-ground one.

In a dense-medium hydrocyclone, where the forces acting are much stronger than the gravity force and the velocity gradients and shears produced by cyclone action reduce the structural viscosity of the dense medium, separation can be extended down to a lower particle size limit of 0.3 to 0.5 mm.

Suspension density γ' and volumetric solids content σ are related to the average s.g. of the solids by

$$\Delta = (\gamma' - 1 + \sigma)/\sigma.$$

Corresponding values of σ, γ' and Δ are presented in Table 1.2.

The relationships

$$\gamma' = \sigma\Delta + (1 - \sigma)$$

Table 1.2. Average solids s.g. Δ in a dense medium as a function of σ and γ'

$\sigma =$	0.30	0.35	0.40	0.45	0.50
$\gamma' = 1.5$	2.66	2.42	2.25	2.11	2.00
2.0	4.33	3.86	3.50	3.22	3.00
2.7	6.67	5.86	5.25	4.78	4.40
3.2	8.33	7.30	6.50	5.90	5.40

and

$$\Delta = (1 - p)\delta + p\delta'$$

reveal that a suspension of volumetric solids content σ and density γ' contains, in addition to a medium solid of s.g. δ and volumetric solids content $\sigma(1 - p)$, also contaminating solids of average s.g. δ', volumetric solids content

$$\sigma p = \frac{\sigma(\delta - 1) - (\gamma' - 1)}{\delta - \delta'}$$

and weight percent concentration

$$s = \frac{100p\delta'}{p\delta' + (1 - p)\delta}.$$

Figure 1.3 is a set of plots of p and s vs. σ, for $\delta = 7.5$, 5.0 and 2.65, and for $\gamma' = 3.2$, 2.7, 2.0 and 1.5. The percentage abundance p (or s) of a contaminant of average s.g. $\delta' = \gamma'$ in a dense medium of density γ' containing $\sigma\%$ solids prepared with a medium solid of s.g. δ can be read directly off these curves.

The separation of the two most common gangue minerals of ore dressing (quartz, gravity 2.65; limestone, gravity 2.71) requires a process suspension

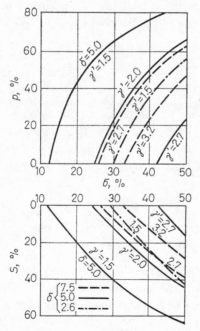

Fig. 1.3. Variation of volume percent $p\%$ (top) and weight percent $s = 100p\delta'/[p\delta' + (1 - p)\delta]$ percent (bottom) of a mud contaminant of s.g. $\delta' (= \gamma')$ vs. σ, with δ and γ' as parameters

of density $\gamma' = 2.7$ to 2.8. For example, a suspension of density $\gamma' = 2.7$, made with $1 - p = 90.4\%$ medium solid of s.g. $\delta = 5.0$, contains $p = 9.6\%$ contaminant of average s.g. $(= \gamma') = \delta' = 2.7$. If the contaminant content of the process suspension is higher, no suspension of density $\gamma' = 2.7$ can be prepared using solids of s.g. $\delta = 5.0$ even at $\sigma = 0.45$. In ore dressing, then, no medium solid of s.g. ~ 5.0 or less can be used.

For example, the relationship

$$p = \frac{(\delta - 1) - \dfrac{(\gamma' - 1)}{\sigma}}{\delta - \delta'},$$

applied to a suspension of density $\gamma' = 2.7$ prepared using galena of s.g. $\delta = 7.5$ at $\delta' = \gamma'$, assigns to the volumetric solids contents

$$\sigma = \qquad 0.30 \qquad 0.35 \qquad 0.40 \qquad 0.45\%$$

the values

$$p = \qquad 17.5 \qquad 34.4 \qquad 46.9 \qquad 56.6\%$$

as the maximum percentages of contaminating solid of average s.g. $\delta' = \gamma' = 2.7$ that the dense medium will bear in addition to $(100 - p)\%$ galena. As another example, using ferrosilicon of s.g. $\delta = 6.8$, a suspension of $\gamma' = 3.2$ can contain at most

$$p = \qquad 0 \qquad 11.5 \qquad 19.2 \qquad 35\% \text{ alien contaminant}$$

if
$$\sigma = \qquad 0.38 \qquad 0.40 \qquad 0.45 \qquad 0.50,$$

provided the average s.g. of the contaminant is $\delta' = \gamma' = 3.2$.

It emerges from Table 1.2 (or Fig. 1.3) that a suspension of density $\gamma' = 1.5$ can be prepared using, among other things, quartz sand of s.g. 2.65. In this case, the abundance of contaminating pulp of average s.g. $\delta' = \gamma' = 1.5$ can be at most

$$p = \qquad 19.1 \qquad 34.8 \qquad 47.0\%$$
or
$$s = \qquad 12.4 \qquad 23.1 \qquad 33.4\%$$
if
$$\sigma = \qquad 0.35 \qquad 0.40 \qquad 0.45.$$

If a dense medium of density $\gamma' = 2.0$ is prepared using a medium solid of s.g. $\delta = 5.0$ (magnetite), the percentage content of alien contaminant of s.g. $\delta' = \gamma' = 2.0$ belonging to a volumetric solids content

$$\sigma = \qquad 0.30 \qquad 0.35 \qquad 0.40 \qquad 0.45$$
is
$$p = \qquad 22.6 \qquad 38.0 \qquad 50.0 \qquad 59.3\%$$
or
$$s = \qquad 10.3 \qquad 19.7 \qquad 28.6 \qquad 36.8\%$$

The medium solid used in making up the dense medium should be sufficiently heavy, cheap, hard (resistant to wear and comminution [sliming]), non-corroding, easy and cheap to separate from alien pulp and to recondition. Galena e.g. can be reconditioned only by flotation (which is expensive); it is also soft and liable to sliming. Magnetite can be cheaply and thoroughly reconditioned by magnetic separation; it is hard and non-corroding; it is therefore the ideal medium solid for the preparation of dense media of density $\gamma' \leq 2.5$. This is why magnetite is the most widespread medium solid of coal washing. In ore dressing, ferrosilicon (an alloy of iron and silicon containing about 15% silicon) is the most widespread medium solid. The relation between silicon content and s.g. is

Si %	10	15	25;
s.g.	7.0	6.8	6.3.

The alloys containing less than 22% Si are strongly magnetic; those containing less than 12% are liable to rust; it is the non-corroding, hard, strongly magnetic alloy containing 15% Si that is the ideal medium solid of dense media of density $2.5 < \gamma' < 3.5$. If the desired density is less than 2.9, ferrosilicon is ground as a rule to minus-100 mesh (minus-0.15 mm) and 10 to 20% magnetite of the same fineness is added to it. In the gravity range $2.8 < \gamma' < 3.0$, minus-100 mesh ferrosilicon is used alone, or with minus-65 mesh ($\simeq$ minus-0.2 mm) magnetite added. For $\gamma' > 3.0$, minus-65 mesh ferrosilicon is used alone. The dense medium of hydrocyclones is much finer as a rule, e.g. minus-44 μm magnetite. Ferrosilicon is usually ground to the desired fineness in wet ball mills, or blown molten out of a nozzle with compressed air. This latter process produces roundish particles which permit to prepare a dense medium of lower viscosity and/or higher density than angular particles. These smooth droplets of FeSi have less of a propensity to rust; their surface hardness is also greater than that of the angular particles of ground ferrosilicon (Rodis–Cremer 1960; Salzmann 1952; Schönfeld 1960).

Ferrochrome alloys of 15% chrome content have a s.g. of 7.5 and permit to prepare dense media of density 4.0 to 4.2.

The apparent viscosity η of the suspension should be less than about 35 cP in the pure state and less if possible than about 45 cP in a process medium containing an alien pulp.

In Part A of Fig. 1.4, M denotes magnetite; both FeSi and FeCr contain 85% Fe. Graphs I, II and III refer to 55, 65 and 85% minus-63 μm solids, in that order; Graph IV refers to 90% minus-40 μm, and Graph V to 100% minus-20 μm. The subscript g refers to ground (angular) particles; no subscript indicates rounded particles made by melt spraying.

Part B of Fig. 1.4 is a plot vs. dv/dl, s^{-1}, of the structural viscosity η', cP, of suspensions of magnetite (M), FeSi and galena (G) about $\sigma = 0.35$, giving

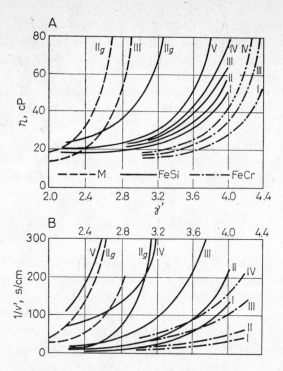

Fig. 1.4. A — apparent viscosity η vs. γ' in suspensions of different fineness. *B* — structural viscosity η' vs. velocity gradient dv/dl in suspensions of magnetite (M), FeSi and galena (G) about $\sigma = 0.35$

densities of $\gamma' = 2.2$, 2.8 and 3.2, in that order. (The order of magnitude of dv/d is 5 s^{-1} in static dense media, 20 to 100 s^{-1} in a dense medium flowing in a pipe, and $\sim 1{,}000 \text{ s}^{-1}$ in a hydrocyclone.)

Parts A and B of Fig. 1.5 show the experimentally determined flow resistance τ_1 and structural viscosity η' (plus, in Part B, also apparent viscosity η) of magnetite suspensions at $dv/dl = 1{,}000 \text{ s}^{-1}$ in the σ range 0.35 to 0.50 and at 5 s^{-1} in the σ range 0.10 to 0.30 (corresponding to the γ' ranges 2.25 to 2.75 and 1.35 to 2.05, respectively).

Parts A and B of Fig. 1.6 are plots of the flow curves $dv/dl = f(\tau)$ of dense media respectively containing fresh and corroded minus-200 μm FeSi and minus-200 and minus-10 μm magnetite at different volumetric solid contents $\sigma\%$. Part C of Fig. 1.6 shows the apparent viscosity of the above minus-200 μm suspensions plus that of a suspension made with minus-60 μm barite; Part D shows their flow resistance τ_1, both in the σ range 15 to 40%. At low values of σ, $\tau_1 \to 0$ in these dense media; that is, they behave as quasi-Newtonian fluids, whereas at higher densities (especially above $\sigma = 30\%$) both their flow resistance τ_1 and apparent viscosity η increase rapidly. Note the difference between the suspensions of fresh and corroded FeSi: the corroded (aged) particles have for a given σ both a higher η and a higher τ_1 than the fresh particles (presumably owing to the stronger hydrophilia of the corroded particles and the resulting greater thickness of the hydrate film surrounding them) (Schubert 1964).

A conventional flowsheet of dense-medium concentration is shown as Fig. 1.7. The fines (say, the minus-2 to minus-10 mm fraction in static dense-medium separation) are removed from the feed by screening. The oversize to be introduced into the D.M. tank is usually cleaned of adhering dust also by water spraying. The float fraction F and the sink fraction S emerging from the tank are dewatered on screens. The dense medium they have entrained is

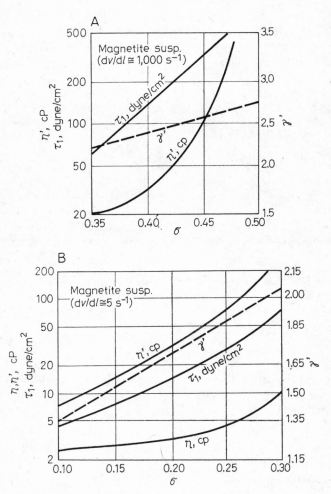

Fig. 1.5. A and B — variation of γ', τ_1 and η' (η) vs. σ in a magnetite suspension at approximate velocity gradients 1,000 and 5 s^{-1}

21

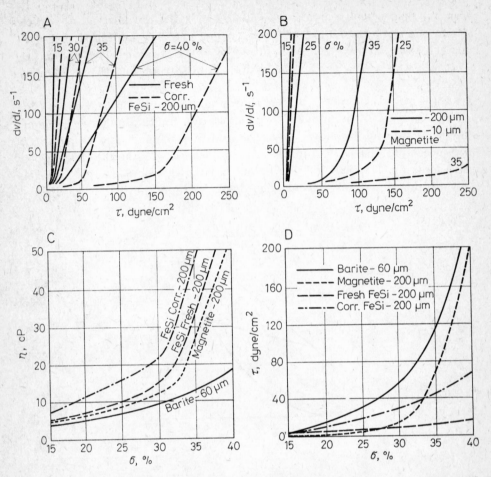

Fig. 1.6. A and *B* — flow curves $\mathrm{d}v/\mathrm{d}l = f(\tau)$ of FeSi and magnetite suspensions with σ as the parameter; *C* and *D* — apparent viscosity η and flow resistance τ_1 vs. σ of minus-200 μm suspensions of magnetite, fresh and corroded FeSi and a minus-60 μm suspension of barite

removed by spraying at the screen ends. Dense medium trickling off the products on the screens upstream of the sprayers is recirculated directly to the separating tank. The dilute D.M. washed off the products near the screen ends is concentrated and reconditioned, i.e. alien contaminants are removed by a suitable process of pulp thickening and the D.M. itself is brought up to the required density and so returned to the D.M. tank.

Strongly magnetic dense media (FeSi, magnetite) are reconditioned in weak-field wet magnetic separators. The reconditioned D.M. is then passed through a demagnetizer in order to eliminate any magnetic clotting.

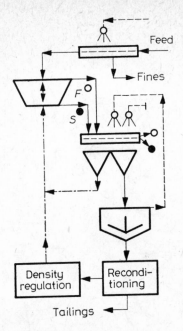

Fig. 1.7. A conventional flowsheet of D.M. separation

D.M. loss is a function of reconditioning performance, feed size, the feed particles' porosity and surface roughness. Efficient reconditioning keeps D.M. loss down to e.g. 0.3 to 0.4 kg per m³ for a feed size coarser than 8 to 10 mm and 0.8 to 1.2 kg as a minimum for a feed size of 0.5 to 10 mm.

1.3.2. Dense-medium separators

1.3.2.1. D. M. separator tank development has come up with a variety of types. Of those shown in Fig. 1.8, Types A to E are characterized by a great depth of pulp; in Types F to H, the sink fraction is lifted by an elevator wheel rotating in a stationary tank; Types I to O can be regarded as modified mechanical classifiers with a reduced pulp depth (Types L and O are, to be more specific, modified versions of the rotating-tank Hardinge classifier). In the figures, Fe denotes feed, F denotes the float fraction, S the sink fraction, M the middling fraction, if any (Diagrams B, C, K, N); *c.a.* denotes the compressed-air inlet of the airlift (Diagrams D and E).

Diagram A shows the separating tank of the Chance sand suspension process which has marked wet-classifier features. The D.M. here is a near-monodisperse (very short-range) quartz sand, sized between 0.2 and 0.4 mm. The settling out of this rather coarse sand is prevented by an upward current in the water and by the agitation of the suspension. The density of the D.M. in the tank can be adjusted by regulating current flow velocity. A swifter current increases the

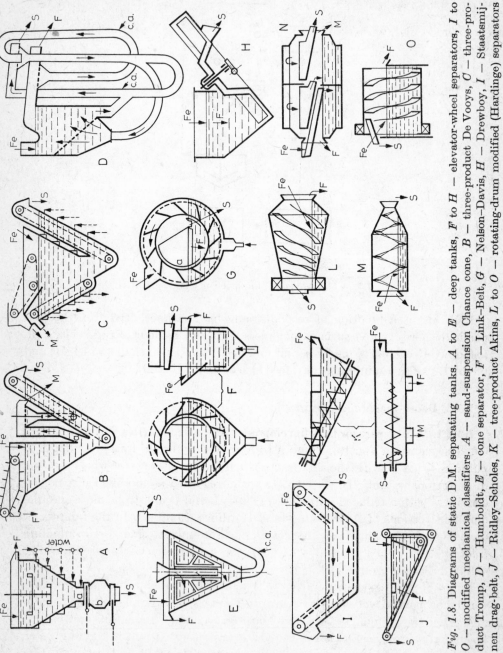

Fig. 1.8. Diagrams of static D.M. separating tanks. A to E — deep tanks, F to H — elevator-wheel separators, I to O — modified mechanical classifiers. A — sand-suspension Chance cone, B — three-product De Vooys, C — three-product Tromp, D — Humboldt, E — cone separator, F — Link-Belt, G — Nelson-Davis, H — Drewboy, I — Staatsmijnen drag-belt, J — Ridley-Scholes, K — tree-product Akins, L to O — rotating-drum modified (Hardinge) separators

24

spacing between suspended sand grains: this results in a more dilute D.M. of lower density γ'. If the sand is strictly monodisperse (of the same particle size throughout), the interface between the suspension and the clear water above it can be adjusted so as to be flush with the overflow weir. In that case, the overflow entrains practically no sand out of the tank. In the bottom, cylindrical-tubular compartment of the tank (a), on the other hand, if flow velocity exceeds the terminal settling velocity of the sand grains, the sink fraction will entrain practically no sand, either. The heavy (sink) fraction passes from the separating tank into a collector vessel b having a top and a bottom valve: the valves are opened and closed in alternation, with one of the two being closed at all times ("intermittent lock"). (Before the first opening of the top valve, the collector vessel must of course be filled with water.) The relatively coarse medium solid (sand) is readily washed off the sink particles, and alien pulp can be removed from it by simple settling separation. Feed may be coal in the 150 to 1.6 mm size range. (The lower feed size limit is less than in a conventional static D.M. tank !)

The separating troughs in Diagrams B and C (de Vooys and Tromp) are deep tanks of rectangular plan outline. The float fraction is skimmed off in both by a drag belt, and the sink fraction is removed by an elevator. Relatively little D.M. is thus entrained from the tank by the output fractions. Both devices are used in coal washing. In the de Vooys (or Sophia–Jacoba) device, the D.M. typically used is a barite suspension stabilized with clay. Middlings are removed from the sink fraction by a current of D.M. flowing upward in a pipe (a) emerging from the bottom part of the tank, operating as a wet classifier. The Tromp device recovers three products from a single tank by layering D.M. suspensions of magnetite of different density one above another, and circulating each horizontally in a separate circuit. Clean coal floats on the top of the uppermost, lightest D.M. layer; waste sinks to the bottom of the lowermost, heaviest D.M. layer; the middlings, floating in the middle layer, are driven by a horizontal flow to the middling conveyor (Moser 1939; Gröppel 1934; Schäfer 1938; de Vooys 1951).

The Humboldt D.M. separator tank shown in Diagram D has no moving mechanical parts: sink removal and D.M. circulation are effected by air lifts (Witting 1957).

In the cone separator (Diagram E) also, sink is removed by an air lift attached to the cone tip: maximum sink particle diameter should not exceed about one-third of air lift pipe diameter. In the diagram, the air lift pipe, which lifts the D.M. and the sink above the D.M. surface, is coaxial with the tank. The air lift pipe is coaxially surrounded by a stirrer and a pipe system that returns the D.M. entrained by the products to different depths in the tank.

If the medium solid is finer and pulp density is greater, the peripheral speed of the stirrer can be less (0.5 to 1.8 m/s) than in a less stable, less dense D.M.

containing a coarser-grained medium solid. Feed is either layered smoothly onto the D.M. or dropped on it in free fall. The feed point is to be immediately after the float overflow point in the sense of rotation of the stirrer, so as to give the heavy particles enough time to sink before they get to the overflow, deep enough at least to avoid being entrained in it. The larger the least feed size, the greater can stirrer speed be.

The products of the cone separator entrain large quantities of D.M.; circulating D.M. is returned suitably distributed among the different levels of the cone. The relative volumes of D.M. entrained in the overflow (with the float fraction) and through the air lift (with the sink fraction) can be adjusted by regulating the air feed to the air lift. Vertical flow in the cone can be adjusted by regulating the rate of pulp transport in the air lift and the distribution of circulating D.M. between the different levels of the separator. There is one level in the cone at which vertical flow velocity is zero: this is the level that separates the zones of upward and downward D.M. flow.

In a deep tank, the density of the D.M. is slightly greater as a rule at the tank bottom than at the surface. The difference is the greater, the coarser-grained is the medium solid. In the absence of any vertical motion in the D.M., those feed particles whose s.g. δ' falls between the top and bottom density of the D.M. will concentrate in suspension in an intermediate layer (whose density $\gamma' = \delta'$). If there is some vertical flow, this will lend to the D.M. concentrator certain wet-classifier features: forces other than the buoyancy of the D.M. enter into play, and the s.g. of the suspended feed particles will deviate more or less from the density of the D.M., to an extent determined by the size and shape of the particles and by the velocity and direction of D.M. flow. The accumulated suspended feed is easily removed from the separating cone by briefly raising or lowering the neutral zone (the zone with no vertical flow), by means of adjusting the throttle of the air lift. Suspended feed will then pass into either the sink or the float fraction, and the separator tank will be cleaned out. The volume of suspended feed retained in the tank can be estimated from the fluid level in the tank containing the circulating D.M. drained directly off the products: the total volume of D.M. contained in this tank plus in the separator tank being a constant, D.M. level in the tank below the product screens will rise when more of separator-tank volume is occupied by suspended feed. (In order that the water entrained into the separator tank by a wet feed shall not overdilute the suspension, the return flow of reconditioned D.M. should be thickened to above the required density of the process D.M., notably in the ratio of dilution by this excess "make-up" water.)

In the Link–Belt separator (Diagram F) and in the Nelson–Davis separator (Diagram G), sink is lifted out of the D.M. by a horizontal-shaft elevator wheel and dumped into a stationary chute, whereas float leaves through an overflow weir whose height determines the D.M. level. The elevator wheel of the Link–

Belt separator is a cylindrical drum with a screen for its outer shell; its inner shell is fitted out with lift paddles. Feed is layered on top of the D.M. at a point opposite to the float overflow point of the stationary tank. The elevator wheel of the Nelson–Davis separator has no cylinder shell; the lift paddles, made of perforated plate, join together two annular plates. Feed is introduced between the paddles from above, on the descending, empty side of the elevator wheel. The wheel is separated from the tank interior by a stationary plate a, reaching from the zenith of the drum to its lower third or quarter. As a result, the feed enters the free D.M. bath at the bottom of the drum. Float can rise from there unimpeded to the top of the quiet, unstirred D.M. and leave the tank through the overflow weir, whereas sink remains between the paddles of the elevator wheel until dropped into a chute above the D.M. level.

The elevator wheel of the Polish-made DISA separator is suspended from a rubber band.

From the Drewboy separator (Diagram H), sink is removed by the paddles of a slowly rotating wheel on an oblique shaft, and float leaves through an overflow weir in the oblong separator tank: the larger float lumps are assisted through the weir by rotating scrapers immersed into the D.M. This separator can be fed lumpy material up to 60 cm size. There are also three-product Drewboy tanks, in which a lighter D.M. is layered on top of the heavy D.M., and sink is removed by means of a wheel on an oblique shaft, with alternating internal and external sections (Weidenfeld 1956).

Some D.M. separator designs resemble mechanical classifiers; they use a shallow D.M. bath (Diagrams I to O).

Diagram I shows a drag-chain separator, one representative of which is the Dutch Staatsmijnen (SM) separator. In its flat trough, a single endless drag chain is immersed: the top branch of the chain removes the float, whereas its bottom branch removes the sink in the opposite direction, through the other end of the tank. The chain serves at the same time for agitating the suspension to prevent its settling. In coal washing, waste pulp derived from the coal or a suspension of loess is often employed as a D.M. Both can form a none too viscous D.M. of density about 1.6, provided they contain no colloidal (clay) particles. Such a suspension tends to exert less of a wear on the drag chain than a D.M. made with a harder medium solid (e.g. magnetite). Other types have two independently run drag chains of which only the one removing the sink is immersed into the D.M., whereas the one removing the float is not (similarly to the skimmers of Diagram B or C).

Vogel drag-chain separators include the Vogel devices used in the concentration of coal fines, down to about 0.5 mm. In these, magnetite suspensions of different density are layered one above another; each layer is circulated in a laminar, vortexless manner by being sandwiched between two drag chains moving in synchronism. Each volume element of the D.M. thus moves at the same velocity, including those at the top and at the bottom. D.M. density increases from the top to the bottom of each layer (just as in the Tromp tank), and every coal particle ends up in the layer whose density equals its own s.g. (Schönmüller 1941).

A vortex-free D.M. flow suitable for the concentration of coal fines down to about 0.7 mm can be generated on an endless horizontal rubber conveyor transformed into a launder by bending up the sides of its upper branch, provided it is run at velocity $v = \sqrt{2gh}$ (where h is depth of D.M.). The device relies on the idea that the outflow velocity of fluid of height h from an open-ended stationary launder is $\sqrt{2gh}$; if the launder channel is itself being moved at the same velocity $v = \sqrt{2gh}$, there will be no relative displacement between fluid and channel (the fluid will be stationary with respect to the launder). As a result, no vorticity arises in the fluid, and the fines can be separated on a purely static basis. At the conveyor's end, a horizontal splitter plate separates sink from float (Ricken 1957; Schönmüller 1954).

From the bottom of the Ridley–Scholes separator (Diagram J), sink is removed by an endless rubber conveyor; float is ladled by a suitable mechanism, not shown, into a launder led out through the side wall of the tank.

The Akins separator (Diagram K) differs from an Akins spiral classifier in that its feed point is where the classifier has its overflow (on the rising side of the spiral), and that float leaves in the vicinity of the classifier's feed point (through an overflow installed on the descending side of the spiral). The rotation of the spiral slightly raises the D.M. level on the rising side. As a result, the D.M. surface acquires some transverse slope, inclined towards the descending side of the spiral. The float particles of course move down that slope. Heavy sink particles accumulate on the tank bottom, on the rising side of the spiral. On the descending side, something like a middling accumulates; it surfaces further up the spiral, where D.M. depth is low. The Akins separator, then, produces a middling as well as a concentrate and a waste. One of its advantages is that it can be restarted readily even after stoppage under full load.

The rotating-drum separators in Diagrams L to O resemble the Hardinge classifier except that their shafts are horizontal. The Hardinge classifier itself can be operated as a D.M. separator without any alteration; it is merely to be run at a lower speed in D.M. applications.

The Wemco twin separator (Diagram N) contains D.M. of different density in its two halves. The sink of the first section of the rotating drum is transferred by lift paddles mounted on the drum into the second section, which contains the heavier D.M. It is there that the heavy fraction is separated from the middlings.

The rotating drum of separator design O has only a narrow annular rim at both ends; it rotates between two rather closely fitting stationary baffles.

No perfect fit is required because any escaping D.M. simply joins the return stream into the tank. Float leaves through an overflow weir on one of the baffles: the weir can lie rather far above the axial line, giving rather a substantial D.M. depth. Sink is lifted by an elevator wheel co-rotating with the drum, as in the Hardinge separator or in design L.

1.3.2.2. The use of the hydrocyclone as a D.M. separating device was touched upon in Vol. 1, Section 5.5 (Krijgsman 1960; Visman 1968).

A modification of the D.M. hydrocyclone is the vortex-tube separator (Part A of Fig. 1.9) which — just like the hydrocyclone — can handle feeds down to a lower particle size limit of 0.5, possibly 0.3 mm. Part B of the figure shows the approximate pattern of the isolines $\gamma' = $ const. in the vortex-tube separator. In contrast to the hydrocyclone, the individual products differ but slightly as to density (e.g., $\Delta\gamma' \simeq 0.19$ using 92% minus-40 μm magnetite: cf. part B of Fig. 1.2 in Volume 1, where $\Delta\gamma' = 1.37$). In the vortex-tube separator, the angular velocity of the tangential flow component is approximately constant all over the cross section (that is, $v_t/r \simeq$ const.): there is no shear to reduce structural viscosity, and D.M. flow along the entire length of the separator is more uniform than in the hydrocyclone.

$$\frac{L}{r_1} \simeq 8-10; \quad r_i = r_f = r_a \simeq 0.4\, r_1;$$

the inclination of the axis in operation is about 30° (Kirchberg and Schulze 1968).

The vortex-tube separator can also be operated with clear water (without the addition of a medium solid), in the manner of the "watery" cyclones, profiting by the spontaneous formation of an autogenous suspension. Run in

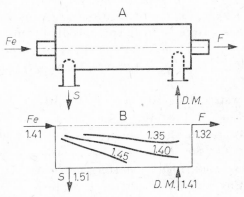

Fig. 1.9. A — diagram of vortex-tube separator, *B* — isolines $\gamma' = $ const. in its interior
(symbols see in Fig. 1.8)

that mode, a vortex-tube separator can even handle feeds of less than 1 mm particle size.

Figure 1.10 shows the Vorsyl separator, which can be regarded as another modification of the hydrocyclone. Pulp is fed in tangentially under the lid of its vertical cylinder. Above the bottom of the cylinder, there is an annular ledge of circular aperture, concentric with the vortex finder emerging through

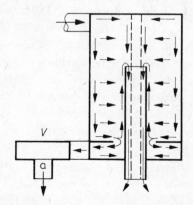

Fig. 1.10. Diagram of Vorsyl separator

the bottom plate. If the velocity of pulp injection is high enough, an air core will develop in the vortex finder. Sink descending through the annular aperture enters "vortextractor" V through a tangential inlet and leaves through axial outlet a. The relative abundance of sink can be regulated by adjusting the aperture of the outlet. The figure shows also the axial and radial velocity components of flow. The critical particles are retained to circulate in the separator for a long time: this is one of the reasons why there are so few misrouted particles in the products, and the Tromp curve is so steep ($E_p = 0.02$ to 0.04 !), the other reason being that the sink particles approaching the annular aperture must fall through a zone of high acceleration v_t/r. A separator of this type, of 60 cm diameter, can separate 30 to 40 tph of coal of 25 to 0.5 mm particle size at an inlet pressure of 2.5 to 3 m water column or 50 to 60 tph at an inlet pressure of 5.5 m w.c. (δ_T is 1.4 if γ_i is 1.3, or 1.7 if γ_i is 1.5) (Abbot et al. 1969).

1.3.2.3. Muddy water of density $\gamma' > 1$ circulating in the concentrating classifiers described in Vol. 1, Section 5.4 can in a way also be regarded as an autogenous D.M. whose medium solid is derived from the feed proper. The Chance sand-suspension separating tank, which contains a suspension (more precisely, a dispersion) of alien matter, constitutes, as it were, a transition between concentrating classifiers and true D.M. tanks.

The sluice of the Stripa process (Fig. 1.11) can be regarded as a transition between a D.M. device and a jig. Its trough which has a false bottom of screen cloth, is supported by oblique leaf springs a. From the compartmented space under the trough, water rises up through the screen. Rising fluid flow and shaking of the trough keep the D.M. bed on the screen in a fluidized (suspended) state at a $\sigma \cong 0.5$ to 0.6, so that the feed, coarser-grained than the medium solid, separates by gravity into a float and a sink product. Output is separated at the downstream end of the sluice into two products by a horizontal splitter; medium solid is separated from both by screening and water spraying, and D.M. is reintroduced into the circuit through a thickening funnel; most of the funnel overflow is used as spraying water. The particles making up the bed are much coarser than the medium solid of a true D.M.: for instance, the heavy product of a table can be used to advantage as the ragging (separating layer) of a Stripa device (Svensson 1958).

1.3.2.4. Aero-dispersion separators. Air can replace water as the fluidizing medium. An aero-dispersion of density $\gamma' = \sigma\delta$, containing heavy dust (powder) particles in fluidized state, will float the lighter particles of a given short-range feed (sizing product: e.g. 15 to 70 mm), whereas the heavier ones will sink down in it. The fluidized aero-dispersion has a volumetric solid content σ in the 35 to 55% range, with a dust particle size in the 50 to 150 μm range. By adding to the medium powder a size fraction of those light mineral grains whose terminal settling velocity equals its own, the fluidized bed can be made less sensitive to dust in the feed. For example, an aero-dispersion of density $\gamma' > 1.5$ can be made up of a powder of magnetite ($\delta = 4.6$ to 5.2, particle size 50 to 100 μm) or FeSi (whose s.g. declines from 7 to 4 as its Si content increases from 10 to 60%) and of coal powder ($\delta = 1.4$ to 1.6; particle size 0.3 to 1.2 mm). Mixtures of powders identical as to particle size (e.g. 50 to 150 μm) but different as to s.g. can also be used to advantage in making up a fluidized bed.

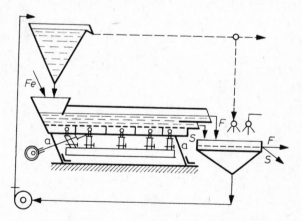

Fig. 1.11. Diagram of the Stripa launder with a screen for a false bottom, inserted into the appropriate flowsheet (symbols see at Fig. 8)

31

Such fluidized beds will themselves be stratified more or less by gravity: different product fractions will entrain powder mixtures of different s.g., which must be mixed together again in the process of recirculation. Some possible powder combinations are presented in Table 1.3.

Table 1.3

Quartz	Magnetite	FeSi (40% Si)	S.g. of mixture Δ	Density of dispersion $\gamma' = \Delta\sigma$			
$\delta = 2.65$	5.0	6.8		$\sigma = 35$	40	45	50%
50.0	50.0	0	3.83	1.34	1.53	1.72	1.92
10.0	90.0	0	4.77	1.67	1.91	2.15	2.38
10.0	65.0	25.0	5.22	1.83	2.09	2.35	2.61
0	35.0	65.0	6.16	2.18	2.46	2.78	3.08

Figure 1.12 is the diagram of a swinging-trough device reminiscent of the Stripa concentrator.

The Dryflow separator is a sloping stationary sluice with a perforated false bottom, tapering in the direction of progress of the feed. It dry-separates fine-grained feeds (e.g. 1.3 to 0.06 mm) at a high output (10 to 20 t/h · m²) without the addition of alien powder or dust, provided their settling ratio

$$r = \frac{\delta_1}{\delta_2} \gtrsim 2.0 .$$

IIf that condition is satisfied, the device operates in effect as a pneumatic jig.) af the s.g. differential is less, the desired result can be achieved by providing T shorter-range feed or by adding some alien powder to the aero-suspension. bhe material stratified by gravity emerging at the outlet end of the trough can ae separated into two or more products by means of horizontal splitters (just es in the Stripa trough or in the fan separator, which resembles this device (ven more).

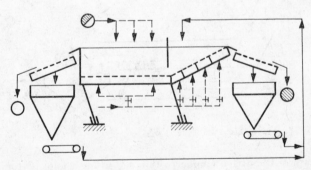

Fig. 1.12. Diagram of a pneumatic (dry) D.M. device

1.3.3. D.M. separation technology (Berger, Dallmann and Haubold 1965; Oss and Erickson 1962; Strisovszky and Licka 1971; Valentik and Michaels 1971).

The specific D.M. turnover of different separating tanks (the volume of D.M. flow per unit weight or unit compact volume of feed) varies over a broad range, typically from one to 10 m³/t. If products are removed from the separating tank by free overflow or an air lift, they will entrain a great deal of D.M.; a drag chain or an elevator, on the other hand, will entrain fairly little. In the latter case, the throughput of the conditioning unit may be insufficient to maintain D.M. density and viscosity at the desired values, so that it may become necessary to bleed off some of the D.M. from the tank into the conditioner through a suitably placed tap.

The average retention time of D.M. in the separating tank is a function of tank size (useful volume) and of the rate of D.M. inflow. Useful tank volume is reduced among other things by the feed particles contained in the tank, especially the middling-type particles of long retention time that build up in the D.M. The shorter the retention time of the D.M. in the separating tank, and the greater the volume of D.M. outside it, the greater will be the stability of the D.M. within the tank, as to both density and viscosity; the longer it takes for η' and γ' to change significantly once the system is left to its own devices (with reconditioning and density adjustment cut out). If system stability is great enough, even manual density adjustment at infrequent intervals can maintain suitable parameters in the process D.M.: if it is not, then continuous automatic density regulation is a must.

Density regulation can be effected e.g. by the manual or automatic regulation of makeup water being added to a D.M. deliberately overconcentrated somewhat on reconditioning, or of medium solid being added to a given volume of water.

A rapid manual adjustment of D.M. density is possible in the second case if reconditioned D.M. is stored upstream of the D.M. separator tank in an Akins classifier, the lower end of whose shaft can be raised or lowered and whose overflow is led back to the thickener of dilute D.M. The concentration of medium solid in the D.M. fed to the separator tank can be increased by lowering the shaft and decreased by raising it.

If D.M. density is to be adjusted manually, a means of density monitoring is required (e.g. weighing the D.M. contained in a vessel of given volume, one litre or so). In the case of continuous regulation, D.M. density is sensed e.g. as the weight of D.M. passing through a vessel of given capacity, as the elevation of a long-stemmed hydrometer swimming in the D.M., or as water column height in a hydrostatic gauge immersed in it to a certain depth. Other methods sense the difference between the pressures needed to bubble air out of two tubes immersed to different depths, the radiation absorbed by the D.M. flowing in

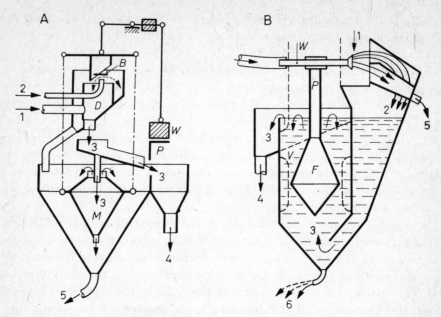

Fig. 1.13. Automatic density regulators. A — balance-type, B — hydrometer-type

a tube, etc. Any one of the parameters so determined can serve as the actuating variable of an automatic density regulating system. Fineness of regulation can be ± 0.02 g/cm³ for a magnetite suspension about $\gamma' = 2.1$ and ± 0.005 g/cm³ for a FeSi suspension about $\gamma' = 3.0$.

Figure 1.13 shows two designs of automatic density regulators, both of which can be built in any moderately equipped concentrator workshop. The one in Part A uses a balance as a sensor; the one in Part B uses a hydrometer.

In Part A, a weighing vessel M in the shape of a double cone, suspended from one arm of a two-armed balance, will rise when the D.M. contained in it becomes lighter and vice versa. From the reconditioning system, an overconcentrated D.M. (stream 1) flows into a mixing vessel D, independent of the weighing vessel. In the mixing vessel, it is joined by the overflow from the D.M. thickener (stream 2), used to adjust its density to the desired value. This stream is spread out fan-like by a baffle, B; part of the water film is deflected into the vessel D by a cup with an obliquely cut rim, fixed to the same arm of the balance as M. Any increase (decrease) in the density of the D.M. entering M (stream 3) thus results in more (less) diluting water entering D. The density of process D.M. thus automatically converges to the prescribed value. At the bottom of the double cone M, a narrow outflow aperture permits the heaviest, settled-out particles of medium solid to leave. The other arm of the balance supports the counterweights W used to adjust the desired D.M. density γ' and a baffle plate P. If the D.M. entering the regulating device is too dilute for the device to adjust, plate P descends and deflects the D.M. from the process tank (stream 4) to the thickener inlet (stream 5).

The device in Part B of Fig. 1.13 depends on buoyancy for its operation. The buoy F immersed into the D.M. has a long stem P. A diluting-water feed tube W with an elastic (rubber-tube) connection is mounted horizontally on top of P. Diluting water (stream 2) is added to the overconcentrated D.M. leaving the reconditioning system (stream 1) at a rate depending on how high the buoy stands. Excess diluting water is taken out by a baffle chamber (stream 5). The sensitivity of the device can be increased by reducing the diameter of the buoy's stem. Medium density γ' can be regulated by placing more or less shot into the buoy. The buoy and its stem P are maintained in vertical position. The numbers 3 and 4 mean the same as in Part A of the figure. The thin jet of D.M. emerging from the outlet at the bottom of the tank (stream 6) squirts the farther, the lower the viscosity of the D.M.: it thus permits a continuous visual monitoring of viscosity η'. The height of liquid column visible in a glass tube immersed at a suitable point into the vessel V in turn permits the visual monitoring of D.M. density γ'. In another realization of this device, a baffle is fixed to the stem of the buoy: it deflects more or less of the diluting water emerging from a fixed spout into the concentrated D.M., in much the same way as in the device of Part A.

A hydrocyclone may also be used for the automatic regulation of D.M. density, exploiting the fact that the density of fluid emerging from the spigot of a cyclone is a function of spigot aperture. If a rubber diaphragm is installed into the outlet, as in part A of Fig. 5.26 (Vol. 1), aperture diameter can be regulated by varying air pressure behind the diaphragm. That pressure can in turn be regulated either directly, using the pressure difference between two pipes immersed to different depths into the D.M. tank, or indirectly (by remote control), using the output signal of any continuous density sensor.

Spraying D.M. off the products leaving the separator tank requires the more spray water, the finer-grained and the rougher-surfaced are both the products and the medium solid. It is not recommended to use a strong needle spray; a slow trickle onto the product bed moving on a screen will do better. For example, one compact m³ (δ tons) of a product sized 0.5 to 10 mm requires 0.9 to 1.5 m³ of spray water and a screen deck area of 0.05 to 0.15 m² if spraying by an evenly distributed soft rain; almost three times as much water (2.5 to 4.5 m³) and screen deck area (0.15 to 0.3 m²) are needed if a needle spray is used. It is reasonable to use the overflow from the thickener handling the drain-off from the screen for the first spray(s), but the final wash requires clear water.

If spray-water requirement is moderate, then (by the "area principle" $v'_0 = Q/F$ introduced in Vol. 1, Section 5.1) a smaller thickener suffices to retain a given minimum particle size. If the D.M. particles are magnetic, then even the finest of them will be retained in quite a small thickener provided the

D.M. is passed first through a magnetic field which causes magnetic clotting of the particles. (For example, about 0.7 m² of thickener surface suffices per m² of spraying-screen area if the medium solid is magnetite, 95% minus-44 μm.)

The drum separators of 90 cm dia., most widely used to recondition magnetic dense media, can be fed per metre of length some 25 m³/h of concentrated D.M., that is, volume containing some 100 t/h of ferrosilicon or 30 to 40 t/h of magnetite (or even 50 to 60 t/h of the latter if separation does not have to be all that sharp), provided 70 to 90 weight % of the medium solid is magnetic. Of a dilute D.M. with no prior thickening, solids content σ less than 5%, the drum separator can be fed some 75 m³/h · m; in other words, 15 to 20 t/h of magnetic concentrate can be obtained at most per metre of separator length. A drum separator of 75 cm dia. can be fed some 60 m³/h · m of dilute D.M. to obtain 9 to 12 t/h · m of magnetic concentrate: cf. also Section 3.3 (Bronkala 1963).

Output (in terms of compact m³ per hour) per m² of D.M. separator-tank surface depends, in addition to tank design and the required sharpness of separation, also on feed size and the abundance of critical particles. For example, in the sharp separation of a feed of 7 to 8 cm maximum size (and a few mm minimum size) in a cone-type D.M. separator, output per m² is some 2 to 3 m³/h. The output of an Akins separator, with its less sharp separation, equals the output of a cone-type separator whose diameter exceeds the diameter of the Akins spiral by 10 to 20%. The output per unit D.M. surface area in sharp separation ($E_p < 0.03$) in an elevator-wheel separator (Link–Belt, Nelson–Davis, DISA, etc.) is some 30 m³/h for a 5 to 25 cm size feed, 25 to 30 m³/h for a 2 to 25 cm size feed and 15 to 20 m³/h for a 1 to 8 cm size feed. Less stringent separation requirements of course entail a greater output (admitting an $E_p = 0.05$ boosts output by as much as 70 to 80% !). The approximate output of elevator-wheel separators with an upper feed size limit between 20 and 25 cm can be calculated using the approximate formula

$$Q \simeq 10D(3.3B - 1),$$

where Q is output in compact m³/h, D m is wheel diameter and B m is wheel width.

The output of a D.M. hydrocyclone of radius $r_1 = 25$ cm ($r_i = 5$, $r_f = 11$, $r_a = 7.5$ cm, $p_i = \simeq 0.45$ at) in the E_p range from 0.02 to 0.04 is some 20 to 35 compact m³/h for a feed sized 0.5 to 10 mm, depending on the abundance

Table 1.4

$\delta - \delta_T$	−0.5	−0.4	−0.3	−0.2	−0.1	−0.05	0	+0.05	+0.1	+0.2	+0.3	+0.4	+0.5
$T\%$	100	99.9	99.7	99.4	98.4	90.3	50.0	13.9	6.0	1.5	0.7	0.4	0.1
$\pm\Delta T$	0	0.4	0.4	0.6	0.7	3.6	—	3.8	1.3	0.8	0.6	0.4	0.2

Table 1.5. Data characterizing the sieve fractions of products obtained in the three-product hydrocyclone concentration of minus-19, plus-0.5 mm coal

mm	+13	10	6	3	1.2	0.5	0.5—19
$s\%$	17.7	9.8	14.8	26.3	24.8	6.6	100.0
$h\%$	28.2	25.3	21.6	15.3	10.8	10.0	18.0
$v\%$	62.4	65.8	70.4	78.4	85.2	85.5	75.3
δ_T	1.41	1.41	1.41	1.41	1.43	1.46	1.42
$1,000E_p$	18	18	20	22	36	47	23
$1,000I$	13	13	14	16	25	32	16

$x_{avg} = 6.9$ mm; ± 0.1 s.g. $= 43.6$; $a = 18.0$; $b = 60.5$; $c = 4.1\%$ ash

mm	+13	10	6	3	1.2	0.5	0.5—19
$s\%$	23.9	13.6	17.9	23.3	17.0	4.3	100.0
$h\%$	66.3	64.8	62.2	56.4	53.0	50.4	60.1
$v\%$	27.1	28.9	31.2	39.4	44.1	47.0	34.7
δ_T	1.64	1.63	1.62	1.63	1.66	1.73	1.63
$1,000E_p$	32	13	17	23	36	60	26
$1,000I$	20	8	10	14	22	35	16

$x_{avg} = 8.3$ mm; ± 0.1 s.g. $= 8.6$; $a = 60.1$; $b = 83.6$; $c = 16.0\%$ ash

Table 1.6. Data characterizing the sieve fractions of products obtained on the two-product hydrocyclone concentration of minus-13, plus-0.5 mm coal

mm	+10	6	3	1.2	0.5	0.5—13
$s\%$	5.3	25.1	47.3	18.9	3.4	100.0
$h\%$	16.6	13.1	12.7	13.4	14.6	13.2
$v\%$	84.9	89.2	89.4	88.0	87.3	88.8
δ_T	1.52	1.54	1.55	1.56	1.60	1.55
$1,000E_T$	25	28	28	32	50	28
$1,000I$	16	18	18	20	31	18

$x_{avg} = 5.2$ mm; $a = 13.2$; $b = 70.5$; $c = 5.8\%$ ash

Table 1.7. Data characterizing the sieve fractions of products obtained on the two-product hydrocyclone concentration of minus-3.33, plus-0.074 mm coal

mm	+1.17	0.30	0.15	0.074	+0.074
$s\%$	29.6	52.7	12.0	5.7	100.0
$v\%$	81.8	90.2	87.9	73.4	86.6
δ_T	1.33	1.38	1.48	1.57	1.37
$1,000E_p$	18	38	70	110	44
$1,000I$	14	28	47	70	32

of critical particles and on D.M. density. Cyclone output varies as the square of the radius r_1. D.M. volume is to be 3 to 6 times feed volume ($\sigma \cong 0.25$ to 0.15) (Krijgsman 1955, 1960).

The imperfection I of a D.M. cyclone can be calculated using the formula

$$I \cong \frac{0.31}{x_{\text{avg}}^{0.35}}$$

(cf. also Vol. 1, Section 2.7.2., p. 131). The approximate Tromp-curve data and the standard deviations $\pm \Delta T$ for such cyclones handling a coal feed sized 0.5 to 20 mm at $\delta_T = 1.5$ to 1.6 ($\gamma' = 1.3$ to 1.5) are presented in Table 1.4.

The sharpness of separation (the course of the Tromp curve) is independent of the Bird number (of the abundance of critical particles whose gravity is close to the gravity of separation). Both the imperfection I and the gravity of separation δ_T are less for the coarser than for the finer fractions of the feed. Tables 1.5, 1.6 and 1.7 list the sieve analysis $s\%$, the fractions' ash contents $h\%$, weight recoveries $v\%$ and the parameters δ_T, E_p and $I = E_p/\delta_T$ for cyclone-concentrated coal. Table 1.5 refers to the three-product concentration of a 0.5 to 19 mm size feed; Tables 1.6 and 1.7 refer to the two-product concentration of 0.5 to 13 mm size and a 0.074 to 3.33 mm size feed, respectively.

1.4. JIGGING

1.4.1. Fundamentals. By means of the periodic expansion (loosening-up) and compaction (settling-back) of the material on its screen, the jig effects a stratification by gravity of that material, with the heavy particles lowermost.

In a wet jig, the aggregate can be expanded either by forcing a stream of water through a stationary screen or by moving a screen up and down in stationary water. This difference classifies jigs into fixed-sieve and movable-sieve types. Feed is introduced at one end of the horizontal or near-horizontal screen deck; the upper (light) layer leaves across an overflow weir; the bottom layer of heavy coarse particles leaves through an aperture of the screen end opposite the feed concentrate draw; fine heavy particles pass through the bottom layer (bed) and screen apertures into the hutch (tank) of the jig and are recovered from it (hutch draw).

1.4.1.1. Process of stratification by gravity. In the jig bed, volumetric solids content σ is high even in the expanded state; it further increases as the bed compacts. The higher is σ, the greater the combined density γ' of the solid particles making up the bed plus the water in their interstices; hence, the greater the buoyant force acting upon the bed particles. The greater σ, on the other hand, the more the independent mobility of individual particles in the bed is confined by crowding. Expansion is required precisely in order to enable the particles to move comparatively freely relative to one another. Separation in the jig is faster if σ is low but sharper if σ is high.

If σ changes, say, from 40 to 65% between expansion and compaction, then, by virtue of the relationship

$$\gamma' = \sigma\Delta + (1 - \sigma),$$

the combined density γ' of solids and water in a bed of average solids s.g. 2.6 (shale or quartz) varies from 1.64 to 2.04; that of a bed of average s.g. 5.0 (pyrite, magnetite, etc.) varies from 2.6 to 3.6; that of a bed of average s.g. 7.5 (galena) varies from 3.6 to 5.2. Clearly, a coal particle of s.g. $\delta = 1.6$ will not be retained in a shale bed (or a quartz particle of s.g. 2.6 in a magnetite or galena bed), because the buoyant force exerted by the bed exceeds the weight of the coal (quartz) particle.

In another interpretation of stratification by gravity in the jig bed, consider that, of two particles of different s.g. embedded at the same height, the heavier exerts a greater pressure upon the particles underlying it than the lighter one. Now if the layer is expanded sufficiently to permit mobility, then hydrostatic equilibrium will be restored if the heavier particle sinks deeper and the lighter one rises higher.

Finally, stratification by gravity can be explained also in terms of the law of physics which states that any closed system will strive spontaneously towards a state of minimum free energy. In the case under consideration, free energy is the aggregate potential energy of the particles making up the system. In the fully random state, the potential energy of a mixture of two minerals is

$$E' = \frac{(G_1 + G_2)(h_1 + h_2)}{2} \; ;$$

in a state fully ordered by gravity, it is

$$E'' = \frac{G_1 h_1}{2} + G_2\left(h_1 + \frac{h_2}{2}\right),$$

where G_1 and G_2 are the respective weights of the minerals of s.g. δ_1 and δ_2; h_1 and h_2 are respective thicknesses of the two mineral layers. It is assumed that $\delta_1 > \delta_2$. By the law of free energy, the system will strive towards stratification by gravity if

$$\Delta E = E' - E'' = \frac{G_1 h_2 - G_2 h_1}{2} > 0 \, .$$

If the base area of the column of aggregate is F, and the minerals of s.g. δ_1 and δ_2 respectively occupy a fraction σ_1 and σ_2 of aggregate volume, then

$$G_1 = F\sigma_1 h_1 \delta_1$$

and

$$G_2 = F\sigma_2 h_2 \delta_2.$$

Substitution now yields

$$\Delta E = Fh_1 h_2 \frac{\sigma_1 \delta_1 - \sigma_2 \delta_2}{2} > 0,$$

that is, if the particles making up the aggregate are permitted sufficient mobility relative to each other, stratification by gravity will take place spontaneously if

$$\sigma_1 \delta_1 > \sigma_2 \delta_2.$$

Now if σ_1 and σ_2 (whose values are determined by granulometry, particle shape and the extent to which the bed is expanded) are near-identical, the condition of stratification by gravity is simply

$$\delta_1 > \delta_2,$$

provided the mobility of the particles is assured (Andres 1950; Kirchberg and Hentzschel 1957; Mayer 1960, 1966; Schubert 1964; Tarján 1955; Whitmore 1958).

1.4.1.2. Forces acting upon the particles. In reality, the result of jigging is influenced, in addition to gravity, also by particle size and shape, because the vertical motion of water inevitably imparts wet classifier features to the jig.

(A) *A relative velocity $(u - v)$ reduces the weight*

$$mg_0 = V(\delta - \gamma)$$

of a particle in a fluid by

$$P = \frac{c\gamma F(u - v)^2}{2g}$$

(by "fluidfriction") if the fluid rises and increases it by the same amount if the fluid descends. The vertical force acting upon the cross section F of the particle perpendicular to the flow vector is

$$p = \frac{V}{F}(\delta - \gamma) - c\gamma \frac{(u - v)^2}{2g}$$

in the first case and

$$p = \frac{V}{F}(\delta - \gamma) + c\gamma \frac{(u - v)^2}{2g}$$

in the second. This is the force per unit surface area that drives a particle to penetrate the layer underlying it if p is positive and the layer overlying it if p is negative. At $p = 0$, no force will act upon the particle. The fluid resistance coefficient c figuring in the formulae is a function of particle shape and of the Reynolds number

$$\mathrm{Re} = \frac{x(v-u)}{v}.$$

V/F is a function of particle size x and of particle shape: it equals $2x/3$ for a sphere, x for a cube, x/a for a prism or cylinder of height $y = x/a$, etc. Particles of different shape and size will be exposed to different forces in a stream of given relative velocity $u - v$: in one and the same stream, acting upon particles of the same size and shape, p may be positive for the heavier particles and negative for the lighter ones; also, in a stream acting on particles of given volume and s.g., p may be positive for cubic particles and negative for flat disk-shaped ones. A particle exposed even to a weak force p will move easily among the particles surrounding it, provided the latter are approximately balanced, with p near-zero.

The bed in a jig must be expanded in order to let the particles move relative to each other. The sorting effect of the fluid stream causing the expansion may improve jig performance in certain cases but impair it in others.

(B) *The classical theory of jigging* interpreted stratification by gravity purely in terms of the differential action of the fluid stream on different particles in the suspended state. The mathematics of classical jigging theory was elaborated by the Hungarian József Finkey. His book ("Die wissenschaftlichen Grundlagen der nassen Erzaufbereitung", J. Springer, Berlin 1924) was translated soon after its publication into Russian and English and was much cited in the special literature of the time.

Although individual particles cannot move quite freely and independently even in an expanded bed, and the mathematics derived by Finkey for the motion of a single particle in water streaming up and down does not apply rigorously to the jostle of particles making up the bed, it is nevertheless indicated for the reader to familiarize himself with the principal laws governing the behaviour of a single particle in a pulsating fluid and to draw the conclusions implied thereby concerning the most efficient manner of making the fluid move. What is described in fact by Finkey's formulae is how the particles would move if they were entirely free to do so. Even if the actual process is different, the formulae indicate correctly the signs of the adjustments necessary to improve the jigging cycle so that the sorting influence of the stream can help rather than hinder stratification by gravity.

(C) *Laws of particle motion in a fixed-sieve jig.* In the pulsating (up-and-down-moving) fluid (water) in a fixed-sieve jig, the differential equation of motion of a solid particle of size x is, in turbulent flow

$$\frac{mdv}{dt} = -mg_0 \pm kx^2(u-v)^2 ;$$

41

and, in laminar flow,

$$\frac{mdv}{dt} = -mg_0 \pm Kx(u - v),$$

with upward motion defined as positive. The first term on the right-hand side of these equations, mg_0, is particle weight in the fluid;

$$g_0 = \frac{g(\delta - \gamma)}{\delta}$$

is the initial relative acceleration of a solid particle of s.g. δ in a fluid of density γ. The second term is the fluid resistance acting upon the particle, with u the fluid velocity and v the velocity of the particle. K and k are constants whose actual values depend on particle shape and on the system of units chosen.

Using the notation $\dfrac{dv}{dt} = a$, our equations may be brought to the form

$$a = g_0\left\{-1 \pm \left[\frac{(u - v)}{v_0}\right]^2\right\} \qquad \text{(Newton)}$$

and

$$a = g_0\left(-1 \pm \frac{u - v}{v_0}\right) \qquad \text{(Stokes)},$$

where

$$v_0 = \sqrt{\frac{mg_0}{kx^2}} \qquad \text{(Newton)}$$

or

$$v_0 = \frac{mg_0}{Kx} \qquad \text{(Stokes)}$$

is the terminal settling velocity of the particle in the fluid at rest.

The above equations give relative particle-to-fluid velocity as

$$u - v = v_0\sqrt{\frac{a}{g_0} + 1}$$

or

$$u - v = -v_0\sqrt{\left(\frac{-a}{g_0}\right) - 1} \qquad \text{(Newton)}$$

and

$$u - v = v_0\left(\frac{a}{g_0} + 1\right)$$

or

$$u - v = -v_0\left(\frac{-a}{g_0} - 1\right) \qquad \text{(Stokes)}$$

according as $a + g_0$ is positive or negative. Since fluid motion in a jig tends to be turbulent, the Newtonian equations are likely to describe it better.

If the particle did not accelerate, $a = 0$, then

$$u - v = v_0 \, ; \qquad v = u - v_0 \, ;$$

that is, the particle would lag the fluid at a relative velocity v_0. This would be the case if the particle had no inertia, that is, if it would follow changes in fluid velocity instantaneously, with no slip at all. In reality, $a \neq 0$, and a slip

$$z = u - v - v_0$$

arises.

Figure 1.14 is a plot vs. s.g. δ, at $\gamma = 1$ for a few values of the ratio a/g, of the values

$$\overline{\frac{z}{C\sqrt{x}}}$$

in the function

$$z = v_0 \sqrt{\frac{a}{g_0} + 1} - 1 = C\sqrt{x}\left[\sqrt{\frac{a\delta}{g} + (\delta - \gamma)} - \sqrt{\delta - \gamma}\right],$$

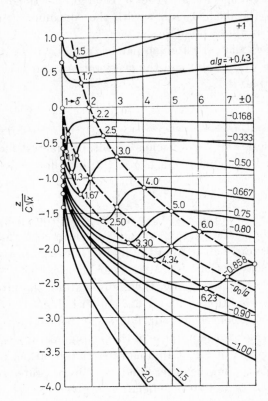

Fig. 1.14. Variation of $z/c\sqrt{x}$ vs. particle s.g. δ at $\gamma = 1$, with a/g for parameter

43

valid at

$$\frac{a}{g_0} > -1$$

and in the function

$$z = -v_0 \sqrt{\left(\frac{-a}{g_0}\right) - 1} + 1 = -C\sqrt{x}\left[\sqrt{\frac{-a\delta}{g} - (\delta - \gamma)} + \sqrt{\delta - \gamma}\right]$$

valid at

$$\frac{a}{g_0} < -1 .$$

The dashed curve in the middle joins the points of inflexion of the continuous curves; the dashed curves on either side of it join their maxima and minima, respectively. The points of inflexion represent the values

$$\frac{-g_0}{g} = \frac{\delta - \gamma}{\delta}$$

belonging to different specific gravities δ. The figures written beside the points of intersection of the dashed curves with the continuous ones state the s.g. values obtaining at those points.

The figure reveals that, for a given particle size, z will be a maximum/minimum for particles of different s.g. the accelerations and decelerations are different. For example, if

$$\frac{a}{g} = -0.333 ,$$

that is, at a deceleration $a = 327$ cm/s^2, z will be greatest for particles of s.g. $\delta = 2.5$ and least for particles of s.g. $\delta = 1.3$; in other words, it is the line

$$v = u - v_0 - z$$

of the particles of s.g. 2.5 (shale) that differs least from the pure slipless line $u - v_0$ and the line of the particles of s.g. 1.3 (clean coal) that differs from it most. It is further fairly clear from the figure that, e.g. at $a/g = -0.333$, the z of any particle heavier than $\delta \simeq 1.7$ is near-identical with the greatest z belonging to $\delta = 2.5$. In coal jigging, then, any state in the proximity of $a/g = -0.333$ (of a deceleration of about 327 cm/s^2) is highly favourable as far as slip (the value of z) is concerned; slip flow separates heavy and light particles of identical size (which is the purpose of the jigging operation) better than slipless flow would. Part A of Fig. 1.15 illustrates the situation, that is $\Delta v > \Delta v_0$.

In the jigging of ores, on the other hand, the slip generated by a deceleration of 327 cm/s^2 or less is not so beneficial: at a given particle size, the gangue grains of s.g. 2.6 to 2.8 experience about the same slip as the heavier ore grains.

44

In fact, z is somewhat less for the heavier particles: these fall somewhat further behind the pure slipless line $u - v_0$ than the lighter gangue grains. Hence, slip impairs jigging performance (albeit not too significantly): the heavy and light particles are separated somewhat less well than they would be in the absence of slip ($\Delta v \lesssim \Delta v_0$).

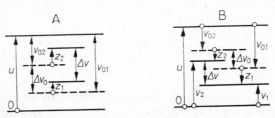

Fig. 1.15. A and *B* — influence of slip at a given a/g upon the velocity difference $\Delta v \neq \Delta v_0$ of particles different as to s.g. δ

At greater decelerations, the difference in slip will be beneficial also in the jigging of ores. At $a/g = -0.667$, e.g., the least z will be at s.g. 2.5 and the greatest at s.g. 4.0. The situation will thus once again be as shown in Part A of Fig. 1.15.

If a/g is positive, then the z curves (Fig. 1.14) have minima only, all at specific gravities equal to or less than 2 (at 2.0 if $a/g = 0$; at 1.7 if $a/g = 0.43$, and at 1.5 if $a/g = 1.0$).

In coal jigging, e.g., clean coal of s.g. 1.3 and shale of s.g. 2.5 have practically the same slip if $a/g = 0.43$, and any particle with a s.g. in between will also have that slip. At higher accelerations (e.g. at $a/g = 1.0$), the slip of clean coal of s.g. 1.3 to 1.5 is somewhat less than that of waste of s.g. 2.5, improving jigging performance (Part B of Fig. 1.15: $\Delta v > \Delta v_0$). Also in ore jigging, the slip of the lighter mineral will be less; in other words, the slip caused by acceleration (a positive a) is invariably beneficial, and the more so, the greater the acceleration. The advantage, however, is always rather substantially less than at optimum deceleration (a negative a).

The equations

$$u - v = v_0 \sqrt{\frac{a}{g_0} + 1}$$

and

$$u - v = - v_0 \sqrt{\frac{-a}{g_0} - 1}$$

yield after the substitutions

$$v_0 = C \sqrt{\frac{x(\delta - \gamma)}{\gamma}}$$

and

$$g_0 = \frac{g(\delta - \gamma)}{\delta}$$

the equations

$$u - v = C\sqrt{\frac{x}{\gamma}\left[\delta\left(\frac{a}{g} + 1\right) - \gamma\right]}$$

and

$$u - v = -C\sqrt{\frac{x}{\gamma}\left[\delta\left(\frac{-a}{g} - 1\right) + \gamma\right]}.$$

The equation of $u - v$, then, has the same structure as the equation of v_0, the only difference being that δ in the formula of v_0 is replaced by

$$\delta\left(\frac{a}{g} + 1\right)$$

in the formula of $u - v$.

There is the correspondence

$a =$	0	$-g_0$	$-g$
$u - v =$	v_0	0	$-C\sqrt{x}$

(cf. Fig. 1.16). That is,

(1) the curves $u - v$ vs. a of all particles of equal terminal settling velocity ($v_0 = $ const.) intersect in the axis of ordinates ($a = 0$), at its point v_0;

(2) the curves of all particles equal as to s.g. ($\delta = $ const. implying $g_0 = $ const.) intersect in the axis of abscissae ($u - v = 0$), at its point $a = -g_0$;

(3) the curves of all particles of identical size ($x = $ const.) intersect in the vertical $a = -g$. The curves have points of inflexion at $-g_0$ on the axis of abscissae and are centrally symmetrical about them (that is, the $u - v$ value at the point $-(2g_0 + a)$ is equal and opposite to the $u - v$ value at a). For example,

$$a = -2g \qquad \text{at} \quad u - v = -v_0',$$
$$a = -g + 2(g - g_0) = g - 2g_0 \qquad \text{at} \quad u - v = C\sqrt{x},$$

etc.

Given e.g. a feed of constant terminal settling velocity emerging from a classifier ($v_0 = $ const.), the $u - v$ curve of the heavier particles ($\delta_1 > \delta_2$) runs above that of the lighter particles in the interval $a > 0$ (where acceleration prevails), and the situation desirable in jigging, with the heavier particles deeper in the bed, arises only if $a < 0$ (that is, in the zone of deceleration).

Of two particles of equal s.g. ($\delta = $ const.), the curve of the larger particle ($x_1 > x_2$) runs below the $u - v$ curve of the smaller one in the interval $a > -g_0$; in the interval $a < -g_0$ (where deceleration is greater), the situation is reversed,

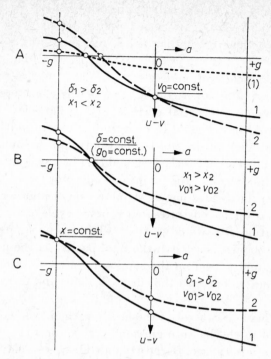

Fig. 1.16. A, B, C — comparison of $(u - v)$ curves vs. acceleration a: A — same s.g., B — same particle size, C — same terminal settling velocity

and water motion carries the smaller particle deeper into the bed. That is, a protracted strong deceleration will collect the smallest particles of identical gravity at the bed bottom even in the expanded state of the bed (when the ordering influence of vertical fluid motion can prevail).

In the jigging of a sized feed ($x = $ const.), the $u - v$ curve of the heavier particles ($\delta_1 > \delta_2$) is below that of the lighter particles over the interval $a > -g$ (that is, wherever acceleration is greater than zero or deceleration is between zero and $-g$). In such cases, then, the heavier particles are collected by vertical fluid motion in the bottom layer of the bed. A strong deceleration (exceeding $-g$), however, is a disadvantage as far as the gravity separation of a closely sized feed in a jig is concerned.

The dotted curve (1) in Part A of Fig. 1.16 is the $u - v$ curve of a very small heavy particle whose v_0 is much less than the v_0 of the light grains ($v_{01} \ll v_{02}$). A comparison of dotted curve 1 and dashed curve 2 accordingly provides information about the jigging of unsized-unclassified material: the ordering influence of vertical fluid motion is sufficient in itself to pull the fine heavy particles below the layer of coarse light particles, in keeping with the jigging principle, only if deceleration is greater than $a = -g_{02}$. At any deceleration

47

less than that, and at any acceleration, large or small, the fine heavy particles will collect above the layer of the coarse light particles.

The fine heavy particles are not, however, drained as a rule from among the lighter coarse particles in the expanded state: it is in fact the fluid flowing at speed (and at a high acceleration-deceleration) downward in the interstices of the "stationary" bed of larger particles, more or less compacted already, that entrains the heavy sub-interstitial particles (those particles small enough to pass through the said interstices). The entraining force (fluid suction) is to be adjusted so that it does not drag to the bed bottom any small light particles starting from the upper layers of the bed, and that it moves only the heavy fine particles through the screen of the jig into its collector tank "hutch product".

Water motion in fixed-sieve jigs may follow one or another of a variety of possible cycles. Figure 1.17 illustrates four types of cycle of vertical fluid velocity U and acceleration $B = du/dt$ vs. time t. There is no supply of back water (wash water from below the screen): the fluid passed on the pulsion (upward) stroke equals the fluid passed on the suction (downward) stroke, whence the areas marked $+$ and $-$ between the curves $U = f(t)$ and the axis of abscissae are equal.

If the volumetric solids content of the bed is σ, then average fluid velocity u and acceleration b in the bed are greater by a factor $1/(1 - \sigma)$ than U and $B = dU/dt$ in the hutch space. In the expanded bed, $\sigma \sim 0.4$; in the compacted bed, $\sigma \sim 0.7$; that is, $1 - \sigma$ varies between 0.6 and 0.3, and $1/(1 - \sigma)$ varies between 1.66 and 3.33, with an estimated average of 2.5. That is, one may use the approximate averages

$$u = 2.5U \qquad \text{and} \qquad b = 2.5B$$

for calculations concerning the bed.

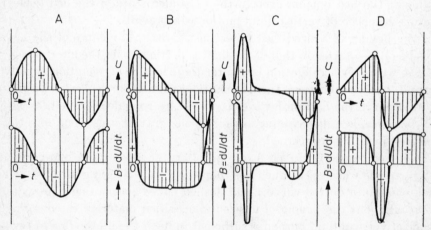

Fig. 1.17. A to *D* — possible variants of the water-velocity (*U*) and water-acceleration (*B*) cycle in a jig

In knowledge of the mechanism used to generate fluid motion, approximate u and b values may be calculated. For example, in a plunger jig whose plunger is driven by a crankshaft (or eccentric) and a rocker arm, the velocity U' of the plunger is an approximate sine function; its acceleration B' is an approximate cosine function. If crank radius is r and speed is n rpm, that is,

$$\omega = \frac{n\pi}{30},$$

then

$$U' = r\omega \sin \omega t$$

and

$$B' = r\omega^2 \cos \omega t.$$

Maxima occur where $\sin \omega t = 1$ and $\cos \omega t = 1$, respectively. The velocity U and acceleration B of the fluid in the hutch space are less as a rule than the U' and B' of the plunger, partly because some of the water (10 to 30%) can flow back through the clearance between the plunger and the jig housing, and partly because screen area is often somewhat greater (by 10 to 30%) than the area of the plunger compartment. That is, with no back water supply,

$$U = kU' \qquad \text{and} \qquad B = kB',$$

where

$$k = \frac{0.7}{1.3} \quad \text{to} \quad \frac{0.9}{1.1} = 0.54 \text{ to } 0.82$$

(about 0.68 as an average). For example, with no back water supplied, $k = 0.68$ and $1(1 - \sigma) = 2.5$ give

$$u = 1.7U' \qquad \text{and} \qquad b = 1.7B'.$$

In plunger jigs for coarse or fine ores, r is typically in the 2.0 to 0.2 cm range and $n \simeq 100$ to 300 ($\omega \simeq 10.5$ to 31.4); in coal jigs, $r \simeq 3.0$ to 1.5 cm, $n \simeq 50$ to 80 ($\omega \simeq 5.2$ to 8.4). In other words,

$$u_{max} \simeq 1.7U'_{max}$$

is about ($\pm$) 36 to 11 cm/s for ores and ($\pm$) 35 to 21 cm/s for coals;

$$b_{max} \simeq 1.7U'_{max}$$

is about ($\pm$) 370 to 340 cm/s² for ores and on the order of ($\pm$) 180 cm/s² for coals.

If back water is being introduced at a uniform rate over the entire jigging cycle (at a constant flow velocity w'), then fluid velocity in the space below the screen is

$$U = k(U' + w')$$

during pulsion and

$$U = k(U' - w')$$

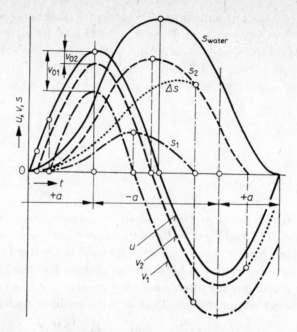

Fig. 1.18. Approximate diagrams of velocity v and displacement s of particles different as to terminal settling velocity v_0 in water in sine-wave motion: u is water velocity

during suction. This means that, in Fig. 1.17, the abscissa axes of the curves $U = f(t)$ must be displaced downward by $w = kw'$. The accelerations B and b remain unaffected by the introduction of back water: displacements of the axis of abscissae do not change the slope of the tangent to the curve.

Figure 1.18 presents approximate diagrams of velocity v and displacement s vs. time t for solid particles different as to both terminal settling velocity, $v_{01} > v_{02}$, and as to s.g., $\delta_1 > \delta_2$, for sine-wave variation of fluid velocity u and zero back water supply. As the velocity u of water passing through the interstices of the compacted bed increases, it begins to expand the top (light) layer of the bed. As flow continues to accelerate, the layers of the bed are expanded in succession from the top down; the heavy bottom layer gets expanded last. (A high-acceleration water pulse, on the other hand, can lift the entire compacted bed as it is; in that case, the bed will expand in the phase of deceleration only !) The degree of expansion will as a result be different in different layers of the bed. The *average* of σ over the entire bed (or over a layer of specified thickness within the bed) is

$$\sigma \cong \frac{\sigma_c h}{h + \Delta s} = \frac{\sigma_c}{1 + \dfrac{\Delta s}{h}},$$

where σ_c is the volumetric solids content of the bed (or layer) of thickness h, and

$$\varDelta s = s_2 - s_1$$

is the difference in displacement (rise) between the top and bottom of the bed (or layer), the ordinate intercept between the curves s_2 and s_1 in the figure (dotted curve). The rise of a given layer culminates (the maximum of its curve s is) where the appropriate v curve intersects the abscissa axis; it has returned to its original (starting) position when the areas below and above the axis of abscissae included (between that axis and the v curve) have become equal (cf. the shaded areas in Fig. 1.19). The lower (heavy) beds reach the peak of their rise and return to their starting position sooner than the upper (light) layers: these latter are still wide open when the lower layers have already compacted.

Figure 1.19 shows expansion $\varDelta s$ (the difference in displacement between the top and bottom) vs. time t for a layer whose compacted thickness is h. Referred to the second axis of abscissa, O_1, the $\varDelta s$ curve traces the variation of $h + \varDelta s$; if calibrated so that $h = 1$, it indicates the variation of

$$1 + \frac{\varDelta s}{h}, \quad \text{i.e. of} \quad \frac{\sigma_c}{\sigma}.$$

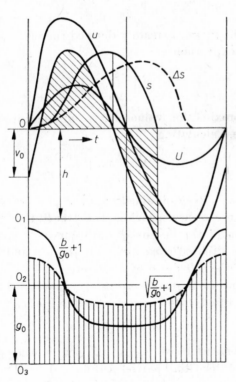

Fig. 1.19. Interrelationship of bed thickness, h, expansion, $\varDelta s$, under-screen water velocity, U, water velocity in the bed, u, and water acceleration in the bed, b

Hence, in possession of σ_c (equal to 0.6 to 0.7 as a rule), one can determine σ, and, in possession of $U = f(t)$, one can determine

$$u = \frac{U}{1 - \sigma},$$

the fluid velocity at any instant in the interstices of the layer. The curve $b = du/dt$ of fluid acceleration can be obtained by plotting the slope of the tangent to the u curve. Neglecting slip at a first approximation (i.e. assuming that the acceleration of the bed particles, $a = dv/dt$, equals the acceleration b of the fluid), velocity v of the particles can be derived from the u curve as shown in the bottom part of Fig. 1.19. Given the initial acceleration g_0 of the particle, and choosing a calibration $g_0 = 1$, the b curve referred to the fourth axis of abscissae O_3 provides the course of

$$\frac{b}{g_0} + 1;$$

the square root

$$\sqrt{\frac{b}{g_0} + 1},$$

shown shaded in the figure, is readily derived therefrom.

Subtracting the expression

$$v_0 \sqrt{\frac{b}{g_0} + 1}$$

from u, a first-approximation value of v is obtained; it can be refined by an iteration procedure. Calculating

$$\sqrt{\frac{a}{g_0} + 1}$$

using the value of $a = dv/dt$ obtained as the slope of the tangent to the first. approximation v curve, a curve providing a better fit to the actual v is obtained) Graphic integration of this more accurate curve provides s (displacement-curves for particles situated respectively at the top and bottom of the layer and a Δs curve for the difference of those, etc.

Bed expansion may be regarded as a fluidization brought about by the surging fluid. In the fluidized state, the static head in the layer of thickness h will be

$$p = h\sigma(\delta - \gamma).$$

The drag (hydrodynamic resistance) of the bed depends greatly on the abundance of finer (par-interstitial) particles, if any, in the interstices of the coarser ones. Early on in the expansion process, these finer particles are prevented from getting classified by joint settling by the compacted aggregate of coarser particles: in fact, since the same hydrodynamic forces act on any volume element of the bed, the aggregate of lighter particles will rise at a greater acceleration than the aggregate of heavier particles. A stratification by gravity can thus come about without any classification by particle size. The gradual expansion of the bed, however, eventually eliminates particle-to-particle contacts:

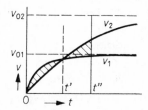

Fig. 1.20. $v = f(t)$ curve for a small heavy particle (*1*) and a large light one (*2*)

the bed is fluidized as a whole, and the particles making it up start to move according to the laws of hindered settling, more or less.

(D) *Particle behaviour in a movable-sieve jig.* In such a device, the screen deck is moved up and down in a fluid that is practically at rest; on the downstroke, the screen is pulled from under the bed, which loses its solid support. In contrast to the fixed-sieve jig, expansion begins in the bottom (heavy) layer of the bed and extends gradually upward to the lighter layers. Stratification by gravity can be interpreted here in terms of different initial acceleration of different particles: the heavier particles have a greater initial acceleration than the lighter ones, regardless of particle size, shape or terminal settling velocity. Figure 1.20 is a plot vs. time of the settling velocity

$$v = v_0 \tanh\left(\frac{g_0 t}{v_0}\right)$$

of a heavy fine particle 1 and a light coarse particle 2;

$$\delta_1 > \delta_2; \quad (g_{01} > g_{02}); \quad v_{01} < v_{02}; \quad x_1 \ll x_2.$$

It is seen that, up to the instant t', particle 1 will settle faster. The area between the two v curves in the interval 0 to t' is the same as in the interval t' to t''. Hence if within a jig cycle the expansion of the layer (during which the particles are more or less free to move relative to one another) is shorter than t'', then the heavy particles will end up in the deeper layer. The difference in displacement of the two particles is greatest at the instant t'; after it, the greater settling velocity of the light coarse particle 2 gradually gains the upper hand, and at the instant t'' (at which the shaded areas become equal), it catches up with the heavy fine particle 1. As far as stratification by gravity is concerned, it is an advantage if expansion starts in the bottom layer of the bed and proceeds up-

53

ward; the σ value perceived by a heavy particle leading the layer just expanding is thus less than that perceived by a slower light particle: that is, "hindered" velocity differentials increase, and so do the critical time intervals t' and t'', as against the situation in which both particles perceive the same σ.

1.4.1.3. Factors influencing jigging performance. Watching through a transparent wall the jigging of a short-range mixture of particles differing both in colour and s.g., one observes a sharply distinct top and bottom layer (possibly with a transitional layer of "middlings" between them). Even with the layers expanded, one has the impression of viewing two immiscible fluids, layered one above the other. A light particle cannot penetrate the heavy layer even if the density of the "fluid" made up of the heavy particles and the liquid is less (especially when expanded) than the s.g. of the light particle. The explanation is found in the order in which the layers of different density expand. If expansion starts at the top of the bed (as in the fixed-sieve jig), then all the particles in a given layer will start rising earlier and will rise higher than the heavier particles in the layer below it. Compaction, on the other hand, begins in the bottom layer of heavy particles: once that layer has closed up, the overlying middlings can no longer penetrate it. Now if expansion in the movable-sieve jig begins at the bottom, so does compaction, too, so that the bottom layer closes up and becomes unpenetrable by the time the middlings settle on it.

(A) *Throughput* is determined above all by the velocity of passage of the heavy particles through the layer of the light ones: it is the greater, the less the resistance of the layer to penetration by the heavier particles, which in turn is the less, the larger the interstices among particles. The longer and stronger the pulse causing expansion, the greater is jig throughput. If the feed is long-range or entirely unsized, however, a comparatively long and strong phase of suction is required (as we have seen) just to make the heavy fine particles pass through the bed: the throughput of such a feed will thus be proportionately less.

Jig throughput is proportional also to the rate of transport by cross water (the horizontal flow of fluid from the feed end to the tailboard), which depends among other things on the mobility of the expanded bed. The velocity of horizontal flow is determined by total feed rate (solids plus fluid), the flow cross section perpendicular to the flow vector and the feed rate of back water (equal to the difference between the volumes of water passing on pulsion and on suction). The horizontal velocity of the top (light) layer of the bed is roughly one-tenth of surface fluid velocity; that of the bottom (heavy) layer is about one-hundredth of surface velocity, provided there are no transverse riffles to keep a ragging in place on the screen. The bottom layer, then, advances much more slowly than the higher layers, which must deliver even the finest of their heavy particles to the bottom layer during their travel along the jig. Achieving this requires a smooth-running operation. If feed rate is too high, feed will pile up on the screen near the feed-end, and its stratification will remain incomplete. If the sufficient expansion of the bed requires a great deal of back water or strong pulsing, water may "boil" (jet through the bed in spots) rather than surge uniformly through the entire interstice area available. Turbulence caused by the tailboards separating jig compartments is another drawback, especially when jigging light feeds (e.g. coal).

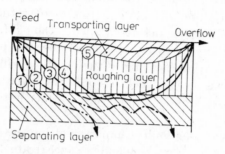

Fig. 1.21. Bed in a fine jig with some particle trajectories. *1* — Heavy particle, *2* — heavy small or par-interstitial particle, *3* — particle of medium s.g., *4* — light coarse particle, *5* — light fine particle

(B) *The bed of a fine jig* operating with hutch discharge is made up of three distinct layers: the bottom bed of heavy coarse particles (the ragging) is the separating layer; there is a roughing layer (a layer of transition) between it and the presenting and transporting layer of light particles at the top. The layers and the trajectories of different types of particles in a jig compartment are illustrated in Fig. 1.21. The ragging is made up of heavy particles larger than the screen apertures; they may be "autogenous" (i.e. derived from the feed) or alien. This layer is also expanded by the pulses: it must exceed a certain minimum thickness in order to ensure a uniform flow of water through the entire cross section and to forestall boiling (localized geyser-like blowouts through the upper layers). Heavy particles smaller than the screen aperture are pulled by suction through the ragging and so delivered to the hutch; lighter particles (irrespective of size and shape) cannot, on the other hand, penetrate the "dense medium" of the ragging. A thicker and heavier ragging (i.e. one of higher density) provides a sharper separation at a lower throughput rate. Output is influenced also by ragging granulometry, the relative magnitudes of pulsion and suction and the degree of expansion of the bed. The roughing layer, consisting partly of middling-type intergrown particles whose composition varies as feed is varied, also contributes to separation: it delivers the light coarse particles to the top (transport) layer and the middling-type supernumerary particles together with the light ones to the concentrate draw. At the top, there is a light, mobile transport layer which receives the feed and spreads it out over the jigging section. Most of the light particles travel in this layer all along; the rest are expelled up from the roughing layer, rising to pass the tailboard at the end of the compartment.

The quantity of heavy grains in the interstices of the ragging and in the bottom part of the roughing layer (that is, the total thickness of heavy material) is of course a function of feed rate and composition. It does not, however, follow changes in feed any too closely, as the number of heavy particles delivered per pulse to the hutchwork (the product discharged through the hutch) is a function of the total number of such particles contained in the jig: from a bed containing a larger number of heavy particles, a larger number will pass through per unit of time. (Misrouted particles leaving in the overflow will, of course, be more abundant also.) Thus a greater thickness of heavy layer in the bed will — for a given magnitude of pulsion — make for a cleaner hutchwork at a reduced component recovery.

In each compartment of a multi-compartment jig, the heavy fraction of the feed is discharged through the hutch and/or concentrate draw; hence, both the abundance and the s.g. of the heavy fraction decline from compartment to compartment. With the cross section unchanged, the reduction in throughput reduces the horizontal rate of progress of the solids, while cross water is increased from compartment to compartment by the back water introduced in each compartment.

(C) *Jigging performance* can be regulated by adjusting the thickness and density of the ragging, the supply of back water, the feed rate, cross flow rate and the pulsion cycle. The throughput of the jig and its separation performance (the steepness of its Tromp curve or the value of imperfection) are correlated. Beyond a certain limit, increasing throughput invariably impairs separation performance, the reason being that any individual particle during its sojourn in the bed requires a certain number of pulses (jig cycles) for being routed into the layer corresponding to its s.g.: a finer feed — which contains more particles per unit weight — has to be jigged at a slower throughput rate than a coarser one. It is in the final reckoning the abundance of critical particles (of the particles whose s.g. is close to the s.g. of separation, as indicated e.g. by the Bird number in a coal) that determines the best feasible combination of throughput and separation performance.

(D) *Further important factors* affecting jigging performance include the following.

The jigging cycle (the force and duration of pulsion and suction) must be suitably adjusted: pulsion should expand and suction compact the entire bed; the dead time between the end of a compaction phase and the beginning of the next expansion should not be too long. Optimum frequency and stroke depend on the feed rate, the s.g. of the feed, its granulometry, bed thickness, the type of jigging cycle employed and the intensity of suction (the supply rate of back water).

In the jigging of a long-range or altogether unsized feed, suction must be strong, but not stronger than what is just necessary. The introduction of back water weakens suction and enhances pulsion. The pulsion must expand the entire bed. The fines in a long-range feed fill out the interstices of the coarser particles, increasing the volumetric solids content of the bed; as a result, a weaker pulse may suffice to expand the entire bed, which means a reduced back-water requirement. If the feed is finer and shorter-range, suction intensity is to be reduced. A heavier and coarser feed requires a stronger pulsion (a faster-rising fluid). A thicker bed is slower to expand, and therefore requires a longer cycle (fewer cycles per minute) than a thinner one: it is therefore reasonable to operate a jig with a bed as thin as is consistent with other considerations of performance.

A large-apertured jig screen facilitates the concentration of fines. Bed compaction starts to impede stratification by gravity while suction is still going on. It is the screen aperture that determines the maximum particle size that can pass through, and also the density (permeability) of the compacted bed.

Vertical fluid flow should be uniform and of equal intensity throughout in the bed. Non-uniform bed distribution tends to result in non-uniform bed mobility. (For instance, more light or fine material may get delivered to one side of the screen than to the other.)

The gravity γ' of the fluid and that of the ragging should be as high as feasible. The fewer the interstices among the bed particles, the less water is required for expansion and the greater will be (including also in the expanded state) the hindered-settling ratio

$$ r' = \frac{(\delta_1 - \gamma')}{(\delta_2 - \gamma')} , $$

beneficial to both the sharpness and the throughput of separation. A high volumetric solids content σ in the bed is best ensured by a suitably graded aggregate containing heavy enough interstice-filling particles. Aqueous dispersions of coarse particles are still mobile enough at a volumetric solids content $\sigma = 0.55$. At such a density, using e.g. in coal washing interstice-filling particles of s.g.

$$ \varDelta \cong 1.8 \qquad 1.9 \qquad 2.0 , $$

one obtains effective densities

$$ \gamma' \cong 1 + \sigma(\varDelta - 1) = 1.44 \qquad 1.50 \qquad 1.55 , $$

in which clean coal particles of s.g. $\delta' < \gamma'$ will float up into the top layer, after the fashion of dense-medium separation.

If the spontaneous comminution granulometry of the feed does not provide interstice-filling particles in sufficient abundance, size and s.g., the deficiency can be made up by recirculating a fine-grained middling. This will, on the one hand, improve the sharpness of separation of hard-to-concentrate feeds containing many critical particles; on the other, it will greatly increase the throughput of the jig. For example, using middling recirculation, specific throughputs achieved were 22 t/h · m² for minus-75 mm coal having a Bird number of 22% ("very hard to wash") and 44 t/h · m² for minus-150 mm coal having a Bird number of 5% ("fairly washable"), whereas the typical specific jigging throughput of unsized coal is $\lesssim$ 10 t/h · m² (Mitchell 1950).

The lower limiting particle size of middlings recirculated for interstice filling should be in the coarse-sand range: slimes are harmful also in this case. Let us consider a case of separating coal of s.g. 1.5 from coal of s.g. 1.6. When jigging a short-range feed in clean water, e.g. with a volumetric solids content $\sigma = 0.45$ in the expanded bed and an average solids s.g. $\Delta \simeq 1.55$,

$$\gamma' \simeq 0.45 \cdot 1.55 + 0.55 = 1.25;$$

on adding a further $\sigma = 0.10$ worth of interstice filling of s.g. $\Delta = 2.0$, on the other hand, an effective density

$$\gamma' \simeq 0.45 \cdot 1.55 + 0.1 \cdot 2.0 + 0.45 = 1.35$$

is obtained, whereas the density of a strongly slimy wash water of volumetric solids content $\sigma = 0.2$ and average s.g. $\Delta = 1.6$ is

$$\gamma' = 0.2 \cdot 1.6 + 0.8 = 1.12.$$

The settling ratio

$$r' = \frac{(\delta_2 - \gamma')}{(\delta_1 - \gamma')},$$

which can be regarded as a measure of separation performance and throughput, is

$r' = 1.20$	1.26	1.40	1.67

for

$\gamma' = 1.00$	1.12	1.25	1.35

if $\delta_1 = 1.5$ and $\delta_2 = 1.6$. The settling ratio is thus increased insignificantly by a slimy wash water compared with a clear one. The higher density of the slimy water thus gives no practical benefit, whereas its greater viscosity impairs fines separation markedly, quite apart from the nuisance of slime films on the products and the excess cost of clarifying a strongly slimy water. (A dense medium of density $\gamma' < \delta_1 < \delta_2$ is nevertheless used on occasion instead of clear water as the fluid in a jig.)

1.4.2. Wet (hydraulic) jigs. Figure 1.22 shows the diagrams of a few types of fixed- and movable-sieve jigs.

1.4.2.1. Fixed-sieve jigs. One of the oldest types is the plunger jig, as represented by the Harz jig (Diagram A), developed at the ore concentrators of the Harz Mountains in Germany. The diagram shows a single-compartment jig, but multi-compartment ones are more frequent, with the screens of successive compartments usually built in so as to form a flight of descending steps. Each compartment is a communicating vessel, with the screen in one of its branches and the plunger in the other. The plunger is not tight, so that some of the water can pass it by. The amplitude of water motion is thus less than that of plunger motion. The loose plunger dampens the impact (acceleration) of water on each change of direction; it also makes possible, the introduction of back water into the space above the plunger. With no back water being introduced (and with the bottom aperture serving for intermittent hutch removal closed), the quantity of water moved is the same on pulsion and suction, and — in the case of an eccentric drive — so is its velocity. If some water is discharged through the bottom aperture, then the abscissa axis of the velocity curve $u = f(t)$ is displaced upward; pulsion is weakened and suction intensified. If back-water is supplied and discharged across the tailboard and through the concentrate draw, pulsion is intensified at the expense of suction: the abscissa of the velocity curve is displaced downward.

More recent types of jig often feature a diaphragm pump instead of a loose plunger. Here, a flexible diaphragm of rubber or leather connects the plunger with the plunger-compartment housing. This device can generate stronger pulses than the loose plunger.

A typical diaphgram device is the Bendelari jig (Diagram B). Its circular plunger is connected by a rubber membrane to a perforated plate a under the screen. The four corners of a are cut away so as to let the hutchwork drop into the bottom part of the jig whence it can be removed periodically or continuously. Concentrate coarser than the screen apertures is discharged through perforated pipe b above the screen. Back water is sucked in under the screen through clack valve c during the down stroke of the diaphragm. By suitably loading the valve, the correct relation of suction to pulsion in the bed may be adjusted. The drive is installed below the jig, so that the screen surface is readily accessible from all sides: the device is comparatively light and requires little space. It is popular on floating dredges concentrating placer deposits.

Another diaphragm-type device is the Pan-American Placer jig (not shown in the figure). It has a square screen deck and a movable conical bottom, moved up and down by an eccentric and connected to the cell housing by a rubber or leather membrane.

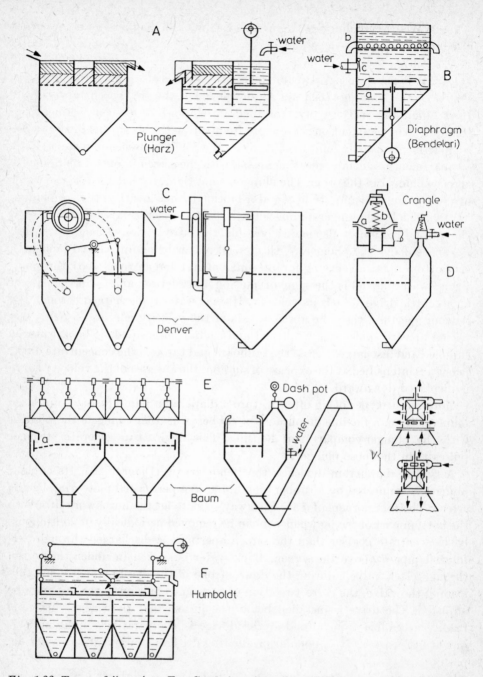

Fig. 1.22. Types of jigs. *A* to *E* — fixed-sieve jigs. *A* — plunger-type (Harz), *B* — dia-phragm-type (Bendelari), *C* — Denver, *D* — pulsator (Crangle), *E* — air-driven (Baum). *F* — movable-sieve (Humboldt) jig

In the Wemco–Remer jig, the screen frame is connected by a rubber diaphragm with a series of funnels moved up and down by eccentrics of different eccentricity and speed, combining a long stroke of low speed with a short stroke of high speed.

Also a diaphragm-type device, the Denver Mineral jig (Diagram C) incorporates an adjustable rotating valve, synchronized with the diaphragm (at n = 250 to 300 cpm), which feeds back water under the diaphragm during a well-defined phase of the jigging cycle (either during pulsion or suction). The machine can thus be adjusted for the sharp separation of long-range feeds as well as for the concentration of placer sands. It is frequently used in ball-mill-plus-mechanical-classifier circuits, inserted between the two devices, for removing from the circuit any unlocked heavy particles as early as possible.

The Krupp jig (not shown in the figure) is of the duplex vibrating type. In the wall separating the two compartments, a vertical diaphragm of horizontal motion is installed; it is driven by a spring-supported unbalanced disk at 500 cpm, with a stroke of 0.5 cm or so. It is suited for handling fine feeds in the 600 to 50 μm size range.

The group of *pulsator jigs* includes the Crangle or Pan-American jig (Diagram D). One of the branches of its communicating vessel is sealed off: through a special valve, rapidly pulsating water (500 to 600 cpm) is introduced under the screen. The machine operates exclusively on pulsion (there is no suction phase). Water pressure acting from below on rubber diaphragm a lifts the valve against spring b, so that water can flow into the hutch. In flowing water, however, static head is reduced by Bernoulli's Law, and the valve is thus closed again by the force of the spring. The frequent pulsions maintain the bed in a permanently expanded state: operating thus with a very dense (quicksand-like) suspension rather than with a bed alternately expanding and compacting, the device is suited for the concentration of fine placer material.

Low-pressure compressed air (at 0.08 to 0.12 gauge atmosphere), moving in and out of an otherwise sealed chamber above the water in a jig through a suitably controlled valve, can pulse the water just as a plunger can. By correctly adjusting the air valve (admittance, expansion with the valve closed, rate of outflow) and the rate of back-water feed, the jig cycle (the relative magnitude of pulsion and suction) can be readily regulated over a broad range. It is in coal washing above all that such pulsated Baum jigs are widespread. Compressed-air demand per m² of screen surface is about 7.5 m³/min in a coarse Baum jig and 3 m³/min in a fine one.

Diagram E of Fig. 1.22 shows a duplex Baum jig together with one of the earlier types of air valve (the piston valve V) in the positions of compressed-air discharge (top) and admission (bottom). More modern Baum jigs tend to be equipped with rotating valves. The full 360° cycle is divided up in the conventional Baum jigs run at n = 45 to 65 cpm approximately as follows: 170° for admission of air, 10° for expansion, 170° for discharging air and 10° for compression. In the more recent machines of greater throughput, operating on the Jeffrey–Bird cycle, at a speed of n = 22 to 28 cpm, the division is about 110°–100°–150°–0°.

In large jigs, large masses of water move to and fro, pendulum-fashion. This motion requires less energy and is smoother with less vorticity if it is kept at its resonant frequency. The centre of gravity of the mass of water moving in each of the two branches of the communicating vessel is in the plane of symmetry of the respective branch: half the distance between the two centres of gravity is the equivalent length L of the "pendulum", whence its period

$$t = 2\pi \sqrt{\frac{L}{g}} \simeq 2\sqrt{L} \text{ s}$$

and frequency

$$n = 60/t \text{ cpm}$$

can be calculated. For example,

$$L = \quad 0.5 \qquad\qquad 1 \qquad\qquad 2 \quad \text{m}$$

gives

$$t = \quad 1.4 \qquad\qquad 2.0 \qquad\qquad 2.8 \text{ s,}$$
$$n = 43 \qquad\qquad 30 \qquad\qquad 21 \quad \text{cpm.}$$

The screen in the first compartment of the Baum jig slopes towards the feed end at a in order to facilitate the direct removal of coarse heavy waste (shale) through a feed-end draw. The tank of the older Baum jigs used to have a U- or V-shaped cross section of uniform depth along its whole length rather than the pyramidal one shown in the diagram: it had the waste and the middling elevator on its two sides; into the launders of these, hutchwork and the waste from the draw between compartments was introduced by screws installed at the tank bottom, of opposite (outward-moving) thread in the two sections. The dams confining the draw are omitted in many of the more recent designs, and the stratified bed of the first compartment is transferred smoothly, turbulence-free into the second compartment.

The air chambers can be installed not only lengthwise, parallel to the screen decks, but also crosswise, under them. In this manner, a uniform water flow

Table 1.8

mm	+80	50	30	18	12	6	3	0.5
δ_T	1.47	1.49	1.53	1.51	1.51	1.56	1.56	1.71
$1{,}000E_p$	40	55	70	85	95	—	—	—

can be ensured in the entire width of the screen even in large machines (of a width of 5 m and more in the Tazub and Batac jigs) (Hoffmann and Mihalovski 1965).

Washing a minus-150, plus-0.5 mm coal in a Baum jig gives rise to a granulometry characterized e.g. by the δ_T and E_p values listed in Table 1.8. The minus-12 mm fractions contain some circulating middling.

1.4.2.2. Movable-sieve jigs incorporate large plane screens (length 6 to 7 m, width 0.6 to 1 m) moving up and down in a tank filled with stationary water. The tank under the screen is compartmented, and the hutchwork, whose s.g. decreases downstream can be drawn from each compartment either intermittently or continuously. In order to make the material progress along the screen, this latter is moved on a short inclined-arc trajectory rather than purely up and down. Travel per stroke equals the horizontal projection of the arc.

The several types of movable-sieve jigs differ primarily as to screen-moving mechanism. In the Humboldt jig, shown as Diagram F of Fig. 1.22, the screen is suspended from linkages actuated by eccentrics and connecting rods. In other machines, the screen connected to suspension rods is actuated e.g. by a cam disk. The upward motion of the deck is limited by striking blocks which cause it to rebound on the down stroke and thereby assure a cleaner detachment of the screen from the material resting on it.

The hand jig is also a movable-sieve jig. A bow with a screen for its bottom, filled with the material to be jigged, it is held under water and moved slowly upward and fast downward, either directly by hand or by a jig pole, a two-arm lever which has the jig box suspended from its shorter arm. After sufficient stratification of the feed, the light layer on top is removed and the box is filled with fresh feed. When the heavy bottom layer has grown thick enough as a result of several repetitions, it is also removed.

1.4.2.3. Coarse and fine jigs. The main difference between the two is in the manner of removing the heavy products (gate draw, hutch draw). In jigs handling unsized feeds, the two types of draw are often applied in combination. Screen apertures are smaller than the particles of the material to be jigged in the coarse jig but larger in the fine jig; hence, a coarse-grained ragging made up of heavy particles has to be layered onto the screen of the fine jig. The ragging may be lighter than the heavy particles to be concentrated but must always be heavier than the light fraction or the coarse middlings.

Concentrate collecting in the bottom layer is often drawn from the screen of the coarse jig by a so-called gate-and-dam discharge devices, with the gate having an adjustable underpass edge and the dam having an adjustable overflow edge (a weir). Part A of Fig. 1.23 shows a typical gate-and-dam design; Part B shows a cup-and-pipe design. In the expanded bed, a striving for hy-

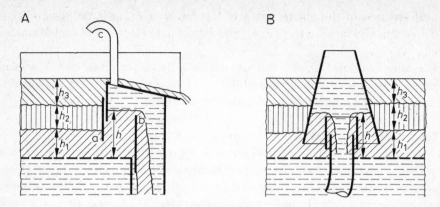

Fig. 1.23. A and *B* — concentrate draw in a coarse jig

drostatic equilibrium arises between the heavy layer h inside the gate and the layers in the jig bed, $h_1 + h_2 + h_3$.

At hydrostatic equilibrium, the relationship

$$h\gamma_1' = h_1\gamma_1' + h_2\gamma_2' + h_3\gamma_3'$$

holds, where γ_i $(i = 1, 2, 3)$ denotes the effective densities of the respective layers ($\gamma_i' = \sigma_i\delta_i + 1 - \sigma_i$, the s.g. of the mixture of solids and water). The underpass edge of the gate a must reach down into the heavy layer to be drawn, called upon as it is to hold up the particles of the upper layers. If hydrostatic equilibrium were complete, the thickness h_1 of the heavy layer in the bed could be adjusted independently of the abundance of heavy particles in the feed, simply by regulating the height h of dam b. Changing h causes an abrupt, temporary change in the draw rate but, after the h_1 corresponding to the new equilibrium has set in, that rate will again equal the input rate of heavy fraction in the feed.

Pipe c connects the pen (the closed space above the dam) with the outer atmosphere. In the absence of such an outlet, water as an incompressible fluid could not move up and down to expand the layer of height h: that is, the forces bringing about hydrostatic equilibrium could not enter into play, and the layer would be held up behind the gate and dam.

Even in the expanded bed, however, hydrostatic equilibrium does not prevail sufficiently to make height h_1 entirely independent of any changes in the abundance of heavy fraction in the feed (always assuming h to be unchanged). Hence, changes in feed rate and/or composition will sooner or later impair the purity of overflow or concentrate if the gate and dam are not readjusted: misrouted particles will appear in one of the products. The stability of a jig (expressed as the length of time over which product quality remains unimpaired after a change of feed rate or quality, with the gate and dam unmoved) is the greater, the heavier the load on the screen (that is, the thicker the bed and the larger the screen area). Adjusting concentrate draw by varying the aperture of the outlet so as to adapt it to changes in feed is the task of the jig operator. Even the most careful regulation by hand is, however, surpassed in performance by automatic concentrate-draw regulators, used on large coal jigs above all.

1.4.2.4. Automatic draw regulators. Diagrams of three such devices are shown in Fig. 1.24.

In Diagrams A and B, the automatic draw regulator for the waste layer is actuated by float a immersed in the roughing layer. If the thickness of the

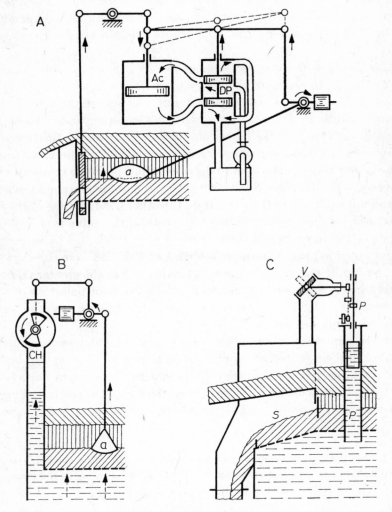

Fig. 1.24. Automatic concentrate-draw regulators used in jigs. A — hydraulic, B and C — backpressure-regulating types. A and C regulate gate draw; B regulates hutch draw

waste layer increases, the float rises, initiating the process indicated by arrows in the diagram: the dual piston DP rises up; oil under pressure between the pistons is forced above the piston in actuator cylinder AC, moving it downward, thus widening the aperture through which the waste layer is discharged, until the dual piston, moving downward, has returned to its original position, at which time the oil feeds to the actuator are shut off. The upper linkage bar then remains in the position shown dashed in the figure until the float moves again, upward or downward.

Part B shows an automatic regulator for hutch draw. Rising, the float closes valve a through which air chamber CH, connected with the hutch space under the screen, communicates with the outside atmosphere. With the valve closed, less of each pulsion is bypassed: the pulsions are thus forced to expand the jig bed more and to exert a stronger suction, resulting in a more vigorous hutch draw.

The automatic gate-draw regulator shown in Part C operates on a similar principle. As the thickness of the heavy layer increases, so does the hydraulic resistance of the bed as a whole. As a result, the amplitude of water-column oscillation in tube P, communicating with the hutch space, will increase, and the float in the tube will rise higher on pulsion. Pin p on the float stem thereupon actuates a mechanism which opens valve V wider. The valve opens the chamber above the gate and dam to the outer atmosphere, so that water pulsating in the pen (in the space S between gate and dam) can expand the material there and unload it across the dam. If on the other hand, the rise of the float in P is reduced because the heavy layer is too thin, the valve is closed and the aggregate settles in the pen in the absence of a strong enough pulsation. (Much the same would happen if the pipe in Part A of Fig. 1.23 were closed.) [The increased hydraulic resistance of the bed, resulting from the greater thickness of the heavy layer, will increase the strength/amplitude of pulsation in the pen in any case (provided the height of the dam is fixed), even without benefit of any special regulating device.]

There are numerous other designs of automatic regulators for concentrate draw, most of them controlled by changes in the s.g. of the roughing layer (the layer of transition), either through a float immersed in it (as in Parts A and B of Fig. 1.24), or by a direct measurement of the s.g. of the solids making it up, by a device using a source and sensor of nuclear radiation or by some other means.*

* Nuclear radiation is absorbed gradually by the matter it traverses, transferring energy to it. The intensity of gamma radiation decreases according to the formula

$$I = I_0 e^{-\mu \delta l}$$

where I_0 is radiation intensity on emission, μ is the mass absorption coefficient (cm²/g), δ is the s.g. of the absorbing material (g/cm³), l is the length of the path of radiation in

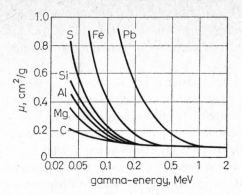

Fig. 1.25. Mass absorption coefficient μ (cm²/g) for some chemical elements vs. gamma-radiation energy

The sensor may actuate the dam and/or gate confining the drawoff aperture either by some direct means as in the three designs of Fig. 1.24, or by electro-mechanical or pneumatic control, but it may also adjust the discharge rate of the heavy concentrate e.g. by regulating the speed of the rotary scraper remov-ing it from the collector bucket under the slot between compartments.

1.4.2.5. Jigging technology. In each compartment of the jig, one stage of concentration is performed: each compartment accordingly furnishes one con-centrate only. It is therefore necessary as a rule to have several compartments in series, depending on the nature of the feed. Even a feed composed of just two minerals, however, often requires at least two compartments, with the concen-trate and/or hutchwork of the first as the finished heavy product (pay product in ore dressing, waste in coal washing), and that of the second a middling, and the overflow of the second compartment entraining the finished light product. By inserting further compartments, cleaner products may be obtained. The number of products invariably equals the number of compartments plus one. For example, a three-compartment ore jig furnishes in succession a con_ centrate, a rich middling, a lean middling and a waste (the latter as the over_

---

it (cm). The value of μ depends on the chemical composition of the material and on the energy spectrum of the radiation. The variation of μ vs. gamma-radiation energy is shown for a few chemical elements in Fig. 1.25. At gamma-quantum energies above one MeV, μ is small, independent of the chemistry of the absorbent and quasi-independent of radiation energy also. The choice of the radioactive isotope source depends on the compo-sition and thickness of the material to be irradiated. The greater the thickness and the s.g. of the material, the stronger a source emitting, the harder a gamma radiation is to be chosen.

flow of the last compartment). It is reasonable in such a case to further unlock the two middling fractions separately, comminuting the richer middling less, so as to obtain the pay mineral in the form of the largest possible grains.

In adjusting and regulating a jig, a number of parameters can be varied, including screen aperture; pulse strength, cross water and its back-water component; the relative rate of water discharge from the hutch; feed rate, bed thickness and the thickness of each individual layer; the presence or absence of alien ragging, etc. (Mitchell 1950: cf. also Section 1.3.1.).

Screen-aperture size depends on ragging granulometry: it should be as large as is consistent with a given ragging size in order to reduce screen drag, to forestall clogging and to promote hutch discharge.

Strength of pulse is a function of frequency (n) and stroke ($l = 2r$). In a fixed-sieve jig, it determines the expansion of the bed together with back-water feed rate. Hutchwork-discharge rate in a fine jig varies as ln^2. The stroke should be as short as possible in order to prevent the geyser-like boiling of the bed and the resulting churn-up of the layers. Expanding a coarser aggregate to the same relative pore volume requires a longer stroke, with pulse frequency reduced appropriately (but not proportionately). A full jigging cycle takes a certain time, not less than about 0.2 s in ore dressing practice. Pulse frequency is accordingly seldom higher than 300 cpm; its lower limit is about 120 cpm in ore jigging. The corresponding strokes vary from about 0.5 to 5 cm. The high-speed Crangle and Krupp pulsator jigs ("vibrating jigs") are not true jigs: they represent a transition towards the dense-medium sluice of the Stripa process. The speed of coarse Baum coal jigs used to be 50 to 70 cpm earlier (it is about 25 cpm nowadays); that of the fine jigs is 70 to 90 cpm. The usual water stroke is 8 to 13 cm in the first and 3 to 7 cm in the second.

Cross water varies as strength of pulsion. Each pulsion discharges across the tailboard of each compartment a water layer whose thickness varies as pulsion stroke. Water leaves the jig for good across the tailboard of the last compartment. Cross water is made up of water added to or contained in the feed (top water) plus back water (the back-water feed rate can be adjusted to regulate the duration of expansion and the relative length of suction and pulsion). The specific water consumption of jigs (m³ of water per ton of solids) varies over a wide range, depending on feed granulometry, s.g. distribution and jig design. On an average, 5 m³/t per compartment should be envisaged in ore jigging and 2 to 3 m³/t in coal jigging in a fixed-sieve jig, giving e.g. about 20 m³/t for a four-compartment ore jig and 4 to 6 m³/t for a two-compartment coal jig. Movable-sieve jigs require much less water (0.5 to 1 m³/t).

Bed thickness is determined by the height of the tailboard above the screen. The bed should be as thin as feasible, with the heavy bottom bed remaining safely below the overflow edge of the tailboard even on full expansion, to avoid boiling the bed. Conventional bed thickness is provided by the rule-of-thumb formula

$$H \cong 33x^{0.6} \, (\pm 20\%),$$

where x is maximum particle size in the bed. Hence, e.g.

$$\text{at } x = 2 \quad 10 \quad 50 \quad 100 \text{ mm}$$
$$\text{we have } H = 5 \quad 13 \quad 35 \quad 52 \text{ cm.}$$

The thickness of the individual layers can be regulated most simply by means of automatic drawoff control for the heavy layer. Manually it can be regulated by adjusting the concentrate discharge (drawoff) aperture or the height of the tailboard in coarse jigs, by adjusting ragging thickness in fine jigs and by adjusting cross water flow rate in both. A faster cross water flow results in a faster discharge of the top, lightest layer above all. The adjustment of back-water feed rate influences the relative strengths of pulsion and suction, and hence bed expansion and, through it, the cleanness of the products.

Feed rate and product cleanness (sharpness of separation) are interdependent. The quality of the top layer is more sensitive as a rule to changes in feed rate than that of the bottom layer. Specific output in tons per hour per square metre of screen surface varies widely from one jig design to the next; it is greatly influenced also by the nature of the feed. At a very rough estimate, it is 8 t/h · m² in a two-compartment plunger jig (for both ores and coal), 4 t/h · m² for a finer feed (< 10 mm), assuming a feed moderately amenable to jigging. Output will be greater for a smaller abundance of critical particles and conversely. For example, the rule-of-thumb output of two-compartment plunger or Baum jigs is 5 to 12 t/h · m² for a coarse coal jig, 3 to 8 t/h · m² for a fine one, 8 to 12 t/h · m² for a jig handling unsized feed and 4 to 6 t/h · m² for a cleaner jig, depending on the washability of the coal.

Sustainable feed rate of a Baum jig per metre of screen width is 120 (max. 160) t/h of unsized coal ($\lesssim 100$ mm), or 50 (max. 65) t/h of fine coal ($\lesssim 12$ mm). Discharge rates of heavy product, towards the top of the range, are 33 (max. 45) t/h per metre of screen width in the first (waste) elevator and half as much, 16 (max. 23) t/h in the second (middling) elevator. Total heavy product, D t/h · m² removed by the two elevators is 2 to 3 when handling a very poorly washable fine coal, 4 to 5 for a medium-washable unsized coal and 6 to 7 for a readily washable one. Approximate values of imperfection are furnished by the formula

$$I \cong \frac{D}{40} + I_0 \, (\pm 0.05),$$

where I_0 is about 0.15 for the minus-12 mm, plus-0.5 mm fraction, about 0.10 for the minus-25, plus-12 mm fraction and about 0.08 for the plus-25 mm fraction.

In the jigging of polymetallic ores, as many as 5 to 7 compartments may be needed, in view of the fact that the difference in s.g. between the minerals to be separated is rather slight. Output referred to the aggregate screen surface of the compartments is small, not more than 0.3 to 1 t/h · m².

The output of diaphragm jigs is 10 to 20 t/h · m² for the Bendelari, Pan-American, etc., 25 for the Denver and 50 to 70 for the Crangle. The dual Krupp pulsator jig discharges 1.5 to 2 t/h · m² if fed a minus-0.6, plus-0.05 mm feed.

Screen surface area in plunger-type ore jigs is in the 0.25 to 1.25 m² range for a width of 0.4 to 1 m. Aggregate screen surface area in two-compartment coal jigs is 5 to 16 m² for a typical width range of 1.5 to 2.2 m (but there are also giant machines with 5 or 6 m screen width, such as the Baum–Batac). The width of the plunger compartment is 0.8 to 1.1 times the width of the screen compartment in coarse jigs and 0.45 times that width in fine jigs. Screen area is 0.36 or 1 m² for the square screens of diaphragm jigs, 0.09 or 0.2 or 0.36 m² in the Crangle and 0.06 to 0.54 m² (20 cm by 30 cm to 60 cm by 90 cm) in the single- or dual-compartment Denver whose screens are oblong with a 1.5 to 1 side ratio.

Power draft per m² of screen area is about 0.4 kW for fine and 1.8 kW for coarse ore jigs and about 0.7 kW for fine and 1.7 kW for coarse coal jigs.

The first mechanized concentrators of ore dressing, jigs once were in wide-spread use handling feeds over a broad size range (80 to 0.3 mm), short-ranged for polymetallic ores and long-ranged for simple ores. After the appearance of shaking tables at the turn of the century, tabling has overtaken jigging in popularity in the concentration of sands finer than about 1 mm. Since flotation gained ground (in the 1920s and 1930s), jigging has been almost entirely superseded in the dressing of sulphide ores (so has also tabling, for that matter). The expansion of D.M. concentration (in the 1940s) drove the jig out of the coarse particle-size domain, so that, as compared with the past, the scope of application of jigging has been much reduced both in ore dressing and in coal washing.

It would nevertheless be wrong to regard the jig as an obsolete concentrating device. It is still an up-to-date means of handling ore feeds in the 1 to 10 mm size range and coal in the 0.5 to 10 mm size range. In these size ranges, its main competitor since the 1950s has been the D.M. hydrocyclone, a device that permits a sharper separation albeit at a much higher operating cost. The jig can still compete with the more expensive D.M. method even in coarser size ranges in coal washing and in the dressing of certain ores (iron, manganese, etc.), especially when handling feeds poor in critical particles or ores in which the s.g. of both minerals to be separated is higher than the density of conventional dense media. For example, readily washable coals of very long range, from 150 to 200 mm down to about 0.5 mm, are handled unsized in a single pass by large jigs of great output. The sharpness of separation (Tromp curve) of the modern high-duty Batac jigs vies with that of the D.M. process in the concentration of both coarse (≈ 10 mm) and fine particles. The more recent types of diaphragm and pulsator jigs, on the other hand, have started to replace the sluices previously used for handling minus-1 mm feeds in the concentration of placer deposits. Lately, jigs have been employed also for the removal, as early as possible, of coarser-grained precious metal and sulphide particles from ball-mill-and-classifier circuits.

1.4.3. Dry (pneumatic) jigs. If the jig is operated with air rather than water for a fluid, no slimes are produced and the need for de-watering the product does not arise. Jigging in air, on the other hand, produces less sharp a separation. For example, a coal dispersion of average s.g. $\Delta = 1.6$ at a volumetric solids content $\sigma = 0.5$ has a fluid density of 0.8 in air and of 1.3 in water. Putting e.g. $\delta_1 = 1.7$ and $\delta_2 = 1.5$, the hindered-settling ratio

$$r' = \frac{(\delta_1 - \gamma')}{(\delta_2 - \gamma')}$$

will be 2.00 in water and 1.28 in air: putting $\delta_1 = 2.2$ and $\delta_2 = 1.4$, it will be 9.0 in water and 2.33 in air. Corresponding values of the free-settling ratio

$$r = \frac{(\delta_1 - \gamma)}{(\delta_2 - \gamma)}$$

are 1.40 and 1.13 in the first case and 3.0 and 1.57 in the second. (Separation by gravity becomes practically impossible at $r < 1.25$.)

The difference in settling ratios makes it abundantly clear that separation by gravity is more of a problem in air than in water. No acceptable jigging of a poorly washable coal (a coal of a high Bird number) can be expected of a pneumatic jig, even if the feed is very closely sized.

The essential feature of the pneumatic jig, just as of the wet one, is a horizontal or slightly sloping screen carrying the material to be separated, with a vertically pulsating fluid (air) flowing through both. The fluid flow expands (fluidizes) the bed so that the particles of the aggregate become mobile with respect to one another; as a result, the heavy particles can collect at the bottom and the light ones on top. Pneumatic jigs operate on pulsion only, without suction. Their principal field of application is in coal preparation: more seldom (in arid, desert regions), they are used in ore concentration also.

1.4.3.1. Types of pneumatic jig. The different types differ in the mode of transport and discharge of the layers of the bed stratified by gravity.

There are fixed-sieve and movable-sieve pneumatic jigs. The former agree in all respects with the wet fixed-sieve jigs; the latter, however, differ in their mode of operation from the wet movable-sieve jig: screen motion is not up

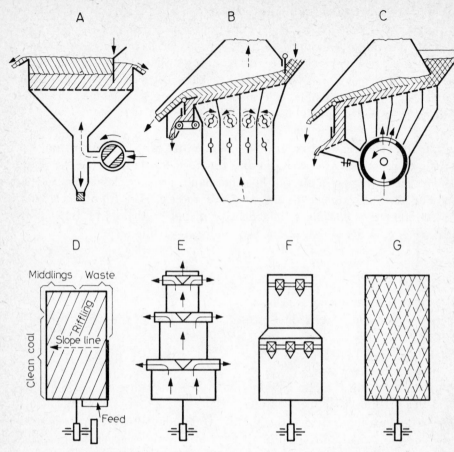

Fig. 1.26. Pneumatic jigs. *A* to *C* — fixed-sieve. *A* — ore-concentrating, *B* — Finkey machine, *C* — Martiny machine. *D* to *G* — diagrams of pneumatic jigs of the movable-sieve type ("pneumatic tables") in plan view

and down but in the deck plane (as in a wet table), and the screen does not move in a stationary medium: there is instead an upward current of air passing through it. The most widespread make of this type recalls a wet shaking table both as to external appearance and the mode of product discharge: this is why, in some languages, it is misnamed a "pneumatic table". In reality, these movable-sieve devices are true jigs and not tables: they incorporate screens, and it is the vertical flow of medium through the screen apertures that orders the bed by gravity.

In Fig. 1.26, Parts A, B and C are diagrams of fixed-sieve pneumatic jigs; Parts D to G are diagrams of movable-sieve ones.

In the fixed-sieve devices, the light top layer is discharged invariably across a tailboard opposite to the feed end, just as in the wet jigs, but hutchwork is removed from each by a different draw mechanism.

Part A is the diagram of a machine suited for ore concentration. The gate-and-dam discharge of the heavy layer is right behind the feed end (as e.g. in the wet Baum jig); hutchwork collects in a bucket under the rotating air valve, whence it can be drained off at intervals.

Parts B and C are the diagrams, respectively, of Finkey's and Martiny's pneumatic-jig designs, both of Hungarian make.

Finkey's machine uses rotating valves for making the air flow pulsate: under them, there are butterfly valves for regulating the distribution of air among the compartments along the length of the screen. The heavy product, separated from the overflowing top layer by an adjustable horizontal splitter, discharges into a bucket from the bottom of which it is removed by a short endless conveyor of adjustable speed.

Fixed-sieve pneumatic jigs of foreign make tend to differ from Finkey's machine essentially in the design of the waste discharge only. The Kirkup or the Carlshütte jig, e.g., have ribbed rotating drums, the SKB (Schüchtermann & Kremer–Baum) jig has a rocking valve to replace the short endless conveyor under the heavy-product bucket of the Finkey machine. The arrangement of the rotating and butterfly valves is also different.

In the Martiny jig, a rapidly rotating valve routes air pulses in succession into successive compartments, so that the pulses seem to run along the screen. By suitably adjusting valve speed, the coal bed on the screen can be brought to a state of resonant fluidization: separation by gravity is rapid in this quasi-fluid bed. The air-supply requirement (and hence also the power draft) of this machine is substantially less than in those in which air flows uniformly through the entire screen surface. Above the coal bed, the velocity of air blown in a thin blade through the screen decreases abruptly owing to the increase in free cross section, and most of the dust entrained out of the coal (coarser than e.g. 100 μm) is dropped onto the top of the bed. By means of a suitable splitter, this layer of dust can be separated from the coarser-grained clean coal if the need arises.

Air velocity (gauge pressure) in a pneumatic jig must be sufficient to keep the coal bed in suspension (to fluidize it), but not high enough to cause boiling. The hazard of boiling is also less in the Martiny jig than in other types of dry fixed-sieve pneumatic jigs, because the thin blade of air blown in can expand in the coal bed proper. Accordingly, at the bottom of the bed, where the heavy particles of waste are to be found, air velocity will be higher for a given σ than at the top of the bed where the lighter particles with a greater propensity to boil lie.

If the aim is to win middlings also, fixed-sieve pneumatic jigs with two or three compartments are often used. The gate draw of the first compartment is "clean waste", the overflow of the second is clean coal; its gate draw is a middling which is either returned to the feed end of the first compartment or sold for boiler fuel. Three-compartment jigs are best suited for handling hard-to-jig coals and/or coal fines.

Each of the types of movable-sieve pneumatic jigs in Parts D to G of Fig. 1.26 is a shaking screen supported by inclined elastic legs, shaken by an eccentric and a rocker arm; transport of the bed is caused by the motion of the screen. (On the sloping deck of the fixed-sieve machines, the fluidized bed flows off the slope spontaneously.) Shaking results in the rhythmic heaving of the bed, or at least in a rhythmic variation of its pressure on the screen, because the vertical component of the force of inertia is now added to the force of gravity, now subtracted from it. In movable-sieve pneumatic jigs, the air will pulse through the bed even if no pulsator is used.

The screen deck in Part D of the figure has a sideways tilt and a somewhat oblique, near-diagonal riffling. Thanks to the shaking of the deck, the riffles drive the bottom (waste) layer upward: the layer of clean coal, which is not in contact with the riffles, trickles off the deck just as in a wet shaking table. In the design of Part E, the top (clean-coal) layer is skimmed off and discharged sideways by suitably designed skimmers adjustable vertically, whereas the bottom (waste) layer moves on under it in the direction of shaking. In Part F, the bottom (waste) layer drops through slots between wedge-shaped deflectors, while the top (coal) layer moves on, overflowing the deflector rims. What is left on the screen is the roughing layer (the middling), which flows on towards the next point of discharge. The decks of Designs E and F get narrower after each discharge, in order to keep the thickness of the bed and, together with it, the resistance to air flow roughly uniform. In the design of Part G, there are two sets of crossing riffles, one above the other, deflecting in opposite directions the bottom layer of waste and the top layer of clean coal as the horizontal screen deck is being shaken.

The screen of a recent type of pneumatic jig, developed by the Steinkohlenbergwerke A. G. of Essen, is driven by a vibrator in order to ensure a suitable progress of the bed: the machine is identical with the fixed-sieve machines in all other particulars. Under its slightly inclined screen, there are five compartments, each fitted with an air valve and a pulsator. Waste is separated from clean coal at the discharge end by a splitter that can be raised or lowered. It is controlled by a gamma-radiation meter which, installed at adjustable height in the midline of the deck, senses the intensity of the residual radiation from two gamma-ray sources installed on either side of the machine. Automatic drawoff regulation has eliminated the principal previous drawback of fixed-sieve pneumatic jigs, their notorious lack of stability. For de-dusting a feed, the first two compartments can be run without pulsators, as an air separator. The output of the machine is some 25 t/h · m² for a feed of unsized minus-10 mm coal (Bartelt 1966).

1.4.3.2. Technological parameters of pneumatic jigs. The optimum thickness of the bed and the required gauge pressure of the fluidizing air are determined by feed granulometry. In a movable-sieve pneumatic jig, where the motion of the screen deck itself will pulse the air flow, a gauge pressure of 25 to 40 mm of water column may be sufficient. In a fixed-sieve machine, gauge pressure is typically in the range of 70 to 180 mm of water column.

Approximate specific throughput is given by the formula

$$T \simeq 3x_{\text{avg}}^{0.7}$$

for fixed-sieve machines, by the formula

$$T \simeq 2.5 + 0.3x$$

for movable-sieve ones and by the formula

$$T' \simeq 12 + 0.9x$$

for both, where T is in tph per m² of screen area, T' is in tph per metre of screen width, x_{avg} is average grain size and x is maximum grain size, both in mm. x seldom exceeds 25 mm, but may on occasion be as high as 60 mm. The specific air requirement of the Finkey machine and of similar designs is in the range of 1,000 to 2,000 m³ per ton of coal, depending on feed size and granulometry.

Surface moisture of coal fed to a pneumatic jig should not exceed 5 to 6%. The rule of thumb is that any coal that can be screened can also be handled by a pneumatic jig, but there are exceptions to this rule. On occasion, even a surface moisture content as low as 2% will appreciably impair performance. For example, a soft waste readily crumbling under the influence of moisture has a propensity to clog up screen apertures, upsetting the uniformity of air distribution. On the other hand, pneumatic jigs will readily handle a feed of significantly higher moisture content provided the waste it contains is hard and comminutes to fragments of cubic or prismatic shape. The surface moisture content of the fines tends to be higher than that of the coarser particles. This is one of the reasons why the pneumatic jigging of finer particle-size ranges is more difficult and less successful as a rule. In one concrete case, the percentage abundance of the plus-1.6 s.g. fraction in the feed (a), in the concentrate (b) and in the tailings (c), the percentage tailings yield (v) and component recovery for plus-1.6 s.g. particles (m) and the efficiency of separation (η) for a 10 to 5 mm and a 5 to 0.4 mm grain size fraction were as stated in Table 1.9. Separation efficiency is seen to be rather dramatically less for the finer fraction.

Vertical fluid motion endows pneumatic jigs with pronounced classifier features, what with the phase of suction, called upon to cancel such features to some extent, being absent. The influence of particle size and shape is thus enhanced against that of s.g. This is why, in the output, the fines tend to have a higher s.g. (and ash content) than the coarser fractions. (This is something of an advantage if a feed is available whose coarser fractions are higher in ash than the finer ones, as in that case the ash contents of the product fractions of different size will differ less.) Separation by shape in a pneumatic jig lets flat pieces of shale float rather easily to the top of the coal bed: within one and the same grain size fraction, flat particles, lighter than cubic or prismatic ones,

Table 1.9

mm	a	b	c	v	m	η
10—5	10	3	53	14	74	67
5—0.4	6	5	53	2	18	17

are readily lifted to the top of the bed by the vertical air current (Yancey and Black 1931.)

The lower limiting grain size of feeds that can be successfully handled by pneumatic jigs is 0.3 mm or so. Pneumatic jigging will remove pyrite from coal fairly efficiently. True, wet washing produces a washed coal lower in ash, but it increases the moisture content of the product by 3 to 6%: the net calorific value of such wet coal might well be less than that of the drier albeit ashier coal produced by pneumatic jigging.

A heavy powder fluidized in a rising current of air can be used as a fine dry dense medium to separate by gravity a coarser-grained feed (r.o.m. ore or coal). (Cf. Fig. 1.12 or the Dryflow separator.)

1.5. SLUICING AND TABLING

1.5.1. Fundamentals. Both sluices and tables essentially depend for their separating action on water flowing down a sloping surface. The surface may be smooth, rough or riffled; the water may be shallow (a sheet or film) or deep, laminar or turbulent. The essential difference between a sluice and a table is in the depth of water. Nature and depth of flow are determined by the water feed rate, the width and slope of the surface and various other factors (e.g. fluid viscosity, friction between the fluid and the bottom, combinations of currents in several directions, non-uniform feed distribution in the sheet of water, etc.).

1.5.1.1. Behaviour of a thick bed in a sluice. A thickish bed of particle aggregate moved by a current of water in a stationary launder is arranged by s.g. and particle size, with the fine heavy particles at the bottom and the coarse light ones at the top, the reason being that flow velocity is not uniform all over the cross section of the launder: it is less in the proximity of the bottom and of the sides than in the mainstream where the flow is markedly turbulent as a rule. Both the vorticity of the flow and the relative slip and rotation of fluid elements moving at different velocities facilitate the motion of particles relative to one another: by the law of least free energy, a spontaneous stratification by gravity can take place, with the heavier particles nudging the lighter

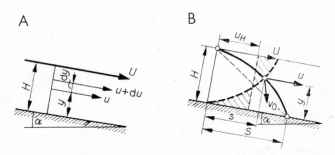

Fig. 1.27. A — notation for the discussion of sheet wash velocity distribution, *B* — trajectory of a settling particle in a thin sheet of laminar wash on a gentle slope

ones out of the deeper layers. At the same time, finer particles of the same s.g., fitting into the interstices of the coarser ones, can find their ways to the bottom of the appropriate layer (Heidenreich 1929).

1.5.1.2. Behaviour of particles in a thin sheet of water (Gaudin 1939). The bottom film, a few molecules thick, of a thin sheet of water flowing down a smooth surface will adhere to the surface if the surface is wetted by it. There is a gradual transition between this stationary film and water moving at full speed. The thickness of the layer of transition moving at less than full speed depends among other things on viscosity (and thus indirectly on temperature) and on the slope of the surface (on the velocity gradient). There are similar closely adhering semi-rigid water films passing into fully mobile water also on the particles' surfaces. The top of the water sheet will move at slightly less than full speed, owing to friction against the air at rest above it. Apart from this effect, the velocity of water in laminar flow increases parabolically from the bottom up. The downslope component of fluid weight over any given water layer tends to accelerate the flow: viscous fluid resistance tends to hinder it. In terms of the notation introduced in Fig. 1.27, in the steady state,

$$F(H - y)\gamma \sin \alpha = F\mu \frac{du}{dy},$$

where F is a surface of arbitrary size, parallel to the bottom and at height y above it, γ is the density and μ the viscosity of the fluid. That is,

$$\mathrm{d}u = \frac{\gamma \sin \alpha}{\mu} (H - y)\, \mathrm{d}y.$$

Integration yields

$$u = \frac{\gamma \sin \alpha}{\mu} \left(Hy - \frac{y^2}{2} \right) + C.$$

If the fluid wets the bottom, then $u = 0$ at $y = 0$, giving $C = 0$. Surface velocity (at $y = H$), neglecting air friction, is

$$U = \gamma \sin \alpha \frac{H^2}{2\mu}.$$

On multiplying the thickness y (cm) of the bottom layer of water by u_y (cm/s), the average velocity of the layer, the layer discharge rate per centimetre of height from the bottom up per second is obtained as

$$q = \int_0^y u\, \mathrm{d}y = \frac{\gamma \sin \alpha}{\mu} \left(\frac{Hy^2}{2} - \frac{y^3}{6} \right) + C.$$

If $u = 0$ at $y = 0$, then $C = 0$ and

$$u_y = \frac{q}{y} = \frac{\gamma \sin \alpha}{\mu} \left(\frac{Hy}{2} - \frac{y^2}{6} \right).$$

For the entire water sheet $(y = H)$,

$$Q = \gamma \sin \alpha \frac{H^3}{3\mu}$$

or

$$H = \sqrt[3]{\frac{3\mu Q}{\gamma \sin \alpha}},$$

implying

$$u_H = \gamma \sin \alpha \frac{H^2}{3\mu} \quad \left(= \frac{2U}{3} \right).$$

A particle settling at velocity v_0 in the sheet of water of parabolically varying velocity u moves on a parabolic trajectory, as shown in part B of Fig. 1.27. The element of downslope component $\mathrm{d}s$ of the particle's progress per time element $\mathrm{d}t$ is

$$\mathrm{d}s = u\, \mathrm{d}t;$$

its component perpendicular to the bottom is

$$dy = v_0 \cos \alpha \, dt,$$

giving

$$ds = \frac{u \, dy}{v_0 \cos \alpha}.$$

Inserting the expression of u and integrating between $y = H$ and $y = 0$ provides the downslope travel of the settling particle as

$$S = \frac{H u_H}{v_0 \cos \alpha} = \frac{Q}{v_0 \cos \alpha}.$$

That is, a particle settling at velocity $v_0 = $ const., starting from the surface of the water sheet whose velocity u varies with depth as specified above, will touch bottom at the same distance downslope of its point of immersion as if it had sunk at the constant velocity u_H. From the settling–velocity relationship

$$v_0 = x^2 \frac{\delta - \gamma}{18\mu} = \frac{Q}{S \cos \alpha},$$

particle size x cm can be calculated if Q cm³/s · cm, S cm, μ, γ, α and δ are known. For example, if

$$Q = 10 \text{ cm}^3/\text{s} \cdot \text{cm}, \quad \alpha = 5°, \quad S = 15 \text{ cm}, \quad \mu = 10^{-5} \text{ gs/cm}^2,$$

$$H = 0.15 \text{ cm}, \gamma = 1,$$

then

$\delta = $	7.5	5.0	2.65	1.5

gives

$x \cong$	43	55	85	155 μm;

or, for $Q = 5$ cm³/s · cm, $\alpha = 5°$, $S = 30$ cm, $H = 0.12$ and $\delta = 18$ (gold), $x \cong 13$ μm.

The relationship

$$S = \frac{Q}{v_0 \cos \alpha}$$

states that, of a set of particles fed in at the surface of the water sheet, those of a lower terminal settling velocity will touch bottom farther downslope (and later in time) than those of a higher terminal settling velocity. In near-horizontal flow, particles are classified by joint settling, with the heavy large grains touching bottom soonest and the light small ones getting farthest, and the small heavy ones falling where the large light ones go.

In laminar flow with a parabolic velocity function, mean velocity u_H is related to maximum (surface) velocity by

$$k = \frac{u_H}{U} = 2/3 \,.$$

In turbulent flow, k is in the range 3/4 to 7/8; in the zone of transition, it increases from 2/3 to 3/4. The vertical velocity component u_f in the eddies of a turbulent flow is a function both of mean fluid velocity u_H and the roughness of the bottom. In a sluice or on a table, the maximum u_f of turbulent flow is roughly 5 to 15% of mean fluid velocity u_H. In turbulent flow, all particles whose $v_0 < u_f$ remain suspended. Such particles move downstream at roughly the mean fluid velocity u_H. Particles whose $v_0 > u_f$ do not remain suspended: they either move along the bottom, sliding or saltating (bouncing), or adhere to it. Saltation, an alternation of settling out and entrainment into suspension, is due to local variations in the vertical eddy component u_f or to the Magnus effect acting on the rolling-spinning particles.

Downstream transport of non-suspended particles is a function of fluid velocity u_p. It is least at the bottom and increases above it (parabolically in laminar flow). Accordingly, of the particles in contact with the bottom, the larger ones are exposed to a stronger entraining force (wash) than the smaller ones. If e.g. a large particle is just moving along, then the smaller non-suspended particles of the same s.g. are not moved at all by the wash. The entraining effect of the flow is greatest on the light large particles and least on the heavy small ones. Particle shape also makes an important contribution. If they do not hinder one another, particles will come to rest on the bottom lying on their faces of least curvature, exposing their least cross section to the wash and opposing the greatest resistance to being overturned. Flat particles lying on their plane faces are pressed more strongly against the bottom by the wash passing over them. Of all particles of the same mass, the flat ones are least ready to slide or be rolled downslope in the flow: cubic-angular ones slide or are rolled more readily, and spherical ones easiest. Of all particles having the same size and shape but differing as to s.g., the heavier ones move slower, what with their greater mass exposed to the same entraining force. In the final reckoning, then, restricting analysis to the particles sliding and rolling on the bottom, the lighter, larger and more rounded particles will move faster downstream in a sheet of fluid.

Resistance to downslope motion is greatly increased for small particles by the roughness of the bottom, especially if the elements of unevenness are of the same size or slightly larger than the particles proper. (Roughness may well be due to fine particles settled on the bottom!) Among the fine particles protected from the wash by the roughness, eddies are formed; their rising branches will pick up the lighter particles and carry them into suspension. Eddies accordingly concentrate fine heavy particles on the bottom, whereas the fine particles taken into suspension are entrained by the more rapid wash higher up.

Let the velocity of a particle of size x sliding down a table of slope α be v. In laminar flow, using the mean fluid velocity u_x instead of the actual velocity which changes from layer to layer, the fundamental equation of particle motion, if friction between particle and fluid is expressed by the Newtonian relationship, is

$$m\frac{dv}{dt} = mg_0 \sin \alpha - fmg_0 \cos \alpha + Kx^2(u_x - v)^2,$$

where f is the coefficient of sliding friction against the table. The particle attains constant velocity in a very short time. At constant velocity, $dv/dt = 0$, and hence,

$$(u_x - v)^2 = \left(\frac{mg_0}{Kx^2}\right)(f \cos \alpha - \sin \alpha) = v_{0N}^2(f \cos \alpha - \sin \alpha)$$

and

$$v = u_x - v_{0N}\sqrt{f \cos \alpha - \sin \alpha}.$$

Taking into account also the velocity component u_f of turbulent flow, $fmg_0 \cos \alpha$ in the expression of $m \, dv/dt$ is replaced by

$$fmg_0 \cos \alpha - P_f,$$

where

$$P_f = c\gamma \frac{Fu_f^2}{2g} = K'x^2u_f^2$$

and, if $K' = K$ implying $c = 0.43$,

$$v = u_x - v_{0N}\sqrt{f\left[\cos \alpha - \left(\frac{u_f}{v_{0N}}\right)^2\right] - \sin \alpha}.$$

If resistance against the motion of the particle relative to the fluid is described by the Stokesian relationship, i.e. at Reynolds numbers

$$\mathrm{Re} = (u_x - v)\frac{x}{\nu} < 1,$$

then the differential equation of motion of the particle is

$$m\frac{dv}{dt} = mg_0(\sin \alpha - f \cos \alpha) + kx(u_x - v),$$

which, for $dv/dt = 0$, gives

$$v = u_x - v_{0S}(f \cos \alpha - \sin \alpha).$$

The analysis of these velocity formulae v reproduces the results obtained above: for two particles of s.g. $\delta_1 < \delta_2$, disregarding differences in friction coefficient, if any,

$$v_1 > v_2 \quad \text{if} \quad x_1 \simeq x_2 \text{ (or } u_{x1} \simeq u_{x2})$$

or

$$v_{01} \simeq v_{02}, \text{ that is, } x_1 > x_2 \text{ (or } u_{x1} > u_{x2});$$

that is, regardless of whether the feed has been sized or classified by terminal settling velocity, of all the particles in contact with the table, the lighter ones will move faster downslope than the heavier ones.

Putting $v = 0$ and inserting the expressions

$$u_x = \frac{\gamma \sin \alpha}{\mu} \left(\frac{Hx}{2} - \frac{x^2}{6} \right)$$

and

$$v_{0N} = C \sqrt{\frac{x(\delta - \gamma)}{\gamma}}$$

or

$$v_{0S} = \frac{x^2(\delta - \gamma)}{18\mu}$$

into the formula

$$u_x = v_{0N} \sqrt{f \cos \alpha - \sin \alpha}$$

or

$$u_x = v_{0S}(f \cos \alpha - \sin \alpha)$$

gives either the limiting particle size x_{crit} which, for a given triplet of f, α and H, will stay put on the table (will not move downslope) as a function of s.g. δ in a laminar flow, or the critical table slope angle α_{crit} at which particles of a given combination of x and δ will stay put.

The introduction of v_{0N} yields a complicated relationship, of the third degree in x:

$$\left(\frac{x}{H} \right) - \frac{2}{3} \left(\frac{x}{H} \right)^2 + \frac{1}{9} \left(\frac{x}{H} \right)^3 = \frac{4C^2\mu^2(\delta - \gamma)(f \cos \alpha - \sin \alpha)}{H^3\gamma^3 \sin^2 \alpha} =$$

$$= \frac{4C^2\mu(\delta - \gamma)}{3Q\gamma^2} \left(\frac{f}{\tan \alpha} - 1 \right),$$

whereas the introduction of v_{0S} yields a simple handy linear relationship:

$$\frac{H}{x_{\text{crit}}} = \frac{1}{3} + \frac{\delta - \gamma}{9\gamma} \left(\frac{f}{\tan \alpha} - 1 \right).$$

Some manipulation converts this formula into

$$\cotan \alpha_{crit} = \frac{9\gamma \left(\dfrac{H}{x} - \dfrac{1}{3} \right)}{(\delta - \gamma)} + 1 }{f} .$$

The critical slope angle, then, at which particles will stay put in laminar flow on a stationary table, is a function of particle size x and s.g. δ, of the friction coefficient f between particle and table and of the thickness of the water sheet.

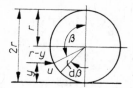

Fig. 1.28. Wash velocity u at central angle β (height y) of a sphere

Critical slope angle increases as particle size, s.g. and the friction coefficient and inversely as the thickness of the water sheet referred to particle size.

Using instead of the average fluid velocity u_x the actual (variable) fluid velocity u, the entraining force due to the relative motion of particle against fluid at the bottom of a thin sheet of water in laminar flow may be obtained by adding up the forces acting on the successive surface elements of the particle.

In a viscous fluid, resistance between particle and fluid is Stokesian. For example, for a sphere of radius r,

$$P = 6\mu\pi r(u - v),$$

where $2\pi r$ is the circumference of the sphere. Fluid resistance per circumference element $r\,d\beta$ (cf. Fig. 1.28) is

$$dP = 3\mu(u - v)r\,d\beta,$$

where u is fluid velocity at β.
Now

$$u = \frac{\gamma \sin \alpha}{\mu} \left(Hy - \frac{y^2}{2} \right),$$

but

$$y = r + r \cos \beta = r(1 + \cos \beta),$$

implying

$$u = \frac{\gamma \sin \alpha}{\mu} [Hr(1 + \cos \beta) - r^2(1 + \cos \beta)^2].$$

Hence,

$$dP = 3\gamma \sin \alpha [Hr^2(1 + \cos \beta) - r^3(1 + \cos \beta)^2]\,d\beta - 3\mu vr\,d\beta\,,$$

which gives the entraining force of the wash as

$$P = 3\gamma \sin \alpha Hr^2 \int_0^{2\pi} (1 + \cos \beta)\,d\beta - 3\gamma \sin \alpha x^3 \int_0^{2\pi} (1 + \cos \beta)^2\,d\beta - 3\,\mu vr \int_0^{2\pi} d\beta\,.$$

After expanding the expression

$$(1 + \cos \beta)^2,$$

the integration can be performed:

$$\int \cos^2 \beta\,d\beta = \frac{\sin^2 \beta}{4} + \frac{\beta}{2} + C\,,$$

giving

$$\int_0^{2\pi} \cos^2 \beta\,d\beta = \pi\,.$$

The upshot is

$$P = 6\pi\gamma \sin \alpha Hr^2 - 4.5\pi\gamma \sin \alpha r^3 - 6\pi\mu rv =$$
$$= \pi\gamma \sin \alpha r^2(6H - 4.5r) - 6\pi\mu rv\,.$$

The differential equation of motion of a particle of mass

$$m = 4r^3\,\frac{\pi\delta}{3g}$$

sliding down a smooth table in a laminar sheet of water is accordingly

$$\frac{4r^3\pi\delta}{3g}\,\frac{dv}{dt} = \frac{4r^3\pi}{3}\,(\delta - \gamma)\,(\sin \alpha - f \cos \alpha) + \pi\gamma \sin \alpha r^2(6H - 4.5r) - 6\pi\mu rv\,.$$

That is,

$$\frac{dv}{dt} = \left[(\delta - \gamma)(\sin \alpha - f \cos \alpha) + \gamma \sin \alpha \left(\frac{9H}{2r} - \frac{27}{8}\right) - 4.5\mu\,\frac{v}{r^2}\right]\frac{g}{\delta}\,.$$

The terminal downslope velocity, practically attained in a very short time by the sliding particle, is obtained on putting $dv/dt = 0$:

$$v = \frac{\left[(\delta - \gamma)(\sin \alpha - f \cos \alpha) + 4.5\,\dfrac{H\gamma}{r} \sin \alpha - 3.375\gamma \sin \alpha\right]r^2}{4.5\mu}\,,$$

that is,

$$v = \frac{rH\gamma}{\mu} \sin \alpha - r^2\left[\frac{3}{4\mu}\,\gamma \sin \alpha + \frac{(\delta - \gamma) \sin \alpha \left(\dfrac{f}{\tan \alpha} - 1\right)}{4.5\mu}\right],$$

or

$$v = \frac{\gamma \sin \alpha}{\mu}\left[Hr - r^2\left(\frac{3}{4} + \frac{(\delta - \gamma)\left[\dfrac{f}{\tan \alpha} - 1\right]}{4.5\gamma}\right)\right].$$

Sliding velocity, then, is obtained as the difference of two terms, respectively linear and quadratic in r, if the layer-by-layer variation of fluid velocity in the laminar wash is taken into account.

The equation for v may be rewritten in terms of a suitably modified form of the Stokesian formula for terminal settling velocity:

$$v_0 = \frac{2r^2(\delta - \gamma)}{9\mu} ;$$

the result obtained is

$$v = v_0 \sin \alpha \left[\frac{4.5\gamma}{\delta - \gamma}\left(\frac{H}{r} - \frac{3}{4}\right) - \left(\frac{f}{\tan \alpha} - 1\right)\right]$$

or, substituting $x = 2r$,

$$v = v_0 \sin \alpha \left[\frac{9\gamma}{\delta - \gamma}\left(\frac{H}{x} - \frac{3}{8}\right) - \left(\frac{f}{\tan \alpha} - 1\right)\right].$$

The function $v = f(x)$ is a parabola which has a maximum at a certain particle size x. The shape of the parabola and the position of its maximum depend on the parameters of the v formula (α, H, δ, f, etc.). Figure 1.29 shows three $v = f(x)$ parabolas; they differ because of differences in the s.g.'s and friction coefficients of the particles. The sliding velocity of particles of low s.g. and f is seen to increase monotonically up to the limit $x = H$. Another set of particles attains maximum speed at an $x < H$ and is slowed beyond it; if either the s.g. or f or both are great, then particle velocity may drop to zero even before attaining the limit $x = H$ (as is the case with the lowermost parabola). The shape of the parabolas (that is, tabling performance) may be in-

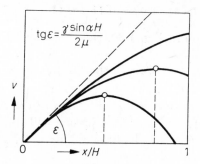

Fig. 1.29. $v = f(x)$ parabolas of particles different as to s.g. and friction coefficient, for given values of α and H

85

fluenced into the desired direction by varying the slope α of the table and the water feed rate (and, through it, the thickness H of the sheet of water).

The critical particle size x_{crit}, all particles larger than which will adhere to the table rather than slide down it, is obtained by putting $v = 0$:

$$\frac{H}{x_{crit}} = \frac{9}{24} + \frac{\delta - \gamma}{9\gamma}\left(\frac{f}{\tan \alpha} - 1\right).$$

Some manipulation now yields

$$\cotan \alpha_{crit} = \frac{1}{f}\left[\frac{9\gamma}{\delta - \gamma}\left(\frac{H}{x} - \frac{9}{24}\right) + 1\right].$$

The above two equations differ from those obtained under the assumption of constant fluid velocity u_x only in that they contain the term $9/24 = 0.375$ instead of $1/3 = 8/24 = 0.333$. They accordingly give a slightly greater H/x_{crit} (a slightly smaller x_{crit}/H). The values furnished by them differ to an insignificant extent if $x_{crit}/H < 1$: if, on the other hand, $x_{crit}/H > 1$, that is, critical particle size is larger than the thickness of the water sheet, then all particles not emerging from the sheet get swept off the (stationary) table. The maxima of the parabolas $v = f(x)$ have the locus $x = x_{crit}/2$.

At a slope angle greater than the critical, the particle is entrained downslope by the wash. During its slide, the coefficient of sliding friction, which is less than rest friction, is to be reckoned with.

Some of the mineral grains will roll rather than slide down the table. (Spherical particles will invariably roll.) Mineral grains can often be described for simplicity as prisms of n faces. If the forces attack the grain in its centre of gravity (this is the tacit assumption made when using the mean water velocity u_x), then a prism will start to roll when, for

$$n = 3 \qquad 4 \qquad 6 \qquad 8 \qquad 12 \qquad 24,$$

the coefficient of sliding friction exceeds

$$1.73 \quad 1.00 \quad 0.71 \quad 0.41 \quad 0.27 \quad 0.16.$$

In terms of the notation in Fig. 1.30, the condition of rolling is

$$Gfa > Gb, \qquad \text{that is,} \quad f > \frac{b}{a}.$$

Typical values of the friction coefficient f are in the 0.2 to 0.6 range, which means that three-, four- and six-edged prisms will slide, 24-edged prisms will roll and 8- and 12-edged ones will either roll or slide, depending on the actual value of the friction coefficient.

Effective water pressure (in laminar flow) will, however, attack a grain lying on the table above its centre of gravity. Integrating the elementary

86

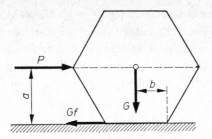

Fig. 1.30. Forces determining the sliding or overturning of a prism on a table

torques dM acting on the "equatorial" plane of the particle,

$$dM = \frac{x}{2} \cos \beta \, dP,$$

and putting $v = 0$, the relationship

$$M = \frac{3\pi\gamma}{8} \sin \alpha \, x^3 \left(H - \frac{x}{2} \right)$$

is obtained. Torque equals force P into lever arm k; that is, the effective force attacks at a distance

$$k = \frac{M}{P} = x \, \frac{2H - x}{8H - 3x}$$

above the equatorial plane. For very small values of x, k tends to $x/4$; for the greatest relevant value $(x = H)$ it equals $k = x/5$. That is, the vector of water pressure attacks small particles at height measured from the bottom

$$\frac{x}{2} + \frac{x}{4} = 0.75x$$

and large particles at height

$$\frac{x}{2} + \frac{x}{5} = 0.70x,$$

provided $v = 0$ as stipulated. Inserting into the condition $f > b/a$ the average value $a = 0.725x$, we find that prisms having

| $n =$ | 3 | 4 | 6 | 8 | 12 | 24 |

faces will not roll if their "critical" friction coefficient exceeds the value

| | 1.20 | 0.69 | 0.40 | 0.29 | 0.19 | 0.11. |

That is, three- and four-edged prisms will invariably slide, 12- and 24-edged ones will invariably roll, and six- and eight-edged ones may or may not roll.

If the particle is moving on the table ($v > 0$), the velocity differential ($u - v$) will, as indicated in Fig. 1.31, retard it with a resultant force P_1 of lever arm a_1 acting on its lower part and accelerate it downslope with a resultant force P_2 of lever arm a_2 acting on its upper part. The net result is a torque whose lever arm a, to be introduced into the critical friction formula $f > b/a$,

$$a = \frac{P_2 a_2 + P_1 a_1}{P_2 - P_1},$$

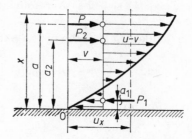

Fig. 1.31. Distribution of forces acting on a sliding particle in a sheet wash

is invariably greater than when the particle is at rest ($v = 0$). The critical frictions separating rolling from sliding motion are therefore even less in actual fact than those listed above.

The above derivation is borne out fairly well by observation. For example, cubes of galena are seldom seen to roll; scales of gold and mica do not roll in any case, whereas particles of irregular or roundish shape do roll down the table as a rule.

In our derivation of the critical friction coefficient, we have assumed the table to be completely smooth. If it is in fact rough, and the roughness of its surface tends to restrain sliding particles, those will be forced to roll rather than slide even more often. The situation appears as if the friction coefficient had increased (possibly beyond unity). On a rough table, these augmented friction coefficients are to be used also in calculating H/x_{crit} and cotan α_{crit}.

Many of the particles entrained down a table by the wash of a sheet of water will alternately roll and slide. Rolling will tend to predominate at higher velocities and sliding at lower ones. The transition is continuous in some of the cases and abrupt in others.

In the case of rolling, $f = 0$; that is, the term containing f disappears from the expression of sliding velocity v (or H/x_{crit} or cotan α_{crit} or dv/dt). Accordingly, the downslope velocity of the rolling particles becomes

$$v = v_0 \sin \alpha \left[\frac{9\gamma}{\delta - \gamma} \left(\frac{H}{x} - \frac{3}{8} \right) + 1 \right].$$

88

Downslope velocity increases in rolling and decreases in sliding as the s.g. of the mineral increases. The rolling velocity of a grain is always greater than its sliding velocity: the two velocities are related by

$$\frac{K \tan \alpha}{K \tan \alpha - f},$$

where

$$K = \frac{9\gamma}{\delta - \gamma}\left(\frac{H}{x} - \frac{3}{8}\right) + 1.$$

It is an advantage in tabling if light minerals roll and heavier ones slide. In rolling, the term quadratic in x is positive — that is, the v parabola takes the form shown in Fig. 1.32 — if

$$\frac{\delta - \gamma}{\gamma} > \frac{27}{8} = 3.375$$

(that is, $\delta > 4.375$ for $\gamma = 1$). In sliding, the term quadratic in x is invariably negative for the combinations of α, f and δ encountered in tabling practice ($\alpha < 8°, f > 0.1, \delta < 19$).

The value of x_{crit}, particles larger than which will adhere to the table rather than roll down it, can be obtained from the velocity equation of rolling by putting $v = 0$ or from the H/x_{crit} equation of sliding by putting $f = 0$:

$$\frac{H}{x_{crit}} = \frac{3}{8} - \frac{\delta - \gamma}{9\gamma}.$$

For $\gamma = 1$, this gives a physically meaningful (positive) solution as long as $\delta < 4.375$, and the solution is invariably less than $3/8 = 0.375$: that is, x_{crit} is invariably greater than $8H/3 = 2.66H$. In other words, every particle prone to rolling and covered by the sheet of water ($x < H$) will be entrained off the table by the wash.

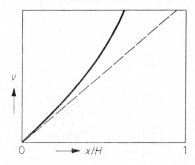

Fig. 1.32. The $v = f(x)$ parabolas of rolling particles heavier than $\delta = 4.375$ are concave upward

The general form of the velocity equation is

$$v = AHx + Bx^2,$$

where A is invariably positive, B is negative in sliding and negative or positive in rolling. The substitution $H = cx$ (where $c > 1/a$) gives the form

$$v = (Ac + B)x^2;$$

hence, v varies as x^2. If the bed on the table is only one particle deep, then its thickness varies as x: hence, the throughput of such a table (that is, the throughput of a smooth table) per unit of time will vary in theory as x^3. No particles larger than the thickness of the sheet of water are to be fed to a smooth table.

1.5.1.3. Influence of the riffling and of shaking. The throughput of a smooth table carrying a bed one particle deep is very small when fed a fine-grained feed. On increasing throughput (feed rate), a bed several particles deep will build up, in which case the heavier particles gravitate downward, expelling from the bottom layer the large, roundish, light ones above all, just as in the sluice, which is operated with deeper water and a thicker bed.

In tables run with a bed several particles deep and in sluices, it is usual to forestall easy sliding on a smooth bottom by using a rough or riffled bottom plate. Creating eddies, these obstacles give rise to turbulent flow and retard or hold up the bottom layer. The upper layers have in that case to slide, roll or saltate down a stationary bottom layer. At the bottom of the bed accumulated upstream of a riffle, the fine heavy particles will collect: above them, heavy particles of gradually increasing size are found, with fine light particles in their interstices. The large light particles collect in the top layer overflowing the riffle, provided their weight is not great enough to make them penetrate the deeper layers. Particles of such weight can be eliminated e.g. by pre-treating the feed in a wet classifier. The situation is illustrated by Fig. 1.33. The abrupt change of cross section h downstream of the riffle causes an especially strong turbulence.

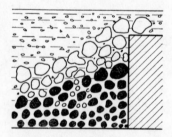

Fig. 1.33. Distribution of light and heavy (white and black) particles in a bed upstream of a riffle

Shaking-table surfaces are provided with a close-spaced riffling (ribbing). The troughs between riffles are filled with settled-out particles, and asymmetric shaking along the riffling makes those particles move in the troughs by jerks in one direction. If the wash is strong enough, eddying between the riffles will entrain the fine particles of light minerals from the interstices of the larger heavy particles, but the heavy fine particles collected at the bottom are not taken into suspension by the eddies.

The particles will adhere to the table, at relative rest to it (or its troughs) as long as friction is sufficient to overcome the forces acting on them, i.e. as long as the acceleration of the table in its own plane is less than the acceleration of adhesion

$$G_0 \frac{f}{m} = g_0 f,$$

which is the maximum acceleration that will not break the adhesion of the particle to the table (will not overcome its friction at rest). Here, G_0 is the weight, measured in a fluid of density γ, of a particle of mass m;

$$g_0 = \frac{G_0}{m} = g \frac{\delta - \gamma}{\delta}$$

is its s.g.-dependent gravity acceleration in the fluid, and f is the rest-friction coefficient between particle and table. If, on the other hand, the acceleration of the table exceeds the acceleration of adhesion, then rest friction will be insufficient to key the particle to the table (to transmit the abrupt change of velocity), and particles will slide along, with the table being pulled out from under them as it were. The maximum possible acceleration of this sliding motion equals $g_0 f$, that is, the "acceleration of adhesion".

Heavier particles (whose friction coefficient is greater) acquire with their greater acceleration of adhesion a greater velocity within the time available, and can thus progress farther in the direction of shaking. Particles progress in a jerk on each stroke in the direction of shaking, provided the acceleration of the table out of one of its neutral points is greater than the acceleration of adhesion of the particles but less out of its other neutral point. Larger and heavier particles (of greater mass/inertia) in contact with the table are moved farther by each stroke than smaller and lighter particles. On smooth tables, then, where the bed is just one particle deep, and every particle is in direct contact with the table, sheet wash down the slope preferentially transports the lighter, larger and more rounded particles (provided $x < x_{crit}/2$), whereas table motion perpendicular to the slope preferentially transports the heavier and larger particles. Parts A, B and C of Fig. 1.34 show the velocity (or displacement) vectors and their resultants illustrating this process. On tabling a feed pre-classified by joint settling ($v_{01} \cong v_{02}$; Part B), the vectors of particles

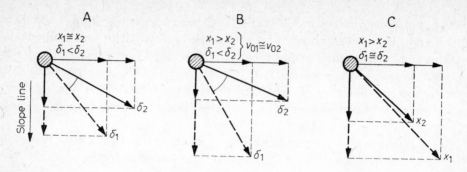

Fig. 1.34. A, B, C — velocity (or displacement) vectors of two particles relative to each other on a table shaken crosswise to its slope. A — same particle size x, B = same terminal settling velocity v_0, C — same s.g. δ

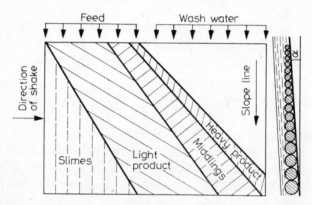

Fig. 1.35. Arrangement of different types of particles on a shaking-table deck

different as to s.g. will differ more than in the case of a sized feed ($x_1 \cong x_2$; Part A). The resultant vectors of particles of roughly equal s.g. ($\delta_1 \cong \delta_2$; Part C) will be quasi-collinear, but the larger particle will move faster. Particle shape also affects the outcome: the wash exerts a weak entraining force on flat particles hugging the bottom, so that these will move preferentially in the direction of shaking rather than down the slope.

The feed to be tabled is introduced at the top corner of the table: it crosses the table as shown in Fig. 1.35. Slimes suspended in the water will flow down-slope from the feed point; the light product remains comparatively close to the fall line of the feed point, whereas the bands of heavier products are farther from it along the direction of shaking. Within each band of particles of equal s.g., arrangement is by particle size: fine particles move farther in the direction of shaking, whereas larger ones remain closer to the fall line of the feed point. Hence, in a fall-line cross section of a given band, one finds the smaller particles higher up and vice versa, as illustrated by the fall-line profile in the inset of

Fig. 1.35. The reason for this arrangement is that, as long as any other arrangement prevails, the smaller particles, protected by the larger ones from the wash, will lag behind until they take up appropriate positions.

If the bed on the table is several particles deep (on a riffled table), table motion is transmitted to the upper layers by the lower ones with a certain loss and phase lag, so that the upper layers (which are also exposed to wash) do not progress as far in the direction of shaking as the lower ones do. Shaking action at the surface of the sheet of water is negligible, whereas the bottom of the sheet moves together with the table. On a table performing symmetric oscillations, the amplitude of water motion is an exponential function of height above the table, with the exponent including the square root of shaking speed and height above the bottom. At $n = 300$ cpm, for example, the oscillation ampitude of water at height

0.2	0.5	1 mm

above the bottom is

45	14	2%

of the bottom layer's (i.e., the table's) amplitude. This proves that fluid motion due to the shaking becomes negligible comparatively close to the table. Accordingly, the velocity difference figuring in the fluid resistance term P of the equation

$$m \frac{dv}{dt} = mg_0 f \pm P$$

expressing the motion of a particle in the direction of shaking will differ as to magnitude, and possibly even as to sign, between the lower and the upper part of a larger particle in direct contact with the table, keyed to or sliding along it. The difference in the magnitude (and, a fortiori, in the sign) of relative velocity causes the particles to rotate; this in turn causes the bed to expand (σ to decrease) against its state of rest, a situation that permits a rapid segregation by gravity.

The troughs of the riffled table lead the material collected in them in the direction of shaking: they also protect its heavy bottom layer from entrainment in the wash down the slope. It is only the light particles collected in the top layer that are so entrained. Standard riffling most often extends from the feed edge ("mechanism end") of the table to the diagonal between the feed point and the corner opposite to it, with riffle height gradually decreasing towards the diagonal. As a result, the bed stratified by gravity in the troughs is gradually exposed to sheet wash from its top down as it proceeds in the direction of shaking. On the smooth part of the table, the heavy product is cleaned of fine light particles. On some tables, however, riffles are of uniform height all across the table. This is the case e.g. on the so-called rougher tables used to produce pre-concentrates.

On a table, maximum feed particle size just equals the thickness of the sheet of water, not more than one or two mm if the table is smooth. On a riffled table, it is determined by the height of riffling. In coal washing, riffles up to 20 mm height are being used. Riffle spacing should be at least three times the maximum particle size. For the tabling of coarser feeds, it is usual to choose higher riffles comparatively close-spaced in order to cause a stronger turbulence between riffles ("sand tables"), whereas on "slime tables" riffles are lower and their spacing is wider as a rule, in order to permit a stationary pulp to form, from which fines also can settle out. Slime tables are always unriffled, partly at least (Yancey and Black 1931).

Stationary tables and certain sluices rely for concentration by gravity on the action of water flowing down a gentle, near-horizontal slope. In such cases, it is the width-to-length ratio of the bottom plate, in addition to depth of water, that determines whether the device is to be called a sluice or a table. The bottom plate of either may be smooth, ribbed or riffled, and both may be operated in the continuous or the batch mode. Moving tables (vanners, bumping tables, shaking tables) rely for concentration on the moving of the table in its own plane or nearly so, in addition to the wash action of a thin sheet of water. In addition to the non-moving (stationary) low-slope devices (rheolaveur, cascadyne sluice, blanket table, round table, etc.), there are also sluices of steeper slope (15 to 20°), e.g. the Humphreys spiral, fan separator, etc.

1.5.2. Sluices. There are sluices of batch and continuous mode of operation.

1.5.2.1. Sluices of batch operation are used locally in ore dressing, mainly in the concentration of placer deposits of gold, platinum, tin, etc., where a heavy fine pay mineral occurs amid a coarser-grained waste. The riffled-bottom sluices used for the purpose are taken out of service at intervals to recover the product. Their depth varies from 15 to 120 cm or so; their slope depends mainly on maximum feed particle size and on the quantity of water available; their length depends on the fineness and s.g. of the pay mineral, but even more often on distance to the tailings area. Finer pay grain size or a feed that must disaggregate in the water require a longer sluice. Width (30 to 300 cm approximately) can be derived from the required depth, flow velocity and pulp throughput rate.

Maximum feed particle size is less than 10 cm as a rule, although lumps of rock up to 80 cm size are occasionally washed down sluices of appropriate size. Riffling type also depends on particle size. It is to be the higher and the closer-spaced, the larger the particles, and the stronger the wash required to move the largest of those.

Flow of water and riffling are to be matched so that the sand settling upstream of a riffle can constitute a yielding, plastic bed that can be penetrated by the heavy particles without the heavy fines being entrained by the turbulence.

For making the bed move, a steep smooth bottom and a deep rapid wash would be best, but both conditions impair metal recovery; moreover, high velocity also results in strong wear. Disaggregation of the feed is promoted by strong rolling and rubbing action which can be generated by letting the pulp flow in a thin sheet down a strongly riffled steep bottom and by inserting "cascades" of some 30 cm height. Water feed rate is to be about ten times the solids feed rate for a maximum feed particle size of about 1 cm, 15 times for 8 cm, 16 to 20 times for 20 cm or above, and even up to 80 times if the feed contains significant numbers of half-metre boulders. A cemented feed requires twice or three times as much water.

At intervals, the concentrate collected on the sluice bottom must be removed. The upstream sections of long sluices are cleaned more often than the others. In the section to be cleaned out the bottom riffling is taken up, starting with the lowermost riffle; the material settled out between riffles is washed by raking under a sheet of water flowing fast enough and then removed (shovelled) from the sluice; this can then be put back in operation after replacing the riffling.

A short batch-type sluice is the blanket (corduroy) table, frequently used even today e.g. to recover free gold from the tailings of flotation plants. The fine scales of gold are retained by the pile or mesh of a fur, velvet or woollen cloth out of the tailings pulp flowing over it. The best is corduroy, with its pile facing the flow. The gold is readily removed from the corduroy by shaking it out in a tank of stationary water.

1.5.2.2. Sluices of continuous mode of operation (Naguib 1971).

(A) The fan separator (Fig. 1.36) is a short smooth-bottomed steep sluice ($\alpha = 16°$ to $20°$) run with a dense pulp ($\sigma = 0.2$ to 0.4). Over a length of 60 to 90 cm, it tapers downstream from a top width of 14 to 30 cm (typically 23 cm) to a bottom width of 1 to 4 cm (typically 2.5 cm). Depth of pulp increases with the taper. The pulp, stratified by gravity, fans out as it overflows the end of the sluice, its speed being higher at the top than at the bottom. This "fan" is often directed against a quarter-circular oblique baffle: the pulp trickling down this latter is separated into a concentrate, middlings and waste

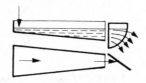

Fig. 1.36. Diagram of fan separator

by wedges that can be fixed in suitable positions about its arc. The device can be used to concentrate feeds pre-treated in a wet classifier, of about 2 to 0.05 mm size, provided

$$r = \frac{(\delta_2 - 1)}{(\delta_1 - 1)} > 1.7 \, .$$

The pulp stream whose depth is increased by the taper can of course be divided in two or three part-streams also without benefit of a baffle, e.g. by means of horizontal splitters installed at suitable height. This is how the Cannon concentrator, incorporating 48 short tapering sluices arranged radially to save space, is operated. Space can be saved also by arranging tapering short sluices side by side, alternately head to tail. Throughput is 0.2 to 1 tph per sluice (Helfricht 1966).

By elimination of the side walls of the close-spaced channels constituting an annulus in the Cannon concentrator, one obtains the now so widely used Reichert cone with its large output and cheap owning and operating cost.

(B) The Humphreys spiral is a smooth-bottomed steep sluice of continuous operation, wound at constant outer radius of ∼30 cm about a vertical axis. The deformed quarter-circle profile of the cast iron launder used in its construction is shown in Fig. 1.37. On the inner rim of this, there is a small water launder, from which wash water can be introduced as required at any point of the pulp (large) launder. In ore dressing, a five-turn spiral is most often used, with a slope of 35 cm per turn; in coal washing, a six-turn spiral with

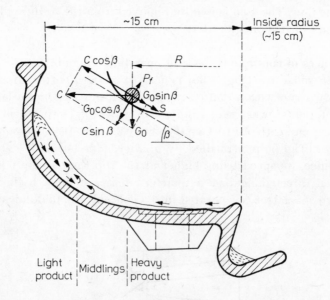

Fig. 1.37. Cross section of the launder of a Humphrey spiral and vector diagram of the forces acting on a particle

a slope of 25 cm per turn is preferred. The width of the launder in the radial direction is about 15 cm. Feed is introduced in the form of a pulp of middling density ($\sigma = 12$ to 20% typically, but up to 30% for coarser feeds) at the top of the spiral. Heavy product is removed through discharge apertures on the inner side of the spiral, spaced half-turns apart. The apertures closer to the feed end (to the top) discharge the heavy product; the lower ones discharge a middling. Each product is led in rubber tubing to a separate vertical collector pipe close to the axis of the spiral. The light product remains in the launder and is discharged at its bottom. Heavy particles may be deflected towards the discharge apertures by semicircular disks provided with vertical-radial scoops, placed in the apertures. Some apertures may be shut off by suitable plugs. As a rule, only five to seven discharge apertures are in operation at any one time.

Instead of cast iron, the spirals may be made of segments of a rubber-lined plastic that can be assembled by bolting. Three segments make up a turn: the spiral may have 3, 5, 8 or 10 turns. A spiral launder of variable pitch can be made up of truck tires cut in two, pulled apart more or less strongly.

In the spiral, a combined radial and downslope force acts on the particles. The balance of forces is shown by the vector-diagram inset of Fig. 1.37, neglecting cross-flow effects for the time being. Here,

$$G_0 = V(\delta - \gamma)$$

is particle weight measured in the fluid,

$$C = \frac{G_0 v^2}{gR}$$

is the centrifugal force,

$$P_f = \frac{c\gamma F u_{2f}}{2g}$$

is the vertical force of turbulent flows,

$$S = f(C \sin \beta + G_0 \cos \beta - P_f)$$

is friction and

$$C \cos \beta - G_0 \sin \beta \pm S = 0.$$

Neglecting the friction S, the relationship

$$\frac{C}{G_0} = \frac{v^2}{gR} = \tan \beta$$

is obtained. In other words, the position of equilibrium is at radial distance R from the axis; R is the greater, the higher the speed at which a particle is travelling. Particle velocity v being greater in the higher layers of the bed (where the lighter particles collect); lighter particles will be swept farther out than heavier ones.

The separation of heavy and light particles is enhanced by a radial (cross) flow arising in the curved launder. Such cross flows invariably arise in any curved flow (in canals and natural streams just as well as in closed conduits or, for that matter, in a hydrocyclone). The pulp wending its way down the spiral will flow radially inward near the launder bottom and radially outward near the pulp surface; this means that the top, light layer of the bed stratified by gravity is washed outward, to the outer wall of the launder and the bottom, heavy layer is washed inward. The radial (cross) flow component is due to the fact that the sheet of water flowing down the spiral launder moves more slowly at its bottom than at its top (the centrifugal force acting upon the fluid particles moving at higher speed being stronger). Wash water, if introduced at an angle, will also contribute to the driving outward of the top layer of water.

In practice, it is usual to run several Humphrey spirals in parallel: uniform feed distribution must in that case be ensured by means of a suitable feed box.

Maximum particle size in the feed to a Humphrey spiral is 1.5 to 2 mm for ores and 5 to 6 mm for coals, but it is best kept below about one mm for ores and 3 mm for coals. For such feeds, at $\sigma = 12$ to 15%, throughput is on the order of one ton per hour. A coarser feed (ore $\lesssim 1.7$ mm or coal $\lesssim 5$ mm) should have a higher pulp density ($\sigma = 25$ to 30%). Throughput is thus increased to about 2 tph. For feeds finer than the usual, pulp density must be reduced; throughput is also reduced thereby. Throughput is of course a function also of the concentrability of the feed (of the ratio of relative gravities or of the Bird number) and of the desired sharpness of separation. It should be decided after suitable testing whether the aggregate to be concentrated can be fed direct to the Humphrey spirals, or whether it has to be split beforehand into two or three fractions in a wet classifier.

Slimes tend to remain suspended and to leave the spiral together with the light product. Hence, if clean separation is desired, the ratio of the largest to the finest feed particles should not exceed, if possible, about four times the ratio of relative gravities. The presence of slimes incidentally confers to the pulp certain dense-medium features: this in itself ought to promote separation, but the concomitant increase in viscosity tends to cancel or outweigh the advantage.

Owning and operating costs of Humphrey spirals are low. The bulk of operating cost is due to the power draft of the pump moving the pulp into the feed box distributing the feed among the spirals and to the replacement of worn pump parts. One or two operators can handle a battery of several hundred units. The spirals require no foundations and little space; also, if no very sharp separation is required, their throughput is large. They can therefore be used to concentrate low-grade feeds for which any other process would be out of the question (low-grade placer deposits, retreatment of old tailings and the like) (Brown and Erck 1949: Hubbard et al. 1953).

(C) The swinging spiral launder serves for the concentration of fine pulps (e.g. tin ore pulps of 5 to 15 μm particle size). It is a launder of about 90 cm outer diameter and a pitch of 5.1 cm per turn, twisted to and fro at a frequency

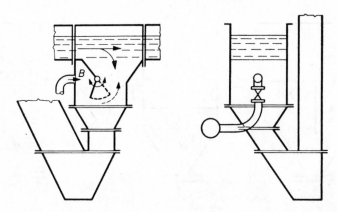

Fig. 1.38. Diagrams of discharge devices (pockets) of coarse rheolaveurs

of about 600 cpm and an amplitude of about 3.2 mm. It can be fed 0.4 to 0.65 m³ pulp per hour at solids contents of 5 to 10% by weight. At the optimum setting, the launder bottom and the pulp move at the same speed on the down stroke, so that no shear arises; on the up stroke, shear is a maximum.

(D) Rheolaveurs are smooth-bottomed, gently sloping straight launders used in coal washing. From these, the heavy bottom layer (the waste first, followed by the middling) is drawn through slots running the full width of the launder bottom, with suitable discharge mechanisms installed under each. The light product (washed coal) leaves with the pulp flowing out of the discharge end of the launder.

Rheolaveurs used to concentrate coarse coal (10 to 120 mm) differ from those for fine coal (about 0.5 to 10 mm) in their discharge mechanisms. In the coarse rheolaveur (Fig. 1.38) there is a tilting valve of circular segment shape made of perforated plate, which at intervals empties the heavy product collecting above it into the pocket of the discharge device or into the sump of the product elevator. Back water can rise through the perforations in the valve. The principal role of back water is to make up for the volume of solids falling from the launder into the pocket, in order to keep the flow in the launder eddy-free. Only as a side-effect does it operate as a wet classifier, returning to the launder the particles of clean coal with their lower terminal settling velocity. Such particles of coal are few and far between in the pocket anyway, what with the separation of clean coal from the bottom layer of heavy particles having taken place before, in the launder section upstream of the pocket. If there were no valve, the entire bed in a coarse rheolaveur would flow down into the pocket. The slot must be wider than about three times the maximum particle size to be discharged through it, e.g. more than 30 cm for $x_{max} = 100$ mm.

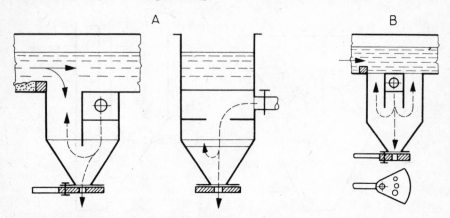

A   B

Fig. 1.39. A and *B* — diagrams of discharge devices (pockets) of fine rheolaveurs

The fine rheolaveur has no moving parts (Fig. 1.39, Parts A and B). The discharge aperture and the pulp outflow rate of the heavy product can be regulated by suitably turning a disk provided with orifices of increasing diameter. A small riffle immediately upstream of the slot holds up the waste (bottom) layer; the waste sliding over the riffle is slowed down so that it can drop into the pocket more safely than if it would slide at speed down the smooth bottom of the launder.

In the washing of coarse coal, it is usual to employ one rheolaveur with two pockets, the first producing the waste and the second a middling. It is reasonable to direct, in addition to the true middling, also some waste and clean coal to the middling discharge, in order to obtain cleaner end products (coal and waste). The middling is often returned to the launder upstream of the first pocket. Recirculation increases the concentration of middling in the launder, which is an advantage because a thicker middling (roughing) layer can separate clean coal better from the waste.

For coals of poor washability, several rheolaveurs with more pockets are used. Flowsheets of coarse rheolaveur batteries with 3, 4 and 5 pockets per unit are shown in Parts A, B and C of Fig. 1.40, indicating feed rates, launder sizes (widths) and the weight percentages of the products. Recorded performance of the three flowsheets in the washing of raw coals containing comparatively little waste is presented in Table 1.10, stating weight percentages

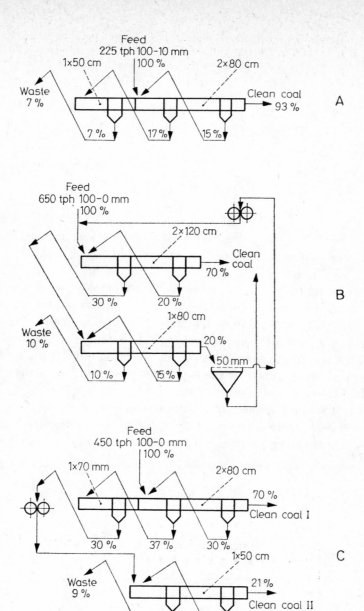

Fig. 1.40. Flowsheets and product parameters of rheolaveur arrangements. *A* — one three-pocket rheo, *B* — two two-pocket rheos, *C* — one three-pocket and one two-pocket rheo

Product	3		4		5	
	pockets employed					
	weight %	+1.6	weight %	+1.6	weight %	+1.6
Feed	100	7.6	100	10.2	100	8.3
Clean coal	93	1.0	{ 70	1.2	70	0.3
			{ 20	3.0	22	2.7
Waste	7	95.0	10	88.0	8	94.0

for the products and the percentage of the plus-1.6 s.g. fraction. Water consumption was 1.90 to 1.95 m³ per ton of raw coal in each of the three arrangements.

In the washing of fine coal, it is usual to employ several launders of 10 to 25 m length installed one under another, with several fine rheos, spaced 1.4 to 2.5 m apart, installed in each launder. The upstream end of the launder, in a length of 2 to 6 m, is made steeper (13 to 33 cm/m): this gives the pulp sufficient momentum to flow along the main section of the launder despite its gentler slope (1 to 4 cm/m), at the expense of less head loss than if the entire launder had the same slope throughout.

Figure 1.41 is the flowsheet of a five-launder device cleaning the minus-10 mm washed-coal fraction produced by the five-pocket flowsheet of Part C, Fig. 1.40. The numbers written into the flowsheet are the ash percentages

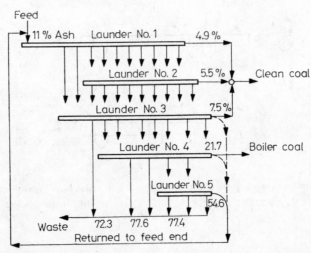

Fig. 1.41. Flowsheet of a five-launder fine rheo cleaning the minus-10 mm fraction of the washed coal emerging from the flowsheet in Part *C* of Fig. 1.40

obtained with a feed of 11% ash content making the full-line circuit. Operated on the dashed-line circuit, the waste had an ash content of 68.4% for a feed ash content of 12%, and the ash contents of the launder overflows were respectively

| 5.7 | 6.9 | 7.3 | 11.4 | 18.2% |

for the launders

| No. I | II | III | IV | V. |

The length H m and width S cm of each launder, the number of pockets used and their average spacing L m, as well as the length H' m and slope h cm/m of the steep initial sections of the launders are listed in Table 1.11.

Throughput per decimetre (per 10 cm) of launder width is 10 to 15 tph in a fine rheo (handling a minus-10 mm feed), 15 to 25 tph in a coarse rheo (for plus-10 mm feeds), and 10 to 30 tph when handling unsized coal, minus-100 mm. Water demand is in the 1.9 to 4 m³/t range (that of coal jigs is 4 to 6 m³/t). The power demand of the rheolaveur proper is negligible: only the discharge valves and elevators of the coarse rheos need driving. Total power draft of pumps, screens, elevators, etc., is 1.5 to 1.8 kW h/t (it is about 2 to 2.2 kW h/t in a coal-jig washery). Owning and operating costs are also less than in jig washeries. There being no mechanical vibration, the concentrator building can be lighter: the need for changing moving parts and screens as in a jig does not arise. Separation performance, on the other hand, is less good as a rule than in a jig (E_p is greater and the Tromp curve is less steep).

A modified design of rheo pockets is encountered in the short cascadyne launder (5 to 6 m), usually provided with two pockets. This has a tiltable-adjustable plate both upstream and downstream of each bottom slot. The size of the pocket aperture can be varied by means of these plates so as to adapt it to the nature of the feed (to constitute a stationary bed of suitable thickness and length upstream of the first plate). For removing excess water between pockets, screens with boxes under them are sometimes inserted in the bottom (Gründer 1960).

Table 1.11. Fine rheolaveurs shown in Fig. 1.41. Length H, width S, number of pockets (pcs), average spacing between them, L, length H' and inclination h of the steeper upstream section

	H m	S cm	pcs	L m	H' m	h cm/m
I	24	58	10	1.45	6.1	17.7
II	17	36	9	1.45	2.5	16.6
III	21	36	8	2.13	3.0	16.6
IV	15	25	4	2.45	4.0	13.0
V	8	25	3	2.45	2.1	15.6

1.5.3. Tables. There is no essential difference between a stationary table are a sltice it is merely the difference in the length-to-width ratio and in the thickness of the sheet of water that justifies the distinction. The bed settling out of a thinner or thicker sheet of pulp flowing down a gently sloping plane may be uneven, with irregular runnels, in which a stronger flow may churn up the separated fractions. The bed formed between riffles may be too compact, so that the freshyl arriving heavy particles, unable to penetrate it, will move on and get lost in the tailings. All these drawbacks may be overcome in stationary tables and in certain sluices by manual action (by raking the bed so as to smooth it and loosen it up). Raking may of course be performed also by some mechanical means. Using a band slowly moving upward instead of a stationary deck, the settled-out bottom layer can be continuously removed and washed clean by a trickle of water upward of the feed point. Blanket tables are operated in this way in some concentrators.

1.5.3.1. Older types of tables. The oldest and simplest type of table, a rectangular sloping plate, used a thin film of water. Its inclination was adjusted for heavy particles to settle down on it while light ones were swept off by the wash. The bed was smoothed manually by upward raking; the slope of the deck was gradually increased at intervals. The operating surface of these old tables was the rough surface of the bed rather than the smooth plate proper.

Later on, the table was suspended from chains and moved by a cam disk. Its return stroke was arrested by bumping blocks. The impact of collision drove the heavy particles settled out on the bottom up the slope.

Prior to the spread of flotation, round tables were used in the concentration of fine pulps. The slightly conical operating surface of the stationary round table was a layer of smooth-polished concrete. With the centrally introduced pulp flowing down and radially outward, both the thickness and velocity of the pulp sheet decreased gradually; particles different as to size, shape and s.g. settled out on the table in successive rings about the feed point: of the particles identical as to size and shape, the heavier ones settled out first. The uniformity of the bed was ensured and the formation of runnels prevented by slowly rotating soft brushes. Operation was of batch type: feed inflow was interrupted at intervals and the individual product rings on the slope were shovelled off.

Stationary round tables were built also with an inward slope and peripheral feeding. The heavier particles settled out near the rim; the rest was entrained by the water flowing at increasing speed towards a central outlet.

Both types of round table (convex and voncave) were designed also for continuous operation.

All these types of table are obsolete and encountered no more in operating practice. Devices still used in the concentration of fine pulps include the tilting slimer and the vanner. The tilting slimer consists of several (usually five) gently sloping smooth rectangular stationary tables mounted one above another. At intervals, the feed is shut off, the decks are tilted into the washing position by a timer-actuated mechanism, and the heavy fines adhering to the decks are washed off. The vanner is a sloping endless rubber belt with a shallow rim at either edge, symmetrically oscillated sidewise ("side-shake"), lengthwise ("end-shake") or rotated. The conveyor transports upslope the heavy fines shaken to the bottom of the bed, whereas the light particles shaken to the top of the bed are entrained by sheet wash. Shaking promotes stratification by gravity and prevents the formation of runnels in the bed. Tilting slimers and vanners are used to treat plus-10 to 20 μm and minus-150 to 300 μm feeds, much the same ones as the round tables used to handle.

1.5.3.2. Of the **tables moved asymmetrically,** crosswise to the slope, the bumping table has become obsolete: the type in modern use is the shaking table.

(A) The rectangular smooth plate of the bumping table is pushed away crosswise to the slope by a cam disk working against a spring. On release, the spring throws the table back until it is stopped abruptly by a bumping block. The particles on the table move on in the direction of the throw; heavy particles move farther than lighter ones.

(B) In the shaking table, the asymmetric motion crosswise to the slope is generated by a suitable mechanism called the head motion, in such a manner that the acceleration of the table in its own plane is less out of one of the dead points of the stroke than the acceleration of adhesion of the particles but greater out of the other dead point. The table is riffled in the direction of the shake, that is, crosswise to the wash. Shallow troughs between the riffles conduct the heavy particles shaken to the bottom of the multi-layered bed in the direction of the shake, whereas the light particles collecting on the top of the bed are entrained downslope by the wash.

Sizes, shapes, materials, riffling designs and head motions of tables vary widely. Parts A, B and C of Fig. 1.42 show e.g. the standard, finishing and roughing riffling used on Wilfley tables of conventional size; in the riffling of Part D of the figure, every third or fourth riffle is twice as high as the others. Part E shows the riffling of a Deister–Overstrom diagonal-deck table; Part F shows a (small) Concenco table; Part G shows the riffling of a slime table. (The last three are diagonal tables of rhomboidal plan outline.) In designs E and F, every fourth or fifth riffle is substantially higher than those in between. This enables the table to hold a thicker sheet of water, making it suited for the handling of coarser feeds (up to 3 cm maximum size). On the slime table (Part G), there is an extensive unriffled surface, and such riffling is wide-spaced with broad hollows in between to reduce turbulence.

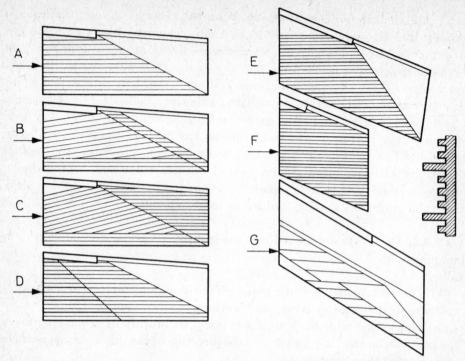

Fig. 1.42. Decks of shaken tables in plan view. A — standard-riffle Wilfley, B — finishing-riffle Wilfley, C — roughing-riffle Wilfley, D — alternating high and low riffles ("1623" Wilfley), E — Deister–Overstrom, F — Concenco, G — slime table

The diagonal shape results in a material saving and increases the useful deck area. It is obtained by cutting away from a Wilfley table the unriffled part where practically no solids appear in operation anyway and by adding a more or less equivalent area downslope, in the direction of progress of the particles. The product that would trickle off the tailing edge of a Wilfley table is processed further on a Deister, which permits the latter to handle a longer-range feed or a greater throughput of a short-range feed than a Wilfley table of equal area.

In designs B and C, there is, in addition to the riffling parallel to the shake, also a riffling mounting the slope at a gentle angle. As a result, the retention time of the particles in the sheet wash is longer, in much the same way as if the downslope dimension (width) of the table were greater. The bed moving between the oblique riffles is being overturned in the process, too, which is an advantage as well as a drawback: the bed stratified by gravity gets churned up, but the misrouted particles, if any, can still find their way to where they belong.

The surface of the table may be of linoleum, rubber, glass, concrete, aluminium, etc. The riffling may be cast in the same operation as the table (e.g. in the case of rubber, glass, etc.) milled into the surface, or made of some other material fixed onto a plate (e.g. wooden cleats held by brads or galvanized steel angles). The material constitution of the table affects the friction coefficients of the diverse minerals and, through it, also overall tabling performance.

Tables are often placed side by side or one above another and connected to a common drive. In the first case, they can be connected in parallel only, whereas in the second — which permits also a substantial saving of space — they can be connected either in parallel or in series. Each of the tables in a vertical stack, connected in series and fixed to a common frame with alternating slopes, may be longer than the one above it. A heavy product is drawn off each deck; the rest of the bed trickles off to form the feed of the next table below.

Some of the head motions of shaken tables, generating their asymmetric shake, are shown diagrammatically in Fig. 1.43.

The Wilfley and the Overstrom (Concenco) head motions (A and B) are of the pitman-and-toggle type. The far end (the one away from the pitman) of one toggle is fixed (more accurately, is adjustable within a narrow range to permit the regulation of its inclination), whereas the far end of the other toggle, confined to horizontal motion by a yoke, is attached to the table. The common articulation of the toggles and pitman moves on a circular arc about the fixed end of the first toggle. The tangent to the arc is steeper at one dead point than at the other: hence, the acceleration of the table is greater out of the first than out of the second. Stroke length can be regulated by adjusting the inclination of the fixed-point toggle. The Plat-O and Deister head motions (C and D),

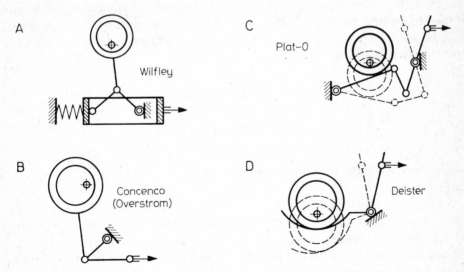

Fig. 1.43. Head motions of shaking tables. *A* — Wilfley, *B* — Overstrom (Concenco), *C* — Plat-O, *D* — Deister

107

incorporate an eccentric disk sliding-rolling on an arm with a fixed pivot. In the Plat-O motion, the end of this arm is connected by a toggle with a rocker arm. In the Deister motion, the part of the fixed-pivot rocker in contact with the eccentric disk is a circular arc of radius greater than that of the disk; the latter rolls down on the former as it rotates. In both diagrams, the situation with the eccentric rotated by 180° is shown dashed. Length of stroke can be adjusted by moving the fixation of the connecting-rod end towards or away from the rocker-arm pivot. The arrows in the diagrams indicate the direction of motion which detaches the particles from the deck (that is, the high-acceleration stroke).

The head motions of Fig. 1.43 move the table in its own plane. Other tables are mounted on oblique leaf springs in the manner of shaking screens (cf. Vol. 1, Section 4.7.3.1); on these, the bed will proceed in one direction even if the shake is symmetric, provided the maximum acceleration of the deck in the direction of swinging (perpendicularly to the springs),

$$r\omega^2 > \frac{g_0 f}{\cos \beta + f \sin \beta},$$

where β is the angle that the supporting springs include with the vertical. The motion of such a spring-supported table may be any one of the designs presented in Vol. 1, Section 4.7.3.1, used to generate symmetric swinging in shaking screens (e.g. an eccentric and connecting rod, a rotating unbalanced mass, etc.). Electromagnets may also be used to drive shaking tables.

(C) In any type of shaking table, it is possible to adjust the splitters dividing the products, water feed rate, and also the slope of the deck and the length of the stroke (the latter two often with the machine running). The length of slope is typically in the 10 to 35 mm range; speed is 130 to 380 cpm in practice. Useful rule-of-thumb formula are

$$l \simeq 18\sqrt[4]{x_{95}}.$$

and

$$n \simeq 250/\sqrt[5]{x_{95}},$$

where l mm is length of stroke, n cpm is speed and x_{95} mm is the 95-per cent particle size.

Given a feed of constant composition and density introduced at a constant rate, the width and direction of particle bands of different s.g. can be regulated by varying the water feed rate, deck slope, length and speed of stroke. In order to obtain clean end products, it is indicated to route thin side bands of concentrate and tailings into the middlings. Table throughput per unit table area (T t/h·m²) varies as the size and average s.g. of the feed, and as the free settling ratio of the minerals to be separated. Shaking-table throughput for a typical ore feed is furnished by

$$T \simeq K\sqrt{x}$$

or

$$T = \frac{x_{95}}{5},$$

for coals by the formula

$$T = K'x^{0.65},$$

where T is in $\text{t/h} \cdot \text{m}^2$; x and x_{95} are, respectively, the maximum and 95-per cent feed particle size; K varies from 0.3 to 0.5 and K' from 0.2 to 0.4. Another empirical formula of table throughput is

$$Q \simeq \frac{(Axr)^{0.6}\delta}{15} \quad \text{tons per hour,}$$

where A m² is table area, x is the maximum particle size, δ is the average s.g. of the feed and

$$r = \frac{\delta_2 - 1}{\delta_1 - 1}$$

is the free-settling ratio.

Maximum feed particle size may be about 6 mm for ores and 20 mm for coals; shaken slime tables provide an acceptable separation down to a lower limiting particle size of 30 to 40 μm for ores and 40 to 50 μm for coals. Water consumption is 4 to 5 m³/t for ores and about 2 m³/t for coals (higher for fine pulps). One-half to three quarters of the water is introduced with the feed, the rest as wash water. In cleaning a rougher product, or in handling a finer-grained feed, water feed rate and slope are to be reduced, stroke is to be reduced, shortened and speed is to be increased. Power draft of a conventional-size table (2.5 to 5 m long and 1.2 to 2.5 m wide) is 0.5 to 0.8 kW.

Shaking tables are used nowadays in the concentration of certain ores containing fine free gold, cassiterite, zinc ores in coarse dissemination, occasionally iron ores and (in America) in the cleaning of coal fines. Tables used to have a wide field of application in the 1920s and 1930s, but the concentration of copper, lead and zinc sulphide ores has been taken over by flotation and the processing of oxidic or partly oxidized copper, zinc (and gold) ores by hydro-metallurgy. Small tables are widespread in flotation shops, but as a means of monitoring flotation performance rather than as concentrating devices in their own right. On trickling some of the tailing pulp onto the table, the appearance of a pay mineral streak gives a direct visual demonstration of loss of pay metal in the flotation process.

1.6. LITERATURE ON CONCENTRATION BY GRAVITY

ABBOT, J.—K. W. BATEMAN—S. R. SHAW: The Vorsyl separator. *Min. Proc. & Extr. Met.*, 9, CMMC, London 1969, 201—221.

ANDRES, W.: Die Schichtung des Setzgutes nach der Wichte. *Glückauf* 1950, 17—19.

BANIEL, A.—A. MITZMAGER: Use and recovery of tetrabromethane (TBE) in mineral dressing. *IMPC*, London 1960, 611—619.

BARTELT, D.: Trockenaufbereitung von Feinkohlen mit Austragregelung durch Radioisotope. *Glückauf* 1966, 1120—1129.

BELUGOU, P.—E. CONDOLIES: Der Lavodune, ein neuer Sortierapparat. 3. *ICPC*, Liège 1958, 423—433.

BERGER, W.—W. DALLMANN—S. HAUBOLD: Einige Hinweise für die Überwachung und den Betrieb von Schwertrübeanlagen. *Bergakademie* 1965, 422—427.

BRONKALA, W. J.: How to select wet magnetic separators for heavy media plants. *E/MJ* 1963, 98—102.

BROWN, W. E.—L. J. ERCK: Humphrey's spiral concentration on Mesabi Range ores. *Min. Eng.* 1949, 187—193.

CARTA, M.—G. FERRARA—G. DEL FÁ: Preparation of fine coal by the "Multidune" process. 5. *ICPC*, Pittsburgh 1966, B.2.

DOUGLAS, E.—T. WALSH: New type of dry, heavy medium gravity separator. *Trans. IMM* 1966, 226—232; 1967, C142—C144.

DeVOOYS, G. J.: Die Entwicklung der Schwerflüssigkeitsverfahren zur Aufbereitung von Steinkohle. *Glückauf* 1951, 921—926.

FINKEY, J.: *Die wissenschaftlichen Grundlagen der nasser Erzaufbereitung*, J. Springer Verlag, Berlin 1924.

GAUDIN, A. M.: *Principles of Mineral Dressing.* McGraw-Hill, New York—London 1939.

GÖTTE, A.: Austragregelung von Setzmaschinen. *Der Bergbau* 1936, 263—271.

GRÖPPEL, K.: Steinkohlenaufbereitung mit Schwerflüssigkeit nach dem Verfahren Sophia-Jacoba. *Glückauf* 1934, 429—435.

GRÜNDER, W.: *Sortierung in Rinnenwäschen. Der deutsche Steinkohlenbergbau, Bd. 4.* Aufbereitung der Steinkohle. Verlag Glückauf, Essen 1960, 208—215.

HAMPEL, M.—M. BECKER: Sortierung von Rohschlämmen in einem Wasserzyklon. *Glückauf* 1970, 584—587.

HEIDENREICH, H.: Beiträge zur Theorie der Sortenbildung im Rheobett. *Mont. Rundschau* 1929, 473—479.

HELFRICHT, R.: Optimale Betriebsbedingungen von Fächerrinnen. *Freib. Fh. A401* 1966, 223—240.

HELFRICHT, R.—H. SCHUBERT: Die Fächerrinne, ein Dichtesortiergerät für die Anreicherung feiner Körnungen. *Freib. Fh. A281* 1963, 171—192.

HOFFMANN, E.: Grundlagen der Setzarbeit und technische Entwicklung der Setzmaschinen. *Glückauf* 1960, 481—494.

HOFFMANN, E.—B. MIHALOVSKI: Neuartige Setzmaschinen für grosse Aufgabeleistungen. *Glückauf* 1965, 637—643.

HUBBARD, J. S.—I. B. HUMPHREYS—W. E. BROWN: How Humphrey's spiral concentrator is used in modern ore dressing practice. *Mining World* 1953, No. 6, 40—45.

JOHN, P.: Die Wirbelschicht-Sinkscheidung als modernes Trockensortierverfahren. *AT* 1971, 140—146.

KIRCHBERG, H.: *Aufbereitung bergbaulicher Rohstoffe. Vol. I.* Wilhelm Gronau Verlag, Jena 1953.

KIRCHBERG, H.—W. BERGER: Study of the operation of shaking concentration tables. *IMPC* London 1960, 537—551.

KIRCHBERG, H.—W. HENTZSCHEL: Neuere Erkenntnisse über den Setzvorgang. *Erzmetall* 1957, 526—530.

KIRCHBERG, H.—G. SCHULZE: Über einige Untersuchungen zu den Strömungs und Entmischungsverhältnissen in einem zylindrischen Zyklon (Bauart Dyna-Whirlpool). *Freib. Fh. A437* 1968, 39—46.

KLASSEN, V. I.—V. I. LITOVKO—N. F. MYASNIKOV: Improvement of physical and mechanical properties of ferrosilicon suspensions with help of reagents. 7. *IMPC*, New York 1964, 95—101.

KÖHLER, H. J.: Sortiererfolg einer Schwertrübe-Setzmaschine. *Aach. Bl.* 1956, 36—56.

KRIJGSMAN, C.: Versuchs- und Betriebsergebnisse mit Hydrozyklonen. *Chem. Ing. Techn.* 1955, 190—192.

KRIJGSMAN, C.: The Dutch State Mines dense-medium cyclone washer. *Coll. Eng.* 1960, 328—332, 383—386.

MAYER, F. W.: Der Entmischungsvorgang als physikalischer Aufbereitungsprozess. *Bergbauarchiv* 1950, 82—94.

MAYER, F. W.: Neue Erkenntnisse über den Setzvorgang auf Grund der Potentialtheorie. *Glückauf* 1960, 1297—1302.

MAYER, F. W.: Stand der Erkenntnisse vom Setzprozess aufgrund der Potentialtheorie. *AT* 1966, 543—559.

MITCHELL, D. R.: *Coal preparation.* AIME, New York, 1950.

MOSER, H.: Die Schwerflüssigkeitsaufbereitung nach Tromp. *Z. VDI* 1939, 53—57.

NAGUIB, A. G.: New considerations in design and application of sluice separators. *Min. Congr. J.* 1971 Sept., 123—128.

OSS, D. G.—S. E. ERICKSON: Instrumentation and control of the heavy media process. *Trans. AIME* 1962, 225—229.

RICKEN, E.: Erfahrungen mit dem Bandsinkscheider bei der Nachwäsche von Feinzwischengut der Zeche Hannover. *Glückauf* 1957, 17—25.

RODIS, F.: Herstellung und Eigenschaften von Ferrosilizium für die Schwerflüssigkeitsaufbereitung. *Erzmetall* 1955, Beiheft 145—150.

RODIS, F.—J. CREMER: Why an atomized ferrosilicon proves superior for heavy media plants. *Mining World* 1960 March, 36—39.

SALZMANN, G.: Ferrosilizium als Schwerstoff. *Erzmetall* 1952, 114.

SCHÄFER, O.: Die Aufbereitung nach dem Schwerflüssigkeitsverfahren von Tromp. *Glückauf* 1938, 581—586.

SCHÖNFELD, W.: Untersuchungen zur Beeinflussung der Konsistenz von Schwertrüben durch oberflächenaktive Mittel. *Aach. Bl.* 1960, 121—131.

SCHÖNMÜLLER, J. R.: Das Laminarstromverfahren nach dr. Walter Vogel. *Glückauf* 1941, 93—101.

SCHÖNMÜLLER, J. R.: Die Sortierung von Feinzwischengut in Bandsinkscheider. *Glückauf* 1954, 1268—1276.

SCHUBERT, H.: Zum gegenwärtigen Stand der Setztheorie. *Bergakademie* 1964, 748—755.

STRISOVSKY, M.—M. LICKA: Zur Frage der Überwachung von Regenerationskreisläufen in Schwertrübe-Aufbereitungsanlägen. *AT* 1971, 637—642.

SVENSSON, J.: Das Stripa-Schwimm-Sink-Aufbereitung für Erze. *Erzmetall* 1955, 147—152; 1958, 189—190.

TARJÁN, G.: Principles of concentration of gravity. *Acta Technica*, 1955, 12.

VALENTIK, L.: Rheological properties of heavy media suspensions stabilized by polymers. *Trans. AIME* 1972, 99—105.

VALENTIK, L.—E. L. MICHAELS: Kontrolle und Arbeitsweise von Schwertrübescheidern. *Bergbauwiss.* 1971, 86—95.

111

VALENTIK, L.—R. L. WHITMORE: Controlling the performance of dense medium baths. 7. *IMPC*, New York 1964, 87—94.

VISMAN, J.: Integrated water cyclone plants for coal preparation. *Can. M. M. Bull.* 1968, 365—370.

VOLIN, M. E.—L. VALENTIK: Control of heavy media plants for the production of gravel aggregate. *NSGA Circular* 1969, No. 105.

WEIDENFELD, W.: Der Drewboy, ein robuster Schwerflüssigkeits-Sinkscheider für die Kohlenaufbereitung. *Schlägel und Eisen* 1956, 101—107.

WHITMORE, R. L.: Principles of jig washing: an experimental approach. *J. Inst. Fuel* 1958, No. 204, 3—11.

WITTING, W.: Erfahrungen bei der Sortierung von Setzmaschinenzwischengut im Humboldt-Sinkscheider. *Glückauf* 1957, 258—264.

ZIEMER, U.: Grenzen der Feinkornsortierung in Schwertrüben. *Bergbauwiss.* 1958, 65—70.

YANCEY, H. F.—C. G. BLACK: The effect of certain operating variables on the efficiency of the coal-washing tables. *Bu. Mines RI 3111* 1931.

YANCEY, H. F.—M. R. GREER: Coal-cleaning performance — Comparison of pneumatic jig, pneumatic table and Baum-type jig. *Trans. AIME* 1946, 208—223.

YANCEY, H. F.—M. R. GREER: Laboratory cleaning trials on a Pennsylvania anthracite in a Baum-type jig and a dense-medium pilot plant. *Bu. Mines RI 5308* 1957.

YANCEY, H. F.—C. B. PORTER: Pneumatic tabling of coal; effect of specific gravity, size and shape. *Bu. Mines*, Tech. Paper 536, 1932.

2. FLOTATION

Most important of the processes of concentration based upon differences in the surface adhesion properties of minerals, flotation is based on the different adhesion to air and water of different mineral surfaces. The other processes of this kind rely for their operation on differences in adhesion to oil, fats or greases, mercury, etc. and to water.

The adhesion between water or air and the surfaces of solid particles can be modified (increased or decreased) by the addition of suitable surface-active agents (surfactants): these can even invert the propensity of a particle to adhere, say, to water in preference to air. If air bubbles are dispersed in a pulp, the mineral grains having an affinity to air (aerophilia) and a disaffinity to water (hydrophobia) will attach themselves to the bubbles which will lift them to the pulp surface. If suitable reagents are added, the bubbles do not burst at once but survive for a longer or shorter time at the pulp surface, forming a more or less stable froth. The grains of mineral species rendered hydrophobic by a succession of chemicals can be selectively removed in the froth, while the aerophobic-hydrophilic grains wetted by water remain dispersed in the pulp.

2.1. FUNDAMENTALS

2.1.1. Phases. In flotation, each of the three common states of matter (solid, liquid and gaseous) plays a role.

2.1.1.1. Differences in the nature of gas phase in the bubbles do not have any substantial influence on flotation performance: air may be replaced by some other gas or by water vapour. The floatability of a mineral is, on the other hand, affected if a chemical reaction takes place between the gas phase and the grain surfaces (or the liquid phase or the reagents dissolved in it). Oxygen e.g. acts as an oxidizing, hydrogen sulphide as a sulphuretting agent, on dry mineral grains as well as in an aqueous solution. Hydrogen sulphide or carbon dioxide affect also the pH (the hydrogen ion concentration) of the aqueous phase.

8

2.1.1.2. The liquid phase in flotation is invariably water or, more precisely, a dilute aqueous solution. Water is a powerful solvent and ionizing agent: its molecules have a propensity to associate among them and to hydrate alien ions. All this is due to the asymmetric, polar nature of the water molecule, in which the centres of action of the positive and negative charge do not coincide. The water molecule accordingly behaves as an electrically charged dipole (quite rigorously speaking, a quadrupole). In liquid water, molecules associate, so that the positive half of one faces the negative half of its neighbour; as a result, loose tetrahedral aggregates of several molecules are constituted, forming and falling apart all the time. In the process, one aggregate may end up with a proton surplus and the other with a proton deficit: as a result, both acquire the nature of ions:

$$(mH_2O \cdot H)^+ \text{ and } (nH_2O \cdot OH)^-.$$

The arithmetic product of the concentrations of hydrated hydrogen and hydroxyl ions in water is a constant at a givent temperature. Disregarding all the associated neutral water molecules, one may write

$$[H^+][OH^-] = K.$$

The brackets denote molar concentrations (grammolecules per litre). For example,

at t =	0	18	25	50	100 °C,
10^{14} K =	0.1	0.6	1.0	6.0	59.0.

In an acid solution, the concentration of hydrogen ions is greater than in pure water; in an alkaline solution, it is the concentration of hydroxyl ions that is greater. In pure water at 25 °C, $K = 10^{-14}$, and hence,

$$[H^+] = [OH^-] = 10^{-7};$$

in acid solutions,

$$[H^+] > 10^{-7};$$

in alkaline solutions,

$$[H^+] < 10^{-7}.$$

By convention, acidity or alkalinity is expressed as minus one times the exponent of 10 on the right-hand side (the negative Briggsian logarithm of hydrogen ion concentration); it is called the hydrogen ion exponent and denoted pH.

In the vicinity of the neutral pH = 7 of pure water, even the addition of small amounts of acid or alkali will shift the pH appreciably. (It is for example not simple at all to make distilled water of pH = 7, since the carbon dioxide that it absorbs from the air usually reduces its pH to below 6.) Comparatively much acid or alkali is required, on the other hand, to change the pH from, say, 1 to 0 or 13 to 14.

Owing to the phenomenon of hydrolysis, the aqueous solutions of most salts are not neutral. If the ions liberated on the dissociation of a salt in water are not of equal strength, then they constitute either a weak acid and a strong base or the other way round. For example, the aqueous solution of aluminium chloride is a fairly strong acid because the chlorine ion is much stronger than the aluminium ion:

$$AlCl_3 + 3H_2O \rightleftarrows Al(OH)_3 + 3H^+ + 3Cl^-;$$

a solution of sodium carbonate is alkaline for a similar reason:

$$Na_2CO_3 + H_2O \rightleftarrows 2Na^+ + OH^- + HCO_3^-.$$

Salts of either type, if dissolved in water, act as a buffer, as a pH-stabilizing influence. For example, on adding hydrochloric acid or sodium hydroxide to water containing some aluminium chloride, the pH of the solution changes much less than if the water were pure. Ferrous and ferric sulphate, present in almost every mine water, also have a buffering effect. Whereas the acidity of the solution as determined by titration varies as the concentration of the Fe^{2+} and/or Fe^{3+} ions, the pH varies much less. In a log-log net with its abscissa axis calibrated in Fe ion concentration (Fig. 2.1), the graphs of acidity as expressed in terms of equivalent $CaCO^3$ concentration are straight lines of slope $+1$ (solid lines), whereas the average slope of the pH graphs (dashed lines) is about -0.5. That is, if the Fe ion concentration in the solution is augmented by a factor of one hundred, titrable acidity (the concentration of SO_4^{2-} ions) also increases by that factor, whereas hydrogen ion concentration increases by a factor of about 10 only.

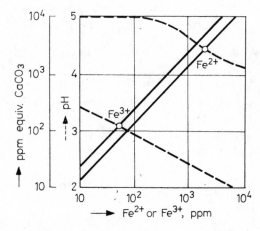

Fig. 2.1. Variation of acidity (of the pH) vs. Fe ion concentration in the pulp

In the absence of buffering, if a strong acid or alkali is added to change the hydrogen ion concentration by ΔpH, then the original pH of the pulp changes to

$$\text{pH}' = \text{pH} + \Delta\text{pH} - 7.$$

For example, on adding 250 mg/l H_2SO_4, of molecular weight 98, to a pulp, the molar concentration of hydrogen becomes

$$\frac{0.25}{49} = 5.1 \cdot 10^{-3}[\text{H}^+];$$

on adding 250 mg/l $Ca(OH_2$, of molecular weight 74, the molar concentration of hydroxyl becomes

$$\frac{0.25}{37} = 6.75 \cdot 10^{-3}[\text{OH}^-].$$

The corresponding ΔpH is

$$3 - \log 5.1 = 2.29$$

in the first case and, since

$$\frac{10^{-14}}{6.75 \cdot 10^{-3}} = 1.48 \cdot 10^{-12},$$

it is

$$12 - \log 1.48 = 11.83$$

in the second. That is, assuming the original pH of the pulp to have been 6.5, it is changed by the additions to pH$'$ = 1.79 in the first case and pH$''$ = 11.33 in the second (in the absence of buffering and of chemical or physical [e.g. adsorption] reactions that would affect the concentration of hydrogen or hydroxyl ions in the solution) (Petersen 1936).

In water, it is not only the hydrogen and hydroxyl ions that get hydrated, but also the other ions in solution. For example, the Na^+ and Cl^- ions of solid rock salt react with water according to the equation

$$(m + n)H_2O + Na^+ + Cl^- \rightleftarrows (Na \cdot mH_2O)^+ + (Cl \cdot nH_2O)^-.$$

2.1.1.3. The solid phase. The crystals making up the solid phase contain lattice defects that affect their behaviour appreciably. One cubic centimetre of crystal is made up of 10^{23} to 10^{24} elementary building blocks (atoms or ions). Reckoning with an average ionic radius of 0.5 to 1 Å, one ion occupies a volume of 1 to 8 Å^3; the number of ions per cubic centimetre is obtained as

$$\frac{1}{(10^{-8})^3} \text{ to } \frac{1}{8(10^{-8})^3} \simeq 10^{24} \text{ to } 10^{23}.$$

Even if the density of lattice defects is not greater than one per one million lattice positions, there are 10^{17} to 10^{18} lattice defects per cubic centimetre of crystal! Such defects affect not only the strength and electrical properties of the solid, but its flotation behaviour also.

A lattice defect may be a cation or anion missing from a lattice position (defect of the Schottky type), or a cation or anion occupying an irregular position (defect of the Frenkel type). An excess electron or the absence of an electron from where there should be one also constitutes a defect. The fact that the effective technical (macroscopic) strength of solids is less by several orders of magnitude than their molecular strength is due to lattice defects, and so are the electric properties of semiconductors (the latter are imparted

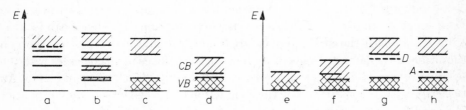

Fig. 2.2. Energy levels and bands of atoms

by the deliberate creation of lattice defects in the production process). Holes in the lattice endow it with ionic conductivity; a surplus or deficit of electrons, compensating for the charges of excess cations or anions in a crystal not quite true to the chemical formula (electron holes) gives rise to electronic conduction. Electrical conductivity and floatability are greatly influenced also by the presence of atoms alien to the formula. Some of the elements making up a crystal lattice may be replaced by other elements having about the same size and polarization properties, but a different valence: the balance of electric charges, however, must be maintained, and this is usually achieved by the incorporation of an alien ion of opposite charge. In certain well-defined cases, the result is the formation of isomorphs, both the lattice energy and the surface energy of which may deviate substantially from that of the pure crystal. There are numerous natural semiconductor minerals, especially among the sulphides, selenides, tellurides, arsenides and oxides. Surface lattice defects also affect the adsorption of surfactants quite appreciably.

The electric conductivity or resistivity of a solid is determined by the energy bands of the outer (valence) electrons of the elements making it up. Conditions are illustrated by Fig. 2.2 (Finkelnburg 1964). In isolated atoms or atoms sufficiently far apart, the energies of the inner electrons have well-defined levels (diagram *a*). The energy of the outer, more or less free electron(s) can change within the range shown shaded. Atoms close-packed (e.g. in a crystal) will interact; as a result, the energy band of the outermost electron(s) grows wider, and the energy levels of some electrons situated further inward also

117

broaden into bands (diagram *b*). There remain, however, forbidden zones between bands.

In the rest of the diagrams, we shall confine our concern to the two uppermost energy bands. Cross-hatching indicates that the band in question is saturated with electrons. If the lower of the two top bands is saturated, and its electrons do not have sufficient energy to jump over into the upper (highest) one, across a gap which in this case is very wide (diagram *c*), then the solid behaves as an insulator, a substance whose outer electrons are not available for conduction. The jump from the saturated band to the free one above it requires an energy of several electron volts (eV) in this case. In pure crystalline semiconductors (diagram *d*), on the other hand, this gap is much narrower, less than one eV, so that some of the electrons can jump from the valence band *VB* to empty positions in the conduction band *CB* simply thanks to the ceaseless thermal vibration of the lattice. In good conductors, the valence band coalesces with the conduction band (diagram *e* for a monovalent, diagram *f* for a bivalent metal). An "electron gas" is constituted by the conduction electrons. Free to move about in the crystal, these electrons are available for charge transfer (for constituting a current). In bivalent metals, the top energy levels partly overlap as a result of strong interaction between the valence electrons. Diagrams *g* and *h* represent semiconductors, respectively of type *n* and *p*. In the *n* type, there is a surplus of electrons; in the *p* type, there is a deficit, due to natural or deliberate "doping" with atoms having more or fewer electrons than the atoms making up the bulk of the lattice. The electron surplus/deficit represented by these doping atoms is comparatively free to move about in the lattice. For example, if a crystal of four-valent silicon or germanium is doped with five-valent phosphorus or arsenic, then four of the valence electrons of this latter are strongly tied down by the neighbouring atoms of the lattice, but the fifth one is comparatively loose. It is therefore separated by a gap having the width of just a few hundredths or tenths of an eV from the unsaturated conduction band, indicated by the *D* (donor) line in diagram *g*. This means that the energy of thermal vibration is quite sufficient to elevate it into the conduction band. Diagram *h*, on the other hand, represents a shortage of valence electrons. For example, if a Si or Ge lattice is doped with a small quantity of trivalent atoms, or a metal oxide is doped with excess oxygen (tantamount to a deficit of metal), then the attachment of the doping atom to the neighbouring lattice atoms is short of one electron. A neighbouring valence electron can jump across comparatively easily to fill this defect, leaving a hole where it has been before; another valence electron can jump across to fill this hole and create another one, and so forth. The energy condition of such atoms can thus be illustrated by the *A* (acceptor) line in diagram *h*. Exposed to a voltage, the holes will move in the crystal just like electrons, but in the opposite direction, behaving as free virtual positive-charge carriers.

118

In flotation, it is the surfaces of the mineral grains that count; their interiors are largely irrelevant. The internal structure of a crystal, on the other hand, has a great importance in determining surface properties.

Table 2.1 lists distances between the constitutents of certain anion complexes. Table 2.2 states the atomic numbers Z, atomic weights, ionic and atomic radii of the elements occurring in minerals. The ionic radii of cations are plotted vs. valence in Part A of Fig. 2.3, the ionic radii of anions are plotted in Part B. The anions with their adventive electrons are seen to be larger than the cations, which have some/all of their valence electrons removed, the reason being that the radius of an ion is in effect the radius of action of its outermost electron(s). For example, in sulphur, the radius of

	S^{2-}	S^0	S^{4+}	S^{6+}
is	1.85	0.96	0.37	0.32 Å;

in lead, the radius of

	Pb^{4-}	Pb^0	Pb^{2+}	Pb^{4+}
is	2.15	1.74	1.20	0.84 Å.

As a result, in ionic lattices, it is the packing of the large anions that determines lattice structure first and foremost, whereas the smaller (polyvalent) cations occupy the interstices of the anions.

In Table 2.2, cationic radii refer to heteropolar compounds in sixfold coordination; anionic radii refer to the most common coordination; atomic radii refer to a coordination of 12 (but U refers to fourfold, Te to two-fold and H and the non-metallics Br, Cl, F, J, O, S and Se to single coordination). The factors of conversion to other coordination numbers are, for cationic radii,

coordination:	3	4	6	8	10	12,
conversion factor:	0.90	0.95	1.00	1.04	1.07	1.10;

Table 2.1. Spacing of constituents in some XO_3 and XO_4 anion complexes, Å. The Si—O spacing is 1.61 Å in all other Si—O complexes (including finite groups with several nuclei, infinite chains, layers or grids such as $Si_2O_7^{6-}$, $Si_6O_{18}^{12-}$, SiO_3^{2-}, SiO_2)

(Å) : BO_3^{3-}	: B—O	1.36
CO_3^{2-}	: C—O	1.27; O—O 2.21
NO_3^-	: N—O	1.24
SO_3^{2-}	: S—O	1.43
ClO_3^-	: Cl—O	1.57; O—O 2.52
SO_4^{2-}	: S—O	1.51; O—O 2.46
SiO_4^{4-}	: Si—O	1.61; O—O 2.63
PO_4^{3-}	: P—O	1.53; O—O 2.59
CrO_4^-	: Cr—O	1.65
MnO_4^-	: Mn—O	1.59

Table 2.2. Ionic and atomic radii of elements

Z		Atomic weight	Cationic radius							Anionic radius		Atomic radius
			1+	2+	3+	4+	5+	6+	7+			
Ag	47	107.87	1.26	0.89								1.44
Al	13	26.97			0.57							1.43
As	33	74.92			0.58		0.47					1.45
Au	79	196.97	1.31		0.85							1.44
B	5	10.81			0.25							0.96
Ba	56	137.34		1.46								2.24
Be	4	9.01		0.34								1.13
Bi	83	208.98			0.96		0.74					1.82
Br	35	79.91					0.48		0.39	Br^{1-}	1.96	1.14
C	6	12.01				0.16						0.87
Ca	20	40.08		0.99								1.97
Cd	48	112.40		0.97								1.56
Ce	58	140.12			1.07	0.94						1.82
Cl	17	35.45					0.34		0.27	Cl^{1-}	1.81	0.99
Co	27	58.93		0.69	0.63							1.26
Cr	24	52.00		0.83	0.63			0.52				1.28
Cs	55	132.91	1.65									2.70
Cu	29	63.54	0.96	0.76								1.28
F	9	19.00							~0.1	F^{-1}	1.36	0.73
Fe	26	55.85		0.74	0.64							1.27
Ga	31	69.72			0.62							1.35
Ge	32	72.59				0.53						1.39
H	1	1.008							1.40	H^{1-}	1.36	0.37
Hf	72	178.49				0.78						1.59
Hg	80	200.59		1.10								1.55
In	49	114.82			0.81							1.65
Ir	77	192.2				0.68						1.35
J	53	126.90					0.62		0.51	J^{1-}	2.20	1.33
K	19	39.10	1.33									2.39
La	57	138.91			1.14							1.88
Li	3	6.94	0.68									1.57
Mg	12	24.31		0.66								1.60
Mn	25	54.94		0.80	0.66	0.60			0.47			1.30
Mo	42	95.94				0.70		0.62				1.40
N	7	14.01			0.18		0.15					0.56
Na	11	22.99	0.97									1.92
Nb	41	92.91				0.79	0.69					1.47
Ni	28	58.71		0.69								1.24
O	8	16.00								O^{2-}	1.40	0.66
Os	76	190.2				0.69		0.69				1.35
P	15	20.97			0.45		0.35					1.30
Pb	82	207.19		1.20	0.84					Pb^{4-}	2.15	1.74
Pt	78	195.09		0.80	0.65							1.38
Ra	88	226.0		1.43								?
Rb	37	85.47	1.47									2.56

Table 2.2 (continued)

z		Atomic weight	Cationic radius							Anionic radius		Atomic radius
			1+	2+	3+	4+	5+	6+	7+			
Re	75	186.2				0.72		0.55	0.56			1.37
S	16	32.06				0.37		0.32		S^{2-}	1.85	0.96
Sb	51	121.75			0.76		0.62			Sb^{3-}	2.42	1.62
Sc	21	44.96			0.81							1.64
Se	34	78.96				0.51		0.42		Se^{2-}	1.91	1.10
Si	14	28.09				0.42				Si^{4-}	1.98	1.30
Sn	50	118.69		0.93		0.71				Sn^{4-}	2.15	1.59
Sr	38	87.62		1.12								2.15
Ta	73	180.95					0.68					1.47
Te	52	127.60				0.89		0.56		Te^{2-}	2.11	1.43
Th	90	232.04			1.15	1.02						1.80
Ti	22	47.90		0.80	0.76	0.68						1.47
Tl	81	204.37	1.47		0.95							1.71
U	92	238.04			1.12	0.97		0.80				1.55
V	23	50.94		0.88	0.74	0.63	0.59					1.36
W	74	183.85				0.70		0.62				1.41
Zn	30	65.37		0.74								1.39
Zr	40	91.22				0.79						1.60
Y	39	88.91			0.92							1.82
Yb	70	173.04		0.91	0.86							1.93

and for atomic radii,

coordination:	3	4	6	8	12,
conversion factor:	0.82	0.88	0.96	0.97	1.00.

Polarization effects as well as transitional, hybrid forms of bonding are due in the final reckoning to the oscillation (resonance or mesomerism) of a given bond between different types, in its quest for a state of least energy. In graphite, for example, any C atom is attached to three other C atoms in the same plane, with bonds of length 1.42 Å; the fourth bond is perpendicular to the plane thus defined and its length is 3.40 Å. Now the length of a C—C bond is 1.54 Å, and that of a C=C bond is 1.33 Å; the distance of 1.42 Å is the result of averaging (resonance) between two single bonds and a double one (Kleber 1956).

In flotation, mineral-grain surfaces tend to capture more or less hydrated ions, which wet them (endow them with a water film), but the surface ions of the grains may themselves acquire hydrate shells as well. Ions of higher ionic potential (of higher valence and smaller ionic radius) tend to hydrate more strongly. The anions with their longer ionic radii for example are less hydrated as a rule than the cations with their shorter ones. Of the monovalent alkali cations, those of a smaller ionic radius (Li, Na) are more strongly hydrated

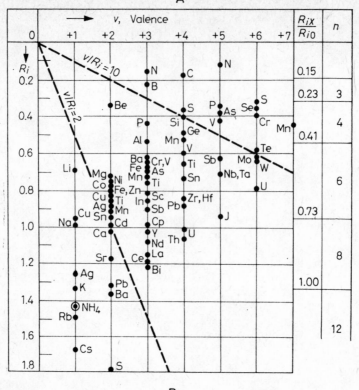

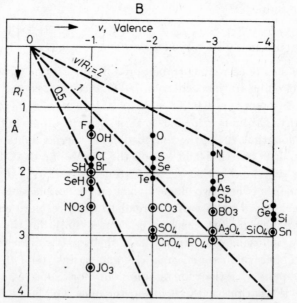

Fig. 2.3. A — ionic radii of cations, B — ionic radii of anions

than the larger ones (K, Rb, Cs). As a result, small Li^+ taken together with its thick hydrate shell is larger than large Cs^+ with its thinner one. Each polyvalent hydrated cation presumably has a hydrate shell of 6 to 8 water molecules. Molecules of substances dissolving in water in a non-ionic manner may also be hydrated to a greater or smaller extent.

Cations (anions) may replace each other in a lattice if they are of roughly the same size (isomorphic substitution). If the replacing ion is of different valence, then the resulting charge imbalance has to be offset somewhere else in the crystal. For example, in the feldspars, whose three-dimensional lattice of tetrahedral silica ions greatly resembles the quartz lattice, some of the Si^{4+} cations of quartz are replaced by Al^{3+} cations. The resulting charge deficit is compensated by the incorporation of a monovalent cation (Na^+) in albite, which contains one aluminium ion per molecule ($NaAlSi_3O_8$), and by a divalent

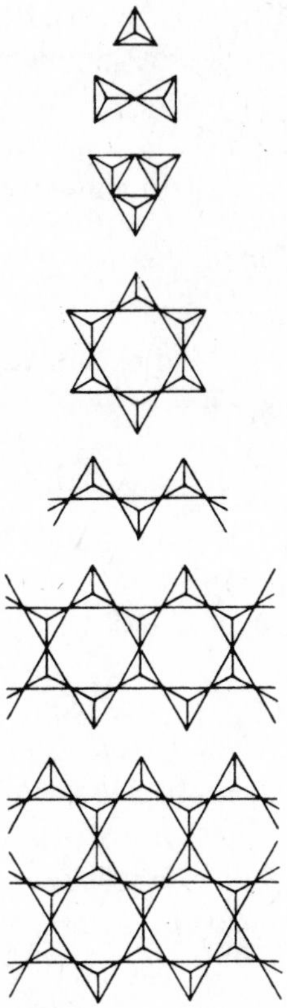

n	Structure	Formula	O/Si
0		$[SiO_4]^{4-}$	4
1		$[Si_2O_7]^{6-}$	$3\frac{1}{2}$
2		$[Si_3O_9]^{6-}$	3
2		$[Si_6O_{18}]^{12-}$	3
2		$[SiO_3]^{2-}$	3
$2\frac{1}{2}$		$[Si_4O_{11}]^{6-}$	$2\frac{3}{4}$
3		$[Si_2O_5]^{2-}$	$2\frac{1}{2}$
4	Tri-dimensional grid	$[SiO_2]$	2

Fig. 2.4. Building blocks of silicates

one (Ca^{2+}) in anorthite, which contains two ($CaAl_2Si_3O_8$). There is full iso-morphism between albite and anorthite (because Na^+ and Ca^{2+} are of roughly the same size), but not between either of those and orthoclase ($KAlSi_3O_8$), because K^+ is much larger. Of the anions, O^{2-}, F^- and OH^- are about the same size and can therefore readily replace one another. Replacement between mono- and divalent anions often compensates for replacement between mono- and divalent cations in the same lattice.

The lattice building blocks making up the structures of the silicates (which constitute most of the terrestrial crust and hence also the gangues of most of the r.o.m. ores) are presented in Fig. 2.4 (Aplan and Fuerstenau 1962; Evans 1954). The Si^{4+} cation constitutes the silicate anion in a tetrahedral configura-tion with four O^{2-} ions. The lattice building blocks differ in the arrangements of the tetrahedra. In the figure, n is the number of bonds by which a tetra-hedron is attached to other tetrahedra. As explained above, some of the Si^{4+} ions may be replaced by Al^{3+}; charge compensation is ensured in such cases by the incorporation of other ions. Other cations and anions in the silicate lattice may also enter isomorphic substitution relations, however. For example,

$n = 0$ in the orthosilicates: olivine: $(Mg, Fe)_2SiO_4$; willemite: Zn_2SiO_4; zircon: $ZrSiO_4$, etc.;

$n = 1$ in hemimorphite: $Zn_4Si_2O_7(OH)_2 \cdot H_2O$;

$n = 2$ in the chain-structured pyroxenes or in ring-structured beryl,

$$Al_2Be_3Si_6O_{18};$$

$n = 2.5$ in the double-chain amphiboles;

$n = 3$ in the flaky micas and clay minerals of excellent cleavage;

$n = 4$ in feldspars and quartz.

2.1.2. Phase interfaces (Wolf 1957)

2.1.2.1. The liquid–gas interface. At this interface, at atmospheric pressure, the density of matter changes by a factor of about 1,000 within a distance of one nanometre (nm) or so.

If a pure liquid whose molecules do not associate (e.g. carbon tetrachloride) is in contact with its own vapour, then molecules will continually pass from the liquid to the gas phase (evaporation) and back (condensation). At equi-librium, the rate of evaporation equals the rate of condensation. In water, molecules associate in the liquid phase but not in the vapour phase; hence, transition from the one phase to the other entails a change in bonding between molecules. (This is why the heat of evaporation of water is so great.) In the case of heteropolar molecules such as alcohols, organic acids, amines, etc., the process of evaporation and condensation is greatly influenced by the pre-ferred orientation of the molecules in the boundary layer (which prefer to have their alkyl radicals pointing towards the gas phase rather than in any random direction).

There is a contractile force, called the surface tension, acting in the plane of the gas–liquid interface. Surface tension has the nature of a potential and, by the second law of thermodynamics, the free energy that it represents strives to become a minimum; it can achieve that by reducing the surface area of the interface. The interior of a homogeneous phase is statistically isotropic: the bonding of atoms, molecules or ions with their neighbours is statistically the same in all directions. At the interface, however, there are practically no bonds reaching out into the tenuous vapour phase (whose density is less by a factor of 1,000 or so): its attraction therefore is much less than that of the liquid phase. Equilibrium can prevail only if the missing bond energy is made up for by total surface energy:

$$\varepsilon = a - \frac{T\partial a}{\partial T}.$$

Here, a, the free energy of the surface is numerically equal to surface tension; the second term is latent surface energy, a function of the temperature gradient of surface tension, $\partial a/\partial T$, where T is absolute temperature. Latent energy is invariably negative. At the critical temperature (above which the liquid and its vapour cannot coexist), surface tension disappears because the interface proper disappears. The creation of one cm^2 of liquid surface requires a work input a if the process is adiabatic (with the system permitted to cool) and a work input ε if the process is isothermal. For example, in water at 20 °C ($T = 293$ K),

$$a = 72.8 \text{ erg/cm}^2, \ \partial a/\partial T = -0.15, \ \varepsilon = 116.7 \text{ erg/cm}^2.$$

Surface tension in a liquid is a close function of bond type. In liquid inert gases, it is on the order of one dyne per cm; in most organic liquids, it is 20 to 30 dynes/cm; in ionic solutions or melts, it is in the 70 to 200 dynes/cm range; it is 487 dynes/cm in mercury at 15 °C and even higher in other molten metals (e.g. 750 in zinc at 480°, about 800 in silver at 970°, 1,100 in copper at 1,130°, about 1,820 in platinum at 2,000°); it increases as temperature decreases.

Surface tension in a mixture of miscible organic liquids equals by and large the (weighted) average of the components' surface tensions. The surface tension of a solution of an inorganic salt or salts differs but slightly from that of water (about 70 dynes/cm), even if the surface tension of a pure melt of the salt is remote from that figure. The surface tension of an aqueous solution of an organic compound or compounds, on the other hand, is substantially less than the weighted average of the components' surface tensions.

The adsorption of dissolved substances by the boundary layer (its excess concentration as compared with the interior of the solution) is expressed by

Gibbs' law of adsorption as

$$u = -\frac{c}{RT}\,\frac{\partial a}{\partial c},$$

where u is adsorption in moles per cm^2, c is the concentration (strictly speaking, the activity) of the dissolved substance in moles per litre, a is surface tension in dynes per cm, T is absolute temperature in kelvins, and

$$R = 8.32 \cdot 10^7 \text{ erg/K}$$

is the gas constant. $u = 0$ if $c = 0$ or $\partial a/\partial c = 0$; u is positive if $\partial a/\partial c$ is negative (that is, if the dissolved substance decreases the surface tension of the solution, as organic compounds do in water), and negative if $\partial a/\partial c$ is positive (e.g. in aqueous solutions of inorganic salts). In the latter case, the concentration of

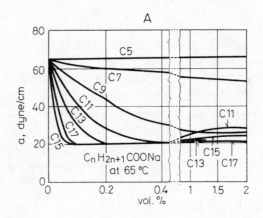

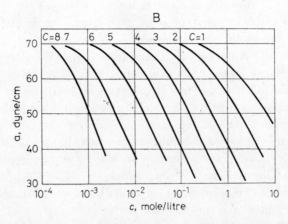

Fig. 2.5. Surface tension in the aqueous solution of an organic chemical decreases as concentration increases. A — sodium soaps at 65 °C; B — alcohols

the dissolved substance is greater in the interior of the solution than close to its surface. Gibbs' equation may be rewritten to read

$$u = -\frac{1}{RT} \frac{\partial a}{\partial \ln c},$$

since

$$\partial \ln c = \partial c/c,$$

That is, u varies as the slope of the tangent to the curve a plotted in a coordinate net linear in a and logarithmic in c. Figure 2.5 presents surface tension

Table 2.3. Surface tension of aqueous solutions of methyl alcohol (C1) and ethyl alcohol (C2) at 20 °C and at different volume percent concentrations

C1	vol. %	10	25	50	60	80	90	100
	dynes/cm	59.0	46.4	35.3	32.95	27.26	25.36	22.65
C2	vol. %	34	48	60	72	80	96	100
	dynes/cm	33.2	30.1	27.6	26.3	24.9	23.0	22.3

vs. concentration in volume percent or moles per litre for fatty acids (soaps) (Part A) and for aqueous solutions of n-alcohols (Part B). Surface tension at 20 °C and at different volume percent concentrations is given in Table 2.3 for the aqueous solutions of methyl alcohol (methanol, C1) and ethyl alcohol (ethanol, C2).

A fresh surface forming in the aqueous solution of a surfactant that reduces surface tension initially contains fewer surfactant molecules than are required

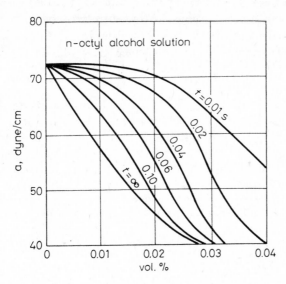

Fig. 2.6. Surface tension vs. concentration in an aqueous solution of n-octyl alcohol

for equilibrium. The diffusion of more surfactant molecules towards the interface and the offsetting diffusion of water molecules into the interior of the liquid until equilibrium is attained take some time. The time to steady-state or equilibrium surface tension is stated by the equation of diffusion to be in the order of 10^{-3} to 10^{-2} s. In reality, it is 10^{-1} s in solutions of short-chain non-ionizing (non-electrolyte) hydrocarbons, and up to 10^{5} s in solutions of

Table 2.4. Surface tension vs. time in a 0.025% sodium stearate ($C_{17}H_{35}COONa$) solution, after Gaudin (1957)

t, minutes	1/6	1/4	1/2	1	2	4	8	16	30	60
a, dynes/cm	72	69	63	58	54	51	47	43	39	36

ionizing long-chain ones. For example, the surface tension a of an aqueous solution of n-octyl alcohol vs. volume percent concentration varies with time t (s) as shown in Fig. 2.6 (Addison 1945; Gaudin 1957).

The variation vs. time of surface tension in a 0.025% sodium stearate ($_{17}H_{35}COONa$) solution is presented in Table 2.4.

The surface tension in aqueous solutions of a given molar concentration of a homologous series of organic compounds decreases as the length of the hydrocarbon chain increases. By Traube's rule, each additional CH_2 link attached to the chain reduces by about one-third the concentration required to attain a given surface tension. (Cf. e.g. Part B of Fig. 2.5; Gaudin 1957.) Of the higher members of a homologous series, then, very small amounts will suffice to reduce the surface tension of an aqueous solution to a given value. Passing from molar concentrations to concentrations in mg/l units, the concentration required to attain $a = 60$ dynes/cm and r, the approximate ratio of equilibrium concentrations in the surface layer and in the interior of the solution are stated for alcohol molecules in Table 2.5 as functions of chain length.

The required concentration of long-chain alcohols and other hydrocarbon derivatives is so small and the concentration gradient between the surface and the interior of the solution so great that, in flotation practice, no equi-

Table 2.5. Concentration c needed to attain a surface tension $a = 60$ dynes per cm and equilibrium ration r of the numbers of alcohol molecules in the boundary layer and in the interior of the solution vs. carbon number C of the alcohol molecule

C	2	5	8	12	16
c, mg/l	29,000	1,530	73	0.9	0.01
$\sim r$	18	300	6,900	$55 \cdot 10^4$	$45 \cdot 10^6$

librium is attained at all when such compounds are being used: it simply takes too long a time to set in.

The surface pressure, F dynes/cm, of an insoluble surfactant (e.g. a long-chain fatty acid, alcohol, amine, etc.) spreading out on the surface of water in a monomolecular layer and the area available per molecule, $\bar{A}$ ångström², are related at a first approximation by

$$F\bar{A} = kT,$$

where k, the Boltzmann constant, $1.38 \cdot 10^{16}$ ergs per degrees centigrade, is the ratio of the gas constant R and the Avogadro number, and T is temperature in kelvins. The equation of these two-dimensional surface layers is analogous to the equation $PV = RT$ of their three-dimensional counterparts, the ideal gases.

van der Waals' correction of the ideal-gas equation furnishes the relationship

$$\left(P + \frac{a}{V^2}\right)(V - V_0) = RT;$$

similarly, for surface films,

$$\left(F + \frac{\alpha}{\bar{A}^2}\right)(\bar{A} - \bar{A}_0) = kT.$$

The equation fits experimental findings best at relatively low pressures F (that is, where the film behaves most like a gas). Higher pressures produce condensed films whose tri-dimensional analogues are the liquids and solids. There is a state of transition between the "gaseous" and the condensed state of the film, called the "expanded-liquid" state, which has no analogue in three dimensions (Schoefield 1925—1926; Shoefield et al. 1926).

Figure 2.7 represents the surface pressure function of myristic acid ($C_{13}H_{27}COOH$) at 14 °C (Adam 1941). Gaseous behaviour is seen to prevail above $\bar{A} = 800$ Å² per molecule, where F increases as Å decreases, albeit at a rate slower than stipulated by the hyperbolic formula $F\bar{A} = kT$. Between $\bar{A} = 800$ and 50, $F \simeq 0.2$ dynes/cm, increasing very slightly. This is where the gaseous and the non-gaseous phases coexist. The gaseous phase disappears at $\bar{A} \lessapprox 50$. At $\bar{A} = 35$, there is another break in the F curve. Below $\bar{A} = 25$, beyond the break, F increases steeply and more or less asymptotically, up to $F = 50$ dynes/cm at $\bar{A} = 20.5$ Å². Further on, the film becomes wrinkled and multi-layered. The inset shows curves at temperatures 5, 9, 14 and 22 °C for the interval $\bar{A} < 50$.

The spacing of molecules at the critical values of $\bar{A}$ (at the breaks of the diagram) can be obtained by taking the square root of $\bar{A}$:

$\bar{A} =$	800	50	45	20.5,
$d = \sqrt{\bar{A}} =$	28.3	7.1	5.9	4.5 Å.

9

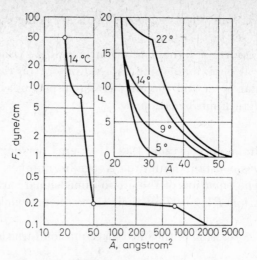

Fig. 2.7. Isotherms of the monomolecular boundary layer of myristic acid ($C_{13}H_{27}COOH$) in the surface tension — area per molecule (F dynes per cm — $\bar{A}$ ångstrom² per molecule) space

In the zigzag chains of saturated hydrocarbons (paraffins, C_nH_{2n+2}), the spacing of the C atoms is 1.54 Å; two consecutive links of the chain include an angle of 109° 28'. That component of the C-atom spacing which is collinear with the chain axis is 1.25 Å (that is, e.g., a chain made up of 13 C atoms has length $12 \cdot 1.25 = 15$ Å). In solid paraffin crystals, adjacent molecules are spaced about 4 Å apart. In the condensed state of the monomolecular layer, the hydrocarbon chains are straight and close-packed, as in a crystal (Fig. 2.8). In the expanded phase, the molecules are not rigidly fixed in the regular zigzag shape. The chain is in permanent motion, with shorter or longer segments swivelling about any one of the bonds between the C atoms. In the

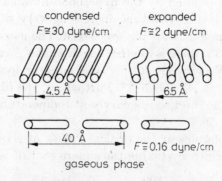

Fig. 2.8. Arrangement of molecules in a monomolecular film: condensed, expanded and gaseous

gaseous phase, the axes of the molecules lie in the plane of the film (Gaudin 1957).

In a monomolecular condensed layer of an aliphatic hydrocarbon, the molecules are arranged in a preferred orientation, with their long axes including a certain angle with the water surface. Each molecule occupies an area of about 20.5 Å² of the water surface (oleic acid: 20.5, palmitic acid: 19.5, stearic acid: 18.5 Å², but a glyceryl monostearate ester [stearin] molecule takes 25 Å²). The thickness of the film is determined by the length of the molecule. Heteropolar molecules are arranged with their polar ends touching the water. In the gaseous state of the film, the molecules lie flat or almost so on the surface of the solution.

After the addition of more surfactant than is needed for the creation of a monomolecular film, equilibrium surface pressure, F dynes/cm, sets in when the excess has spread out evenly on the water surface available. Equilibrium surface pressure is specific for the substance added. At 20 °C, it is $\sim$20 dynes/cm for stearic acid, $\sim$30 for palmitic and oleic acids and 38 to 45 for cetyl alcohol. The thickness of the monomolecular layer is about 20 Å $= 20 \cdot 10^{-8}$ cm; that is, pressure in the film — say, in the case of stearic acid — is about

$$\frac{20}{20 \cdot 10^{-8}} = 10^8 \text{ dynes/cm}^2 = 100 \text{ at (!).}$$

Substances having a higher surface pressure displace those of lower surface pressure from the surface. For instance, when a gout of oleic acid is dropped onto a layer of stearic acid at equilibrium pressure, this latter will wrinkle and contract until its pressure matches that of the oleic acid. If a foil of hydrophobized metal is pulled slowly and perpendicularly out of water with a film of stearic acid on it, the foil also gets coated with a monomolecular layer of stearic acid, with the non-polar ends of the stearic acid molecules facing the foil. If a foil so coated enters into contact with a free water surface, it will be wetted by the water. On the other hand, if the metal enters into contact with water carrying a stearic-acid film, it acquires a second monomolecular layer, orientated opposite to the first. This is not wetted by the water, so that the foil can be pulled dry out of free-surfaced water. By repeating immersion and extraction several times, the foil can be coated with a "thick" layer of stearic acid, exhibiting colours of interference, every monomolecular layer making up a coating orientated opposite to the two adjacent ones.

2.1.2.2. The solid–gas interface. Such an interface comes to exist e.g. when a solid crystal is crushed in air. Fracture means that bonds between adjacent molecules (atoms, ions) of the crystal have snapped. If the residual bonds holding a molecular lattice together are broken, then the fresh surface differs but slightly from the interior of the crystal. When covalent bonds snap, the electrons that were shared previously end up with one or the other of the nuclei that shared them, giving rise to ionized surfaces. The electrostatic state of the fracture surfaces of an ionically bonded crystal also differs essentially from the state of the crystals' interior, what with all neighbouring ions being removed from opposite the ions exposed on the surface. These latter acquire polarization, with the result that their distance from the ions of the next layer underneath is reduced. The severance of metallic bonds also changes the density of the freely moving electron cloud and the cation spacing of the surface layer.

In the final reckoning, then, broken residual bonds give rise to non-polar surfaces, whereas broken chemical (covalent, ionic and metallic) bonds give rise to polar ones. These latter possess an excess of energy as compared with the interior of the phase; the result is a propensity to enter physical and chemical reactions. At any solid–gas interface, some physical adsorption of gas molecules and their fixation by residual bonds invariably takes place. The quantity of gas adsorbed per unit of surface depends on the material nature of the solid and gas and on gas pressure. (Gibbs' formula holds for the physical adsorption of gases also !) A chemical reaction may, however, also take place between the adsorbed gas and the adsorbing surface. For example, oxygen is bound on charcoal at a low temperature by physical adsorption, just as, e.g., argon is. At a higher temperature, the C and O atoms combine to form carbon monoxide at the surface. If the CO molecules cannot escape, then the entire surface gets coated by a process called chemisorption with a layer of combined C and O atoms. If the CO molecules do escape, chemisorption continues as long as oxygen and carbon remain available: the process is tantamount to the burning of charcoal. In other cases, where more than one gas is present, the surface of the solid adsorbent can trigger between them reactions that would not take place in its absence, but in which the adsorbent itself is not involved (or, if it is, regains its original state by the end of the process). This phenomenon is called contact catalysis.

2.1.2.3. The solid–liquid interface. The surfaces of minerals immersed in water become solid–water interfaces: they attain a hydrated or hydroxidated state as a rule; removal of solid from the surface into the liquid (solution) also takes place.

The surface atoms or ions of a solid immersed in a fluid are attracted on one side by the atoms (ions) next to them on the solid side, and by the atoms, molecules or ions of the liquid on the other side. At the surface of an ionic crystal, for example, the arrangement of atomic nuclei and electrons differs from that in the interior of the crystal: if the liquid is a polar one (like water), then its ions, dipole molecules and/or molecular aggregates get attached to the surface of the solid. These sorbate ions and molecules do not remain fixed at well-determined points: rather, they achieve a sort of statistical equilibrium between hydrated ions/molecules wandering from the interior of the liquid to the surface and back. A similar statistical equilibrium prevails between hydrated and un-hydrated ions. The hydration and dissolution of the ions resembles that type of reaction at a gas–solid interface when the reaction products can escape. Crystals having molecular lattices have much less of a propensity to adhere to water or to dissolve in it than ionic crystals. Even if they are soluble in water to a certain extent, their dissolution is a phenomenon akin to simple evaporation. Their hydrate shells are therefore thinner and easier to remove or penetrate than the thicker and more strongly bonded hydrate shells of ionic crystals.

Native (natural) floatability of a degree is confined to non-ionic crystal surfaces (crystals with molecular lattices: iodine, sulphur and some hydrocarbons such as paraffin) and such crystals, flaky as a rule, whose faces of excellent cleavage carry residual bonds only (boric acid, talc, graphite). In one group of crystals of organic substances, the molecules are held together by residual bonds; the snapping of these bonds gives rise to non-polar surfaces endowed with a native floatability. (The group includes, in addition to hydrocarbons, also hydrogenless halogen carbides such as fluorocarbons.)

The crystals of some other organic compounds contain ion or hydrogen bonds in two or three dimensions. Fatty acids, soaps, primary amines, amine salts, primary alcohols, etc. constitute flaky crystals by means of two-dimensional bonding, with the molecules arranged so as to face one another alternately with their ionic and non-ionic ends. The energy of an ion or hydrogen bond is higher than that of a residual bond. Crystals of this type accordingly tend to break apart by the fracture of the weak residual bonds, so that the fracture surface becomes overwhelmingly non-polar as in a crystal with a molecular lattice. Those organic compounds, on the other hand, whose molecules possess two or more polar radicals, and are connected together tridimensionally by ionic or hydrogen bonds, have no flaky cleavage and their surfaces of fracture are rendered polar by broken hydrogen or ionic bonds. It is the relative abundance of residual bonds vs. ionic and/or hydrogen bonds that determines the degree of native floatability of these crystals.

The rate of dissolution of a solid in an unsaturated solution depends on the concentration gradient next to the solid and on the size of the exposed surface. The relationship

$$\frac{dc}{dt} = k(c_s - c)$$

holds, where c is concentration within the solution; c_s is concentration of the saturated solution; and the proportionality constant k is a function of the exposed surface area S of the solid and of the thickness of the viscous liquid

133

film adhering to the solid. Putting

$$k = K \frac{S}{V},$$

where K is a rate constant and V is the volume of the solution, integration gives

$$k = \frac{V}{tS} \ln \frac{(c_s - c_1)}{(c_s - c_2)},$$

where c_1 is the initial concentration and c_2 is concentration after a time t. (k is in cm/min if V is in cm³, S in cm² and t min.)

Rate constant K differs from one substance to the next and depends also on the intensity of agitation of the liquid. Agitation affects the thickness of the viscous film adhering to the solid, in which flow remains laminar even if the interior of the liquid is in turbulent motion. Layers in laminar flow do not mix: as a result, any changes of concentration in them are due to diffusion caused by the thermal motion of the molecules, just as in liquids at rest. Convective transport due to turbulence increases rates of dissolution quite considerably. The thickness of the adhesive, non-mixing laminar layer is 20 to 25 μm if the liquid is being agitated vigorously, and about 150 μm on gentler agitation. It depends also on the relative velocity of the liquid streaming past the solid (inversely as its 2/3 to 4/5 power). The thickness of the adhesive viscous layer of liquid and the rates of diffusion through it affect not only rates of dissolution but also rates of adhesion and chemical reaction rates between the reagents of flotation and the surfaces of mineral grains (Gaudin 1957).

If the aqueous solution contains ions, the interfaces will be the sites of electrical phenomena. If a solid soluble by a non-ionic mechanism is placed in pure water, its molecules get dissolved until the solution saturates. Saturation means that the chemical potential of the molecules becomes the same in the solution as in the solid phase. If, on the other hand, a metal — say, silver — is placed into pure water, it will release Ag cations into solution: the free electrons left behind in the metal endow it with a negative charge, while the solution becomes positive. Against this increasing positive charge, it is increasingly difficult for the cations of the metal to go into solution, and equilibrium sets in when the difference in chemical potential equals the electric potential to be overcome. Here, it is the electrochemical potential of the cation,

$$\bar{\mu}_i = \mu_i + z_i e_0 \psi,$$

that must be equal in the solid phase and in the solution [μ_i is the chemical potential of the ion; z_i is the number of its charges (its valence); e_0 is the elementary charge and ψ is electrostatic potential]. The chemical potential of the solution can be increased by adding silver nitrate to it; that of the solid silver remains practically unaffected thereby. As a result, Ag^+ ions will move

134

from the solution onto the metal, turning it positive, while the solution is made negative by an excess of NO_3^- anions.

The charge on the solid phase attracts ions of opposite charge out of the solution; as a result, an electric double layer is constituted next to the phase boundary. One half of the double layer is attached to the boundary (to the solid surface); the other is constituted by a diffuse cloud of ions gathering in the solution. At a certain concentration of the potential-determining ion (Ag^+ in the case under consideration), the passage of ions from one phase into the other ceases, statistically speaking: the electric double layer disappears and the solid surface retains no excess charge, negative or positive, due to the presence of surplus electrons or cations. The critical concentration in question defines the zero point of surface charge and the isoelectric point of the solution, respectively.

If the solid placed in the water is a two-ion compound (e.g. silver iodide) rather than a metal (silver), then the double layer forming at the solid–liquid interface contains two potential-determining ions, a cation (Ag^+) and an anion (I^-). At equilibrium, the electrochemical potential of each is as great in the solid phase (s) as in the liquid (l):

$$\bar{\mu}_{Ag^+}^s = \bar{\mu}_{Ag^+}^l \quad \text{and} \quad \bar{\mu}_{I^-}^s = \bar{\mu}_{I^-}^l .$$

Moreover, the product of their activities in the solution is a constant:

$$a_{Ag^+} \cdot a_{I^-} = K = 10^{-16},$$

activity being the product of molar concentration c and the activity coefficient λ:

$$a = \lambda c .$$

In dilute solutions, λ differs little from unity and it is permissible to replace a by c. The expression

$$pAg = -\log a_{Ag^+}$$

can be interpreted in analogy to the pH,

$$pH = -\log a_{H_+} = -\log [H^+] .$$

The zero charge point of silver iodide is at $pAg = 5.5$, rather than at the $pAg = 8$ that would correspond to equal ionic concentrations: in other words, from a chunk of solid silver iodide placed in water, more silver ions are dissolved than iodine ions, so that the chunk acquires a negative charge. It takes a very high concentration of Ag^+ ($pAg < 5.5$) for the chunk to become positive.

Metal sulphides (PbS, ZnS, Ag_2S, etc.) are also two-ion compounds in which potential is determined jointly by the metal cation and the sulphide anion. The sulphide ion, however, is readily hydrated in the solution, a process that gives rise to HS^- and H_2S as well as to H^+ and OH^- ions. All these can be regarded as potential-determining in the sense of the formulae below, each of which states the condition of equilibrium between the solid sulphide and the aqueous solution:

$$S_s^{2-} = S_l^{2-};$$

$$S_s^{2-} + H_2O = HS_l^- + OH^-;$$

$$S_s^{2-} + 2H_2O = H_2S_l + 2OH^-;$$

$$S_s^{2-} + H^+ = HS_l^-.$$

If the pH of the solution is unchanged, then the relationships

$$\Delta\mu_{S^{2-}} = \Delta\mu_{HS^-} = \Delta\mu_{H_2S} = -\Delta\mu_{Pb^{2+}}$$

hold: that is, as viewed from the solution, it is immaterial whether S^{2-}, HS^- or H_2S is chosen as the potential determinant. The influence of the pH is evident from the equilibrium equations.

The potential-determining role of H^+ and OH^- ions is even more conspicuous in the case of solid oxides. The two immediate potential determinants of those are the metal (or alkali earth) cation and the oxygen anion. One may further write

$$O_s^{2-} + H_2O = 2OH^-$$

and, e.g. in the case of Fe_2O_3 (haematite)

$$Fe_s^{3+} + 2H_2O = Fe(OH)_2^+ + 2H^+.$$

In addition to the complex ion $Fe(OH)_2^+$, the solution contains hydrated Fe^{3+} ions, FeO_2^-, $FeOH^{2+}$ and $Fe_2(OH)_2^{4+}$ ions and neutral $Fe(OH)_3$ molecules also. At equilibrium, the concentrations of all these ions and of the neutral molecules are unequivocally defined. Figure 2.9 presents the shifts of equilibrium concentration due to changes in the pH. The solubility of haematite is indicated by the bold curve. The flat plateau of the curve is due to the evanescent concentration of complex ions as compared with that of undissociated $Fe(OH)_3$. The isoelectric point of the solution (the zero charge point of the solid surface) is at pH $\cong 8.5$, where the concentrations of $Fe(OH)_2^+$ and FeO_2^- ions are equal. The concentrations of the other cations are so minute there as to be negligible against $Fe(OH)_2^+$ (DeBruyn and Agar 1962).

Surface charge in an oxidic mineral is determined by the equilibria of adsorption and by the dissociation of the compounds formed at the surface. The hydration of surface ions also plays a role, and so does the polarization of water molecules adsorbed by the polyvalent cations of small ionic radius present at the surface. For example, any fresh surface of fracture of a crystal of quartz or corundum carries broken Si—O and Al—O bonds, respectively. The negatively charged O ions of the surface may obviously interact directly with

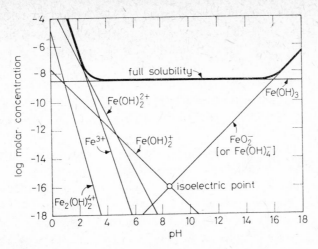

Fig. 2.9. Equilibrium concentration vs. the pH of the soluble ions and neutral molecules of haematite, Fe_2O_3

the H^+ ions of the solution. The hydration of the Si or Al ions, on the other hand, can create charges interacting with the H^+ ions as follows:

$$-\overset{|}{\underset{|}{Si}}^+ + OH_2 \rightleftarrows -\overset{|}{\underset{|}{Si}}^+OH_2 \rightleftarrows -\overset{|}{\underset{|}{Si}}-OH + H^+ \rightleftarrows -\overset{|}{\underset{|}{Si}}-O^- + 2H^+,$$

$$>Al^+ + OH_2 \rightleftarrows >Al^+OH_2 \rightleftarrows >Al-OH + H^+ \rightleftarrows >Al-O^- + 2H^+.$$

The surface charge of an oxidic mineral, then, is pH-dependent (Schubert 1964). The electrochemical properties of a metal oxide depend, however, also on its prehistory. The surface of an originally neutral MOH may change into either $M^+ + OH^-$ or $MO^- + H^+$.

The position of the isoelectric point is affected greatly by the relatively alkaline or acidic nature of the solid crystal. The zero charge points of the oxides of amphoteric elements (such as Fe_2O_3 or Al_2O_3) are in the vicinity of the neutral pH, whereas acidic oxides such as SnO_2 or WO_3 will be negatively charged even at low pH's and basic ones such as Ag_2O or MgO will be positively charged even at high ones.

Clay minerals, whose general chemical formula is

$$Al_2O_3 \cdot (0.3 \ldots 8)SiO_2 \cdot (0.5 \ldots 19)H_2O,$$

behave specially because their flaky faces are invariably negatively charged, regardless of the electrolyte content of the solution. In a clay mineral, an octahedral layer, with Al^{3+} or Mg^{2+} ions at the centres of the octahedra, surrounded by oxygen and hydroxyl ions in sixfold coordination, is sandwiched between

137

two layers of Si–O tetrahedra. The three layers, the octahedral one at the middle and the two tetrahedral ones on either side of it, are bound together by O atoms forming covalent bonds. Such triplets are stacked together card-pack fashion to constitute the mineral. In talc or pyrophyllite, the triplets are held together by weak van der Waals forces (residual bonds); these minerals have excellent flaky cleavage and a fair native floatability. In the typical clay minerals, certain of the Si^{4+} ions of the tetrahedral Si–O layers are replaced by Al^{3+}, and the charge deficit is offset by the incorporation of alkali metal cations (Na^+ or K^+). In water, these cations are leached off, and the tetrahedral layers become negatively charged as a result, regardless of the pH of the solution (with the alkali cations in solution constituting the diffuse half of the double layer). Fracture perpendicular to the flakes involves the snapping of Si–O or Al–O bonds: at such surfaces, any change of pH will result in a change of charge just as in a simple oxide mineral. For such surfaces, then, the H^+ and OH^- ions are potential-determining, so that the surfaces perpendicular to the flaky faces may be positively charged while the flaky faces themselves retain their permanent negative charges.

Clay minerals often affect flotation adversely: they impair selectivity, increase the consumption of reagents, stabilize froth for good, etc. This is why they are often removed (washed out) beforehand from flotation feeds.

Figure 2.10 illustrates the layer structures respectively of kaolinite, pyrophyllite, muscovite and montmorillonite (Aplan and Fuerstenau 1962). Every

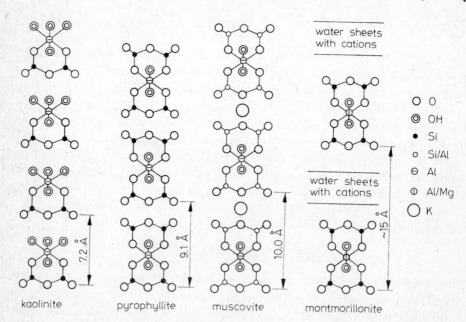

Fig. 2.10. Structures of layered Si_2O_5 minerals (phyllosilicates)

Table 2.6. Potential-determining ions, solubility products K (at 25 °C), pM$^+$ parameters (negative logarithms of cation concentration) at the isoelectric point of some ionic minerals and the sign of their charges in their saturated solutions

Ionic minerals (crystals)	Potential-determining ions		Solubility product, K	pM+		Charge in saturated solution
Ag_2S	Ag^{2+}	S^{2-}	$5.7 \cdot 10^{-51}$	pAg$^+$	10.2	—
AgI	Ag^+	J^-	$1.0 \cdot 10^{-16}$	pAg$^+$	5.5	—
AgBr	Ag^+	Br^-	$6.3 \cdot 10^{-13}$	pAg$^+$	5.4	—
AgCl	Ag^+	Cl^-	$1.6 \cdot 10^{-10}$	pAg ?	4.0	—
Fluorite CaF_2	Ca^{2+}	F^-	$1.7 \cdot 10^{-10}$	?		+
Calcite $CaCO_3$	Ca^{2+}	CO_3^{2-}	$4.7 \cdot 10^{-9}$	?		—
Barite $BaSO_4$	Ba^{2+}	SO_4^{2-}	$1.5 \cdot 10^{-9}$	pBa^{2+}	3.4	+
Gypsum $CaSO_4 \cdot 2H_2O$	Ca^{2+}	SO_4^{2-}	$2.4 \cdot 10^{-5}$	?		—
Anglesite $PbSO_4$	Pb^{2+}	SO_4^{2-}	$1.3 \cdot 10^{-8}$	pPb^{2+}	3.9	+
Celestite $SrSO_4$	Sr^{2+}	SO_4^{2-}	$7.6 \cdot 10^{-7}$	pSr^{2+}	3.1	+
Scheelite $CaWO_4$	Ca^{2+}	WO_4^{2-}	$8.0 \cdot 10^{-13}$	pCa^{2+}	4.8	—

lattice in the group incorporates layers of SiO_4 tetrahedra. Each tetrahedron is bonded by three oxygen atoms into endless layers of bulk formula $(Si_2O_5)^{2-}$. In kaolinite, these alternate with layers of $Al(OH)_3$. The free (unbound) apices of the tetrahedra all point in the same direction. The bond between the oxygen ions of the tetrahedra and the OH radicals is a weak one, and kaolinite has an excellent cleavage there. In pyrophyllite, the free oxygens at the apices of two adjacent layers of $(Si_2O_5)^{2-}$ face each other, and there is an $Al(OH)_3$ layer between them. If the two layers facing one another have instead a layer of $Mg(OH)_2$ between them, then talc is the resulting mineral. The crystals have an excellent cleavage between the $(Si_2O_5)^{2-}$ layers turned back-to-back: the cleavage surface is hydrophobic (McHardy and Salman 1974). From pyrophyllite, the muscovite lattice can be derived by replacing every fourth Si^{4+} by an Al^{3+} ion and offsetting the excess negative charge by the insertion of K^+ ions; the montmorillonite lattice results when some of the Al^{3+} ions replacing Si^{4+} ions and all the Al^{3+} ions in octahedral positions are replaced by Fe^{2+} and/or Mg^{2+}. The cations required for charge compensation are inserted between the layers: it is their hydration and absorption of water that is responsible for montmorillonite's swelling. (Montmorillonite is the principal mineral of bentonite.)

In whichever mineral H^+ and OH^- play a potential-determining role (as in the oxides), the pH has a great influence on flotation performance; it is less important in the flotation of ionic crystals in which the ions of the mineral rather than the H^+ and OH^- ions are the potential determinants.

Table 2.6 lists the potential-determining ions of some ionic minerals, the K constants of their ionic (activity or solubility) products, the cation concentra-

Table 2.7. Solubility products K at temperature t °C of some compounds; solubility in water of some compounds at 20 °C

Solubility products K of some compounds at temperature t °C

	$t°$	K		$t°$	K		$t°$	K
$AgCl$	20	$1.3 \cdot 10^{-10}$	$CuCO_3$	25	$2.4 \cdot 10^{-10}$	$Mn(OH)_2$	18	$4.0 \cdot 10^{-14}$
Ag_2CO_3	25	$6.1 \cdot 10^{-12}$	CuS	18	$8.5 \cdot 10^{-45}$	MnS	18	$7.0 \cdot 10^{-16}$
Ag_2S	25	$5.7 \cdot 10^{-51}$	Cu_2S	18	$2.0 \cdot 10^{-47}$	$MnCO_3$	25	$5.0 \cdot 10^{-10}$
$Al(OH)_3$	18	$6.0 \cdot 10^{-13}$	$Cu(OH)_2$	25	$5.6 \cdot 10^{-20}$	NiS	20	$1.1 \cdot 10^{-27}$
$BaCO_3$	18	$7.2 \cdot 10^{-9}$	$Fe(OH)_3$	18	$3.8 \cdot 10^{-38}$	$PbCO_3$	25	$1.5 \cdot 10^{-13}$
$CaCrO_4$	18	$1.6 \cdot 10^{-10}$	$Fe(OH)_2$	18	$4.8 \cdot 10^{-16}$	$PbCrO_4$	18	$1.8 \cdot 10^{-14}$
$BaSO_4$	25	$1.1 \cdot 10^{-10}$	$FeCO_3$	25	$2.1 \cdot 10^{-11}$	PbF_2	20	$3.2 \cdot 10^{-8}$
$CaCO_3$	25	$8.7 \cdot 10^{-9}$	FeS	18	$3.7 \cdot 10^{-19}$	$Pb_3(PO_4)_2$		$1.0 \cdot 10^{-54}$
CaF_2	18	$3.4 \cdot 10^{-11}$	HgS	18	$3.0 \cdot 10^{-54}$	PbS	18	$3.4 \cdot 10^{-28}$
$Ca_3(PO_4)_2$		$1.3 \cdot 10^{-32}$	Hg_2S	18	$1.0 \cdot 10^{-47}$	$PbSO_4$	25	$1.6 \cdot 10^{-8}$
$CaSO_4$	10	$2.0 \cdot 10^{-4}$	$MgCO_3$	25	$1.0 \cdot 10^{-5}$	$SrSO_4$	25	$2.8 \cdot 10^{-7}$
$CaSO_4 \cdot 2H_2O$	25	$2.4 \cdot 10^{-5}$	$Mg(OH)_2$	25	$5.5 \cdot 10^{-12}$	$Zn(OH)_2$	25	$1.3 \cdot 10^{-17}$
CdS	18	$5.1 \cdot 10^{-29}$	MgS	25	$2.0 \cdot 10^{-15}$	ZnS	25	$1.1 \cdot 10^{-24}$

Solubility products K of some other compounds at 18 °C

C_6H_5OH	$7.0 \cdot 10^{-11}$	H_2S	$1.0 \cdot 10^{-7}$	$Pb(OH)_2 \cdot H_2O$	$1.3 \cdot 10^{-11}$
H_2CO_3	$4.1 \cdot 10^{-7}$	H_2SO_3	$1.7 \cdot 10^{-2}$	$Pb(OH)^+$	$1.5 \cdot 10^{-8}$
HCO_3^-	$4.8 \cdot 10^{-11}$	HSO_3^-	$5.0 \cdot 10^{-6}$	Pb ethyl xanthate	$1.7 \cdot 10^{-17}$
H_3CO_4	$7.5 \cdot 10^{-3}$	H_2SO_4	$4.5 \cdot 10^{-1}$	Pb propyl xanthate	$1.6 \cdot 10^{-18}$
$H_2PO_4^-$	$6.2 \cdot 10^{-8}$	HSO_4^-	$1.7 \cdot 10^{-2}$	Pb butyl xanthate	$1.4 \cdot 10^{-19}$
HPO_4^{2-}	$1.0 \cdot 10^{-12}$	$H_2S_2O_3$	$1.0 \cdot 10^{-2}$	Pb amyl xanthate	$7.5 \cdot 10^{-21}$
$HCrO_4^-$	$3.2 \cdot 10^{-7}$	$H_2S_2O_4$	$3.5 \cdot 10^{-3}$	Pb hexyl xanthate	$4.1 \cdot 10^{-22}$
$2HCrO_4^-$	$2.3 \cdot 10^{-2}$	NH_3	$1.1 \cdot 10^{-5}$	NH_4OH	$1.8 \cdot 10^{-5}$

Solubility in water of some compounds at 20 °C in mg/g/kg of water

$AgCl$	1.5	FeS	6.14	KCl $\begin{cases} (20°) \\ (100°) \end{cases}$	$3.40 \cdot 10^5$ $5.67 \cdot 10^5$
$AgCN$	0.22	$FeSO_4 \cdot 7H_2O$	$2.65 \cdot 10^5$	$K_2CO_3 \cdot 2H_2O$	$5.25 \cdot 10^5$

Ag_2CO_3	3.2	$Mg(OH)_2$	9.0	$KHCO_3$	$2.49 \cdot 10^5$
Ag_2S	0.14	MnS	6.2	K_2CrO_4	$6.17 \cdot 10^5$
As_2S_3	0.52	$MnSO_4 \cdot 5H_2O$	$6.29 \cdot 10^5$	$K_2Cr_2O_7$	$1.31 \cdot 10^5$
$BaCO_3$	22.0	$NiCO_3$	0.925	KOH	$11.20 \cdot 10^5$
$BaCrO_4$	3.7	NiS	3.6	$NaCl \begin{cases} (20°) \\ (100°) \end{cases}$	$3.60 \cdot 10^5$ $3.98 \cdot 10^5$
$BaSO_4$	2.4	$PbCO_3$	1.1	Na_2CO_3	$2.15 \cdot 10^5$
$CaCl_2 \cdot 6H_2O$	$7.45 \cdot 10^5$	$PbCr_2O_4$	0.07	$NaHCO_3$	$0.96 \cdot 10^5$
$Ca(OH)_2$	1,650	PbF_2	640	$Na_2HPO_4 \cdot 12H_2O$	$0.77 \cdot 10^5$
CaF_2	16	$PbSO_4$	4.1	$NaOH$	$10.90 \cdot 10^5$
$CaSO_4$	2,000	PbS	0.86	$Na_2S \cdot 9H_2O$	$1.58 \cdot 10^5$
CdS	$9 \cdot 10^{-3}$	Sb_2S_3	1.75	$Na_2SO_3 \cdot 7H_2O$	$2.69 \cdot 10^5$
CuS	0.33	$UO_2(NO_3)_2$	$5.57 \cdot 10^5$	$Na_2SO_4 \cdot 7H_2O$	$4.40 \cdot 10^5$
$CuSO_4$	$2.07 \cdot 10^{-5}$	$ZnSO_4 \cdot 7H_2O$	$5.44 \cdot 10^5$		

tion of the solution at the isoelectric point of the mineral (more specifically, its negative logarithm pM^+) and the sign of the surface charge of the mineral in its saturated solution (Schubert 1964).

The pH in the aqueous suspension of a dissociating mineral depends on the relative strengths of the cation and anion making it up. The cation of a strong base combined with the anion of a weak acid (e.g. calcite, $CaCO_3$; dolomite, $CaMg(CO_3)_2$; scheelite, $CaWO_4$; wollastonite, $CaSiO_3$, etc.) gives rise to an

Table 2.8. Isoelectric point pH of some minerals

Mineral		pH
Albite	$NaAlSi_3O_8$	2.0
Andalusite	$Al_2O_3 \cdot SiO_2$	7.2
Apatite	$Ca_5(PO_4)_3(F, OH)$	4.1—6.4
Augite	$CaMgSi_2O_6$	3.4
Baddeleyite	ZrO_2	6.05
Barite	$BaSO_4$	6.1
Bentonite	$Al_2O_3 \cdot 4SiO_2(xRO)H_2O$	3.3
Beryl	$Be_3Al_2Si_6O_{18}$	3.0
Calcite	$CaCO_3$	8.0—9.5 (10.8)
Cassiterite	SnO_2	(3.0) 4.5—7.3
Celestite	$SrSO_4$	3.5—3.8
Corundum	Al_2O_3	6.7—9.4
Enstatite	$MgSiO_3$	3.8
Fluorite	CaF_2	9.3—10.0
Forsterite	Mg_2SiO_4	4.1
Galena	Pb_5	3.0
Gibbsite	$Al_2O_3 \cdot 3H_2O$	4.8
Goethite	$FeO(OH)$	6.7
Haematite	$\alpha\text{-}Fe_2O_3$	6.7—8.5
Ilmenite	$FeTiO_3$	5.6
Kaolinite	$Al_2O_3 \cdot 2SiO_2 \cdot 2H_2O$	3.4
Kyanite (Disthene)	$Al_2O_3 \cdot SiO_2$	7.9
Magnetite	Fe_3O_4	6.5—9.5
Manganite	$Mn_2O_3 \cdot H_2O$	1.8—2.0
Microcline	$KAlSi_3O_8$	2.0—2.4
Monazite	$(Ce, La)PO_4*$	7.1
Mullite	$3Al_2O_3 \cdot 2SiO_2$	8.0
Pyrolusite	$MnO_2(\alpha\text{-}\beta\text{-}\gamma\text{-}\delta)$	4.5—7.3—5.6—1.5
Quartz	SiO_2	1.5—3.7
Rutile	TiO_2	(3.5) 6.0—6.7
Sillimanite	$Al_2O_3 \cdot SiO_2$	6.8
Tungstite	$WO_3 \cdot H_2O$	0.43
Uraninite	UO_2	4.8—6.6
Zincite	ZnO	9.1
Zircon	$ZrSiO_4$	5.0—6.5

* Monazite $(Ce, La, Yt)PO_4 + ThO_2$ or $ThSiO_4$.

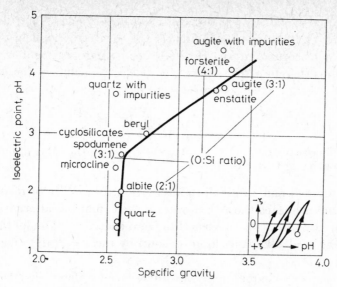

Fig. 2.11. Isoelectric points of some silicates

alkaline suspension. The cation of a weak base combined with the anion of a strong acid (e.g. anglesite, $PbSO_4$; aluminite, $Al_2SO_4(OH)_6$, etc.) gives an acidic suspension, with a pH less than 6; the cation of a strong base combined with the anion of a strong acid (e.g. barite, $BaSO_4$; fluorite, CaF_2, etc.) or the cation of a weak base combined with the anion of a weak acid gives a solution whose pH will be in the 6 to 7 range or thereabouts.

The top part of Table 2.7 lists dissociation constants K for certain compounds (minerals and metal hydroxides); its bottom part lists their solubilities in water. The middle part contains K values for some acids, a few bases and some collector reagents.

Table 2.8 states the pH at the isoelectric points (zero charge points) of some minerals. These values are variable within limits, depending on the impurities present, on the prehistory of the mineral, etc.

Figure 2.11 shows isoelectric points vs. specific gravities for certain silicates and for quartz and states their O : Si ratios also. In silicates the isoelectric point tends to shift towards a higher pH as the s.g., O : Si ratio and/or impurity concentration increase.

The isoelectric point of an oxide is lower as a rule, the greater the ion potential of its cation (the smaller its radius and the higher its charge).

Andalusite (A), disthene or kyanite (D) and sillimanite (S) are of identical composition, $Al_2O_3 \cdot SiO_2$, but their crystal structures are different, and so are, as a result, also their zero-charge points: 7.2 for A, 7.9 for D and 6.8 for S. The Al : Si ratio at their cleavage surfaces is 2 : 1. On treatment with an acid or an alkali, then, more Al than Si dissolves off their surfaces. The zero-charge

143

point of the Si–O bond is lower than that of the Al–O bond. (The ion potential of Si is about 10; that of Al is about 5.5; the isoelectric point of quartz is at pH $\cong$ 2, that of corundum at pH $\cong$ 9.) Alternating treatment with an acid and an alkali is therefore apt to lower the isoelectric points of the $Al_2O_3 \cdot SiO_2$ minerals: for example, the isoelectric point of

	A	D	S
at pH = 7.2		7.9	6.8
decreases to pH = 5.9		7.3	5.6
on being treated	5	3	4

times with an acid and an alkali in alternation. In mullite of related composition, on whose surface the Al : Si ratio is 3 : 1, fourfold alternation reduces the pH from 8.0 to 7.0. The decrease of the zero-charge point under the influence of alternating acid–alkali leaching is shown by the $\zeta = f(pH)$ diagram in the inset of Fig. 2.11.

Shifts in the zero-charge point as a function of different lattice structures are illustrated also by the case of pyrolusite, MnO_2 in Table 2.8, whose zero-charge points range from 1.5 to 7.3.

2.1.2.4. The electric double layer. The surface charge of an immersed particle gives rise to an electric potential against the solution, which, by Coulomb attraction pulls ions of opposite charge to the immediate vicinity of the particle and repels ions of identical charge. As a result, an electric double layer develops about the particle. One half of the double layer adheres tightly to the particle surface: the other half, of opposite charge, is diffuse. The monoionic layer closely adhering to the surface is the Stern layer. Its thickness is a few Å. The hydrate shell of the ions forming the Stern layer together with other solvated water molecules at the surface are to be regarded as belonging to the particle, in the sense of moving along with it whenever it moves relative to the solution. The hydrate shell may be up to 0.1 μm (several hundred molecules) thick. At the surface of the water film moving together with the particle, an electrokinetic or ζ (zeta) potential arises.

The electric double layer is generated in the final reckoning by the equilibrium distribution of the potential-determining ions from the surface of the particle into the solution surrounding it. Assigning to the concentrations c_0 and c_n of some potential-determining ion (e.g. Ag^+ or I in the case of silver iodide) the respective thermodynamic potentials ψ_0 and ψ_n, one may write

$$\psi_n - \psi_0 = \frac{kT}{ze_0} \ln \frac{c_n}{c_0},$$

where k is the Boltzmann constant, T is absolute temperature, z is the valence of the ion and e_0 is the elementary charge (the charge of the electron). With

ψ_0 put equal to zero, c_0 gives the concentration corresponding to the zero-charge point. At $z = 1$ and $T = 298$ K (25 °C),

$$\frac{kT}{ze_0} \simeq 25 \text{ mV};$$

that is, the potential of the surface is given by the formula

$$\psi_n \simeq 25 \ln \frac{c_n}{c_0} = 58 \log \frac{c_n}{c_0}$$

or

$$c_n = c_0 e^{\psi_n/25} = c_0 \cdot 10^{\psi_n/58}$$

where ψ_n is in millivolts.

When exposed to an external potential gradient, the ions constituting the electrical double layer of the particle (the free ions in the solution and the ions of opposite charge attached to the particle) will start moving relative to one another, giving rise to the phenomena of electrophoresis or electroosmosis. In the first, the solution is stationary and the solid surface is moving; in the second, it is the other way round. The relationship

$$\zeta = 141 \frac{u}{E}$$

holds, where ζ is in mV and u in μm/s, is the relative velocity between solution and particles that gives rise to the potential gradient E V/cm.

The diffuse layer is fairly thick (in dilute solutions it may attain 100 μm or so): in it, ion density decreases exponentially with increasing distance from the interface (Part A of Fig. 2.12). Potential decreases from the surface potential ψ_n, determined by the surface charge, to ψ_S at the boundary of the Stern

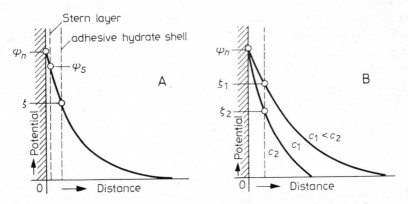

Fig. 2.12. A — variation of the zeta potential with distance from the surface; B — influence of counter-ion concentration on the zeta potential

layer, to ζ at the boundary of the adhesive layer and to zero in the diffuse layer. Approximately,

$$\psi_S = \frac{\psi_n + \zeta}{2}.$$

For example, quartz has its zero-charge point about a pH = 3.7, where

$$[c_0^+] = [H^+] = 10^{-3.7} = 2 \cdot 10^{-4}.$$

At pH = 7,

$$[c_n^+] = 10^{-7}$$

and

$$\psi_n = 25 \ln \frac{10^{-7}}{2 \cdot 10^{-4}} = -190 \text{ mV};$$

also,

$$\zeta - 72 \text{ mV}$$

and, at the boundary of the Stern layer,

$$\psi_S \cong \frac{\psi_n + \zeta}{2} = -131 \text{ mV}.$$

The thickness of the diffuse layer is best described in terms of the thickness d of a hypothetical layer of identical electrostatic effect, assumed to contain all the ions of opposite charge ("counter-ions") of the diffuse layer. The relationship defining d is

$$d = 97/\sqrt{c},$$

where d is in ångströms and c is ion concentration in millimoles per litre (Gaudin 1957). This states, for example, d to be about 3 Å in a molar solution, about 100 Å in the millimolar solutions usual in flotation practice, and about 3,000 Å at the micromolar concentrations prevailing in distilled water.

The zeta (ζ) potential depends not only on the magnitude of the surface charge ψ_n but, given a constant ψ_n, also on the concentration in the solution of the diffuse layer's counter-ions. If this latter increases, then the diffuse layer is compressed and the zeta potential decreases (part B of Fig. 2.12).

The surface adsorption density u mole/cm^2 of the potential-determining (unhydrated) ions and their concentration, c mole/litre, in the solution are related by

$$\log u = a + b \log c$$

or

$$u = 2rce^{-W/kT}.$$

Here, a and b are constants; r is the ionic radius of the adsorbed ion, W is energy of adsorption (enthalpy), obtained as the sum of an electrostatic component

$$W_p = ze_0\psi_n$$

146

due to the polar radical and the enthalpy Φ due to the non-polar part of the ion. The latter includes also the energy of association (free enthalpy) Φ'. For alkyl compounds,

$$\Phi' = sf\varphi(m - 1) ,$$

where s is the degree of association;

$$\varphi = -1.39kT$$

is the change of free enthalpy per $-CH_2-$ group in the case that association is complete; f is a factor accounting for prior associations in the solution (dimers, micellae, etc.). Both s and f may assume any value from zero to unity. m is the "effective" carbon (C) number of the hydrocarbon chain. (m equals the number of C atoms in straight chains and that of the longest chain in forked chains. If the chain includes rings, the equivalent C number of those is to be taken: it is, e.g., 3.5 for a benzene ring.) In other words,

$$\ln u = \ln(2r) + \ln c - ze_0\frac{\psi_n}{kT} - sf\varphi\frac{m - 1}{kT} .$$

If u, ψ_n, s and f remain constant as m changes, then

$$\frac{\partial \ln c}{\partial m} = \frac{sf\varphi}{kT} = - 1.39sf .$$

The electrokinetic or zeta potential ζ mV, the ion concentration c mole/litre and specific surface charge σ cm^{-2} (charge units [charges of monovalent ions or electrons] per cm^2) are related by

$$\sigma \simeq 1.42 \cdot 10^{12}\zeta\sqrt{c} .$$

For example, on a particle of quartz immersed in a NaOH solution of $c = 0.01$ mole per litre concentration,

$$\zeta = -52 \text{ mV},$$

that is,

$$\sigma \simeq 7.4 \cdot 10^{12}/\text{cm}^2.$$

The charge density of a close-packed monoionic layer would be much greater, about $4 \cdot 10^{14}$ cm^{-2}. Surface charge is in fact due to ions adsorbed by a surface in excess of what is needed for charge compensation. Figure 2.13 illustrates water molecules, hydrated cations and anions in and near the Stern layer. In the diffuse layer, it is the counter-ions (the ions whose charge is opposed to the ion surplus of the surface) that are in excess, but this does not imply that the layer contains no ions having the same charge as the surface at all. The anion-to-cation abundance ratio in the diffuse layer is a function of the zeta potential. For example, at $\zeta = +100$ mV, that ratio is about 7; at $\zeta = +25$ mV, it is about 2. In addition to the potential-determining ion, the

10*

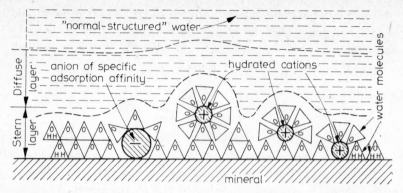

Fig. 2.13. Illustration of adsorbed ions and water molecules in the Stern layer

mineral surface may adsorb also other ions from the solution, often in fact in much greater abundance. For example, if the mineral surface adsorbs a collector reagent with great avidity, then this reduces the influence of the potential-determining ions on the outcome of flotation.

The adsorption of an ion by the mineral surface is the stronger as a rule, the less soluble is the compound that the ion can constitute with one of the ions of the mineral. The adsorption of ions by polar mineral surfaces out of an otherwise indifferent electrolyte depends, however, in addition to the solubility of the ion, also on its valence and radius and on the hydration of the adsorbed complex. A fair idea of the conditions is provided by Hofmeister's ion sequences. The sequence for cations is

$$Li^+ - Na^+ - K^+ - Rb^+ - Cs^+ - NH_4^+ - Cu^+ - Ag^+ - Cu^{2+} - Fe^{2+} - Zn^{2+} -$$
$$- Mg^{2+} - Ca^{2+} - Sr^{2+} - Ba^{2+} - Al^{3+} - Fe^{3+} - \ldots H^+;$$

the sequence for anions is

$$\tfrac{1}{2}SO_4^{2-} - F^- - NO_3^- - Cl^- - Br^- - I^- - CNS^- - \ldots OH^-.$$

An ion further back in the sequence tends to be adsorbed more avidly than those preceding it.

Any ion adsorbed in the Stern layer (and not only the potential-determining ion(s) in the strict sense) has a direct influence on the magnitude of the surface charge ψ_n and of the zeta potential. The ions of indifferent electrolyte have no specific affinity to the mineral surface: their distribution in the electric double layer is determined by the electrostatic forces present. The way that the zeta potential of a mineral is influenced by various electrolytes permits to infer whether there is a special affinity between this or that ion and the mineral surface.

The variation of the zeta potential vs. the concentration of various electrolytes is shown in Fig. 2.14A, B for quartz, in Fig. 2.15 for corundum and in

Fig. 2.16A, B for haematite. Part A of Fig. 2.14 shows the influence of various chlorides. The potential-determining ion is H^+, but the Ca^{2+} and Ba^{2+} ions affect the zeta potential of quartz almost as much. Both these and the Al^{3+} ion, which turns the surface charge of quartz positive even in very small concentrations, are adsorbed by quartz just as preferentially as the potential-determining ion; NaCl on the other hand is an indifferent electrolyte, whose rising concentration merely compresses the diffuse part of the double layer. (The rise of the zeta potential in the low NaCl concentration range is presumably due to an unavoidable error of measurement, the contribution of the surface conductivity of quartz to the conductivity of the solution, which is not negligible at low electrolyte concentrations.) The sequence of increasing adsorption from Na^+ through Ca^{2+} and Ba^{2+} to Al^{3+} is consistent with the Hofmeister sequence. The avid adsorption of trivalent Al can even explain the change of polarity (Schubert 1964).

Part B of Fig. 2.14 illustrates the influence of various sodium salts and of ammonium acetate (marked NH^+) and various amine acetates (marked 8C to 16C according to the number of C atoms in their hydrocarbon chains) upon the zeta potential of quartz. The zero-charge or zero-potential (isoelectric) point of quartz is seen to be at pH = 3.7. At any pH greater than 3.7, quartz immersed into pure water (an electrolyte of concentration $c \leq 10^{-7}$) is negatively charged ($\zeta = -72$ mV at pH = 7; $\zeta = -122$ mV at pH = 10). The curves shown in the figure all belong to a pH = 7.

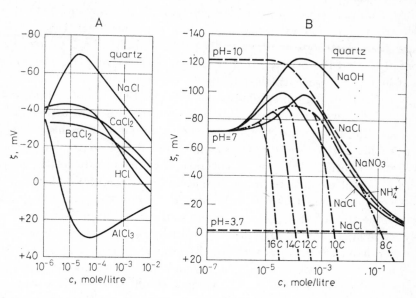

Fig. 2.14. A, B — zeta potential of quartz vs. electrolyte concentration in various electrolytes

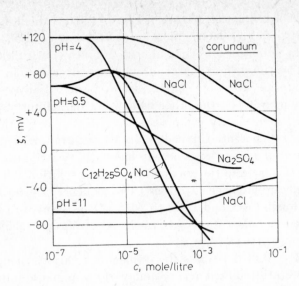

Fig. 2.15. Zeta potential of corundum vs. electrolyte concentration in various electrolytes

Ammonium acetate and the various sodium salts affect ζ about equally; the negatively charged quartz surface adsorbs the cations NH^+ and Na^+ by pure electrostatic attraction; this is revealed by the fact that, as the concentration of either increases, it drives ζ towards zero but does not change its sign. Ammonium acetate and the sodium salts (NaCl, NaNO$_3$, NaOH), then, are electrolytes indifferent to quartz (Gaudin and Fuerstenau 1955).

NaCl is an electrolyte indifferent also to corundum (Fig. 2.15), whose zeta potential ($\zeta = +120$ mV at pH $= 4$ or $\zeta = +67$ mV at pH $= 6.5$) drops to zero at high NaCl concentrations owing to the adsorption of Cl^- ions.

The SO_4^{2-} ion of sodium sulphate and the $C_{12}H_{25}SO_4^-$ ion of sodium dodecyl sulphate on the other hand have, over and above their electrostatic attraction, also a specific affinity to corundum (just as amine acetate has to quartz), being capable as they are to repolarize the mineral surface (to change the sign of its zeta potential). At a low concentration, amine acetate relates to quartz as an indifferent electrolyte, much like ammonium acetate; dodecyl sulphate affects corundum much like sodium chloride. Above a certain concentration, however, the affinity of the organic anions to the mineral surfaces rises rapidly. Early on, organic ions get adsorbed individually; in greater concentrations, on the other hand, their hydrocarbon chains associate in the surface layer, similarly to the process of micella formation in a solution. At pH $= 11$, corundum has a negative charge of -65 mV; as a result, it is the Na^+ cations that are adsorbed by its surface, whereas both the organic and the inorganic sodium salts behave as indifferent electrolytes.

The variation of haematite's zeta potential is shown in Fig. 2.16. Part A of the figure shows zeta vs. dodecyl amine concentration at different pH values; Part B shows zeta vs. the pH at different dodecyl amine concentrations. If the pH is adjusted by dosages of HCl and NaOH, the zero charge point of haematite at an amine concentration $c = 0$ (in the presence of monovalent Cl^-, ClO_4^- and NO_3^- anions) is at pH $= 4.75$. As the amine concentration increases, the $\zeta = f(\text{pH})$ curve splits off the curve of $c = 0$ at lower and lower pH's (Part B of the figure). The $\zeta = f(c)$ curves of Part A belong to different (constant) pH values. Zeta does not change below a threshold concentration of amine: above it, however, it rises rapidly. (For example, at pH $= 6.5$, the threshold concentration is $c = 10^{-4}$ mole per litre; above it, zeta increases fast from a plateau of -20 mV.) Above an amine concentration of $c \cong 5 \cdot 10^{-4}$ mole per litre, the zeta potential of haematite is positive at any pH. The specific affinity resulting in repolarization above the threshold concentration can be interpreted also in this case by the micella-like adsorption of dodecyl amine molecules.

The variation of the zeta potential vs. the pH for a number of other minerals is shown in Fig. 2.17. The pH was adjusted also here by dosages of HCl and NaOH.

Part A of Fig. 2.18 is a diagram of the adsorption density, u moles per cm^2, of dodecyl amine (12C) on quartz in the pH range 6 to 7. Up to a concentration of $c = 2 \cdot 10^{-4}$ mole per litre, adsorption is purely electrostatic. The slope of the adsorption isotherm is $1/2$; that is, u varies as the square root of concentration c (consistently with the equation of surface charge σ). At higher concentrations, the ions are adsorbed at the quartz surface in clusters; adsorp-

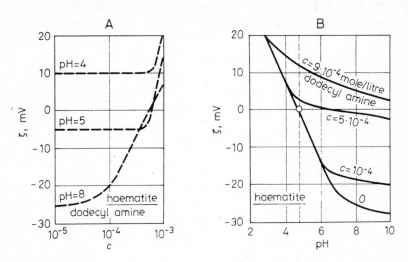

Fig. 2.16. Zeta potential of haematite, A — vs. dodecyl amine concentration at different pH's, B — vs. the pH at different dodecyl amine concentrations

tion u therefore varies as $c^{1.2}$. The number of associated ions may in such cases exceed the number required to form a close-packed monoionic layer. The associated ions may even enclose undissociated molecules among them. Part B of Fig. 2.18 shows the absorption density u vs. concentration c of dodecyl amine on haematite. Here, u varies as $\sim c^{0.6}$ below a concentration $c = 2 \cdot 10^{-4}$ and as $\sim c^{1.6}$ above it (DeBruyn 1955).

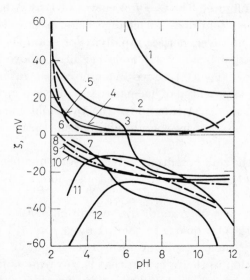

Fig. 2.17. Zeta potential vs. the pH in various minerals. *1* — fluorite, CaF$_2$, *2* —calcite, CaCO$_3$, *3* — pyrite, FeS$_2$, *4* — dolomite, CaMg(CO$_3$)$_2$, *5* — barite, BaSO$_4$, *6* — apatite, (Cl, F)Ca$_5$(PO$_4$)$_3$, *7* — quartz, SiO$_2$, *8* — sphalerite, ZnS, *9* — cassiterite, SnO$_2$, *10* — galena, PbS, *11* — nepheline, NaAlSiO$_4$, *12* — feldspars

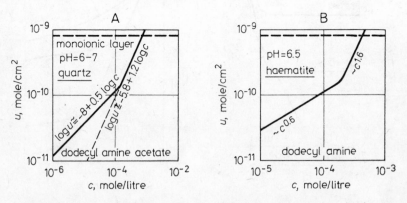

Fig. 2.18. Dodecyl amine adsorption, u mole/litre, on quartz and haematite vs. dodecyl amine acetate (dodecyl amine) concentration

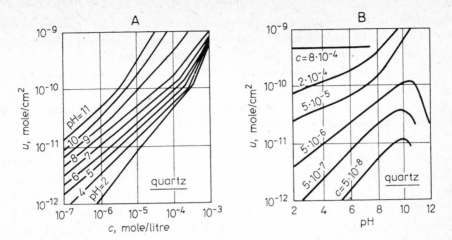

Fig. 2.19. Dodecyl amine adsorption on quartz, u mole/litre, vs. dodecyl amine concentration c mole/litre and the pH

Part A of Fig. 2.19 shows the adsorption density, u moles per cm², vs. concentration, c moles per litre, of dodecyl amine on quartz at various pH values; Part B of the figure shows u vs. the pH at various values of c. In the vicinity of pH = 7, at a dodecyl amine concentration of $c = 2 \cdot 10^{-4}$ mole per litre, the surface adsorption density of quartz is

$$u \cong \frac{\sqrt{c}}{10^8} = \frac{\sqrt{2 \cdot 10^{-4}}}{10^8} = 1.4 \cdot 10^{-10}.$$

A complete monoionic shell requires $u = 8 \cdot 10^{-10}$ mole per cm²: that is, the surface association of the amine ions (the formation of hemimicellae) begins when only

$$\frac{1.4 \cdot 10^{-10}}{8 \cdot 10^{-10}} = 17.5\%$$

of the surface is coated.

According to Part B of Fig. 2.14, quartz in the presence of dodecyl amine (12C) is abruptly repolarized at pH = 7 as the concentration of dodecyl amine changes from $5 \cdot 10^{-5}$ to $2 \cdot 10^{-4}$ mole per litre. At a concentration in the solution of $c_0 = 2 \cdot 10^{-4}$ mole per litre, the concentration c_S belonging to the potential $\psi_S = -131$ mV in the Stern layer is provided by the relationship

$$c_S = c_0 e^{\frac{ze\psi_S}{kT}} = c_0 e^{\frac{\psi_S}{25}} = c_0 10^{\frac{\psi_S}{58}}$$

as

$$c_S = 2 \cdot 10^{-4} \cdot 10^{\frac{131}{58}} = 2 \cdot 10^{-4} \cdot 10^{2.26} = 2 \cdot 1.82 \cdot 10^{-2} = 0.0364 \text{ mole/l.}$$

153

In the interior of the solution, the threshold concentration c_M of micella formation is about 0.014 mole per litre for dodecyl amine (cf. Table 2.9). Association among the hydrocarbon chains of the amine ions adsorbed into the Stern layer (the formation of hemimicellae at the particle surface) begins when concentration in the solution is much lower still ($2 \cdot 10^{-4}$ mole per litre). The hemimicella itself can be regarded as a polyvalent polymer of amine ions and of undissociated amine molecules enclosed by them.

The phases of adsorption into the Stern layer as concentration rises are illustrated by Fig. 2.20. Part A shows individual adsorption at a low concentration; Part B shows hemimicellar-monoionic adsorption at a higher concentration; Part C shows an excess above monoionic adsorption at a high concentration. The potential-determining ions at the mineral surface are represented by small circles (they are anions if the mineral is negatively charged, e.g. in the case of quartz). The heteropolar hydrocarbon ions (e.g. the amine cations) are adsorbed into the Stern layer, whereas (hydrated or unhydrated) counterions (e.g. the acetate anions) accumulate in the diffuse layer (DeBruyn and Agar 1962).

An electric double layer fully analogous to the one found at the solid–liquid interface is observed also at the gas–liquid interface, provided ions can get adsorbed into the surface layer, endowing it with an electric charge. The counter-ions constitute a diffuse layer also in this case. The situation is illustrated by Fig. 2.21 (Gaudin 1957). The surface charge of gas bubbles tends to be negative as a result of the preferred orientation of the water dipole molecules: hence, in combination with the electric double layers of opposite polarity of the mineral grains, a process of electrostatic flotation, so to speak, may come about (Spurný and Dobiaš 1960).

Bubbles coated with surface-active ions in a preferred orientation (with their polar radicals towards the water) can capture ions of opposite charge, colloid particles and even fine slime particles. This is the phenomenon exploited

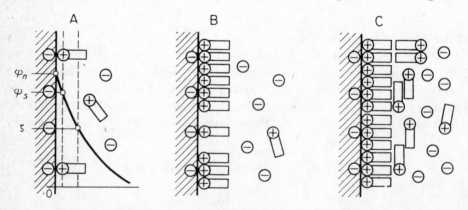

Fig. 2.20. A, B, C — ion adsorption patterns vs. rising concentration

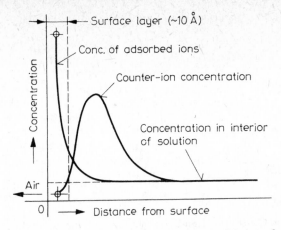

Fig. 2.21. Electric double layer at a water/air interface

in ionic flotation. Hydrocarbons carrying the polar radicals —COOH (car-boxyl), —HSO$_4$ (sulphate), —HSO$_3$ (sulphonate), —H$_2$PO$_4$ (phosphate), —H$_2$PO$_3$ (phosphonate), —SH (mercaptan) are negatively charged; hydro-carbons carrying the radicals —NH$_2$ (primary amine), =NH (secondary amine), ≡N (tertiary amine) or ≡N$^+$ (quaternary ammonium) are positively charged.

2.1.2.5. Micellae. The pronounced hydrophobia of long hydrocarbon chains causes them to form micellae in their aqueous solutions. A micella is an aggre-gate, attaining colloidal size, of organic ions or molecules, made up of densely clotted hydrocarbon chains facing the water with their polar radicals. Micellae tend to be either spherical or cylindrical, with radii approximately equal to the length of the carbon chain, or double-layer lamellae in which the molecules face one another with their non-polar ends and the water with their polar ends. The formation of micellae is analogous in its essence to the adsorption of surfactants in a preferred orientation at a liquid surface: here also, the hydrophobic parts of the molecules or ions are jostled, so to speak, out of the water; the bundle constituted by them is separated from the water by a shell made up of the hydrophilic parts. The size and shape of a micella is determined by the equilibrium between the attraction among the hydrocarbon chains and the repulsion among the electrically charged polar radicals. For micellae to form, the concentration in the solution must exceed a threshold value c_M. Micella size depends on the length of the chain (the number of the C atoms making it up) as well as on the nature of the polar radical. The typical micella is made up of 50 to 100 molecules. Tensids or surfactants (surface-active heteropolar compounds) dissociate less at a mineral–water interface than at a water–air or water–oil interface. Reduced ionization promotes association by

155

Table 2.9. Threshold concentrations of micella formation for long-chain anionic and cationic collector reagents

Threshold concentration c_M of micella formation, mole/litre			c_M mole/litre (R = $C_n H_{2n+1}$)		
Soaps	n	$R_n NH_3 Cl$	$R_n N(CH_3)_3 Cl$	$R_n SO_4 Na$
$R_{11}COONa$ $3.6 \cdot 10^{-2}$ (20° C)	8	$4.5 \cdot 10^{-1}$	—	$1.0 \cdot 10^{-1}$
$R_{11}COOK$ $2.3 \cdot 10^{-2}$ (26° C)	10	$(3.2-5.4)10^{-2}$	$6.1 \cdot 10^{-2}$	$3.3 \cdot 10^{-2}$
$R_{16}COONa$ $3.4 \cdot 10^{-3}$ (70° C)	12	$(1.2-1.6)10^{-2}$	$1.7 \cdot 10^{-2}$	$(5.8-9.9)10^{-3}$
$R_{17}COONa$ $4.0 \cdot 10^{-4}$	14	$(2.8-4.5)10^{-3}$	$4.5 \cdot 10^{-3}$	$(1.5-3.1)10^{-3}$
Na-oleate $2.7 \cdot 10^{-3}$ (20 °C)	16	$8.0 \cdot 10^{-4}$	—	$(3.8-9.9)10^{-4}$
K-oleate $(0.7-1.2)10^{-3}$ (26 °C)	18	$3.0 \cdot 10^{-4}$	—	$(1.0-3.0)10^{-4}$
Na-elaidate $2.5 \cdot 10^{-3}$				

Table 2.10. Constants A and B of the formula $\log c_M = A - Bn$ for some long-chain compounds

Collector reagents	°C	A	B
Sodium soaps	20	2.41	0.341
Potassium soaps	25	1.92	0.290
	45	2.03	0.292
Alcane sulphonates	40	1.59	0.294
	50	1.63	0.294
Alkyl sulphates	25	1.27	0.280
	45	1.42	0.295
Alkyl ammonium chlorides	25	1.25	0.265
	45	1.79	0.296
Alkyl trimethyl ammonium bromides	60	1.77	0.292

van der Waals forces: at the mineral surfaces, micellae may form even if concentration in the solution remains below the threshold concentration c_M.

Threshold concentrations of micella formation (c_M moles per litre) for certain soaps (RCOONa or RCOOK) and sodium n-alkyl sulphates (RSO$_4$Na), primary n-alkyl amine chlorides ($R_n NH_3 Cl$) and trimethyl ammonium chlorides [$R_n N(CH_3)_3 Cl$] are listed in Table 2.9. (R or R_n denotes $C_n H_{2n+1}$.)

The threshold concentration of micella formation c_M in long-chain ($n \geq 8$) alkyl compounds is furnished by the relationship

$$\log c_M \simeq A - Bn = \log a - n \log b$$

or

$$c_M \simeq \frac{a}{b^n} ,$$

where n is the number of C atoms in the hydrocarbon chain. A, B, a and b are constants depending on the nature and number of hydrophilic radicals and on temperature. For one-ion molecules, B is in the vicinity of log $2 = 0.3$. Table 2.10 presents some values of A and B.

The resultant hydrophilia or hydrophobia of a heteropolar compound is determined by the size and strength of the radicals; if these are known, it can be quantified as

$$F = \Sigma\,(\text{strength of hydrophilic groups}) - \Sigma\,(\text{strength of hydrophobic groups}) + 7,$$

where the strength assigned to each hydrophobic group —CH—, —CH$_2$—, —CH$_3$, =CH is 0.475 and the strengths of the hydrophilic groups are as follows:

—SO$_4^-$ (Na$^+$)	38.7;	≡N (tertiary amine)	9.4;
—COO$^-$ (K$^+$)	21.1;	—COOH	2.1;
—COO$^-$ (Na$^+$)	19.1;	—OH	1.9;
—SO$_3^-$ (Na$^+$)	11.0;	—O—	1.3.

The number n of C atoms in the hydrocarbon chain (or the equivalent number in a non-normal, forked or ringed chain) figures in the equations of both F and c_M: one may therefore write

$$\log c_M = \alpha + \beta F.$$

The coefficients α, β, A and B are related by the equations

$$\frac{B}{\beta} = 0.475$$

and

$$\frac{A - \alpha}{\beta} = \Sigma(\text{strength of hydropholic groups}) + 7;$$

that is, for any homologous series, the F values can be derived from the c_M values, and vice versa. For example, for the soaps R$_n$COONa (whose $A = 2.41$ and $B = 0.341$), $\beta = 0.718$ and $\alpha = -16.33$; that is,

$$\log c_M = -16.33 + 0.718\,F;$$

for the alkyl sulphates at 25 °C,

$$\log c_M \cong -25.73 + 0.590\,F;$$

for the alkyl sulphates at 45 °C,

$$\log c_M \cong -26.96 + 0.621\,F.$$

Table 2.11 lists c_M and F values for the homologous series R$_n$COONa and R$_n$SO$_4$Na (at 20 °C for the first and at 25 and 45 °C respectively for the second) (Lin 1971).

Table 2.11. c_M and F parameters of sodium soaps (R_nCOONa) and sodium alkyl sulphates (R_nSO_4Na)

n	R_nCOONa, 20 °C		R_nSO_4Na, 25 °C		R_nSO_4Na, 45 °C		$\sim t_K$ °C
	c_M mole/litre	F	c_M mole/litre	F	c_M mole/litre	F	
8	—	—	$1.07 \cdot 10^{-1}$	41.9	$1.1 \cdot 10^{-1}$	41.9	—
10	$1.0 \cdot 10^{-1}$	21.35	$2.95 \cdot 10^{-2}$	41.0	$2.9 \cdot 10^{-2}$	40.9	—
12	$2.4 \cdot 10^{-2}$	20.40	$8.13 \cdot 10^{-3}$	40.0	$7.5 \cdot 10^{-3}$	40.0	8
14	$4.4 \cdot 10^{-3}$	19.45	$2.24 \cdot 10^{-3}$	39.2	$1.9 \cdot 10^{-3}$	39.0	20
16	$9.0 \cdot 10^{-4}$	18.50	$6.16 \cdot 10^{-4}$	38.1	$5.0 \cdot 10^{-4}$	38.1	31
18	$1.8 \cdot 10^{-4}$	17.55	$1.70 \cdot 10^{-4}$	37.4	$1.3 \cdot 10^{-4}$	37.1	41

The equivalent conductivity of a solution takes an abrupt plunge at the threshold concentration of micella formation. Temperature affects the threshold concentration little enough: solubility increases slowly up to a certain temperature depending on chain length (the Krafft point t_K), and steeply beyond it. The conditions are illustrated by Fig. 2.22. Along the c_M line, the balance of the molecular-disperse and micellar-disperse phases upset at t_K in favour of the latter. The Krafft point is in the vicinity of 23 °C e.g. for $R_{12}NH_3Cl$ and of 55 °C for $R_{18}NH_3Cl$. Krafft points for some sodium n-alkyl sulphates (R_nSO_4Na) are listed in the last column of Table 2.11. The Krafft point of a sodium n-alkyl sulphate with an odd number of C atoms in its chain is near-equal to that of the next lowest even-numbered chain, whereas the threshold concentration of micella formation changes continuously, according to the formula

$$\log c_M = A - Bn.$$

Surface tension in an aqueous solution is least at the threshold concentration c_M: it increases strongly towards the lower and slowly towards the higher concentration range. Likewise, the adsorption of flotation collector reagents by

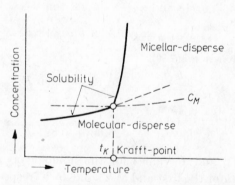

Fig. 2.22. Solubility and threshold concentration of micella formation vs. the temperature

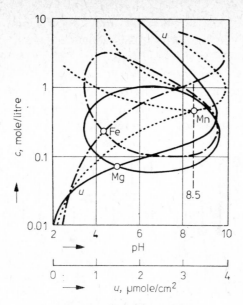

Fig. 2.23. Flotation with oleic acid of orthosilicates, M_2SiO_4, vs. the pH and oleic acid adsorption at a pH = 8.5

the particles' surfaces tends to be greatest at the threshold concentration: above it, the floatability of the particles tends to cease sooner or later. For example, the upper limit of oleate concentration for floating calcite is about $3 c_M$ (Buckenham and MacKenzie 1961). The upper limit may in fact be as low as $\sim c_M$ in the cationic (amine) or anionic (soapy) flotation of certain silicates. For example, the orthosilicates M_2SiO_4 (where M is Mg [forsterite], Fe [fayalite] or Mn [tephroite]) react with oleic acid according to the formula

$$M_2SiO_4 \overset{OH}{\diagup} + \overline{Ol}^- \rightarrow M_2SiO_4 \overset{Ol}{\diagup} + OH^-,$$

which permits their flotation in the c-pH domains shown in Fig. 2.23 (that is, e.g. at pH = 8.5, in the c ranges from 0.07 to 0.77 mole per litre oleic acid for forsterite, 0.10 to 0.86 for fayalite and 0.58 to 0.77 for tephroite). The c_M of oleic acid is 0.86 mole per litre at pH = 8.5. At a lower pH, c_M decreases, but the upper limiting concentration of floatability rises nevertheless. For example, at pH = 6, the floatability range of the three orthosilicates in the above order is c = 0.07 to 1.00, 0.10 to 1.20 and 0.65 to 1.15 mole per litre oleate. A lower limiting concentration (Mg < Fe < Mn) indicates a better floatability; both it and the full floatability range $\varDelta c_M$ vary as the heat of wetting H_n of the minerals. (H_n equals 0.25 cal/m² for forsterite, 0.18 for fayalite and 0.12 for tephroite.) The figure also shows the variation of oleic acid adsorption, u μmole per m²,

159

vs. concentration c, for pH = 8.5. Maximum adsorption by each of the three minerals is in the vicinity of $c_M = 0.86$ (somewhat below it for forsterite and somewhat above it for fayalite and tephroite) (Read and Manser 1972).

The threshold concentration of micella formation is reduced both by inorganic salts whose ions form counter-ions to the micellae (and reduce the zeta potential thereby) and by neutral long-chain organic molecules which are absorbed into the micellae because they reduce repulsion between the ionized polar radi-

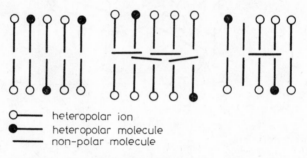

Fig. 2.24. Hydrocarbon molecules and collector ions

cals. (For example, the threshold concentration of dodecyl ammonium chloride is reduced from about $1.3 \cdot 10^{-2}$ mole per litre to about $6.8 \cdot 10^{-3}$ mole per litre by the addition of 0.05 mole per litre NaCl or $2.8 \cdot 10^{-4}$ mole per litre decyl alcohol.) The influence of heteropolar molecules (an alcohol, $C_nH_{2n+1}OH$) and of non-polar ones (an alcane or paraffin, C_nH_{2n+2}) is illustrated by Fig. 2.24 (Schubert 1964). The relationship linking the counter-ion concentration c_i of an electrolyte and the threshold concentration of micella formation c_M is

$$c_M \cong \frac{K}{c_i^p},$$

where K and p are constants ($p = 0.4$ to 0.6).

Being of a more polar nature, double bonds in a hydrocarbon chain reduce the hydrophobia of the chain and, as a result, raise both its c_M and its solubility. This is why the propensity to hydrolyse of an unsaturated fatty acid is less than that of the corresponding saturated one; so is also the propensity to associate of its non-polar radicals (Buckenham and MacKenzie 1961; Pope and Sutton 1972).

The solubility of the neutral molecules formed on the hydrolysis of a weak electrolyte also depends on the length of the hydrocarbon chain. Table 2.12 lists the solubility in water, moles per litre, of primary amine chloride (RNH_3Cl) molecules and undissociated saturated carboxyl acid molecules and of the sodium, magnesium and calcium salts of some n-alkyl sulphonates. Alkyl sulphates constitute "insoluble" compounds with the cations Al, Ba, Cr, Fe, Pb,

160

Table 2.12. Solubility in water of some neutral alkyl compounds

n	RNH_3Cl	$RCOOH$			RSO_3 (25 °C), g/kg		
	1 mole/litre (25 °C)		mg/kg		Na-	Mg-	Ca-
			20 °C	60 °C			
10	$5 \cdot 10^{-4}$	$3 \cdot 10^{-4}$	155	270	45.5	2.68	1.55
12	$2 \cdot 10^{-5}$	$1.2 \cdot 10^{-5}$	55	87	2.53	0.33	0.11
14	$1 \cdot 10^{-6}$	$1 \cdot 10^{-6}$	20	34	0.41	0.033	0.014
16	—	$6 \cdot 10^{-7}$	7.2	12	0.073	0.012	0.005
18	—	$3 \cdot 10^{-7}$	2.9	5	0.010	0.010	0.006

Table 2.13. pK parameters (negative logarithms of solubility products) of some fatty acids and their salts

Cation	Palmitate	Stearate	Elaidate	Oleate	Linoleate	Linolenate
	$C_{15}H_{31}COO^-$	$C_{17}H_{35}COO^-$		$C_{17}H_{33}COO^-$		
H^+	11.9	12.7	11.2	10.9	11.0	11.5
Na^+	5.1	6.0	—	—	—	—
Ag^+	11.1	12.0	10.5	9.4	9.5	9.4
Pb^{++}	20.7	22.2	—	16.8	—	16.9
Cu^{++}	19.4	20.8	—	16.4	—	17.0
Fe^{++}	15.6	17.4	—	12.4	—	—
Mn^{++}	16.2	17.5	—	12.3	—	12.6
Ca^{++}	15.8	17.4	14.3	12.4	12.4	12.2
Ba^{++}	15.4	16.9	—	11.9	11.8	11.6
Mg^{++}	14.3	15.5	—	10.8	—	—

Sr, Zr, whereas their salts of Ca, Cd, Cu, Li, Mg, Mn, Na are fairly soluble. The solubility of alkyl amine salts increases in the following sequence: molybdates, vanadates, silicates $< 2.5 \cdot 10^{-4} <$ carbonates, tungstates, chromates, phosphates $< 7.5 \cdot 10^{-4} <$ sulphates $< 2.5 \cdot 10^{-3} <$ borates, chlorides, fluorides.

The solubilities of soaps (of the metal salts of higher carboxyl acids: 16C to 18C) are stated in Table 2.13 in terms of the negative logarithms of their solubility products. (The solubility product is the product of the ionic concentrations of the ions of a dissolved compound.) The stearates are less soluble than the palmitates, and the oleates are more soluble than both; the soaps of the monovalent metals are more soluble than those of the divalent ones; of the latter, those of the alkali earths are more soluble than those of the heavier metals.

The first three rows of Table 2.13A present the pL values (negative logarithms of the solubility products) of soaps, extrapolated to infinite dilution, at 20 °C. These figures exceed those in Table 2.13 by about one or two units. The last row presents the pL values of metal hydroxides, likewise extrapolated to infinite dilution at 20 °C (Du Rietz 1975).

Table 2.13B presents the solubility products pL_{MA} of some compounds of certain metals, as stated in different handbooks, with the temperature in °C in parentheses.

The solubility of metal salts usually increases with temperature, often quite rapidly. The temperature dependence of solubility is specific for each compound: hence, selectivity of flotation can often be improved by raising the temperature.

Table 2.13A

	H^+	K^+	Ag^+	Pb^{2+}	Cu^{2+}	Zn^{2+}	Cd^{2+}	Fe^{2+}
Palmitate	12.8	5.2	12.2	22.9	21.6	20.7	20.2	17.8
Stearate	13.8	6.1	13.1	24.4	23.0	22.2		19.6
Oleate	12.3	5.7	10.9	19.8	19.4	18.1	17.3	15.4
Hydroxide, OH^-			7.9	15.1	18.2	15.7		14.8

	Ni^{2+}	Mn^{2+}	Ca^{2+}	Ba^{2+}	Mg^{2+}	Al^{3+}	Fe^{3+}
Palmitate	18.3	18.4	18.0	17.6	16.5	31.2	34.3
Stearate	19.4	19.7	19.6	19.1	17.7	33.6	
Oleate	15.7	15.3	15.4	14.9	13.8	30.0	34.2
Hydroxide, OH^-	14.8	13.1	4.9		10.3	32.2	37.0

Table 2.13B

Al^{3+} OH^- $\begin{cases} 12.4\ (15) \\ 14.96\ (18) \\ 14.43\ (25) \end{cases}$

Ag^+ Cl^- 9.81 (25)
OH^- 7.82 (20)
CO_3^{2-} 11.21 (25)
S^{2-} 48.80 (18)

Ba^{2+} CO_3^{2-} $\begin{cases} 8.15\ (16) \\ 8.09\ (25) \\ 8.8 \end{cases}$
SO_4^{2-} 10.0
OH^- 0.7
$P_2O_7^{4-}$ 4.64

Ca^{2+} CO_3^{2-} $\begin{cases} 8.0\ (15) \\ 8.06\ (25) \\ 8.33 \end{cases}$
SO_4^{2-} $\begin{cases} 4.2 \\ 3.71\ (10) \end{cases}$
OH^- $\begin{cases} 3.82 \\ 4.46 \end{cases}$
$P_2O_7^{4-}$ 5.0

Cu^{2+} CO_3^{2-} 9.6
OH^- 19.25
S^{2-} $\begin{cases} 44.07\ (18) \\ 37.5 \end{cases}$
$P_2O_5^{4-}$ 7—8.7

Cu^+ S^{2-} $\begin{cases} 46.7\ (17) \\ 48.6 \end{cases}$

Fe^{2+} CO_3^{2-} 10.7
OH^- 13.78 (18)
S^{2-} 18.43 (18)

Fe^{3+} OH^- 35.96 (18)

Mg^{2+} CO_3^{2-} $\begin{cases} 4.1 \\ 4.58\ (12) \\ 5.0 \end{cases}$
OH^- 10.92 (18)
$P_2O_5^{4-}$ 5.7

Mn^{2+} CO_3^{2-} 10.05
OH^- 13.40 (18)
S^{2-} 14.85 (18)

Ni^{2+} S^{2-} 23.85 (18)

Pb^{2+} CO_3^{2-} 18.48 (18)
OH^- 17.5 (20)
SO_4^{2-} $\begin{cases} 7.97\ (18) \\ 7.6 \end{cases}$
S^{2-} $\begin{cases} 27.47\ (18) \\ 28.17 \end{cases}$
SO_3^{2-} 13.0
$S_2O_3^{2-}$ 9.5
$Cr_2O_4^{2-}$ 13.8

Zn^{2+} OH^- 13.74 (19)
S^{2-} $\begin{cases} 22.92\ (18) \\ 25.1 \end{cases}$

Hg^{2+} S^{2-} $\begin{cases} 52.4\ (18) \\ 48.7 \end{cases}$

2.1.2.6. The three-phase boundary. The contact angle of a solid. Two phases in contact constitute an interface; three phases in simultaneous contact constitute a three-phase boundary line. The angle included by the two interfaces of the liquid phase, as measured in a plane perpendicular to the boundary line, is the angle of contact, ϑ. It is a function of the surface tensions arising at the

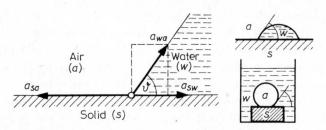

Fig. 2.25. The contact angle ϑ at a three-phase boundary (where the phases s — solid, w — water and a — air meet) is determined by the surface tensions at the phase boundaries

two interfaces. The condition of equilibrium between the three surface-tension vectors in Fig. 2.25 is

$$a_{sa} = a_{sw} + a_{wa} \cos \vartheta,$$

that is,

$$\cos \vartheta = \frac{a_{sa} - a_{sw}}{a_{wa}}.$$

The resultant of the three vectors is perpendicular to the surface of the solid, and its magnitude is $a_{wa} \sin \vartheta$. If

$$\vartheta = 0°, \quad \text{that is,} \quad a_{sa} - a_{sw} \geq a_{wa},$$

then a drop of water will wet the solid completely, i.e. spread out on it, so that the solid–gas interface disappears: the mineral is water-avid, hydrophilic, aerophobic, unfloatable. If

$$a_{sa} = a_{sw},$$

then $\vartheta = 90$; if

$$a_{sa} < a_{sw},$$

then $\vartheta > 90°$ and vice versa. The greater is ϑ, the more hydrophobic (the more floatable) is the mineral. In pure water, the contact angle of no solid exceeds about 110°.

The surface tensions a_{sa} and a_{sw} cannot be measured at all accurately. In the absence of that information, the wetting process of the surface is best characterized by the heat of wetting, which is proportional to surface energy. The heat of wetting (of immersion) can be measured in the liquid phase. Equal to the heat of adsorption of the saturated vapour of the liquid minus its heat of evaporation, it is due to the change in surface energy: it is greater, the greater the difference between the free surface energies of the solid and the liquid at the instant of wetting. By measuring the wetting heats per unit of surface of various solids in one and the same liquid, the relative magnitude of their adsorptivities *vis-à-vis* that liquid can be established (a greater heat of wetting implying an adsorptive bonding of greater energy). By measuring the heats of wetting of a given solid in different liquids, the order of increasing adsorptivities of the liquids *vis-à-vis* the solid in question can be established. Of a liquid with a greater heat of wetting, more is adsorbed more strongly by the solid surface: indeed, such a liquid may even displace a liquid of lower heat of wetting from the surface. Of a solution containing several dissolved components, the component with the greater heat of wetting is adsorbed in greater quantity.

The measured (apparent) angle of contact ϑ is often different at different points of a solid, largely owing to the microscopic unevennesses of the surface. Figure 2.26 reveals how different apparent contact angles ϑ' may come to be measured on an uneven surface, even though the true contact angle ϑ is the same everywhere. Even on an entirely smooth surface, however, the contact angle may be different between the two sides of a drop of water or an air bubble, if the drop or bubble is moving or the contact surface is out of horizontal. In such cases, the greater of the two angles measured is the true contact angle. The drop shown in Fig. 2.27 adheres to a surface of inclination α and has cross sectional area F. The equilibrium of the forces acting on a layer of liquid of thickness dl and density γ g/cm³ $= g\gamma$ dynes per cm³ can be written up as

$$a_{wa}\,dl\,\cos\vartheta' = a_{wa}\,dl\,\cos\vartheta + F\,dl\,g\gamma\,\sin\alpha\,,$$

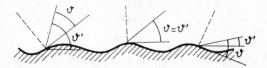

Fig. 2.26. How the hysteresis of the contact angle may be due to microscopic unevennesses of the surface

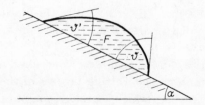

Fig. 2.27. Contact-angle hysteresis on a sloping surface

164

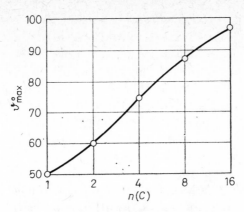

Fig. 2.28. Maximum contact angle attainable with n-alkyl thiols (1C to 16C) on sulphide minerals

that is,

$$\cos \vartheta' = \cos \vartheta + \frac{\gamma g}{a_{wa}} F \sin \alpha .$$

Hence, the deviation in contact angles,

$$\Delta \vartheta = \vartheta - \vartheta',$$

(also called a "hysteresis") is a function also of the size of the drop (through F) as well as of the inclination α (Gaudin 1957).

Comparatively few mineral surfaces possess a native floatabllity (a contact angle $\vartheta > 0$): most minerals are hydrophilic with zero contact angle. These can be endowed with hydrophobia (with a non-zero contact angle, that is, with floatability) by bringing them into contact with a suitable collector reagent (a heteropolar hydrocarbon electrolyte) whose ions are adsorbed in a preferred orientation by the mineral surface (with the hydrocarbon radical on the ion pointing into the liquid phase). The contact angle of the mineral increases as more and more of the collector ion is adsorbed (as u increases); the maximum angle is attained when the entire surface is coated with a monoionic film.

The maximum contact angle that can be attained using a thiol collector depends neither on the nature of the mineral nor on the nature of the collector's polar radical: it depends exclusively on the nature of the hydrocarbon group. For example, the maximum contact angles that can be attained with thiols attached to n-alkyl radicals C_nH_{2n+1} is plotted vs. n (with an error of ± 1 to $2°$) in Fig. 2.28 (Wark 1955). It shows the maximum contact angle to be about $50°$ for the methyl radical, $60°$ for the ethyl, $75°$ for the butyl and $97°$ for the cetyl radical, regardless of the sulphide mineral (galena, sphalerite, pyrite, etc.) or the thiol radical (mono-, di- or trithiocarbonate, mono- or dithiocarbamate, dithiophosphate, mercaptan, etc.) involved.

165

The maximum contact angles achieved by the adsorption of carboxyl soaps and alkyl sulphates also increase as the length of the hydrocarbon chain increases. Part A of Fig. 2.29, e.g., shows the maximum contact angle, ϑ_{max} in the water phase, at oil/water and air/water interfaces, at pH = 12 and 20 °C, on the adsorption of sodium carboxyl soaps and alkyl sulphates different as to chain length (C number). ϑ increases as the temperature increases. Part B of the figure is a plot vs. the pH of the contact angles of barite coated with films of sodium oleate (18C), sodium laurate (12C) and sodium dodecyl sulphate (12C), at oil/water and air/water interfaces.

Figure 2.30 shows the variation of the contact angle of haematite adsorbing dodecyl amine. Part A is a plot of ϑ vs. dodecyl amine concentration c for various pH's; Part B is a plot of ϑ vs. the pH for various values of c. The steeper increase of ϑ at the higher values of c in Part A is due to the micella-like adsorption of the reagent. The maximum contact angle that can be achieved with amines on haematite is about 83°; it is independent of the molecular weight of the reagent (of the length of its hydrocarbon chain), revealing a mechanism of adsorption different from that of the anionic reagents. The dashed curves in Part B of the figure indicate haematite recoveries m% achieved at different concentrations of dodecyl amine.

The contact angle of sylvite (KCl) at a dodecyl amine concentration $c = 5 \cdot 10^{-3}$ mole per litre is 55°; up to that limit, it varies according to the formula

$$\vartheta^0 \simeq 84 + 12 \log c,$$

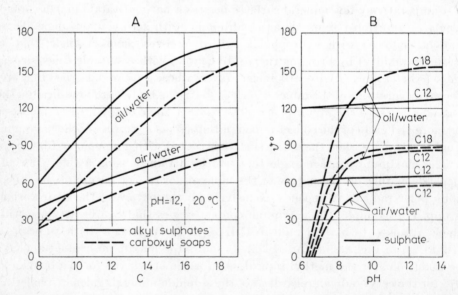

Fig. 2.29. Maximum contact angle attainable with A — alkyl sulphates and carboxyl soaps on barite, B — contact angle of barite coated with different reagent films vs. the pH

166

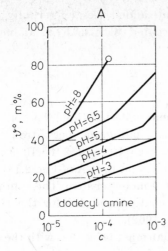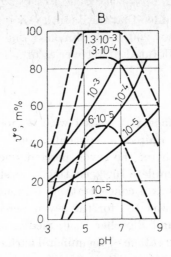

Fig. 2.30. Maximum contact angle attainable with dodecyl amine on haematite, vs. *A* — concentration, *B* — the pH

being e.g. 36° at $c = 10^{-4}$ and 12° at $c = 10^{-6}$. At higher concentrations, it decreases abruptly (e.g., it is 20° at $c = 5 \cdot 10^{-2}$ and 0° at $c = 10^{-1}$), presumably as a result of the formation of a second film of collector, opposite in polarity to the first. The contact angle of sylvite coated with amines (ammonium acetates) of different chain length at a concentration of 10^{-4} mole per litre is stated by the formula

$$\vartheta^0 \simeq 3.2n,$$

where n is the carbon number of the chain. For example,

$\vartheta = 58°$	38°	25°
if $n = 18$	12	8

(Fuerstenau and Fuerstenau 1956).

In flotation practice, the adsorption of the collector does not produce anything like a full monoionic coating: isolated patches unevenly scattered on the mineral surface, get coated with reagent; they are separated by uncoated domains. For example, chalcocite can be flotated out fairly thoroughly using only 10 to 15% of the quantity of butyl or amyl xanthate required for a complete monoionic coating. Galena recovery was found to vary with the dosage of ethyl xanthate, expressed in percent of the theoretical quantity required to form complete monoionic coatings, as follows

ethyl xanthate concentration	25	50	75%;
galena recovery	21	82	96%.

Let it be added that the quantity of xanthate added does not get fully adsorbed even. Minus-200 mesh slimeless quartz coated with dodecyl amine acetate could be flotated at recoveries of

	25	54	92	99%
when only	1	2	4	7%

of its surface was coated with a monoionic collector film! The one percent coating required a concentration of 0.15 milligram per litre $= 5 \cdot 10^{-7}$ mole per litre: the seven percent one required 10 mg/l $= 4 \cdot 10^{-5}$ mole per litre. A complete 100% coating — as shown e.g. in Part A of Fig. 2.18 — would be formed at a concentration of about 10^{-3} mole per litre. The contact angle achieved was 15° for the seven percent coating and 45° for the 100% one (Gaudin and Bloecher 1950; Siedler et al. 1962).

The percentage of the mineral surface that must be coated with the collector to enable a fair flotation performance is a function of particle size also. For example, floating sylvite (KCl) with hexadecyl ammonium chloride, particle sizes

	100	150	200	250 μm

could be flotated out at recoveries

$m =$	100	98	82	50%

with a 10% coating and at recoveries

$m =$	100	100	88	70%

with a 15% coating. The 250 to 200 μm particle size fraction at coating percentages of

	10	20	30	40%

gave flotation recoveries of

$m =$	50	81	93	98%

with hexadecyl ammonium chloride and

$m =$	20	62	86	93%

with dodecyl ammonium chloride.

Attaining full equilibrium of adsorption takes more or less time: the ions pass from the solution to the interface by diffusion through the liquid films adhering to the particles. Attaining the equilibrium contact angle takes more time if the concentration of collector ions is lower: the time can, however, be reduced substantially by agitating the pulp.

Overdosage of collector may entail a reduction of the contact angle (possibly down to zero). This tends to be the case especially with long-chain compounds

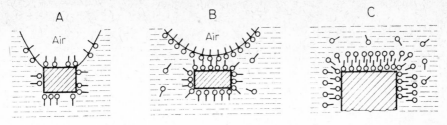

Fig. 2.31. An excessive collector concentration (*B* and *C*) may prevent mineral-to-bubble adherence (as shown in *A*)

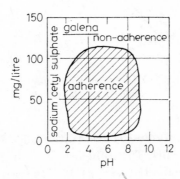

Fig. 2.32. Domain of adherence of galena in the space of sodium cetyl sulphate concentration and the pH

such as alkyl sulphates or alkyl amine salts. The phenomenon may be due to one or both of two causes: (1) the air bubbles also adsorb a great deal of collector, acquiring a rigid armour that prevents the attachment of reagent-coated mineral particles to them; (2) instead of a monoionic film, a double film is formed on the particle, with the polar radical of the outer layer facing the liquid phase and rendering the surface hydrophilic. These conditions are illustrated in Parts B and C of Fig. 2.31, whereas the normal attachment of bubble to mineral is shown in Part A (Bartell and Shepard 1953). Figure 2.32 shows the domain of attachment between bubbles and particles of galena treated with sodium hexadecyl sulphate. Above a collector concentration of about 120 mg/l, the double layers adsorbed turn the mineral particles hydrophilic, despite a pronounced hydrophobia at lower concentrations (Wark 1955).

Galena is endowed with a contact angle of about 83° by a monoionic amyl xanthate film and of about 63° by a monoionic hexadecyl sulphate film. Galena first treated with amyl xanthate and then immersed in a 200 mg/l solution of hexadecyl sulphate exhibits a zero contact angle. Taken out of the solution and washed off, it recovers its contact angle of about 83° against distilled water; that is, the hexadecyl sulphate has not displaced the amyl xanthate film (Rogers 1962).

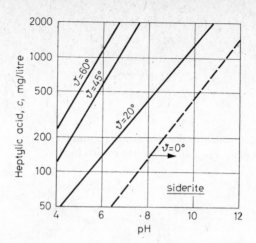

Fig. 2.33. Heptylic acid ($C_6H_{13}COOH$) concentration required to create different contact angles ϑ vs. the pH

In addition to the nature and concentration of the collector, the contact angle depends also on the pH. The influence of the pH is especially strong on those minerals which have the H^+ and/or OH^- ion for potential determinant(s). An increasing OH^- concentration hinders the adsorption of anionic collectors; an increasing H^+ concentration hinders the adsorption of cationic ones, the reason being that ions of identical charge will compete for positions at the mineral surface and, despite their comparatively greater affinity, the collector anions will be displaced from the surface by the OH^- (or H^+) ions if the concentration of these latter is sufficiently high. Figure 2.33 shows for an example the concentration c mg/l of heptylic acid required to endow siderite with different contact angles ϑ vs. the pH (the maximum contact angle ϑ_{max}, being $62°$).

2.1.3. Work of adhesion. When a bubble and a mineral particle in the liquid make contact, the nature of the interface is changed at both surfaces of contact: part of the old liquid–air (*la*) and solid–liquid (*sl*) interface is replaced by a solid–air (*sa*) interface. By the law of least free energy, attachment will take place if the surface energy $E_{la} + E_{sl}$ (ergs per cm²) of the initial state exceeds E_{sa}, the surface energy of the final state, that is, if the work of adhesion

$$A = E_{la} + E_{sl} - E_{sa}$$

is greater than zero. In fact, the greater A, the greater the propensity of the bubbles and grains to stick together, and the less can their attachment be prevented by the other forces present (such as electric repulsion by zeta potentials of identical sign between bubble and grain).

170

Numerically, surface energy (E ergs per cm²) equals surface tension (a dynes per cm): that is,

$$E_{sa} = E_{sl} + E_{la} \cos \vartheta.$$

Substitution gives

$$A = E_{la}(1 - \cos \vartheta).$$

At $\vartheta = 0$, $\cos \vartheta = 1$, and A becomes zero. The work of adhesion is great if $E_{la} (= a_{la})$ is great and ϑ is great. For example, given $a_{la} = 70$ dynes per cm,

$$A = \quad 9.45 \qquad\qquad 30 \qquad\qquad 70 \qquad\qquad 82.4 \text{ erg/cm}^2$$

if

$$\vartheta = 30 \qquad\qquad 60 \qquad\qquad 90 \qquad\qquad 110°.$$

If $\vartheta < 90$, then ϑ decreases as a_{la} decreases: that is, both factors of A decrease. This is why the radical lowering of the surface tension of water is to be avoided in flotation.

A similar consideration yields the work-of-adhesion condition

$$A_a = E_{sa} + E_{la} - E_{sl} = E_{la}(1 + \cos \vartheta) > 0$$

for the attachment of dust particles to water droplets suspended in air. (A_a is invariably greater than zero.) Tearing in two a water column of 1 cm² cross section (giving rise to 2 cm² of new surface) requires a work input

$$K = 2E_{la}$$

to overcome cohesion: that is,

$$\frac{A_a}{K} = \frac{1 + \cos \vartheta}{2}.$$

At $\vartheta = 0$, $A_a = K$; at $\vartheta = 90°$, $A_a = K/2$. A_a would equal zero if ϑ were 180°: that, however, is impossible since the molecular attraction giving rise to adhesion between the solid and the liquid phase cannot be cut out entirely. The maximum contact angle of any solid in pure water is 110° or so.

2.1.4. Force of adhesion. The resultant vector of the surface tensions holding bubble and particle together, of magnitude $a_{la} \sin \vartheta$ dynes per cm, is perpendicular to the solid surface. If the length of the three-phase boundary is L and the resultant vector includes an angle ω with the vertical, then the vertical component of the force of adhesion attaching the particle to the bubble is

$$L a_{la} \sin \vartheta \cos \omega \quad \text{dynes}.$$

It is opposed by the weight, measured in water, of the particle of volume V cm³ and s.g. δ:

$$V(\delta - \gamma)g \quad \text{dynes}.$$

On attachment, the replacement of the solid–liquid and liquid–air interfaces by a solid–air interface reduces the free energy of the system; as a result, the solid–air interface expands spontaneously and immediately to the greatest possible extent. In the case of small particles in contact with a large bubble, the three-phase boundary will coincide with the edges defining that face of the particle which is in contact with the bubble. The particle itself is immersed

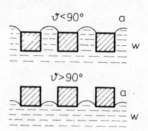

Fig. 2.34. A particle attached to a gas bubble remains in the water phase or passes into the gas phase, depending on the magnitude of its angle of contact

either entirely in the liquid or entirely in the air phase, depending on its angle of contact, as shown in Fig. 2.34 (Gaudin 1957). If the angle included by two faces of a particle is α, then the angle included by the normals to them (the change of the resultant tension vector) is $180° - \alpha$. The attitude of the tension vector a_{la} at the edge — and the angle ω of the resultant vector $a_{la} \sin \vartheta$ — is determined by the equation

$$La_{la} \sin \vartheta \cos \omega = V(\delta - \gamma)g \,.$$

The expression
$$\frac{V}{L} = \frac{a_{la} \sin \vartheta \cos \omega}{(\delta - \gamma)g}$$

is a maximum at $\cos \omega = 1$. The condition provides upper size limits for particles of different shape that can attach themselves to a bubble. For a cube, e.g. ($V = x^3$, $L = 4x$) or for a cylinder whose height equals its diameter ($V = x^3\pi/4$, $L = x\pi$), we have

$$V/L = x^2/4;$$

the maximum floatable particle size is

$$x_{\text{max}} = \sqrt{\frac{4a_{la} \sin \vartheta}{(\delta - \gamma)g}}$$

and the least contact angle ϑ_{min} required to float out a particle of size x is furnished by

$$\sin \vartheta_{\text{min}} = \frac{(\delta - \gamma)gx^2}{4a_{la}}$$

(Tarján 1947).

If surface tension is to keep the bubble and the particle together in the face of a detaching force n times the force of gravity, e.g. in the space exposed to centrifugal action about the impeller of a flotation cell, or in a collision, then g in the above formulae is to be replaced by ng. Figure 2.35 is a plot of the least contact angle ϑ_{min} required for the adherence of cubes of different s.g. δ vs. particle size x (at $a_{la} = 70$ dynes per cm and $\gamma = 1$). For $\delta = 7.5$, graphs are given also for 10 and 100 times the force of gravity (Gaudin 1957).

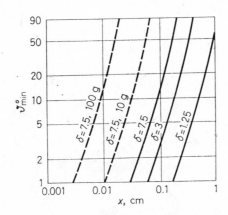

Fig. 2.35. Minimum angle of contact required for the adherence of cubes of different s.g. δ, vs. cube size x

In a flaky or acicular particle, L is comparatively great relative to V: even largish particles of such shape are fairly easy to flotate.

If $\vartheta > 90°$, then the particles pass from the water into the air phase, and the buoyancy reducing their weight disappears. In that case, $(\delta - \gamma)$ is to be replaced by δ in the formulae.

When a particle adheres to ("floats on") the free surface of the liquid rather than attaching itself to a bubble in its interior, it depresses the liquid surface somewhat. The volume of water displaced by the particle is thus greater than the volume of the particle proper: the particles that can be made to float in this way are therefore larger than those which can remain attached to bubbles in the liquid. (A needle or a safety-razor blade will float on water if it is greasy enough to possess a non-zero angle of contact.)

The adhesive force attaching a bubble of volume V to a largish (horizontal) mineral-grain surface with a three-phase boundary circle of radius r and a contact angle ϑ is

$$2\pi r a_{la} \sin \vartheta \quad \text{dynes} ;$$

the force acting on the bubble is

$$V \gamma g \quad \text{dynes} .$$

173

The bubble is detached from the grain if the buoyant force exceeds the adhesive force. The condition of attachment, then, is

$$V \leq \frac{2\pi a_{la} r \sin \vartheta}{\gamma g} \, .$$

If the shape of the bubble is a sphere of radius R flattened on one side, then

$$r = R \sin \vartheta$$

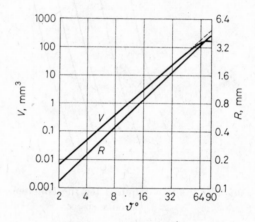

Fig. 2.36. Radius R and volume V of the largest bubble still adhering to a mineral surface, vs. the contact angle

and

$$V \leq R^3 \pi \left[\frac{4}{3} - (1 - \cos \vartheta)^2 \left(1 - \frac{1 - \cos \vartheta}{3} \right) \right] =$$

$$= 4R^3 \frac{\pi}{3} \left[1 - \sin^4 \left(\frac{\vartheta}{2} \right) \left(3 - 2 \sin^2 \left(\frac{\vartheta}{2} \right) \right) \right],$$

implying

$$R^2 \leq 3a_{la} \frac{\sin^2 \vartheta}{2\gamma g} \left[1 - \sin^4 \left(\frac{\vartheta}{2} \right) \left(3 - 2 \sin^2 \left(\frac{\vartheta}{2} \right) \right) \right].$$

For example, given $a_{la} = 70$ dynes per cm and $\gamma = 1$,

$$R \leq \frac{3.27 \sin \vartheta}{\sqrt{1 - \sin^4 \left(\frac{\vartheta}{2} \right) \left(3 - 2 \sin^2 \left(\frac{\vartheta}{2} \right) \right)}} \quad \text{mm} \, .$$

174

Figure 2.36 is a plot of $R_{\max}$ and $V_{\max}$ vs. ϑ. In the log-log net of the figure, both $R_{\max} = f(\vartheta)$ and $V_{\max} = f(\vartheta)$ give straight lines up to about $\vartheta = 50°$; their approximate equations are

$$R_{\max} \cong \frac{\vartheta^{0.825}}{15.5} \quad \text{mm}$$

and

$$V_{\max} \cong \frac{\vartheta^{2.964}}{1,240} \quad \text{mm}^3.$$

2.2. THE REAGENTS OF FLOTATION

Flotation uses organic reagents for frothing agents (frothers) and collecting agents (collectors) and mostly inorganic ones for various modifiers.

The role of a frother is to keep fine air bubbles dispersed (to prevent their coalescence into larger bubbles) and to stabilize the bubbles that have reached the surface (to permit them to constitute a stable froth for more or less time, in order that the hydrophobic particles of the pulp — those endowed with a contact angle — might collect in it).

The role of a collector is to turn hydrophilic minerals (minerals of zero contact angle) hydrophobic, or to increase the contact angles of minerals whose native contact angles are too small, in order to endow them with a propensity to attach themselves to the bubbles.

The role of modifiers is to improve the conditions of separation of the minerals to be separated as far as is feasible, by
— increasing the hydrophilia of the minerals to be kept out of the froth and thus decreasing their floatability (depressing agents or depressants),
— rendering suitable for the adsorption of collectors (and hence, rendering floatable) minerals of insufficient floatability or minerals whose floatability has previously been removed by a depressant (activating agents, activators),
— precipitating harmful ions out of the pulp,
— removing slime films from the minerals to be floated out,
— adjusting the pH of the pulp, etc.

Some reagents can fulfil more than just one role: for example, an agent depressing one mineral may activate another. The actual action of a reagent is a sensitive function of its concentration.

2.2.1. Frothers. Surface tension strives to reduce free surfaces. A droplet of water falling in air or a bubble of air rising in water is basically spherical because the sphere has the least surface area of all the solids of a given volume.

175

Two bubbles making contact coalesce into a larger bubble, the surface of which is smaller than those of the two original bubbles combined. Bubbles rising to the surface of pure water will burst (i.e. "coalesce with the atmosphere"); they can form no stable froth, because the aggregate surface of the bubbles constituting the froth would be greater than the smooth surface of the water. It is difficult to produce thin films of pure liquids, in the face of the contraction caused by surface tension. Heteropolar organic substances adsorbed in a preferred orientation at the water–air interface, on the other hand, tend to reduce the surface tension of water and thus to stabilize liquid films (or a froth made up of such).

The polar part of a heteropolar molecule is water-avid, whereas its non-polar (hydrocarbon) part is water-repellent (not wetted by water). Such molecules adsorbed at a water–air interface accordingly face the water with their polar ends and the air with their non-polar ones. If a liquid film carrying such a heteropolar surfactant is stretched by some external force, the abundance (concentration) of surfactant molecules decreases at the film surface, increasing thereby the surface tension of the surfactant solution and hence also the force that strives to make the film shrink back to its original size. Conversely, if the external influence strives to make the film shrink, surfactant concentration increases and surface tension decreases. The change in surface tension thus works toward the restoration of the original state of equilibrium in any case, opposing the external force regardless of whether it strives to expand or contract the film. This is why stable froths can exist on top of a surfactant solution, and this is why the bubbles in the interior of the solution do not coalesce into larger bubbles.

The mechanism of action can be explained also by the following argument: if the film is thinned out and its surface expanded at a point by an external force, the temporary reduction in the surface concentration of frother molecules results in a local increase of surface tension, attracting more liquid (solvent) from the neighbourhood, and conversely.

Frothing intensity at first increases as more and more frother is added: beyond a critical concentration, however, it starts to decline and in fact attains zero when the solution is saturated with the surfactant. The froth is the more stable, the longer it takes for an equilibrium surface tension to establish itself at freshly formed film surfaces.

In flotation, no very stable froth is needed. Reducing the surface tension of water reduces the angle of contact and hence also the floatability of minerals: $\cos \vartheta$ increases (ϑ decreases) as a_{la} decreases (provided $\vartheta < 90°$). This is why it is usual in flotation practice to add very small doses of frother and to avoid surfactants that reduce the surface tension of water even in minute quantities. Such substances (e.g. soaps, sulphonated or sulphated detergents, saponine, etc.) form stable but sterile froth which have no mineral particles attached to

176

them. Frothers that reduce but slightly the surface tension of water (and hence the angle of contact, the work and the force of adhesion) are non-selective: their froth collects many minerals, including some with comparatively small angles of contact. Frothers that reduce the surface tension of water to a relatively greater degree are selective: their bubbles will pick up mineral grains with wide angles of contact only.

The most widely used frothers are heteropolar hydrocarbons moderately soluble in water (0.2 to 0.5 gram per litre) whose single polar radical has an affinity to water. These compounds are non-electrolytic as a rule. The most frequent polar radical is OH^- (phenol derivatives, terpene alcohols, higher alcohols). Non-electrolytic hydrocarbon compounds carrying one of the polar radicals —CO (ketones, aldehydes), —COO (esters), —COC (ethers), —NH_2 (amines) also find use as frothers. Electrolytes (e.g. compounds carrying the carboxyl radical —COOH) are less suitable frothers in flotation practice, partly because their ions have a collector property also and partly because their solubility (and hence their frothing propensity) is markedly pH-dependent.

In homologous series of compounds [e.g. phenol, C_6H_5OH; cresol, $C_6H_4CH_3OH$; xylenol, $C_6H_3(CH_3)_2OH$ (or $C_6H_4 \cdot C_2H_5OH$); aniline, $C_6H_5NH_2$; toluidine, $C_6H_4CH_3NH$; xylidine, $C_6H_3(CH_3)_2NH$; or methyl alcohol, CH_3OH; ethyl alcohol, C_2H_5OH; propyl alcohol, C_3H_7OH; butyl alcohol, C_4H_9OH; amyl alcohol, $C_5H_{11}OH$, etc.], solubiliby decreases and surface activity increases as the size of the hydrocarbon group increases. For example, the higher alcohols (such as amyl alcohol) are good frothers; the lower ones (such as ethyl alcohol), on the other hand, give no froth because they are too soluble in water. Ready solubility betrays a great affinity of the molecules to water: hence, readily soluble compounds are not enriched to any significant degree at the water–air interface. The hydrophobia of the short ethyl group cannot offset the marked hydrophilia of the OH radical (whereas that of the longer amyl group can). Above carbon numbers of 7 or 8, on the other hand, the frothing effect of alcohols gradually decreases as a result of poor solubility.

One widely used selective frother is cresylic acid, a distillation product of coal tar. Raw cresol, a mixture of meta-, para- and ortho-cresol, $CH_3C_6H_4OH$, invariably contains also some other products of coal-tar distillation, xylenols above all:

Ortho-cresol:

Meta-cresol:

Para-cresol:

The most frequently used non-selective frother is pine oil, extracted from turpentine or won by steam distillation or solvent extraction out of the twigs, branches and stumps of certain conifers. It is a mixture of various terpene hydrocarbons such as pinene, $C_{10}H_{16}$, camphor, $C_{10}H_{18}$, terpene, $C_{10}H_{20}$, hydroaromatic ketones (e.g. kineol, $C_{10}H_{18}O$), terpene alcohols (α- and β-terpineol, borneol, fenchyl alcohol, $C_{10}H_{17}OH$), etc. The alcoholic constituents of composition $C_{10}H_{17}O$ are the most important frother factors in pine oil. Their structural formulae are:

α-terpineol   fenchyl alcohol   borneol

Instead of these reagents of non-standard composition (cresylic acid, pine oil, etc.), standardized synthetic alcohol products (with a carbon number of 6 to 8) have come to be preferred more recently, and so have certain proprietary makes of frothers trade-named flotol, sapinol, etc. Using these, a froth of the desired texture can be produced more consistently. Eucalyptus oil, camphor oil, certain aromatic amines, amyl alcohol, methyl isobutyl carbinol (MIBC), etc., are nowadays being used only locally as frothers. Some of the more recent frothers are fairly soluble in water, e.g. alkyl and alkoxy esters of dicarbon acids, in which the COOH radicals are separated by chains of three or more carbon atoms:

$$ROOC(CH_2)_nCOOR',$$

or polypropylene glycols:

$$HOCH_2(CH \cdot CH_3O \cdot CH_2)_nCH \cdot CH_3OH$$

produced by reacting propylene oxide

$$CH_3-CH-CH_2$$
$$\diagdown \; O \; \diagup$$

with propylene glycol,

$$CH_3-CH-CH_2$$
$$| \qquad |$$
$$OH \quad OH$$

(Dowfroth 200 and 250, Aerofroth 65, Aerosol OT, etc.).

Figure 2.37 presents diagrams of surface tension a in aqueous solution vs. concentration, moles per litre, for normal monovalent aliphatic alcohols ($C_nH_{2n+1}OH$) (Part A) and pine oil and its most important alcoholic constituents (Part B) (Schubert 1964). Cf. also Fig. 2.5.

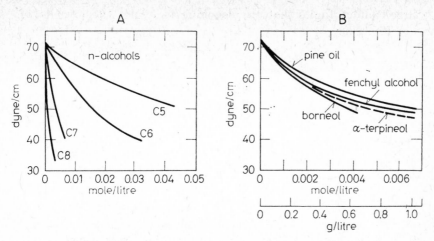

Fig. 2.37. Decrease of surface tension vs. concentration, mole/litre, of *A* — alcohols, *B* — pine oil and its components

Some electrolytes used as collectors, such as long-chain carboxylates (fatty acids, soaps), alkyl sulphates, sulphonates and amines possess a frothing property also.

Usual dosages of some frothers in grams per tonne are 35 (5 to 120) for pine oil, 45 (5 to 180) for cresylic acid and 35 (3 to 120) for methyl isobutyl carbinol.

2.2.2. Collectors. It is the role of collectors to endow the minerals to be floated out with contact angles that are large enough for the purpose. Native floatability is confined to minerals whose surfaces are non-ionic, such as solid hydrocarbons. On being given a hydrocarbon coating all over their surfaces (or indeed in patches only), the mineral particles to be floated out acquire a non-zero contact angle so that they can attach themselves to the air bubbles in their vicinity. Collectors are heteropolar hydrocarbons whose polar radical has an affinity to the mineral to be flotated out. Organic (heteropolar) acids, bases or salts sufficiently soluble in water, i.e. electrolytes whose ions attach themselves selectively with their polar radicals to the surfaces of certain minerals, are generally used for the purpose.

2.2.2.1. Non-ionic or non-polar collectors (kerosene, diesel fuel, coal and wood tar, creosotes, etc.) are also used exceptionally. The molecules of these, however, are in fact also ionized to some extent by tautomerism, hydrolysis or some other process. Oils non-polar in their entire bulk spread out to form thin or even thickish films on "oleophilic" surfaces. It is the hydrophobic minerals with large contact angles that are oleophilic as a rule. As shown by the diagrams of Fig. 2.38,

$$a_{sa} - a_{sw} = a_{wa} \cos \vartheta,$$

$$a_{so} - a_{sw} = a_{wo} \cos \varepsilon,$$

$$a_{oa} - a_{ow} = a_{wa} \cos \Theta.$$

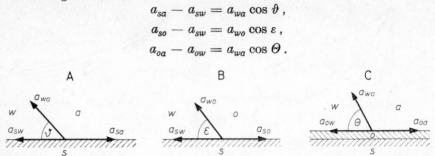

Fig. 2.38. How the boundary angle in the water phase and the positions of the phase boundaries are determined by surface tensions A — at the solid–water–air, B — at the solid–water–oil, C — at the oil–water–air three-phase boundary

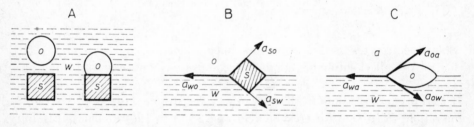

Fig. 2.39. A — attachment of solid particles to oil droplets in water; B and C — vector diagrams of surface tensions for B — a solid particle at an oil–water interface, C — a droplet of oil at an air–water interface

The subscript a (air) in Part A of Fig. 2.38 is replaced by o (oil) in Part B. If a_{sw} is great, then so are both ϑ and ε: hence, any aerophilic (hydrophobic) mineral is oleophilic also. (A mineral is aerophilic if its ϑ is large, and oleophilic if its ε is large.) If $\varepsilon = 0$ (that is, if $a_{so} - a_{sw} > a_{wo}$), then the mineral does not get attached to the oil (it remains in the water phase); if $\varepsilon = 180°$ (that is, $a_{sw} - a_{wo} > a_{so}$), the oil (Part C of Fig. 2.38) spreads out on the mineral and coats it all over: that is, the mineral is transferred into the oil phase. The mineral particle gets attached to the oil droplets in the water (Part A of Fig. 2.39) if the work of adhesion

$$A = a_{wo} + a_{sw} - a_{so} = a_{wo}(1 - \cos \varepsilon)$$

is positive:

$$A > 0 \quad \text{if} \quad \varepsilon > 0, \quad \text{i.e.} \quad a_{so} - a_{sw} < a_{wo}.$$

The solid particles get attached to the interfaces that the water forms with larger drops or bodies of oil if

$$a_{wo} > a_{so} + a_{sw}$$

Table 2.14. Interface tensions of some pure liquids

	a_{oa}	a_{ow}	$a_{oa} - a_{ow}$	$a_{oa} + a_{ow}$	S
Acetylene tetrabromide	49.7	38.8	10.9	88.5	$+15.7$
Nitrobenzene	43.4	25.7	17.7	69.1	-3.7
Oleic acid	32.5	15.6	16.9	48.1	-24.7
Olive oil	35.8	22.9	12.9	58.7	-14.1
Carbon disulphide	31.4	48.4	-17.0	79.8	$+7.0$
Benzene	28.9	35.1	-6.2	64.0	-8.8
Toluene	28.4	36.1	-7.7	64.5	-8.3
n-octyl alcohol	27.5	8.5	19.0	36.0	-36.8
Chloroform	27.1	32.8	-5.7	59.9	-12.9
Carbon tetrachloride	26.7	45.0	18.3	71.7	-1.1
n-octane	21.8	50.8	-29.0	72.6	-0.2
n-hexane	18.4	51.1	-32.7	69.5	-3.3
Ethyl ether	17.1	10.7	6.4	27.8	-45.0

(Part B of Fig. 2.39). Minerals with a small angle of contact do not get smeared with the oil, which prefers to remain emulsified, forming small droplets dispersed in the water (since the free energy of the system is less in that case). If the oil coats the mineral surface, the contact angle Θ of the latter is greatly increased thereby as, in that case, the air–water interface forms a three-phase boundary with the oil rather than with the mineral (cf. Part C of Fig. 2.38). However,

$$a_{oa} - a_{ow} = a_{wa} \cos \Theta$$

is often negative, making $\Theta > 90°$.

Table 2.14 lists interface tensions a_{oa} and a_{ow}, their differences $a_{oa} - a_{ow}$, their sums $a_{oa} + a_{ow}$ and the parameter

$$S = a_{oa} + a_{ow} - a_{wa}$$

for some pure liquids at 20 °C (where $a_{wa} = 72.8$ dynes per cm). With S positive, either the liquid hydrocarbon forms lenticular drops floating on the water, or the other way round; with S negative, one of the two liquids spreads out on the other. The propensity to spread out is the greater, the greater the magnitude of (the negative) S. The table shows that hydrocarbons incorporating polar groups (such as oleic acid, octyl alcohol, ethyl ether) have a much greater propensity to spread out on water than the non-polar compounds.

The non-polar oleaginous hydrocarbons coat all hydrophobic minerals equally: that is, they are non-selective collectors. Well-emulsified non-polar collector oils are used even in today's practice to flotate coals or other minerals of a fair native floatability. Occasionally, small doses of a non-polar oil are added to ionic collectors also, in order to produce a tougher and more stable froth.

2.2.2.2. Ionic (true or chemical) **collectors** are anionic or cationic, depending on the polarity of their hydrocarbon group.

(A) In most widespread use are the anionic collectors in which the hydrocarbon group is part of the anion. This group, then, is the collector in the strict sense. The cation is the hydrogen of the organic acid (or the metal replacing it in a salt). In the undissociated molecule, the metal or the hydrogen that becomes the cation is attached to an oxygen or a sulphur atom: on this basis, oxyhydryl and sulphydryl (thiol) compounds can be distinguished. The first group includes the carboxylates, alkyl sulphates and sulphonates: the second includes the mercaptans, thiocarboxylates, thiocarbonates (xanthates), thioureas, thiocarbamates and thiophosphates.

The anions of these compounds have the structural formulae shown below. In the diagrams, the hydrocarbon group attached to the polar radical is denoted by R (or by R' if there is a second one as well). R' may be replaced by another R or by H. An O marked by an asterisk can be replaced by an S and vice versa.

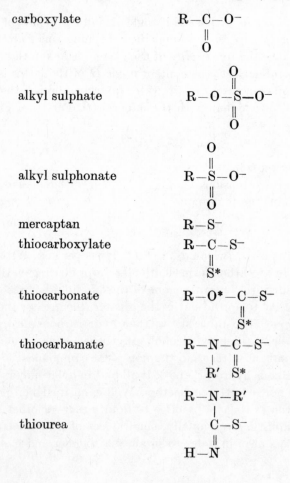

carboxylate

alkyl sulphate

alkyl sulphonate

mercaptan

thiocarboxylate

thiocarbonate

thiocarbamate

thiourea

$$\begin{array}{c} \text{R}-\text{O} \\ \diagdown \\ \text{P}-\text{S}- \\ \diagup \diagdown \\ \text{R}'-\text{O} \quad \text{S*} \end{array}$$

Of the great family of compounds containing the $-\text{COO}-$ (carboxyl) radical, the fatty acids containing alkyl chains and their alkali salts, the soaps, are the most important.

The saturated fatty acids contain no double bond: the general formula of their hydrocarbon chain is $\text{R} = \text{C}_n\text{H}_{2n+1}$. Some unsaturated fatty acids contain one, two or more double bonds: these are termed olefinic or mono-unsaturated ($\text{C}_n\text{H}_{2n-1}$), diolefinic or di-unsaturated ($\text{C}_n\text{H}_{2n-3}$), triolefinic or tri-unsaturated ($\text{C}_n\text{H}_{2n-5}$), etc. Others contain one or several triple bonds (acetylenic fatty acids). The most common representatives of the saturated acids include lauric acid, $\text{C}_{11}\text{H}_{23}\text{COOH}$; myristic acid, $\text{C}_{13}\text{H}_{27}\text{COOH}$, palmitic acid, $\text{C}_{15}\text{H}_{31}\text{COOH}$; stearic acid, $\text{C}_{17}\text{H}_{35}\text{COOH}$; oleic acid, $\text{C}_{17}\text{H}_{33}\text{COOH}$, is olefinic; linoleic acid, $\text{C}_{17}\text{H}_{31}\text{COOH}$, is diolefinic; linolenic acid, $\text{C}_{17}\text{H}_{29}\text{COOH}$, is triolefinic.

Other monocarboxyl compounds include naphthenic acids (in which the hydrocarbon chain is replaced by a complex cyclic hydrocarbon group, e.g. naphthoic acid, $\text{C}_{10}\text{H}_7\text{COOH}$) and resinic acids (in which the C atom of the carboxyl radical is attached to partly-hydrated (hydrogenated) cyclical hydrocarbons: e.g. abietic acid, $\text{C}_{19}\text{H}_{29}\text{COOH}$, principal ingredient of tall oil (talloel), a by-product of paper making, which contains some fatty acids as well, such as oleic acid, linolenic acid, stearic acid, palmitic acid, etc.).

Alkyl sulphates or sulphonates are formed on the treatment of unsaturated alcohols, fatty acids or the esters of those with sulphuric acid (H_2SO_4) or sulphurous acid (H_2SO_3). Typical representatives of the complex mixtures so produced are Turkey-red oil and sulphonated castor oil. The reagents of flotation include many proprietary products of such nature, e.g. Emulsol X-1 or Duponol D (higher alcohol sulphates with 8C to 12C chains) or Ultrawet (sulphonated kerosene with a chain length of 14C on average). The sodium salts of the higher alkyl sulphates (12C, 15C, etc.) find use as detergents also. The hydrocarbon group in these compounds may be an aryl or heterocyclic group as well as an alkyl group. There are many such compounds among the intermediate products of the dye industry. The attachment of dyes to textile fibres is a phenomenon analogous to the attachment of collectors to minerals.

Anionic oxyhydryl collectors are very widely used in flotation. A suitable selection of collector permits the more or less selective (differential) flotation of sulphides, of base metal oxides, alkali earth minerals, mineral salts and numerous silicates. Selectivity can be increased greatly by the addition of suitable modifying reagents.

Of the thiols used as collectors, the mercaptans are the simplest. Their $-SH$ radical is directly attached to the organic group R. Mercaptans are thioalcohols, with the O of the alcohols (ROH) replaced by S. Alcohols are non-electrolytic, and the higher ones are good frothers; mercaptans on the other hand are electrolytes, and the RS^- anion combined with base-metal cations (Hg, Cu, Pb, Ag, Ni, etc.) constitutes practically water-insoluble compounds (mercaptids): this is why it performs so well as a collector of the minerals of those cations.

In some other thiols, it is the O atom attached to the H in the carboxyl radical that is replaced by S. The other O atom may also be replaced by S or NH. The key atom of the carboxyl radical (the C) is attached to the adjacent C atom of the hydrocarbon group R either directly (in the thiocarboxyls) or by the intermediary of an O (or S) atom (in the thiocarbonates) or of a trivalent N atom (in the thiocarbamates and thioureas). In the thiophosphates, the key atom is a five-valent P.

Of the thiols that have C for a key atom, with a polar radical attached to it, the most important are the xanthates (sodium or potassium salts of dithiocarbonates based on an alkyl group, $R = C_nH_{2n+1}$). They can be "home-made" rather simply by letting carbon disulphide, CS_2, and caustic soda or potash (NaOH or KOH) react with an alcohol, ROH (e.g. methylated spirits). Xanthates are the collectors most widely used in the flotation of base-metal sulphides and oxidized lead and copper minerals. The xanthate anions constitute readily water-soluble compounds with the alkali-earth metals, moderately soluble ones with Fe, Mn and Zn and practically insoluble ones with the other base-metal cations (Cu, Pb, Ni). For example,

$$2X^- + Cu^{2+} \rightarrow CuX_2 .$$

The cupric xanthate can decompose into cuprous xanthate and dixanthogen:

$$2CuX_2 \rightarrow 2CuX + X_2 .$$

Oxidation of the xanthate ion also produces dixanthogen:

$$2X^- + H_2O + \tfrac{1}{2} O_2 \rightarrow 2X + 2OH^- .$$

Both the insoluble (non-ionic) base-metal xanthates and the dixanthogens have collector properties, but their performance lags behind that of the xanthate ions. The most frequently used xanthates are ethyl, butyl and amyl xanthate (2C, 4C and 5C, respectively).

The solubility of metal xanthates decreases as the carbon-atom number n of their alkyl radical increases. Table 2.14A presents for certain metals (M) the constants a and b of the relationship

$$pL_{MX_2} = a + bn ,$$

Table 2.14A. Solubility product exponents pL of metal xanthates

M:	Cu^{2+}	Pb^{2+}	Ni^{2+}	Zn^{2+}	Ag^+
a	22.2	14.7	10.5	6.0	17.5
b	1.15	0.97	1.02	1.11	0.55
$n = 2$ $\{c$	24.50	16.64	12.54	8.22	18.6
$\{m$	24.2	16.7	12.5	8.2	18.6
$n = 6$ $\{c$	29.10	20.52	16.62	12.66	20.8
$\{m$	29.0	20.3	16.5	?	20.8
$n = 9$ $\{c$	32.55	23.43	19.68	15.99	22.45
$\{m$	30.0	24.0	22.3	16.2	22.6
$n = 12$ $\{c$	36.80	26.34	22.74	19.32	24.1
$\{m$	37.0	26.3	23.0	19.5	23.8

making shift for the expression

$$pL_{MX_2} = pM^{2+} + 2\,pX^-$$

of the negative logarithm of the solubility product for bivalent metals (or for

$$pL_{MX} = pM^+ + pX^-$$

in the case of monovalent metals), which can be written up for straight-chain "normal" xanthates. The solubility of an isoxanthate tends to be somewhat greater (its pL somewhat less) than that of the corresponding straight-chain are.

The bottom four pairs of rows of Table 2.13C reveal a fair agreement between the measured pL_{MX_2} (marked m) and the one furnished by the formula (marked c for calculated) in the case of ethyl (2C), hexyl (6C), nonyl (9C) and dodecyl (12C) metal xanthates (Du Rietz 1975).

Xanthates are readily soluble in water: they are introduced as a 10 to 20% solution into a pulp that, as a rule, is made weakly alkaline beforehand.

Thiocarbonates can be derived from carbonic acid (H_2CO_3), thiocarbamates from ammonia (NH_3) plus carbonic acid anhydride (CO_2), thioureas from uric acid ($CO(NH_2)_2$), thiophosphates from phosphoric acid (H_3PO_4), by substituting one or several of their H atoms with an R or R' group and one or several of their O atoms with S atoms.

Carbamates are monothio or dithio compounds featuring a monoalkyl ($RNH-$), dialkyl (R_2N-), aryl or heterocyclic group. Monoalkyl dithiocarbamates are comparatively widespread as collectors replacing the xanthates. Of the thioureas, diphenyl thiourea, $CS(NH \cdot C_6H_5)_2$, under the trade name thiocarbanilid, was fairly widely used as a collector before the advent of the xanthates. It is slightly soluble in water but readily soluble in orthotoluidine ($CH_3 \cdot C_6H_4NH_2$): the solution (e.g. 15% thiocarbanilid dissolved in 85% orthotoluidine), called the "T–T mixture", is a frother also. A weak collector of pyrite, it is locally used to this day to flotate galena differentially in the presence of sphalerite and pyrite.

More widely used in flotation practice are dithiophosphates and dithiophosphoric acids under the trade name Aerofloat (or Phosocresol). For example, dicresyl dithiophosphoric acid $(CH_3C_6H_4O)_2PSSH$, is prepared from phosphorus pentasulphide (P_2S_5) and cresylic acid $(CH_3C_6H_4OH)$:

$$P_2S_5 + 4ROH \rightarrow 2HSSP(RO)_2 + H_2S.$$

The number that figures in the designations Aerofloat 15, 25, 31, etc., indicates the quantity of P_2S_5 that went into the making of the product. The liquid contains some free cresylic acid (which is a frother). It is most often introduced into a neutral pulp: it floats pyrite less readily than the xanthates do. In the dithiophosphoric acids or the alkali (e.g. sodium) salts of those, the R is sometimes an alkyl (e.g. diethyl) group rather than an aryl (e.g. cresol) group. The alkyl salts in question are highly water-soluble crystalline compounds with no frothing property.

(B) Cationic collectors. On the dissociation of these, the hydrocarbon group R of the organic compound remains attached to the cation. These are usually designated with a suffix "onium" (ammonium, sulphonium or phosphonium salts and bases), in which a polyvalent central atom (five-valent N or P, four-valent S) attached to the hydrocarbon (cation) group carries a halogen atom (Cl, Br, I . . .) or a hydroxyl radical (OH) that dissociates as an anion. For example,

$$RR_3'NA, \quad RR_2'SA, \quad RR_3'PA,$$

or

$$\langle\,\rangle\ NRA\ \text{(a pyridinium salt),}$$

where A denotes the anion. R′ may or may not be identical with R; it may be a H atom.

The most important cationic reagents are ammonium salts. The amines are the derivatives of ammonia (NH_3). Replacing one, two or all three of the hydrogens in ammonia by a hydrocarbon group R, a primary, secondary or tertiary amine is obtained, respectively. These constitute bases with water or salts with acids (e.g. HCl), just as ammonia does:

$$NH_3 + HOH \rightarrow NH_4OH;$$
$$RNH_2 + HOH \rightarrow RNH_3OH;$$
$$NH_3 + HCl \rightarrow NH_4Cl,$$
$$RNH_2 + HCl \rightarrow RNH_3Cl;$$
$$R_2NH + HCl \rightarrow R_2NH_2Cl;$$
$$R_3N + HCl \rightarrow R_3NHCl.$$

The salt constituted by a tertiary amine and an organic halide (R′Cl) is a tetrammonium salt:

$$R_3N + R'Cl \rightarrow R_3R'NCl.$$

Amines may be alkyl, aryl, or alkyl-aryl compounds, depending on whether the N atom is attached to open-chain or cyclic hydrocarbons or both. Short-chain amines are comparatively well soluble in water; long-chain ones do not dissolve readily. In the case of the latter, colloidal phenomena tend to come to the fore. In primary alkyl amines, e.g., colloidal behaviour arises at 8C and becomes marked at 12, 14 and 16C. The halogen salts of these compounds are much more soluble than the respective free amines or base anhydrydes. The dissociation (ionization) constant K of primary alkyl amines is in the 4 to $4.5 \cdot 10^{-4}$ range: at 25 °C,

$$8C : 4.5;$$
$$9C : 4.4;$$
$$12-13C : 4.3;$$
$$14C : 4.2;$$
$$15-16C : 4.1;$$
$$17-18C : 4.0 \cdot 10^{-4}.$$

The secondary amines are somewhat stronger bases (with a K on the order of 10^{-3}); the tertiary ones are somewhat weaker ($K = 5 \cdot 10^{-5}$). For ammonia, $R = 1.8 \cdot 10^{-5}$. Aryl amines are much weaker bases: K is on the order of 10^{-10} for primary aryl amines and even less for secondary aryl amines, so low in fact that these hardly constitute any stable salts at all. The dissociation constant of cetyl pyridinium bromide is $K = 3 \cdot 10^{-3}$.

Cationic reagents (amine salts) are useful in the flotation of silicates (talc, micas, sericite, kaolin, etc.), quartz, tungstates, molybdates, vanadates and arsenates above all.

2.2.2.3. Chemical and physical properties of collectors are jointly determined by the polar radical and the hydrocarbon group. It depends on the polar radical whether the collector is a strong or weak electrolyte (whether in solution it dissociates into ions to a great or a modest extent). For example, of the long-chain (C >8) organic compounds used in the flotation of non-metallic minerals, the alkyl sulphates and sulphonates, the tetrammonium salts, the sulphonium and pyridinium salts are strong electrolytes; alkyl carboxylates (soaps) and phosphates and primary amines are weak electrolytes. The collector ions of these, in the above succession, are

$$RSO_4^-, \quad RSO_3^-, \quad RN(CH_3)_3^+, \quad RS(CH_3)_2^+, \quad R\langle\text{—}NH^+$$

for the first group and

$$RCOO^-, \ RPO_4^{2-}, \ RNH_3^+$$

for the second.

The dissociation constants of the weak electrolytes are important in that they state the percentage of neutral molecules in the system. Consider for example two hydrolysis reactions. The hydrolysis of a soap gives rise to a carboxylic acid:

$$RCOO^- + H^+ \rightleftarrows RCOOH$$

with $K = 2 \cdot 10^{-5}$ (that is, pK = 4.7) at 25 °C; the hydrolysis of a primary amine salt gives rise to an amine:

$$RNH_3^+ \rightleftarrows RNH_2 + H^+$$

with $K = 2.4 \cdot 10^{-11}$ (that is, pK = 10.6) at 25 °C, implying that the ratio of amine ion concentration to hydrogen ion concentration varies as the concentration of undissociated (molecularly dissolved) free amine (RNH_2). To explain, one can write up directly

$$K = \frac{[RNH_2][H^+]}{[RNH_3^+].}$$

The analogous relationship

$$K = K'K'' = \frac{[RNH_2][H^+]}{[RNH_3^+]}$$

is obtained also from the relationship

$$K' = \frac{[RNH_2]}{[RNH_3^+][OH^-]}$$

that can be written up for the reaction

$$RNH_2 + H_2O \rightleftarrows RNH_3^+ + OH^-,$$

since

$$[OH^-] = \frac{K''}{[H^+]}.$$

That is,

$$pK = pH - \log\left(\frac{[RNH_2]}{[RNH_3^+]}\right)$$

or, stated in a general way,

$$pH = pK + \log\left(\frac{[M]}{[I^+]}\right).$$

For an anionic collector,

$$pH = pK + \log\left(\frac{[I^-]}{[M]}\right),$$

where $[I^+]$ or $[I^-]$ denotes the concentration of the ionic form of the cationic/anionic collecting agent and $[M]$ denotes the concentration of its non-ionic (undissociated) form. That is, if

$$pH = pK,$$

then

$$[I^-] = [M] \text{ or } [I^+] = [M]$$

implies that, in the solution, half of the reagent is ionized and the other half is non-ionized. The ionic form predominates in the solution of an anionic collector if $pH > pK$ and in that of a cationic one if $pH < pK$. For example, the abundances of the two forms are 1 and 99% respectively if

$$pH = pK \pm 2.$$

In possession of the dissociation constant, the concentration of the ionic and the non-dissociated (molecular) forms in the solution can be calculated for any pH. For example, Fig. 2.40 is a plot vs. the pH of the concentration c of dodecyl amine chloride ($R = C_{12}H_{25}$) in ionized form ($I^+ = RNH_3^+$) and non-ionized form ($M = RNH_2$). The full lines (I and M) refer to a dodecyl amine chloride concentration of $2 \cdot 10^{-5}$ mole per litre; the dot-dash lines (b_I and b_M)

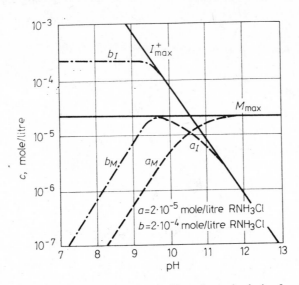

Fig. 2.40. Concentration vs. the pH of the ionic (I) and non-ionic (molecular, M) fractions of dodecyl amine chloride ($C_{12}H_{25}NH_3Cl$) in an aqueous solution, at dosages (a) $2 \cdot 10^{-5}$ mole/litre, (b) $2 \cdot 10^{-4}$ mole/litre

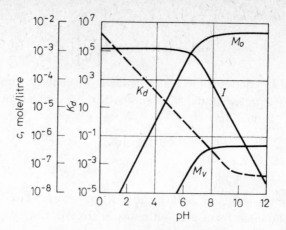

Fig. 2.41. Concentration vs. the pH of the ionic (I) and non-ionic (molecular, M) fraction of dodecyl amine chloride ($C_{12}H_{25}NH_3Cl$) in a mixture of water and iso-octane, at a dosage $c = 1.25 \cdot 10^{-5}$ mole/litre

refer to one of $2 \cdot 10^{-4}$ mole per litre; the dashed lines a_I and a_M refer to the possible maximum quantities (Gaudin 1957).

Figure 2.41 is a plot vs. the pH of the distribution of ionic ($I = RNH_3^+$) and non-ionic ($M = RNH_2$) dodecyl amine dissolved in a concentration $c = 1.25 \cdot 10^{-5}$ mole per litre in the phases of a solvent made up of 77 volume percent water and 23 volume percent isooctane (motor spirit). I is to be found in the water; most of M is to be found in the octane. The variation of

$$K_d = \frac{[I] + [M_w]}{[M_0]}$$

is also shown.

Using the notation

$$D = \frac{[M_0]}{[M_w]},$$

K_d may be written in the form

$$K_d = \frac{[H^+]}{KD} + \frac{1}{D}$$

or

$$\log K_d = -pH - (\log K + \log D),$$

where

$$K = 2.4 \cdot 10^{-11}$$

is the constant of dissociation of the acid RNH_3^+. That is,

$$\log K_d = f(pH)$$

is a straight line of slope -1, from whose ordinate intercept

$$-(\log K + \log D)$$

D can be calculated (in the given case, D is found to equal 10^4). The figure reveals the ionic form to be dominant below a $\mathrm{pH} = 6.5$ and the non-ionic one above it. The latter concentrates in the organic (octane) phase: its concentration in the aqueous phase, M_w, exceeds the ionic percentage I above a $\mathrm{pH} = 10.5$ only (Mellgren and Shergold 1966).

In view of the relationship

$$\log u = a + b \log c,$$

collector concentration c in the solution determines both the adsorption u and the collector-coated percentage of the surface, which is proportional to u. For example, if it is only a multitude of I^+ and H^+ ions (or I^- and OH^- ions) that vie for occupancy of the surface, then, for cationic collectors,

$$[I^+]^\alpha = \frac{C[H^+]^\beta \varphi}{1 - \varphi} ;$$

$$\log u = A + \alpha \log [I^+] + \beta(\mathrm{pH}),$$

and for anionic ones,

$$[I^-]^\alpha = \frac{C[OH^-]^\beta \varphi}{1 - \varphi} = \frac{C' \varphi}{(1 - \varphi)[H^+]^\beta} ;$$

$$\log u = A + \alpha \log [I^-] - \beta(\mathrm{pH}),$$

where α and β may equal unity also.

Collector (or any other) reagents are attached to the surfaces of the mineral particle either by physical adsorption, chemisorption or chemical bonding (a chemical reaction).

Physical adsorption is characterized by rapid reversibility, low energy ($\lesssim 0.1$ eV) and a lack of specificity. There is an approximate relationship

$$a \simeq kc^n$$

between concentration c and adsorbed quantity a (k and n are constants). Others prefer the relationship

$$\frac{c}{a(c_0 - c)} = \left(\frac{1}{ka_0}\right)\left[1 + (k - 1)\frac{c}{c_0}\right],$$

where c_0 is concentration in the saturated solution and a_0 is the maximum quantity that can go into the formation of monomolecular (or monoionic) layers. The equation holds up to

$$c \simeq 0.35\, c_0 .$$

The relationship between

$$\frac{c}{a(c_0 - c)} \quad \text{and} \quad \frac{c}{c_0}$$

is a linear one: the constants can be calculated from the slope and ordinate intercept of the straight line laid through some plotted points.

Chemisorption has a great energy of adsorption ($\gtrsim 1$ eV or $\gtrsim 10$ kcal/mole) and the reaction is specific and irreversible or slowly reversible as a rule.

Chemical reactions at the solid surface are also comparatively high-energy. They can go on until the mineral is entirely consumed, provided the reaction products are soluble. If they are not, then the coating constituted by a reaction product may protect the interior of the mineral grain from further corrosion. (For example, on anglesite immersed in a solution of sodium sulphide, a film of insoluble lead sulphide will form.)

Regardless of whether the phenomenon involved is chemisorption or polar adsorption or non-polar (physical) adsorption, collectors may get adsorbed (1) at the mineral surface proper (or in its Stern layer), (2) on alien (activating) ions attached to the surface, (3) or by means of hydrogen bridges to the hydrate layer tightly bound to the mineral surface.

Association among the non-polar parts of a long-chain collector directly attached to the mineral surface affects energetic conditions rather substantially. Just like the formation of micellae, association is due to the hydrophobia of the non-polar radicals: those strive to present the least possible surface of contact to the water. The energy of association of hydrocarbon chains is $\varphi = -1$ to -1.3 times kT per CH_2 group, where T is absolute temperature,

$$k = \frac{R}{N} = 1.38 \cdot 10^{-16} \text{ erg per degree}$$

is the Boltzmann constant,

$$R = 8.312 \text{ Ws per degree}$$

is the gas constant and

$$N = 6.022 \cdot 10^{23}$$

is the Loschmidt number. The energy of association of alkyl groups of carbon number n is

$$z(n - 1)s\varphi,$$

where $z \leq 1$ is a factor depending on the nature of the non-polar group, and s is the degree of association. The theoretical maximum of φ, which prevails when ordering is ideal, is $-1.39\,kT$. Direct adsorption at the surface is possible if the interaction between the polar radical of the collector and the mineral surface is stronger than that between the mineral surface and the water molecules, as the collector must displace the hydrate shell before making contact.

192

Non-ionic heteropolar or non-polar additives coadsorbed at the mineral surface with an ionic collector (4C to 10C alcohols, 6C to 10C alcanes, various cyclic hydrocarbons) increase the rates of flotation, the particle size of the mineral grains that can still be flotated out, reduce the required doses of ionic (primary) collector, and also influence frothing and froth stability more or less (Schubert 1964).

Non-polar or polar oily additives at first attach themselves in droplets to the hydrophobic mineral surfaces. On contact with a bubble, they spread out to form a thin film: the oil ring formed at the three-phase boundary exerts a capillary suction between mineral and bubble. Attachment to the bubble is reinforced thereby, and the time of induction required for attachment to take place is considerably reduced (Klassen 1960).

Figure 2.42 shows the outcome of flotation of 200 to 250 μm size particles of quartz at a pH = 6, in the presence of $7 \cdot 10^{-6}$ and $8 \cdot 10^{-6}$ mole per litre dodecyl ammonium chloride in a Hallimond tube in the presence of various non-ionic additives, in terms of mineral recovery $m\%$ (and $v\%$) vs. concentration c. (Without the additives, m did not exceed 50% or so in any case.) The

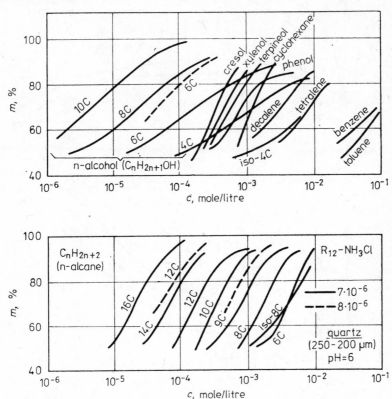

Fig. 2.42. Recovery of narrow (250—200 μm) grained quartz vs. dosages

$m = f(c)$ curves of the non-polar alcanes (C_nH_{2n+2}) are steeper than those of the heteropolar alcohols ($C_nH_{2n+1}OH$), but the latter produce the same effect in smaller doses. Among the cyclic compounds also, the heteropolar ones (the members of the phenol series) are more effective than the non-polar ones (benzene, toluene, tetralene, decalene). The influence of the length and branching, if any, of the alkyl chains is also revealed by the figure: a long straight chain is more effective than a short and/or branching one (Schubert 1964).

Figure 2.43 shows the outcomes of the flotation in a laboratory cell of two quartz fractions (minus-315 μm and 500 to 315 μm, respectively) using three standard dosages of a R_{16-18} ammonium chloride collector (40, 50 and 75 g/t) and various dosages of a diversity of non-ionic additives, in terms of mineral recovery $m\%$ vs. additive dosage in g/t. (Without additives, m ranged from 28

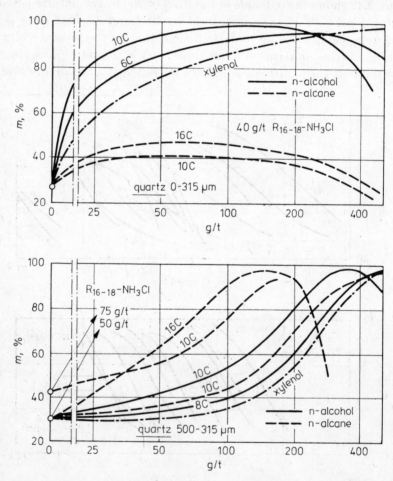

Fig. 2.43. Recovery of fine (0—315 μm) and coarse (500—315 μm) grained quartz vs. dosages

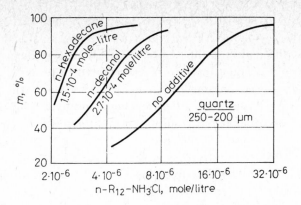

Fig. 2.44. Quartz recovery vs. collector concentration, in flotation with and without fixed dosages of two additives

to 42% for the three standard dosages of alkyl ammonium chloride.) Recovery drops off if too much additive is used. The flotation of minus-315 μm quartz is not promoted by the n-alcanes, whereas the flotation of coarser quartz is, the reason being that collector adsorption density in the coarser fraction, in moles per cm², is just right to make the grains stick to the bubbles, whereas in the finer fraction it is insufficient to counteract the strong froth-destroying action of the alcanes.

Figure 2.44 shows the variation of quartz recovery m% vs. the concentration of the ionic collector (dodecyl ammonium chloride) at constant (and zero) additive concentration (Schubert 1964).

So as to acquire the hydrophobia needed to float it out, a certain percentage at least of a mineral grain surface must acquire a coating with a coadsorptive film (a mixture of ionic collector and non-ionic additive). The presence of some additives will in fact increase the energy of association of ionic collectors. For example, using a collector dosage of 10^{-7} mole per litre n-alkyl ammonium ion on quartz in the 250 to 200 μm size range (corresponding to a surface coating of 27.5%) at a pH = 6 and 20 °C, the addition of

$2.7 \cdot 10^{-4}$	$1.5 \cdot 10^{-4}$	$6.0 \cdot 10^{-4}$ mole/litre
n-decanol,	n-hexadecane,	xylenol

has changed the degree of association of the collector from the $s = 0.21$ prevailing in the absence of any additive to

$s = 0.28$	0.26	0.22.

In other words, the coadsorption of decanol or hexadecane increases the energy of association of the alkyl ammonium ion, whereas xylenol — presumably owing to its ring structure — does not, at the concentration used, get coadsorbed to any significant extent with the collector at the quartz surface. Despite its shorter chain, decanol is more effective than hexadecane: the alcohol presumably penetrates the collector film more deeply than the alcane does. In the figure, the influence of n-decanol can be interpreted in terms of coadsorption: a given state of association (surface coverage) gives about the same mineral recovery, with or without any n-decanol being present. The presence of n-hexadecane, on the other hand, results in a greater recovery for a given surface coverage (state of association), presumably owing to the reduction in the time of induction by the oil droplets in the collector film and to the capillary suction of the oil rings along the three-phase boundaries, resulting in a stronger bubble attachment (Schubert 1964).

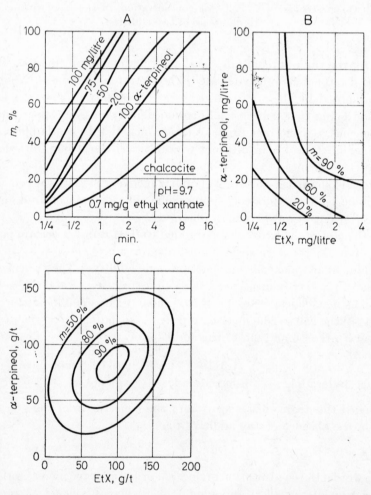

Fig. 2.45. Recovery of chalcocite flotation vs. A — time, B and C — potassium ethyl xanthate dosage, at various concentrations of the frother α-terpineol

The influence of α-terpineol (a frother) coadsorbed with a potassium ethyl xanthate collector is illustrated in Fig. 2.45. Part A of the figure is a diagram of chalcocite recovery vs. time of flotation using a fixed dosage of xanthate and various dosages (0 to 100 mg/l) of α-terpineol; Parts B and C show those combinations of collector and frother that give equal recoveries. Part B refers to the one-minute flotation of pure chalcocite; Part C to the flotation of a chalcocitic copper ore. In the latter case, 80 g/t EtX (ethyl xanthate) plus 80 g/t α-terpineol gave the best result.

If there are alien (activating) ions adsorbed at the mineral surface, the collector may attach itself to those as well. Corundum for example, at a pH < 6, can be flotated with amine cations after the addition of Na_2SO_4; quartz can be flotated with anion-active collectors in the presence of di- and trivalent metal ions such as Ba^{2+}, Ca^{2+}, Al_3^+ or Fe^{3+}. (The isoelectric point of corundum is in the pH range from 6.7 to 9.4; that of quartz is between 1.5 and 3.7; their charges are positive below and negative above. Collector ions of identical charge can attach themselves to these surfaces only by means of "bridges" of opposite charge.) The steps of the process are, in the case of corundum,

$$\rangle Al^+ - OH_2 + SO_4^{2-} \rightleftarrows \,\rangle Al - SO_4^- + H_2O;$$

$$\rangle Al - SO_4^- + R - NH_3^+ \rightleftarrows \,\rangle Al - SO_4^{(-)} \ldots {}^{(+)}NH_3 - R;$$

and in the case of quartz,

$$-\overset{|}{\underset{|}{Si}} - O^- + Ca^{2+} \rightleftarrows -\overset{|}{\underset{|}{Si}} - O - Ca^+;$$

$$-\overset{|}{\underset{|}{Si}} - O - Ca^+ + R - COO^- \rightleftarrows -\overset{|}{\underset{|}{Si}} - O - Ca^{(+)} \ldots {}^{(-)}OOC - R$$

(Schubert 1964).

The collector can attach itself with hydrogen bonds also to the hydrate layer of the mineral grain. For example, hydrated rock salt can be flotated with fatty acids or alkyl phosphates by the mechanism

$$\overset{-Cl}{\underset{-Cl}{-NaOH_2}} + OH_2 \ldots O - \overset{\|}{\underset{O}{C}} - R \rightleftarrows \overset{-Cl}{\underset{-Cl}{-NaOH_2}} \ldots O - \overset{\|}{\underset{O}{C}} - R + H_2O$$

(Rogers 1958). Potash salts cannot be flotated by this mechanism because the K^+ ions, with their large radii and negative hydration, do not get hydrated at the grain surfaces (Schubert 1964).

2.2.3. Attachment of mineral species to collectors

2.2.3.1. To the **sulphide minerals,** xanthates and other thiols are attached by chemisorption and/or chemical reactions. Base-metal sulphides can, however, be flotated, often selectively, also with cationic collectors attached by physical adsorption (Kellogg et al. 1946). For example, chalcopyrite flotated at a pH = 5.6 with tetradecyl pyridinium bromide ($C_{14}H_{29}C_5H_5NBr$) is readily separated from the sulphides of Zn, Pb and Fe (Pusch 1965). Figure 2.46 shows the respective recoveries $m\%$ vs. collector concentration.

2.2.3.2. To **oxides and silicates,** collectors tend to get attached by physical adsorption; they constitute the diffuse outer layer of the electric double layer at the solid–liquid interface. Chemisorption, however, is also possible, as in the

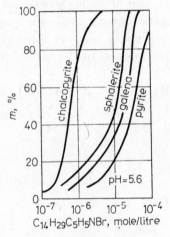

Fig. 2.46. Recovery of metal sulphides vs. the dosage of a cationic collector

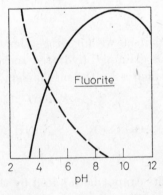

Fig. 2.47. Relative abundance of oleate captured by adsorption (dashed curve) and chemisorption (full line) on fluorite, vs. the pH

198

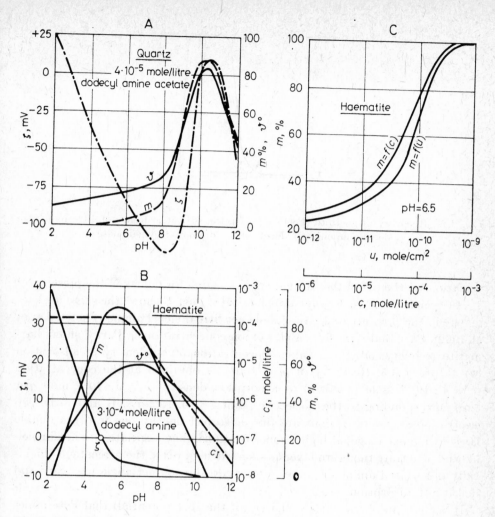

Fig. 2.48. Zeta potential ζ, contact angle ϑ and flotation recovery of A — quartz, B — haematite vs. the pH, at stated dosages of dodecyl amine acetate: C — haematite recovery vs. amine concentration c and adsorption density u

case of zincite (ZnO) or willemite (Zn_2SiO_4), where the adsorption of hexanethiol results in a strong zinc-mercaptan bond. An oleic acid collector may get attached to fluorite, barite and calcite surfaces by chemisorption, forming a strongly adherent coating that is fairly hard to remove. Figure 2.47 shows the relative abundances vs. the pH of oleate, respectively attached to fluorite by physical adsorption (dashed curve) and chemisorption (full curve).

In physical adsorption, there is a close relationship between the physical state of the surface (its zeta potential, density of adsorption, angle of contact ϑ) and the mineral recovery $m\%$ of flotation. Part A of Fig. 2.48 e.g. shows the

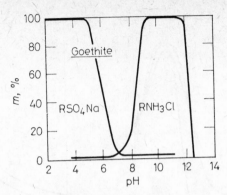

Fig. 2.49. Recovery of goethite (FeO · OH) vs. the pH, at a dosage of 10^{-3} mole/litre dodecyl ammonium chloride and sodium dodecyl sulphate

variation vs. the pH of the parameters ζ, ϑ and m for quartz in the presence of $4 \cdot 10^{-5}$ mole per litre dodecyl amine acetate; Part B shows the same for haematite in the presence of $3 \cdot 10^{-4}$ mole per litre dodecyl amine (Fuerstenau et al. 1962). Part B also includes a plot of ion concentration c_I. Part C shows haematite recovery, $m\%$, vs. amine concentration (c) or density of adsorption (u) at pH = 6.5. Recovery of $m = 100\%$ is obtained at the concentration $(c = 5 \cdot 10^{-4}$ mole per litre) or adsorption density $(u = 9 \cdot 10^{-9}$ mole per cm²) corresponding to the isoelectric point $\zeta = 0$. At any pH above the isoelectric point, amine cations are first adsorbed one by one into the double layer by ion exchange; at higher concentrations, they associate into hemimicellae and penetrate the Stern layer as such. At high pH's, the percentage of ionically dissociated amine decreases, and so do the contact angle, recovery and density of adsorption.

It is the sign of the surface charge (of the zeta potential) that determines whether an anionic or cationic collector should be used. The oxide minerals, which have the H^+ and OH^- ions for their potential determinants, are especially sensitive to changes in pH. Figure 2.49 is the recovery curve $(m\%)$ of goethite vs. the pH at the dosage of 10^{-3} mole per litre dodecyl ammonium chloride on the one hand and sodium dodecyl sulphate on the other (Iwasaki et al. 1962). The zero-charge (isoelectric) point is at pH = 6.7; the zeta potential is positive below it and negative above it. Hence, goethite can be flotated with a cationic collector at pH > 6.7 and with an anionic one at pH < 6.7. Floatability ceases at pH = 12.3 because, at and above that point, hydrolysis of the collector reduces the amine ion concentration overmuch. Other oxide minerals (haematite, corundum, rutile, quartz, etc.) behave similarly: they are to be flotated with anionic collectors (sulphates, sulphonates) at any pH below their zero-charge point and with cationic ones (amines) above it.

The reagent concentration required for flotation changes with the pH, because the zeta potential is also affected thereby. If the zeta potential increases, the adsorption of counter-ions (collector ions) increases: hence, the desirable collector concentration tends to decrease the more, the greater the pH difference against the isoelectric point. Figure 2.50 shows corundum recovery ($m\%$) vs. sodium dodecyl sulphate concentration (c moles per litre) for various pH values (Modi and Fuerstenau 1960). The zero-charge point of corundum is in the pH range 6.7 to 9.4: it cannot be flotated with an anionic collector at any pH higher than that. At pH = 6, floatability takes an abrupt surge at a reagent concentration $c \gtrsim 10^{-5}$ mole per litre: this is where the collector ions begin to associate (to form hemimicellae) in the layer adhering to the surface. Further adsorption and the beginning of ion association at a lower concentration at pH = 4 is due to the increase in surface charge.

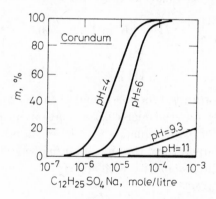

Fig. 2.50. Recovery of corundum (Al_2O_3) vs. sodium dodecyl sulphate dosage at different pH values

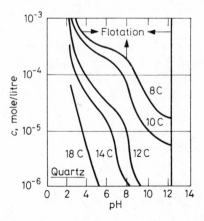

Fig. 2.51. Critical $c = c(\text{pH})$ curves of the floatability (adherence to bubbles) of quartz in the presence of primary amine acetates of different chain length

201

The flotation performance of oxidic minerals is influenced both by the size and nature of the collector reagent's polar radical and the length of its hydrocarbon group. The size of the polar radical influences the strength of adsorption in the adhesive film: its chemical nature determines, over and above the chemical reactions that take place, if any, also the degree of hydrolysis. Collector selectivity is the less, the longer is the hydrocarbon chain: the degree of association of the adsorbed collector ions is also affected by chain length.

Figure 2.51 shows critical-pH curves for the flotation of quartz with primary amine acetates of different chain length (DeBruyn 1955). The ordinate axis is calibrated in total amine concentration, c moles per litre. Quartz can be flotated using these collectors in the domain included between the vertical at $pH = 12.2$ and the applicable curve. At $pH = 12.2$, the concentration of the ionic form of the amine salt which basically is the collecting reagent — becomes too low as related to its total concentration. Since $pK = 10.6$,

$$\log \frac{[M]}{[I^+]} = pH - pK = 12.2 - 10.6 = 1.6 \, ;$$

$$\frac{[M]}{[I^+]} = 40 \, .$$

The presence of an unsaturated (double) bond in the hydrocarbon chain affects both collector solubility and the degree of association of the adsorbed ions. The flotation performance of oxide minerals with long-chain hydrocarbons may be affected greatly by temperature, through its influence on collector solubility. For example, on floating haematite with stearic acid (the saturated 17C fatty acid), mineral recovery was

$$m\% = \quad 10 \quad\quad 98 \quad\quad 100$$
$$\text{at} \quad\quad 25 \quad\quad 50 \quad\quad 75 \,°C \, ,$$

whereas the unsaturated 17C fatty acid (oleic acid) gave a recovery of 98% even at 25 °C.

Collector ions attached by physical adsorption play the role of counter-ions in the electric double layer. Their density of adsorption is a function of their competitiveness with other counter-ions in the solution. This is why any significant concentration of such competing ions (cations in the case of cationic collectors and anions in the case of anionic ones) is harmful in the flotation of oxide minerals. Nor is the presence of neutral molecules a matter of indifference, provided these can get coadsorbed (e.g. in association) with the ionic collector. For example, the flotation of corundum with sodium dodecyl sulphate (at a $pH < 9.4$!) is promoted by additions of decyl alcohol; at a $pH = 6$, collector concentration may be less by a factor of about 10 in a saturated solution ($2.2 \cdot 10^{-4}$ mole per litre) of decyl alcohol than in distilled water. In the presence of decyl alcohol, a given collector concentration gave the same flotation performance at a pH higher by about two units. That is, if selective flotation is to be achieved by pH regulation, then a better performance may be expected on using a pure collecting reagent than on using one that contains impurities.

2.2.3.3. To the surfaces of **salt-type indissoluble minerals** (carbonates, sulphates, fluorides such as magnesite, barite, apatite, rhodochrosite, fluorite, calcite, etc.) long-chain fatty acids or soaps are attached by chemisorption. It is important to condition such minerals prior to flotation, as the reaction between the collector ions and the mineral surfaces takes some time. In the case of physical adsorption (by oxides or silicates), where the collector ions are counterions in a double layer, prior conditioning is superfluous as a rule because an equilibrium is quick to set in anyway at the solid–liquid interface.

2.2.3.4. The flotation of soluble salts in their saturated solutions depends greatly on the crystallographic properties of those, on the one hand (flotation can take place if the collector ion can insert itself into the lattice at the mineral grain surface), and on the affinity of water molecules to the ions at the crystal surface and in the interior of the solution, on the other: according to some authors, the condition for a collector ion to get adsorbed is that the heat of solution of the salt be negative. (If the water molecules have a great affinity to the crystal surface, they may prevent the adsorption of collector ions.) For example, in the case of cubic crystals, the cation of the amine, of radius R_i may penetrate the layer of water molecules of radius 1.4 Å attached to the cations of the hydrated surface, provided the closest spacing d between the centres of adjacent lattice anions (or cations) at the crystal surface is greater than 6 Å. The relationship

$$R_i \leq \frac{d}{2} - 1.4$$

is of general validity: that is, for flotation to be feasible, the radius R_i of the collector ion must be less than $3 - 1.4 = 1.6$ Å.

Table 2.15 lists the molar heats of solution (H, kcal/mole) and the anion spacings (d, Å) of alkali and ammonium halides (top); those of some sodium and potassium salts (nitrates, NO_3; chlorates, ClO_3; bromates, BrO_3; iodates, IO_3, and sulphates, $1/2SO_4$) (middle); and the flotability F (+: floatable, —: non-floatable) of NaCl, KCl and NH_4Cl using various types of collector reagent (bottom). Primary n-alkyl amine collectors will float the salts below the bold line in the top part of the table. Except for NH_4F, the heat of solution of every floatable salt is less than -3 kcal/mole (Prosser and Kiwia 1969). Chlorites of great negative heats of solution (K, NH_4) can — as revealed by the bottom half of the table — be readily flotated using primary amine, sulphate

Table 2.15. Molar heats of solution (H kcal/mole), anion spacings (d Å) and floatability F of halides using different collector reagent types and other potassium and sodium salts

Ionic radius Å		Li^+ 0.60	Na^+ 0.95	K^+ 1.33	R_b^+ 1.48	Cs^+ 1.69	NH^+ 1.43
F^- 1.36	H	−0.7	−0.3	−1.9	−0.5	+1.1	−1.5
	d	4.02	4.62	5.33	5.63	6.01	
Cl^- 1.81	H	+1.1	−0.9	−4.4	−4.4	−4.6	−3.4
	d	5.14	5.63	6.28	6.54		
Br^- 1.95	H	+2.1	−4.6	−5.1	−6.1	−6.9	−4.5
	d	5.49	5.96	6.58	6.55		
I^- 2.16	H	−0.2	−3.9	−5.2	−6.6	−8.5	−3.6
	d	6.00	6.46	7.05	7.24		

Anion	Sodium salt			Potassium salt		
	d	H	F	d	H	F
Nitrate	6.5	+5.1	—	7.0	−8.3	+
Chlorate	6.6	−5.0	+	7.1	−10.0	+
Bromate	6.7	−5.3	+	7.5	−9.8	+
Iodate	7.0	−7.0	+	7.6	−4.1	+
Sulphate	6.1	+0.6	—	?	−5.6	+

Salt	$-N(CH_3)_3^+$	$-NH_3^+$	$-SO_4^-$	$-SO_3^-$	$-COO^-$	$-PO_2OH^-$
NaCl	—	—	—	—	+	+
KCl	—	+	+	+	—	—
NH$_4$Cl	—	+	+	+	+	—

and sulphonate collectors (where R is the alkyl group): these get adsorbed as counter-ions, and some of them even get inserted into the lattice. The large trimethyl amine ion (of radius 2.95 Å), on the other hand, does not fit into the lattices listed (only RbCl and CsCl can be flotated with it). The carboxyl and phosphate ions have a propensity to form hydrogen bonds: the collector ions are attached by such bonds to the water molecules strongly adsorbed on the small sodium ions (Fuerstenau et al. 1962; Rogers 1958; Roman 1970; Singewald 1961). (The ionic radii of the polar radicals of some collector reagents are: 2.4 to 2.7 Å for $-OSO_3^-$, 2.9 for $-SO_3^-$, 2.0 to 2.6 [about 4.4 when hydrated] for $-COO^-$, 1.3 to 1.4 [about 1.85 when hydrated] for $-NH_3^-$, 2.95 [about 4.2 when hydrated] for $-(CH_3)_3N^+$.)

Ions exhibit "remote" and "close" hydration. The former, essentially an orientation by polarization of the surrounding water molecules, is responsible for the bulk of the heats of hydration and solution, whereas the latter is the process that attaches to an ion the water molecules in immediate contact with

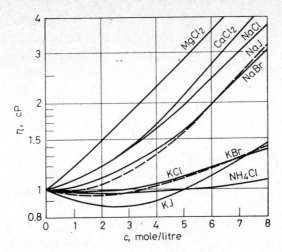

Fig. 2.52. Viscosity η cP of different salt solutions at 20 °C, vs. concentration, mole/litre

it. It is positive if the presence of the ion reduces the mobility of the water molecules, and negative if it increases that mobility by upsetting the structures developed prior to its appearance. Positive hydration means a marked increase of viscosity in the solution as concentration increases: on negative hydration, the rise is slight and may even be preceded by a decline at low concentrations

Table 2.16

+ :	Mg^{2+}	>	Li^+	>	Sr^{2+}	>	Ca^{2+}	>	F^-	>	SO_4^{2-}	>	Na^+	>	Ba^{2+}	
	+80		56		34		28		20		15		14		2	
− :	ClO_4^-		NO_3^-		Br^-		K^+		NH_4^+		Cs^+		I^-		Cl^-		(at 21.5 °C)
	−47		44		39		36		35		31		24		21		

(Fig. 2.52). The phenomenon of positive hydration is observed on mono- and polyvalent ions of small ionic radius; that of negative hydration, on mono-valent ions of large ionic radius (cf. Table 2.16) (Samoilov 1961; Schubert 1964).

2.2.4. Modifying reagents. Most modifying reagents are inorganic. They serve to increase the selectivity of the collectors and the sharpness of separation of the minerals to be separated. The influence of the pH has been referred to repeatedly in the preceding sections, but there are also ions other than the hydrogen and hydroxyl ion that promote or hinder the adsorption of this or that collector on this or that mineral. The promotion of collector action is called activation; its hindering is called depression or deactivation.

pH regulation serves to modify the solubility of salts in the pulp (the concentration of their ions in the liquid phase). Ions deleterious to flotation have to be removed from the solution (by neutralization or precipitation) prior to the dosage of the collecting reagent. For example, metal cations of higher valence (Al^{3+}, Fe^{3+}, Cr^{3+}, Th^{4+}, etc.) generate strong electric charges (a strong zeta potential) even if adsorbed in moderate quantities. These "flotation poisons" or "toxic agents" are precipitated by the OH^- ion in the form of insoluble metal hydroxides. In other instances, an ion present in the solution may consume some of the collector (Ca^{2+} e.g. constitutes insoluble Ca carboxylates with fatty acids or soaps). The precipitation of such ions prior to collector dosage greatly reduces collector consumption. Ca^{2+} and Mg^{2+} may be precipitated with caustic soda (as used in softening drinking water); the precipitation of other cations or the neutralization of acidity can be done cheapest by additions of slaked lime [$Ca(OH)_2$]. It may be possible to eliminate undesirable ions by adding substances with which those form complex salts that dissociate but very slightly. (For example, Cu^{2+} or Fe^{2+} ions can be eliminated as cuprocyanide or ferrocyanide compounds by additions of cyanide.) The ions thus neutralized can subsequently be regenerated and recovered after changing the chemical parameters of the pulp.

pH regulation has a direct influence, beneficial or otherwise, on the competitiveness of the collector for the mineral surface. Figure 2.53 shows recoveries of some pure, granulate minerals vs. the pH: 90 g/t of a terpineol frother was added in each case, plus a potassium amyl xanthate collector in the concentration of 15 g/t in cases 1 and 2, 45 g/t in case 3, 1,350 g/t in case 4 and an isoamyl amine collector in the concentration of 230 g/t in case 5. The pH was adjusted by the dosage of NaOH and HCl (Gaudin 1957).

In the absence of a collector, the H^+ and OH^- ions affect the ionic composition of the pulp and get adsorbed by the mineral surfaces: in the presence of a collector, they affect its adsorption by influencing the electric properties of the surface, the ionic composition of the pulp and the active form of the collector,

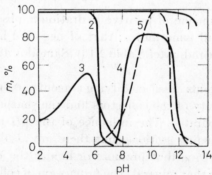

Fig. 2.53. Recoveries $m\%$ of pure granulate minerals vs. the pH using 90 g/t terpineol frother. *1* — chalcocite with 15 g/t potassium amyl xanthate, *2* — pyrite with the same, *3* — sphalerite with 45 g/t potassium amyl xanthate, *4* — malachite with 1,350 g/t potassium amyl xanthate, *5* — chalcocite with 230 g/t isoamyl amine

and also by competing with the active collector ions (H^+ with the cations and OH^- with the anions), by displacing the collector from the mineral surfaces, or by getting coadsorbed with the collecting reagent (and affecting thereby the hydrate shell and the contact angle of the mineral).

The metal recovery in flotation with an anionic collector varies as the product $[R_c][H^+]$, with cationic collector as $[R_c]/[H^+]$, where $[R_c]$ is residual collector concentration in the tailing pulp. If the product is too great, the metal content of the concentrate decreases; if it is too low, metal loss increases. The optimum of the product can be provided by any one of a variety of combinations of $[R_c]$ and $[H^+]$. In order to keep $[R_c]$ (that is, also the collector dosage) as low as possible, it is $[H^+]$ that is to be increased by anionic, and decreased by cationic collector. In case of galena and xanthate, for example, the optimum of the product coincides approximately with the minimum of $[R_c]^2[H^+]$. A given flotation performance can be achieved with less xanthate at a lower pH (by means of a more sparing lime dosage).

2.2.4.1. Depressants. The action mechanisms of depressants are varied: (1) the creation or enhancement of a zeta potential having the same polarity as the ions of the collector; (2) displacement of the collector from the mineral surfaces by means of ions with a stronger affinity to those; (3) precipitation of the activating ions present in the pulp in the form of insoluble compounds; (4) enhancing the hydrophilia (strengthening the hydrate shell) of those parts of the mineral surfaces that wear no collector coatings, e.g. by making them adsorb hydrophilic colloids.

Depressants displacing the collector ions from the mineral surface will be anions if the collector is an anionic one and vice versa.

2.2.4.2. Activators make mineral surfaces capable of adsorbing a collector. There are three action mechanisms: (1) changing the sign or magnitude of the zeta potential; (2) introducing alien ions with a propensity to adsorb the collector into the Stern layer; (3) dispersing or weakening the hydrate shell at those parts of the mineral surface not coated with the collector.

Atomic oxygen is an activator for sulphides and many non-sulphide minerals. The fresh fracture surfaces of sulphide minerals, formed in oxygen-free water, are hydrophilic: in the presence of oxygen, the minerals oxidize gradually, turning hydrophobic even without the benefit of a collector. Oxygen dissolved in water is adsorbed by the sulphide minerals more avidly than are other gases (N_2, CO_2). In an oxygen-free medium, sulphides will adsorb no collector: the quantity of oxygen required to activate a mineral differs from one mineral to the next. In flotation with a xanthate, the quantity of oxygen to be adsorbed for activation to take place increases for some sulphides in the following succession: galena, sphalerite, chalcopyrite, pyrrhotite, arsenopyrite. At the optimum concentration of oxygen, the time required for flotation also decreases markedly, whereas an overdose of oxygen (the overoxidation of the surfaces) tends to impair the minerals' propensity to float. For example, the oxygen adsorption of pyrite is increased far beyond the optimum if the pulp is dosed with enough lime: this is why lime is a specific depressant of pyrite. The oxygen adsorption of chalcopyrite, on the other hand, changes but little even if the concentration of $Ca(OH)_2$ is comparatively high: hence, chalcopyrite is depressed less by lime.

In the flotation of some non-sulphidic minerals (quartz, fluorite, limestone, etc.) with a carboxyl collector and with bubbles of various gases (air, oxygen, nitrogen), the highest recovery was invariably achieved with oxygen. A short burst of nitrogen blown through the pulp decreased the floatability of certain minerals (quartz, fluorite) markedly; a more prolonged blowing eliminated it altogether. The different influences of different gases can be explained in terms of differences in the thickness of the adsorbed collector film and of its mosaic structure. The adsorption of oxygen does not only promote the reaction between mineral and collector, but also reduces the degree of hydration of the patches with no collector coating, increasing their hydrophobia thereby.

The oxygen molecules adsorbed at the surface dissociate into atoms which attach themselves to the metal atoms/ions of the lattice. Adsorption of the competing collector ions is greatly promoted by such incipient oxidation but is hindered if it becomes excessive.

The S^{2-} ions of the metal sulphides of very low solubility are not exchanged by chemisorption for the anions of the collector (a xanthate, say). On a slightly oxidized metal sulphide, however, some of the S^{2-} ions are replaced by $2OH^-$, SO_4^{2-}, $S_2O_3^{2-}$, SO_3^{2-} ions, which do get replaced by the xanthate ions if the solubility of the metal xanthate is less than that of these compounds produced by the oxidation of the sulphide (Du Rietz 1975).

The pL_{MA} values (negative logarithms of the solubility products) of some metal compounds are listed in Table 2.13: Part C (xanthates), Part A (metal soaps and hydroxides) and Part B (some other compounds).

Those of metal xanthates are listed in Table 2.14A.

Let e.g. the anion concentration of ethyl xanthate anion be

$$(EX^-) = 3 \cdot 10^{-5} \text{ mole},$$

giving $pEX^- = 4.52$. For lead, we find

$$pPb^{2+} = 16.7 - 2(4.25) = 7.66 .$$

At the same time, the critical pA values (anion concentrations) of the compounds resulting from the oxidation of galena are

$$pOH^- = \frac{1}{2}(15.1 - 7.66) = 3.72$$

corresponding to a $pH^+ = 10.28$;

$$pSO_4^{2-} = 7.97 - 7.66 = 0.31;$$
$$pS_2O_3^{2-} = 9.5 - 7.66 = 1.84;$$
$$pSO_3^{2-} = 13.0 - 7.66 = 5.34.$$

pA values lower (anion concentrations greater) than this will act as depressants: galena cannot be flotated using a $3 \cdot 10^{-5}$ mole EX^- collector. Using ten times that concentration, $3 \cdot 10^{-4}$ mole EX^-, we have

$$pEX^- = 3.52$$

and

$$pPb^{2+} = 16.7 - 2(3.52) = 9.66;$$

this exceeds the above value, 7.66, by two units. The result is that the critical anion concentrations pA will also be less by two units than the above ones:

$$pOH^- = 1.72 \ (pH = 12.28),$$
$$pSO_4^{2-} = -1.69; \ pS_2O_3^{2-} = -0.16; \ pSO_3^{2-} = 3.34.$$

Using hexyl xanthate, in a concentration of 10^{-6} mole HX^-, on the other hand, we have $pHX^- = 6$ and

$$pPb^{2+} = 20.3 - 2(6.0) = 8.3,$$

and the critical anion concentrations are

$$pOH^- = 3.08 \ (pH = 10.92);$$
$$pSO_4^{2+} = -0.33; \ pS_2O_3^{2+} = 1.20; \ pSO_3^{2+} = 4.70.$$

At pA values lower (concentrations in the pulp higher) than this, galena cannot be flotated at a hexyl xanthate concentration of 10^{-6} mole.

If the metal is Cu^{2+}, then

$$pL_{Cu(OH)_2} = 18.2 \ \text{and} \ pL_{Cu(EX)_2} = 24.2.$$

For example, let $pEX^- = 4.52$. Then,

$$pCu^{2+} = 24.2 - 2(4.52) = 15.16,$$

and the critical OH concentration is

$$pOH^- = \frac{1}{2}(18.2 - 15.16) = 1.52.$$

For metal hydroxides,

$$pL_{M(OH)_2} = pM^{2+} + 2pOH^-,$$

that is,

$$pM^{2+} = pL_{M(OH)_2} - 2pOH.$$

14

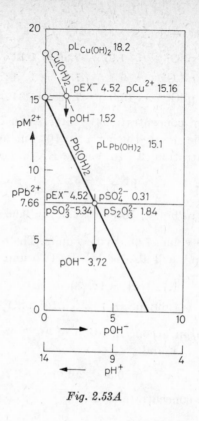

Fig. 2.53A

At $pOH^- = 0$,

$$pM^{2+} = pL_{M(OH)_2};$$

at $pOH^- = 5$,

$$pM^{2+} = pL_{M(OH)_2} - 10.$$

For the metal hydroxides, the graph of $pM^{2+} = f(pOH^-)$ is a straight line of slope -2. Figure 2.53A shows the graph for lead and copper hydroxide, with the pM^{2+} values belonging to $pEX^- = 4.52$, and the corresponding critical anion concentrations pA^{2-} of some other salts (in the case of lead) are also plotted. Higher-than-critical anion concentrations (which depress the mineral in question, forestalling its flotation) correspond to lower values of pA^{2-} (to higher values of pPb^{2+}). The graphs of these are higher in the diagram than the graph of $pPb^{2+} = 7.66$, which corresponds to $pEX^- = 4.52$. It is a fairly general rule, with few exceptions, that the higher graphs representing higher values of pM^{2+} will replace at the mineral surface the anions of the lower graphs.

The penetration of oxygen into the surface layer weakens the bonds between the ions of the lattice, promoting ionization, and also the mobility of the ions, their going into solution and their displacement by collector ions.

The hydrophobizing influence of oxygen may be connected with the semiconducting properties of the sulphides. Galena for example is a mixed semiconductor (one of both p and n type at the same time): its conductivity is partly due to excess electrons and partly to an electron deficit (holes). A fresh galena surface, at which conduction by electrons dominates, adsorbs no xanthate collector. Oxygen adsorption changes the n-type (electronic) conductivity into p-type (hole) conductivity, and the electrons of the xanthate ions can then form bonds with the holes at the galena surface (Plaksin 1960; Plaksin et al. 1957, 1968).

Oxidation lowers the Fermi energy level of a mineral, enhancing its acceptor feature and increasing its adsorptivity vis-à-vis the anionic collectors. The energy levels of a mineral can be modified in many other ways as well, e.g. by irradiation with ultraviolet (or, indeed, visible) light, alpha, beta and gamma rays, X-rays, by bombardment with ions or neutrons, ultrasonic waves, by imparting a triboelectric charge (a contact potential), by a magnetic or electric field, by heat treatment, dry conditioning, gas adsorption, various types of grinding, etc. All these may affect the outcome of flotation (Carta et al. 1970, 1973; Mellgren 1973).

The process of oxidation of a mineral may be inferred from the change of redox potential of the aqueous solution into which it is immersed, because the redox potential (the potential difference between a platinum electrode and a saturated calomel electrode) is proportional to the oxygen content of the solution. For example, the redox potential of a pulp containing sphalerite in a hermetically sealed vessel was found to decrease from -80 mV to

	-220	-270	-300 mV
in	10	20	40 minutes,

revealing the rate at which the oxygen content of the pulp was consumed by its reductive components. Aeration restored the redox potential of the pulp to the original -80 mV.

The voltages measured were

	-150	-110	-80 mV
after aeration for	5	10	20 minutes.

Flotation of a pulp of redox potential -300 mV with nitrogen bubbles (no oxygen) resulted in a sphalerite recovery less by a factor of 2/3 than flotation with air bubbles of a pulp of r.p. -80 mV; the metal content of the concentrate also decreased. Conditions were found to be optimal at -100 mV, where the pulp contained just sufficient oxygen for the adequate oxidation of the sphalerite but not enough the excess oxygen to deploy its harmful effects (Hofmann and Lengler 1969).

Aeration, however, may result in the decrease as well as in the increase of the O_2 concentration in the pulp. Between the redox potential, E_h mV, and the pH of an aqueous solution, the relationship

$$E_h + 60\,\mathrm{pH} = C$$

has often been found to hold; C has been found to vary from 660 to 830 in individual flotation shops (Woodcock and Jones 1969).

The sulphide minerals of a dry-ground ore tend to oxidize differentially and so to acquire different native floatabilities.

Chalcopyrite in hydrothermal copper ores tends to be hydrophobized sufficiently in the process of grinding, whereas the other sulphides accompanying it (pyrite, pyrrhotite, etc.) remain hydrophilic, so that the chalcopyrite can be flotated out at a fair recovery using a frother only. Doing so often permits to achieve a cleaner concentrate and a better copper recovery than using the modifiers and collectors of conventional flotation (Lepetic 1974).

Oxygen oxidizes part of the xanthate dosed to dixanthogen; it is this latter that attaches itself to the grains of Pb, Cu and Fe sulphides, at the grainward sides of their electric double layers. In the absence of dixanthogen, the bubbles and sulphide grains will not stick together, even if there is sufficient xanthate present (Granville et al. 1972; Klymowsky 1973; Usul and Tolun 1974).

Most of the other activating reagents are inorganic salts in which the ion opposite in sign to the collector ion is the activator in the proper sense. Metal cations (e.g. Cu^{2+} for sphalerite, Ba^{2+}, Ca^{2+}, Al^{3+}, Fe^{3+} for quartz) may be used in this way in combination with anionic collectors (xanthates, carboxylates, etc.); silicate, phosphate, etc. anions may be used in combination with cationic collectors. These activators, just like oxygen, must be dosed carefully. Over-dosage may result in the precipitation of the collector ions out of the solution, decreasing their concentration below the minimum required to bring about flotation. (This is the phenomenon called pseudodepression.)

2.2.5. Behaviour of mineral species in the presence of depressants

2.2.5.1. It is usual to flotate *sulphide minerals* with anionic collectors. Depressants of these minerals accordingly tend to be anionic. Any aqueous solution contains OH^- ions; their concentration increases as the pH increases. OH^- functions as a broad-spectrum (non-selective) depressant in the presence of anionic collectors. At higher concentrations, it reduces the floatability of every mineral. Increasing depression by an increasing $[OH^-]$ concentration can be offset by raising the concentration $[I^-]$ of the collector anion. In principle, the condition of constant flotation performance should be

$$\frac{[I^-]}{[OH^-]} = \mathrm{const.};$$

however,
$$\frac{[I^-]}{[OH^-]^b} = C$$

is borne out better by experimental fact, where the exponent $b \neq 1$ and the constant C are specific for the different combinations of mineral and collector. (For example, $b = 0.65$ for galena flotated with potassium ethyl xanthate; 0.52 for sodium diethyl dithiophosphate: it is 0.56, 0.72 and 0.75, in that order, for sphalerite flotated with sodium diethyl, potassium dibutyl and potassium diamyl carbamate.)

Figure 2.54 shows critical collector (sodium diethyl dithiophosphate) concentrations in mg/l for three metal sulphides vs. the pH (or the $[OH^-]$ concen-

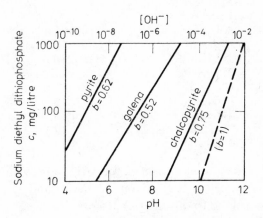

Fig. 2.54. Critical $c = c(pH)$ limits of the floatability of some sulphide minerals with sodium diethyl dithiophosphate

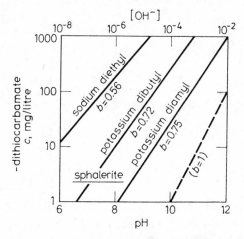

Fig. 2.55. Critical $c = c(pH)$ limits of the floatability of sphalerite with different dialkyl dithiocarbamates

213

tration). The minerals will not float in the domains to the right (below) the lines. In the case of a readily dissociating electrolyte at low concentrations, $[I^-]$ varies as the total concentration $[I]$; hence, the reagent concentration required for a given flotation performance is also proportional to $[OH^-]^b$.

Figure 2.55 shows critical limits of concentration for sphalerite vs. the pH when flotated with different dialkyl dithiocarbamate collectors. Sphalerite will float to the left and will not to the right of the lines.

The critical pH values (above which the minerals will not stick to the bubbles) in an aqueous solution containing 25 mg/l ($= 1.56 \cdot 10^{-4}$ mole per litre) potassium ethyl xanthate are as listed below:

Sphalerite	0
Pyrrhotite	6.0
Arsenopyrite	8.4
Galena	10.4
Pyrite	10.5
Marcasite	11.0
Chalcopyrite	11.8
Covellite	13.2
Bornite	13.8
Tetrahedrite	13.8
Chalcocite	14

In other words, the depressing effect of the OH^- ion (with potassium ethyl xanthate as the collector) is greatest on sphalerite and least on chalcocite. Different sequences belong to different collectors.

For example, the critical pH's (above which no air bubbles will attach to the mineral grains) are found to be for

	sphalerite	pyrite	galena	chalcopyrite
pH =	0	3.5	6.2	9.4

at 32 mg/l sodium diethyl dithiophosphate,

	6.2	10.5	13.5	14.0

at 27 mg/l sodium diethyl dithiocarbamate,

	5.5	12.3	12.1	14.0

at 32 mg/l isoamyl xanthate,

	10.4	12.8	14.0	14.0

at 42 mg/l potassium diamyl dithiocarbamate (Wark 1955).

As the pH ($[OH^-]$) increases, the hydroxyl ion displaces the anionic collector film adsorbed at the surfaces of the mineral grains. Figure 2.56 shows the adsorption density u of potassium ethyl xanthate vs. $[X^-]/[OH^-]$, for differ-

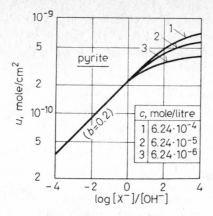

Fig. 2.56. Density of reagent adsorption u mole/cm² on pyrite vs. log [X⁻]/[OH⁻]

ent collector concentrations in the solution. As long as $[X^-]/[OH^-]$ is low, the relationship

$$\frac{u_{X^-}}{u_{OH^-}} = \frac{u_{X^-}}{(u_0 - u_{X^-})} = K \left(\frac{[X^-]}{[OH^-]}\right)^b$$

holds, where u_0 is the number of molecules that can be accommodated per unit surface area. ($b = 0.20$ in the case of pyrite and ethyl xanthate) (Gaudin et al. 1956).

The relationship generalizes to

$$\log u = a - b \, (\text{pH}) \quad \text{or} \quad u = \frac{A}{(\text{pH})^b}$$

for any sulphydryl collector (other workers prefer

$$u = a - b \, (\text{pH}).$$

The percentage surface of the mineral grains covered with a collector film ($\varphi\%$) thus decreases as the pH increases. For example, as revealed by Fig. 2.56, φ is found to be

	100	57	44	31	17%
at pH =	<7	9.5	10.5	11.5	12.5

for pyrite flotated with ethyl xanthate in a concentration $c = 6.24 \cdot 10^{-6}$ mole per litre.

The volume V and surface F of a particle are related by

$$\frac{V}{F} = \frac{x}{k},$$

where x is particle size and k is a form factor ($k = 6$ for spheres). The ratio of the weight, measured in a pulp, of the particle, $V(\delta - \gamma)$, to the collector-covered surface, $F\varphi$, varies as $x/k\varphi$. The greater this ratio, the more liable is the mineral grain to be detached from the bubble by its own weight (that is, the more hydrophobic grains will be left behind in the tailings). For example, the value of

$$\frac{V}{F\varphi} = \frac{x}{6\varphi}$$

belonging at $\varphi = 100\%$ to the particle sizes

	200	100	50	25 μm
is	33	17	8	4;

it is twice (four times) as much at $\varphi = 50\%$ ($\varphi = 25\%$). Hence, the floatability of larger particles ceases sooner with an increasing pH.

Since an anionic collector adsorbed on the grains can be made to desorb by increasing the pH, concentrates flotated out at a comparatively low pH and filtered after the addition of lime will give a filtrate rich in desorbed collector: after precipitating the excess lime (e.g. by means of CO_2 or sulphuric acid), the collector contained in the filtrate can be recycled into flotation (Blake 1972).

Anionic depressants other than the OH^- ion may also compete with an anionic collector for adhesion to the mineral surface. The HS^- ion and especially the CN^- ion serve as depressants more specific than the OH^- ion in the flotation of sulphide minerals. The relationships

$$\frac{[I^-]}{[HS^-]^b} = C$$

and

$$\frac{[I^-]}{[CN^-]^b} = C$$

apply to these: C and b are different for different minerals and different collector ions I^-. The CN^- or HS^- anion is usually introduced into the solution in the form of an alkali salt (NaCN or $Na_2S \cdot 9H_2O$). In the possession of the relevant constants of dissociation, the quantity of anions released by the salts can be calculated for any pH (or $[H^+]$). Table 2.17 states dissociation constants K (and $pK = -\log K$ parameters) for a number of inorganic and organic acids and bases. The dissociation constant of hydrogen cyanide, HCN, is

$$K_{HCN} = \frac{[H^+][CN^-]}{[HCN]} = 4.7 \cdot 10^{-10}$$

at 18 °C (it is $7.2 \cdot 10^{-10}$ at 25 °C); the dissociation constant of hydrogen sulphide, H_2S, is

$$K_{H_2S} = \frac{[H^+][HS^-]}{[H_2S]} = 10^{-7},$$

Table 2.17. Dissociation constants K and pH $= -\log K$ parameters of some acids and bases in water, at 20 °C

	pK	K
Acetic acid	4.75	$1.76 \cdot 10^{-5}$
Acrylic acid	4.25	$5.6 \cdot 10^{-5}$
Aniline	9.42	$3.82 \cdot 10^{-10}$
Benzoic acid	4.19	$6.46 \cdot 10^{-5}$
Caproic acid (18°)	4.83	$1.43 \cdot 10^{-5}$
Chloroacetic acid	2.85	$1.4 \cdot 10^{-3}$
Citric acid 1. (18°)	3.08	$8.4 \cdot 10^{-4}$
Citric acid 2.	4.74	$1.8 \cdot 10^{-5}$
Citric acid 3.	5.40	$4.0 \cdot 10^{-6}$
Dichloroacetic acid	1.48	$3.32 \cdot 10^{-2}$
Diethyl amine	3.02	$9.6 \cdot 10^{-4}$
Diisobutyl amine	3.32	$4.8 \cdot 10^{-4}$
Diisopropil amine	1.95	$1.13 \cdot 10^{-3}$
Dimethyl amine	3.28	$5.2 \cdot 10^{-4}$
Diphenylacetic acid	3.94	$1.15 \cdot 10^{-4}$
Ethyl amine	3.25	$5.6 \cdot 10^{-4}$
Ethylene diamine	4.07	$8.5 \cdot 10^{-5}$
Formic acid (20°)	3.75	$1.77 \cdot 10^{-4}$
Glycine	9.78	$1.67 \cdot 10^{-10}$
Glycol	14.22	$6.0 \cdot 10^{-15}$
Glycolic acid	3.83	$1.48 \cdot 10^{-4}$
Heptylic acid	4.89	$1.28 \cdot 10^{-5}$
Hexylic acid	4.88	$1.31 \cdot 10^{-5}$
Hydrazine	5.52	$3.0 \cdot 10^{-6}$
Hydroquinine	5.33	$4.7 \cdot 10^{-6}$
Hydroquinine (20°)	10.35	$4.5 \cdot 10^{-11}$
Hydroxylamine	7.97	$1.07 \cdot 10^{-8}$
Isopropil amine	3.28	$5.3 \cdot 10^{-4}$
Lactic acid (100°)	3.08	$8.4 \cdot 10^{-4}$
m-chloraniline	10.54	$2.88 \cdot 10^{-11}$
m-cresol	10.01	$9.8 \cdot 10^{-11}$
m-toluidine	9.31	$4.92 \cdot 10^{-10}$
Maleic acid 1.	1.83	$1.42 \cdot 10^{-2}$
Maleic acid 2.	6.07	$8.57 \cdot 10^{-7}$
Malonic acid 1.	2.83	$1.49 \cdot 10^{-3}$
Malonic acid 2.	5.69	$2.03 \cdot 10^{-6}$
Methyl amine	3.36	$4.38 \cdot 10^{-4}$
Methyl diethyl amine	3.57	$2.7 \cdot 10^{-4}$
n-butyl amine	3.39	$4.09 \cdot 10^{-4}$
n-butyric acid (20°)	4.81	$1.54 \cdot 10^{-5}$
n-diethyl amine	7.44	$3.65 \cdot 10^{-8}$
n-dimethyl aniline	8.94	$1.15 \cdot 10^{-9}$
n-diphenyl amine (15°)	13.12	$7.6 \cdot 10^{-14}$
n-methyl aniline	9.30	$5.0 \cdot 10^{-10}$
n-valeric acid	4.82	$1.51 \cdot 10^{-5}$

Table 2.17 (continued)

	pK	K
o-chloraniline (15°)	11.44	$3.77 \cdot 10^{-12}$
o-cresol	10.20	$6.3 \cdot 10^{-11}$
o-toluidine	9.61	$2.47 \cdot 10^{-10}$
Oxalic acid 1.	1.23	$5.9 \cdot 10^{-2}$
Oxalic acid 2.	4.19	$6.4 \cdot 10^{-5}$
p-chloraniline	10.07	$8.45 \cdot 10^{-11}$
p-cresol	10.17	$6.7 \cdot 10^{-11}$
p-toluidine	8.92	$1.18 \cdot 10^{-9}$
Papaverine	8.10	$8.0 \cdot 10^{-9}$
Phenol (20°)	9.89	$1.28 \cdot 10^{-10}$
Phenylacetic acid (18°)	4.28	$5.2 \cdot 10^{-5}$
Phthalic acid 1.	2.89	$1.3 \cdot 10^{-3}$
Phthalic acid 2.	4.41	$3.9 \cdot 10^{-5}$
Picric acid	0.38	$4.2 \cdot 10^{-1}$
Propionic acid	4.87	$1.34 \cdot 10^{-5}$
Pyridine (20°)	8.77	$1.71 \cdot 10^{-9}$
Pyroxylidine	2.89	$1.3 \cdot 10^{-3}$
Quinidine 1. (15°)	5.43	$3.7 \cdot 10^{-6}$
Quinidine 2. (15°)	10.00	$1.0 \cdot 10^{-10}$
Quinine 1. (15°)	5.96	$1.1 \cdot 10^{-6}$
Quinine 2. (15°)	9.87	$1.35 \cdot 10^{-10}$
Quinoline	9.20	$6.3 \cdot 10^{-10}$
Quinoline	9.20	$6.3 \cdot 10^{-10}$
Strychnine	6.00	$1.0 \cdot 10^{-6}$
Tannic acid	4.41	$3.9 \cdot 10^{-5}$
Tetramethylene diamine	3.26	$5.1 \cdot 10^{-4}$
Thiourea	14.96	$1.1 \cdot 10^{-15}$
Trichloroacetic acid	0.70	$2.0 \cdot 10^{-1}$
Triethyl amine	3.24	$5.65 \cdot 10^{-4}$
Triisobutyl amine	3.58	$2.6 \cdot 10^{-4}$
Trimethyl amine	4.26	$5.45 \cdot 10^{-5}$
Urea	13.82	$1.5 \cdot 10^{-14}$
Uric acid (12°)	3.89	$1.3 \cdot 10^{-4}$
α-naphthol	3.70	$2.0 \cdot 10^{-4}$
β-naphthol	4.22	$6.0 \cdot 10^{-5}$
α-naphthyl amine	10.08	$8.36 \cdot 10^{-11}$
β-naphthyl amine	9.89	$1.29 \cdot 10^{-10}$

0.1 to 0.01 *n* inorganic acids and bases

	pK	K
Arsenous acid	9.23	$6.0 \cdot 10^{-10}$
Arsenic acid 1. (18°)	2.25	$5.62 \cdot 10^{-3}$
Arsenic acid 2. (18°)	6.77	$1.70 \cdot 10^{-7}$
Arsenic acid 3. (18°)	11.60	$3.95 \cdot 10^{-12}$
Boric acid 1. (20°)	9.14	$7.3 \cdot 10^{-10}$
Boric acid 2. (20°)	12.74	$1.8 \cdot 10^{-13}$
Boric acid 3. (20°)	13.80	$1.6 \cdot 10^{-14}$

Table 2.17 (continued)

	pK	K
Carbonic acid 1.	6.37	$4.30 \cdot 10^{-7}$
Carbonic acid 2.	10.25	$5.61 \cdot 10^{-11}$
Chromic acid 1.	0.74	$1.8 \cdot 10^{-1}$
Chromic acid 2.	6.49	$3.2 \cdot 10^{-7}$
Hydrazine sulphide 1. (18°)	7.04	$9.1 \cdot 10^{-8}$
Hydrazine sulphide 2. (18°)	11.96	$1.1 \cdot 10^{-12}$
Hydrazine peroxide	11.62	$2.4 \cdot 10^{-12}$
Hydrogen cyanide	9.31	$4.93 \cdot 10^{-10}$
Hydrogen fluoride	3.45	$3.53 \cdot 10^{-4}$
Hydrogen sulphide 1.	7.00	$1.0 \cdot 10^{-7}$
Hydrogen sulphide 2.	14.70	$2.0 \cdot 10^{-15}$
Hypochloric acid (18°)	7.53	$2.95 \cdot 10^{-8}$
m-silicic acid 1.	9.70	$2.0 \cdot 10^{-10}$
m-silicic acid 2.	12.00	$1.0 \cdot 10^{-12}$
Nitric acid (12°)	3.37	$4.6 \cdot 10^{-4}$
o-phosphoric acid 1.	2.12	$7.52 \cdot 10^{-3}$
o-phosphoric acid 2.	7.21	$6.23 \cdot 10^{-8}$
o-phosphoric acid 3. (18°)	12.67	$2.2 \cdot 10^{-13}$
o-silicic acid 1. (30°)	9.66	$2.2 \cdot 10^{-10}$
o-silicic acid 2. (30°)	11.70	$2.0 \cdot 10^{-12}$
o-silicic acid 3. (30°)	12.00	$1.0 \cdot 10^{-12}$
o-silicic acid 4. (30°)	12.00	$1.0 \cdot 10^{-12}$
Pyrophosphoric acid 1. (18°)	0.85	$1.4 \cdot 10^{-1}$
Pyrophosphoric acid 2. (18°)	1.49	$3.2 \cdot 10^{-2}$
Pyrophosphoric acid 3. (18°)	5.77	$1.7 \cdot 10^{-6}$
Pyrophosphoric acid 4. (18°)	8.22	$6.0 \cdot 10^{-9}$
Sulphurous acid 1.	1.81	$1.54 \cdot 10^{-2}$
Sulphurous acid 2.	6.91	$1.02 \cdot 10^{-7}$
Sulphuric acid 1.	0.75	$4.5 \cdot 10^{-1}$
Sulphuric acid 2.	1.91	$1.2 \cdot 10^{-2}$

$$K_{\text{HS}-} = \frac{[\text{H}^+][\text{S}^{2-}]}{[\text{HS}^-]} = 2 \cdot 10^{-15}$$

at 20 °C. In other words, the ratio

$$\frac{[\text{CN}^-]}{[\text{HCN}]}$$

or

$$\frac{[\text{HS}^-]}{[\text{H}_2\text{S}]}$$

increases as H^+ decreases (the pH increases): at a higher pH, more depressant anions (CN^- or HS^-) are released by a given concentration of NaCN or $\text{Na}_2\text{S} \cdot 9\text{H}_2\text{O}$. Conversely, at a higher pH, less reagent salt will suffice to produce

219

a given concentration of depressant anions. (The hydrolysis of the salts in question produces a strong base, NaOH, and a weak acid, HCN or H_2S, respectively.) Figure 2.57 shows the molar percentage distribution vs. the pH of HCN and CN^-, on the one hand, and of H_2S, HS^- and S^{2-}, on the other.

Parts A and B of Fig. 2.58 state as a function of the pH the depressant concentration (NaCN and $Na_2S \cdot 9H_2O$, respectively) required to detach from the bubbles different sulphide mineral grains in the presence of 25 milligrams per litre of potassium ethyl xanthate (KEtX). Bubbles will get attached to the particles below the curves but not above them. The critical NaCN concentration for chalcocite is about 600 mg/l at pH = 9 and 420 mg/l at pH = 13. (Gaudin 1957; Rogers 1962; Wark 1955).

Critical anion concentrations of CN^- or HS^- calculated from the curves in parts A and B of Fig. 2.58 using the appropriate dissociation constants are found to be near-constant over broad pH ranges for each individual mineral.

Figure 2.59 shows for an example the critical concentrations of CN^- in a solution containing 25 mg/l potassium ethyl xanthate, KEtX (Wark 1955). The abrupt breakdown near the right-hand ends of the lines, which are parallel to the axis of abscissae up to there, is due to the OH^- ions compounding the depressing action of the CN^- ions. The "constant" critical CN^- ion concentration that detaches the mineral grains from the bubbles in the presence of 25 mg/l KEtX can be read off the figure. The critical HS^- anion concentrations required to cancel the collector action of 25 mg/l (= $1.56 \cdot 10^{-4}$ mole per litre) KEtX can be calculated by an analogous procedure, starting from the curves in part B of Fig. 2.58. Table 2.18 lists side by side the critical pA^- and mg/l

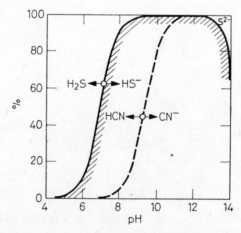

Fig. 2.57. Molar percentage distribution of the abundances of HCN and CN^- and of H_2S, HS^- and S^{2-} vs. the pH

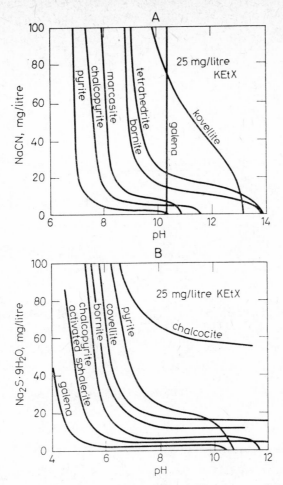

Fig. 2.58. Critical $c = c(\text{pH})$ curves of floatability (adherence to bubbles) for different sulphide minerals using 25 mg/l potassium ethyl xanthate collector, in the presence A — of NaCN, B — of $Na_2S \cdot 9H_2O$

concentrations of the depressant ions OH^-, CN^- and HS^- for some minerals in the presence of 25 mg/l ($= 1.56 \cdot 10^{-4}$ moles per litre) KEtX.

Parts A and B of Fig. 2.60 show graphs of critical concentration of sodium sulphide and HS^-, respectively, for galena and potassium amyl xanthate (KAmX). The graphs separate the domains of adhesion between bubbles and mineral grains (below and to the right) from those of non-adhesion (above and to the left) (Gaudin 1957). By Part B of the figure,

$$\frac{[\text{KAmX}^-]}{[\text{HS}^-]} = 10 ,$$

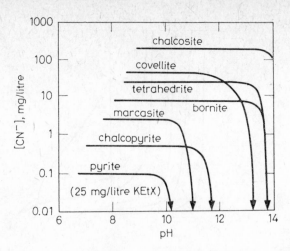

Fig. 2.59. Critical CN⁻ concentration of the floatability of sulphide minerals vs. the pH using 25 mg/l potassium ethyl xanthate collector

regardless of the pH (here, $b = 1$). The exponent b of the equation

$$\frac{[\text{EtX}^-]}{[\text{CN}^-]^b} = C$$

approximately equals 2, e.g. for chalcopyrite. Now if $b = 2$, then the xanthate dosages

$$5 \qquad\qquad 25 \qquad\qquad 625 \text{ mg/l}$$

give almost equal values:

$$C = \qquad 0.5 \qquad\qquad 0.6 \qquad\qquad 0.8,$$

Table 2.18. Critical concentrations of OH⁻, CN⁻, HS⁻ in the flotation of sulphide minerals using 25 mg/l ($= 1.56 \cdot 10^{-4}$ mole/litre) potassium ethyl xanthate

Mineral	pOH⁻	pCN⁻	pHS⁻	mg/l		
				[OH⁻]	[CN⁻]	[HS⁻]
Arsenopyrite	5.22	—	—	0.1	—	—
Bornite	0.046	3.602	4.40	$1.5 \cdot 10^4$	$2.5 \cdot 10^{-4}$	1.3
Chalchocite	0.00	2.162	3.721	$1.7 \cdot 10^4$	$6.9 \cdot 10^{-3}$	6.4
Chalchopyrite	2.046	4.638	5.046	$1.5 \cdot 10^2$	$2.3 \cdot 10^{-5}$	0.3
Covellite	0.523	2.92	4.30	$5.0 \cdot 10^3$	$1.2 \cdot 10^{-3}$	1.7
Galena	3.22	0.00	6.70	10	1	0.007
Marcasite	3.00	4.018	—	17	$9.6 \cdot 10^{-5}$	—
Pyrite	3.155	5.42	4.124	12	$3.8 \cdot 10^{-6}$	2.5
Pyrrhotite	8.00	—	—	$1.7 \cdot 10^{-4}$	—	—
Tetrahedrite	0.046	3.114	—	$1.5 \cdot 10^{-4}$	$7.7 \cdot 10^{-4}$	—

whereas the exponent $b = 1$ gives widely different ones:

$$C = \quad 4.0 \qquad\qquad 9.4 \qquad\qquad 57.$$

The CN^- ion depresses pyrite and sphalerite intensely but has no depressing influence at all on galena ($b \to \infty$!). The HS^- ion, on the other hand, is a strong depressant of galena and a less strong one of pyrite. It does not depress molybdenite at all. (Of the non-sulphides, the HS^- ion depresses e.g. quartz, but not cassiterite.) In an alkaline medium, Na_2SO_4 also depresses every sulphide mineral except molybdenite. (Replacing $Na_2S \cdot 9H_2O$ by Na_2SO_4 increased the Mo content of the concentrate produced in the flotation of one complex ore

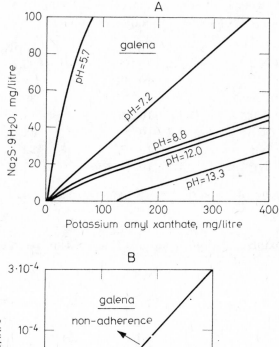

Fig. 2.60. Floatability of galena: critical concentration of A — sodium sulphide, B — HS^- vs. potassium amyl xanthate collector concentration

from 55 to 57 percent, while increasing Mo recovery from 55 to 71 percent.) Molybdenite in its turn is successfully depressed by hydrophilic polymers (dextrin, starch, glue, etc.). For example, 8 mg/l dextrin reduces the contact angle of molybdenite from 86° to 0° and its recovery from 92% to 2%, regardless of the pH.

The depressing action of the CN^- ion is due to the fact that the cyanogen, $(CN)_2$, formed in the course of the reaction constitutes complex metal cyanide anions with the base metal cations (e.g. Cu^{2+}):

$$Cu^{2+} + 3CN^- \rightarrow Cu(CN)_2^- + {}^1/_2(CN)_2;$$

these repel the identically charged collector ions. These complex metal cyanide anions dissociate very little into free metal cations and CN^- anions. The dissociation constants K of some of them are as follows:

	K	$\sim pK$
$Cu(CN)_2^-$	$2 \cdot 10^{-24}$	23.7
$Fe^{III}(CN)_6^{3-}$	10^{-42},	42
$Fe^{II}(CN)_6^{4-}$	10^{-35},	35
$Cd(CN)_4^{2-}$	$1.4 \cdot 10^{-19}$,	18.9
$Hg(CN)_4^{2-}$	$4 \cdot 10^{-42}$,	42
$Ni(CN)_4^{2-}$	10^{-22},	22
$Zn(CN)_4^{2-}$	$1.2 \cdot 10^{-18}$,	17.9

that is, if the concentration of free CN^- ions is, e.g.,

pCN^-	7	5	3,

then the approximate ratio of concentrations of the free metal cation to the complex metal cyanide anion is,

for Cu^+,	9.7	13.7	17.7
for Fe^{2+},	-7	5	17
for Fe^{3+},	0	12	24
for Zn^{2+},	-10.1	-2.1	5.9.

Pyritic ores tend to release a great deal of ferrous sulphate into solution. Let e.g. $pFe^{2+} = 3$ in the solution. Assuming a 4 : 1 dilution, this corresponds to some 0.4 kg per ton Fe_2SO_4, since

$$0.056 \text{ g/l } Fe^{2+} = 0.104 \text{ g/l } Fe_2SO_4 \text{ corresponds to } pFe^{2+} = 3.$$

If

$$pCN = 5$$

then

$$p\left(\frac{Fe^{2+}}{Fe(CN)_6^{4-}}\right) = 35 - (5 \cdot 6) = 5,$$

that is,
$$pFe^{2+} = 3 + 5 = 8.$$

The solubility product of $Fe(OH)_2$ is
$$pL_{Fe(OH)_2} = 13.8$$

$$pOH^- = \frac{1}{2}(13.8 - 8) = 2.9,$$

that is,
$$[Fe^{2+}] = [Fe(OH)_2]$$

at $pH \simeq 11.1$; at any pH less than that, the iron will dissolve, largely in the form of a complex cyanide. In the absence of CN^- ions, on the other hand, a ferrous hydroxide precipitate appears at $pOH^- = \frac{1}{2}(13.8 - 3) = 5.4$, that is, at $pH = 8.6$

$$[OH^-] = 4 \cdot 10^{-6}$$
$$pOH^- = 6 - \log 4 = 5.4$$
$$pH^+ = 14 - 5.4 = 8.6.$$

If the iron in ferrous sulphate were to oxidize to $\sim 10^{-3}$ mole ferric iron, $pFe^{3+} = 3$, then, since
$$p\left(\frac{Fe^{3+}}{Fe(CN)_6^{3-}}\right) = 12,$$

one would have
$$pFe^{3+} = 3 + 12 = 15.$$

The solubility product of ferric hydroxide being
$$pL_{Fe(OH)_3} = 37$$

ferric iron is dissolved at
$$pOH^- = \frac{1}{3}(37 - 15) = 7.3,$$

that is, below a $pH \simeq 6.7$ or, in the absence of cyanide, at
$$pOH^- = \frac{1}{3}(37 - 3) = 11.3,$$

that is, below a $pH \simeq 2.7$. In other words, the concentration of ferrous vs. ferric iron in a solution can be regulated over a broad range by adjusting the concentration of the cyanide ion.

The critical concentration of HS^- is much lower as a rule than that of CN^-. Moreover, the HS^- ion oxidizes rather readily, which makes its concentration harder to adjust in practice than that of the CN^- ion. In greater dosages,

15

it tends to effect the desorption of the collector (xanthate, aerofloat, oleic acid) from the surfaces of flotated-out sulphide mineral grains: it is therefore well suited for cancelling the angle of contact (the floatability) of concentrates of such minerals produced by bulk flotation, as a preliminary to their differential flotation (Mellgren and Lwakatare 1968). It is for a similar purpose that films of amines or other collectors are oxidized with hypochlorites, or carboxyl-type collectors are removed with sulphuric acid from phosphate surfaces prior to the separation by amine flotation of quartz contaminating the concentrate.

Other anions may also exert a depressive action on sulphides. In the separation of lead and zinc sulphides, e.g., alkali sulphites, alkali hydrosulphites or sulphur dioxide may be used. Some other sulphoxy compounds also function as depressants. Sulphurous acid (H_2SO_3), for example, constitutes complex compounds with many metals (Mn, Fe, Co, Ni, Cu, Zn, Ag, Cd, Pt, Au, Hg, etc.): the Hg, Co and Pt complexes thus formed are especially stable. Ag, Pb, Hg, Au and Cu^+ constitute complexes with thiosulphates ($H_2S_2O_2$, $H_2S_2O_3$). Strong oxidizers such as alkali dichromates or permanganates may also have a depressive influence, in some cases by oxidizing xanthate ions to dixanthogen. (Dixanthogen is a less vigorous collector than the xanthate ion.)

Cations that form insoluble precipitates with an anionic collector may be regarded as pseudodepressants. On the other hand, metal cations that vie with a cationic collector for absorption at the metal surface are direct depressants. Chalcopyrite e.g. can be depressed in the presence of some primary or tetra-alkyl amine collectors with zinc sulphate, silver nitrate or lead acetate; it will not, on the other hand, be depressed by copper or barium salts. The depressing action of cations, then, is also specific to different sulphides and collectors.

2.2.5.2. In the **flotation of oxides**, the ions H^+ and OH^- as potential determinants play roles of some prominence. The depression of oxide minerals can be achieved in a number of ways, including changing the sign of the surface charge, making ions compete for adsorption, neutralizing activating ions (by precipitation or by the formation of complexes), initiating direct chemical reactions or introducing hydrophilic colloids.

The first two methods were discussed above in some depth. Neutralizing the activating ions is an excellent method of depressing minerals that can be floated after activation only. The addition of reagents that form complex compounds with the activating ion is important in the flotation of non-ore minerals, where the minerals to be separated are near-identical as to flotation behaviour, so that their separation must of necessity be based on very slight differences. The complex-forming reagents in question reduce the concentration in the solution of those free activating ions that would otherwise get adsorbed at the surfaces of the undesirable mineral, thereby enabling those surfaces to adsorb the collecting reagent instead. Complex-forming reagents used to eliminate

Table 2.19. Logarithms of stability constants (positive values) and of dissociation constants (negative values) of some complex compounds

Ion	Complex-forming compound-radical					
	EDTA	DTPA	Citric acid	$P_2O_7^{4-}$	$P_3O_9^{2-}$	$CO_3^=$
Ca^{++}	10.7	10.74	3.2	5.0	3.48	8.3
Mg^{++}	8.69	—	3.2	5.7	3.31	4.1
Ba^{++}	7.76	—	2.1	4.64	3.35	8.8
Cu^{++}	18.8	21.1	14.2	7—8.7*	—	9.6
Fe^{++}	14.3	16.5	—	(+)	—	10.7
Fe^{+++}	25.1	28.6	—	+	—	—
Al^{+++}	16.1	—	—	(+)	—	—

* $\log K_2 = 3.8$.

various cations include citric acid, tannic acid or quebracho, soda ash, certain phosphates, ethylene diamine tetraacetate (EDTA or complexon), diethylene triamine pentaacetate (DTPA), etc. Their action recalls that of cyanide on the sulphide minerals. For example, EDTA and sodium hexametaphosphate are useful in neutralizing activation by Ca^{2+}, Fe^{2+} and Mg^{2+} ions. Table 2.19 lists the negative logarithms pK of the dissociation constants (solubility products)

$$K = \frac{[ML]}{[M][L]}$$

of certain complexes (where M is the metal and L is the complex-forming anionic reagent).

2.2.5.3. A reagent in common use for the **depression of non-ore minerals** (silicates) and for slimes dispersion is water glass or sodium silicate, Na_2SiO_3. In solution, it forms colloidal polysilicate polymers which get adsorbed at the silicate surfaces, thanks to the chemical similarity between them. The degree of polymerization depends — in addition to the nature of the other alkali salts present in the solution — on the $Na_2O : SiO_2$ concentration ratio. Up to a ratio of 2 : 1, dimers tend to predominate; at higher ratios, polymers tend to abound. By adjusting the ratio, the intensity of depression and, through it, the sharpness of separation may be influenced. (For instance, in the flotation of scheelite in a silicate gangue, optimum recovery was achieved at a pH = 10 in the 2.4 : 1 to 2.9 : 1 ratio range.) Figure 2.61 shows the relative abundances of H_2SiO_3, $HSiO_3^-$, and SiO_3^{2-}, formed on the dissociation of sodium silicate, vs. the pH (Fuerstenau et al. 1968).

Water glass is a commercial product containing 50% or so Na_2SiO_3, readily soluble in hot water. (Solid sodium silicate containing little or no hydrate water is also available but seldom used because dissolving it requires an autoclave,

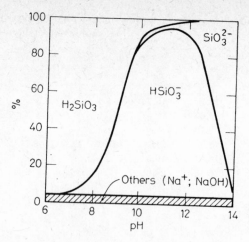

Fig. 2.61. Percentage distribution vs. the pH of the compounds H_2SiO_3, $HSiO_3^-$, SiO_3^{2-} and others formed on the dissociation of Na_2SiO_3

its temperature of dissolution being higher than the boiling temperature of water.)

Hydrophilic organic colloids such as starch, gelatine, gum arabic, proteins, etc. are also used in flotation as depressants. All are large molecules made up by a repetition of more or less identical elements: they often constitute micellae that, in the solution, acquire a charge or an electric double layer. (The charge is due to the dissociation of ionic components from the molecules rather than to the adsorption of alien ions.) These macromolecular "electrolytes" belong to one of three groups: (1) acidic, e.g. with $-COO^-$ radicals (gum arabic) or $-OSO_3^-$ radicals (agar); (2) alkaline, e.g. with $-NH_3^+$ radicals, or (3) amphoteric, such as natural glues or proteins. For the amphoteric compounds, the pH is a potential determinant; as a result, they behave as alkaline (cation-active) colloids below their isoelectric points and as acidic (anion-active) ones above it. Soluble salts also affect the charge of a colloid. Getting adsorbed on mineral particles of opposite charge, these macromolecules forestall the adsorption of a collector. Crystal chemistry presumably also affects the adsorption of colloids at the mineral-grain surfaces. Some organic colloids such as starch, glue, etc., can be used to depress minerals having a native floatability (talc, graphite, hard coals, etc.). The two principal constituents of starch are amylopectin, forming the shells of the starch granules, and chain-shaped amylose, forming their inner parts. The bulk formula of the latter is $(C_6H_{10}O_5)_n$. Cold water dissolves only the light fractions of amylose; in hot water, the granules will swell and burst and constitute a homogeneous jelly (paste, starch gum, dextrin). Amylose leaches out in dilute bases (a fair grade starch solution can be prepared e.g. by boiling a starch paste containing some five weight percent starch in a two percent NaOH solution).

228

2.2.6. Response of mineral species to activating reagents

2.2.6.1. The paradigmatic (and most important) **example of sulphide activation** is the activation of sphalerite by copper sulphate (by Cu^{2+} ions);

$$\boxed{ZnS}^{Zn^{2+}} + Cu^{2+} \rightleftarrows \boxed{ZnS}^{Cu^{2+}} + Zn^{2+}.$$

The solubility of copper sulphide ($3.2 \cdot 10^{-38}$) being much less than that of zinc sulphide ($6.9 \cdot 10^{-26}$), the copper ions constitute an insoluble film of copper sulphide at the sphalerite surface. This film adsorbs e.g. xanthate ions fairly well. Cu^{2+} as an activator may be replaced by other base metal cations (e.g. Pb^{2+}, Ag^+, Hg^{2+}), provided the sulphide compounds of those are less soluble than zinc sulphide. Other sulphides can also be activated by means of copper or lead salts; many non-sulphide minerals can also be activated by means of different cations (e.g. Ca^{2+}, Ba^{2+}, Cu^{2+}, Pb^{2+}, Zn^{2+}, etc.).

The metallic elements may be arranged in a sequence of their "relative potentials", that is, their propensity to get cationized by the loss of one or more electrons (cf. Table 2.20). The values stated in the table are relative voltages E^0_{ox} referred to the hydrogen ion as zero, in volts, at unity activity and 25 °C temperature. The sequence begins with the most negative elements and ends with the most positive ones. A cation farther back in the sequence will displace from its compounds any cation preceding it. (For example, copper displaces zinc, which precedes it, from the sphalerite surface.)

A similar sequence for anions is presented as Table 2.21. Sequences of this style can be written up also for transitions from one cation of a given metal to another of a different valence, from one anion to another of a different valence, for the interactions of elements with acid radicals, for hydrolysis reactions (involving electron loss) of elements and ions (ongoing oxidation), and

Table 2.20. Sequence of relative potentials of metallic elements

Li^+	K^+	Ba^{2+}	Sr^{2+}	Ca^{2+}	Na^+	Mg^{2+}	Th^{4+}	Be^{2+}	U^{3+}	Al^{3+}
3.04	2.93	2.90	2.89	2.87	2.71	2.37	1.90	1.85	1.80	1.66
Ti^{2+}	Zr^{4+}	Mn^{2+}	Zn^{2+}	Cr^{3+}	Te^{2+}	Fe^{2+}	Cd^{2+}	Co^{2+}	Ni^{2+}	Mo^{3+}
1.63	1.53	1.18	0.76	0.74	0.51	0.44	0.40	0.28	0.25	0.20
Sn^{2+}	Pb^{2+}	H^+	Cu^{2+}	Cu^+	Hg^+	Ag^+	Pd^{2+}	Pt^{2+}	Au^{3+}	Au^-
0.14	0.13	0	-0.34	$-0:52$	-0.79	-0.80	-0.99	-1.20	$--1.50$	-1.68

for oxidation or reduction by means of the anions of alkaline solutions (cf. Table 2.22).

One mineral of an ore may often be activated by the more positive dissolved ions of another mineral. Such auto-activation — undesirable because it impairs the selectivity of flotation — can be prevented in a variety of ways. The typical example is the deactivation of sphalerite activated by copper, by means of cyanide ions which constitute cuprocyanide ions ($Cu(CN)_2^-$) and greatly reduce thereby the concentrations of the Cu^+ and Cu^{2+} ions in the solution: the complex ions are not adsorbed by the sphalerite surfaces, nor do they react with the xanthate ions. Figure 2.62 shows the critical NaCN curves of sphalerite at different copper sulphate concentrations, in the presence of 25 mg/l potassium

Table 2.21. Sequence of relative potentials of anions

S^{2-}	Se^{2-}	I^-	Br^-	Cl^-	F^-
$+0.92$	$+0.78$	-0.54	-1.07	-1.39	-2.85

Table 2.22. Relative potentials E_{ox}^0 of some interactions and reactions

		E_{ox}^0			E_{ox}^0
U^{3+}	$\rightarrow U^{4+} + e$	$+0.61$	H_2Te	$\rightarrow Te + 2H^+ + 2e$	$+0.72$
Ti^{2+}	$\rightarrow Ti^{3+} + e$	$+0.37$	AsH_3	$\rightarrow As + 3H^+ + 3e$	$+0.60$
Cu^+	$\rightarrow Cu^{2+} + e$	-0.15	UO_2^+	$\rightarrow UO_2^{2+} + e$	-0.05
Fe^{2+}	$\rightarrow Fe^{3+} + e$	-0.77	$Fe(CN)_6^{4-}$	$\rightarrow Fe(CN)_6^{3-} + e$	-0.36
Mn^{2+}	$\rightarrow Mn^{3+} + e$	-1.51	MnO_4^{2-}	$\rightarrow MnO_4^- + e$	-0.56
Co^{2+}	$\rightarrow Co^{3+} + e$	-1.82	$Cu(CN)_2^-$	$\rightarrow Cu^{2+} + 2CN^- + e$	-1.12
Ag^+	$\rightarrow Ag^{2+} + e$	-1.98	$2NH_4^+$	$\rightarrow N_2H_5^+ + 3H^+ + 2e$	-1.27
$Si + 6F^-$	$\rightarrow SiF_6^{2-} + 4e$	$+1.20$	$Ti + H_2O$	$\rightarrow TiO^{2+} + 2H^+ + 4e$	$+0.89$
$Pb + 2Cl^-$	$\rightarrow PbCl_2 + 2e$	$+0.27$	$Si + 2H_2O$	$\rightarrow SiO_2 + 4H^+ + 4e$	$+0.86$
$Cu + Cl^-$	$\rightarrow CuCl + e$	-0.14	$Ti^{3+} + H_2O$	$\rightarrow TiO^{2+} + 2H^+ + e$	-0.10
$Ag + Cl^-$	$\rightarrow AgCl + e$	-0.22	$Bi + H_2O$	$\rightarrow BiO^+ + 2H^+ + 3e$	-0.32
$Ag + BrO_3^-$	$\rightarrow AgBrO_3 + e$	-0.55	$U^{4+} + 2H_2O$	$\rightarrow UO_2^{2+} + 4H^+ + 2e$	-0.33
$2Ag + SO_4^{2-}$	$\rightarrow Ag_2SO_4 + 2e$	-0.65	$Mn^{2+} + 2H_2O$	$\rightarrow MnO_2 + 4H^+ + 2e$	-1.23
$Au + 4Cl^-$	$\rightarrow AuCl_4 + 3e$	-1.00	$Mn^{2+} + 4H_2O$	$\rightarrow MnO_4 + 8H^+ + 5e$	-1.51

		E_{ox}^0
$Ca + 2OH^-$	$\rightarrow Ca(OH)_2 + 2e^-$	$+3.03$
$Mg + 2H_2O^-$	$\rightarrow Mg(OH)_2 + 2e^-$	$+2.69$
$Zn + S^{2-}$	$\rightarrow ZnS + 2e^-$	$+1.44$
$Pb + S^{2-}$	$\rightarrow PbS + 2e^-$	$+0.95$
$Fe + 2OH^-$	$\rightarrow Fe(OH)_2 + 2e^-$	$+0.88$
$Fe(OH)_2 + OH^-$	$\rightarrow Fe(OH)_3 + e^-$	$+0.56$
$Mn(OH)_2 + OH^-$	$\rightarrow Mn(OH)_3 + e^-$	-1.10

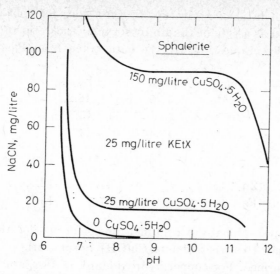

Fig. 2.62. Critical NaCN graphs of sphalerite at different copper sulphate dosages, vs. the pH, in the presence of 25 mg/l potassium ethyl xanthate

ethyl xanthate, KEtX (Wark 1955). These critical curves of bubble adhesion have a plateau over a wide pH range in the vicinity of the stoichiometric CN : Cu ratio. Above that ratio, there is some excess cyanide which practically keeps the copper ions out of solution (i.e., bubbles do not adhere). Below it, there is some excess copper in the solution, so that bubbles can get attached to the sphalerite grains. The depression of sphalerite requires in practice a molar ratio

$$\frac{CN}{Cu} \gtrsim 3$$

in the solution. As this ratio declines below 2, sphalerite starts floating out. At and above 6, there is an overplus of cyanide, and the subsequent activation of sphalerite requires too much copper sulphate.

Any lowering of the copper ion concentration in the solution makes the reaction

$$ZnS + Cu^{2+} \rightleftarrows CuS + Zn^{2+}$$

proceed in the direction of the lower arrow, entailing the dissolution of the CuS film formed at the sphalerite surface. A similar result may be achieved by increasing the concentration of Zn^{2+} ions in the solution. For deactivating sphalerite, zinc sulphate is often used together with or instead of cyanide. It should be established by experiment separately for each lead-zinc ore to be flotated differentially (selectively), what is best: cyanide in itself, zinc sulphide in itself or a combination of the two.

231

The equilibrium ratio of activation by Cu^{2+} ions for sphalerite and pyrrhotite is obtained as a rule of thumb by forming the ratio of solubilities of the metal sulphides in question. By the data taken from Parts A and B of Table 2.13,

M	pL_{MS}	$pL_{M(OH)_2}$
Cu^{2+}	37.5	18.2,
Zn^{2+}	25.1	15.7,
Fe^{2+}	18.4	14.8.

That is,

$$p(Zn^{2+}/Cu^{2+}) = 25.1 - 37.5 = -12.4,$$
$$p(Fe^{2+}/Cu^{2+}) = 18.4 - 37.5 = -19.1.$$

On adding copper sulphate to a normal-run sphalerite-flotation pulp, whose pH typically equals 10 or thereabouts, $Cu(OH)_2$ or some other basic copper salt is immediately formed. For copper hydroxide, $pL = 18.2$, and at $pOH^- = 4$, which is tantamount to $pH = 10$,

$$pCu^{2+} = 18.2 - 2(4.0) = 10.2.$$

The critical pM^{2+} of the replacement of zinc (iron) by copper is, respectively,

$$pZn^{2+} = -12.4 + 10.2 = -2.2$$

and

$$pFe^{2+} = -19.1 + 10.2 = -8.9.$$

These very low values of pM^{2+} correspond to very high concentrations $[Zn^{2+}]$ (or $[Fe^{2+}]$): in view of the low solubility of the available Zn (Fe) minerals or hydroxides (e.g. $pZn^{2+} = 15.7 - 8.0 = 7.7$; $pFe^{2+} = 14.8 - 8.0 = 6.8$ at $pOH^- = 4$), such concentrations do not arise, that is, the activation reaction involving copper continues until either the copper hydroxide or the zinc (iron) sulphide is consumed entirely.

The fact that, in practice, pyrrhotite is activated less than sphalerite is due to the rapid and intense oxidation of the pyrrhotite surface. In the presence of dissolved oxygen, ferrous iron is readily converted to ferric iron; ferric hydroxide, ferric oxide and the alkaline salts of the ferric ion, being practically insoluble ($pL_{Fe(OH)_3} = 37$) can thus form a protective coating on the pyrrhotite surface, forestalling the exchange reaction between the ferric and the copper ions.

At very high pH's, on the other hand, the reactions

$$ZnS + 2\, OH^- \rightarrow Zn(OH)_2 + S^{2-};$$

$$FeS + 2\, OH^- \rightarrow Fe(OH)_2 + S^{2+}$$

will take place. The critical pH is 12.2 for sphalerite and 11.2 for pyrrhotite. The S^{2-} ions thus formed pry the Cu^{2+} ions loose from the surfaces of the mineral grains and precipitate them, increasing thereby the required dosage of copper sulphite. (For example, at pH $= 10.2$, in a pulp containing no free oxygen, both minerals become activated by incorporating Cu^{2+} ions into their surfaces; in the presence of oxygen, on the other hand, only sphalerite is activated, whereas the activation of pyrrhotite is prevented by the coating of ferric salts formed at its surface (Bushell et al. 1961). The equilibrium ratio of activation of sphalerite by Pb^{2+} ions is as low as

$$\frac{[Pb^{2+}]}{[Zn^{2+}]} \simeq 10^3 \, ;$$

that is, a dose of zinc sulphate prevents the activation of sphalerite by lead more readily than its activation by copper.

In the case of pyrite, the reactions

$$FeS_2 \rightarrow Fe^{2+} + S_2^{2-}, \ S_2^{2-} \rightarrow S^0 + S^{2-}, \ Cu^{2+} + S^{2-} \rightarrow CuS$$

take place; they can be condensed into the reaction equation

$$FeS_2 + Cu^{2+} \rightarrow CuS + S^0 + Fe^{2+}.$$

In other words, no sulphide ions are produced at high pH. This implies that pyrite is activated by the Cu^{2+} ion, whether or not there is some free oxygen present. The activation of pyrite can be forestalled by introducing lime (Ca^{2+} ions), which — at high enough OH^- concentrations — presumably constitutes a protective film of calcium peroxide at the grain surfaces. Pyrite depressed by lime can be reactivated with sulphuric acid (by acidizing the solution), or — if it is desired to maintain the alkalinity of the pulp — by the dosage of ammonium salts (the nitrate, sulphate, chloride or carbonate) or of sodium sulphide.

Sphalerite activated by cations of copper or some other base metal can also be deactivated by means of sodium sulphide or some other reagent forming an insoluble precipitate with the undesirable activator. In that case, the copper ions are not leached off the sphalerite surface; it is the adsorbed collector (e.g. xanthate) ions that are displaced by HS^- ions: the activated surface will readsorb the xanthate — and sphalerite will float out — as soon as the HS^- ion concentration is lowered again.

Sodium sulphide is not only a depressant or deactivator of sulphide minerals: it also serves to activate the oxides or carbonates of base metals (cerussite, anglesite, malachite, etc.) — those are more soluble than the corresponding sulphides or sulphides whose surface oxidation has progressed too far. In the process, sodium sulphide forms a sulphide coating at the surfaces of the minerals in question; the usual collectors of sulphide minerals get adsorbed rather readily

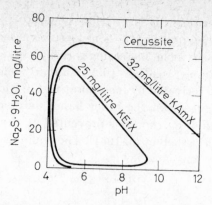

Fig. 2.63. Critical sodium sulphide concentration of cerussite vs. the pH, using 25 mg/l
potassium ethyl xanthate and 32 mg/l potassium amyl xanthate

by that coating. In this sort of sulphidization, however, care must be taken to
use the right dosage because overdoses of sodium sulphide will depress each
and every mineral. Figure 2.63 presents for an example critical sodium sulphide
concentrations for cerussite ($PbCO_3$): the grains will adhere to the bubbles only
within the domains inside the curves (Wark 1955). The sulphidation of cerussite
proceeds fastest in the pH range between 9 and 10.

In sulphidization, alkali sulphides are rather frequently replaced by polysulphides. A hot pulp is an advantage when sulphidizing cerussite, malachite
or oxidic zinc ores, but a drawback when sulphidizing anglesite or chrysocolla.
Sulphidization entails the build-up of CO_3^{2-}, SO_3^{2-} and SO_4^{2-} ions, which impair
flotation performance: in order to remove them, it is indicated to decant the
pulp at intervals and to use fresh water as a makeup.

After the sulphidization of Cu, Pb and Zn oxides or carbonates, polyacrylates
of comparatively small molecular weight are helpful in that they depress
carbonate gangue minerals (calcite, dolomite) and disperse their slimes. Their
dispersing effect is much stronger than that of water glass (Van Lierde 1972).

Prior to the separation into its components of a bulk concentrate of metal
sulphides, the adsorbed collector (xanthate) must be removed from the mineral
grains' surfaces. This can be achieved by introducing sodium sulphide or lime
in fairly large quantities. Prior to separation by differential flotation, the xanthate in the solution is to be removed by decanting the pulp and by adding fresh
makeup water. Hotting up the thickened pulp produced by the collective flotation operation to above 80 °C is another effective means of making the xanthate
hydrolyse and desorb.

2.2.6.2. The main point in activating metallic and non-metallic oxides is the
same as in activating the sulphides: notably, to get ions opposite in charge to
the collector ion adsorbed at the surfaces of the mineral grains to be flotated

out. For example, positively charged corundum (Al_2O_3) cannot be flotated with dodecyl ammonium acetate at a pH $= 6$; it will, on the other hand, flotate well in the presence of $5 \cdot 10^{-3}$ mole Na_2SO_4, which has the effect of turning its zeta potential negative (cf. Fig. 2.15). Sodium sulphate (the SO_4^{2-} ion), then, acts on corundum as an activator in the presence of a cationic collector but as a depressant in the presence of an anionic one.

Quartz can be activated in the presence of an anionic collector (e.g. a carboxylate) using e.g. Ba^{2+}, Ca^{2+}, Cu^{2+}, Pb^{2+}, Al^{3+}, Fe^{3+} cations. In the case of Ca^{2+}, for example, flotation comes about if

$$\frac{[Ca^{2+}]}{[H^+]} > 10^6$$

and

$$\frac{[Ca^{2+}]}{[Na^+]} > 10^{-3}.$$

The attachment of a hydrocarbon chain affects quartz activated with calcium inversely as the minerals that can be flotated without activation using these collectors (e.g. haematite, goethite, etc.). For example, at a given collector concentration, if the pH is increased beyond 9, the floatability of haematite or goethite ceases in the sequence linolenic acid, linoleic acid, oleic acid; the reverse sequence holds for activated quartz. At a pH $= 11$, in the presence of 5 mg/l Ca^{2+} and 10^{-4} mole fatty acid, the recovery of quartz flotation was 100% using linolenic acid ($C_{17}H_{29}COOH$), 96% using linoleic acid ($C_{17}H_{31}COOH$), 47% using oleic acid ($C_{17}H_{33}COOH$) and just 2% using stearic acid ($C_{17}H_{35}COOH$). In order to attain a given recovery, more activator is required in combination with a saturated or less unsaturated collector than with a more unsaturated (less water-repellent) one. Flotation performance depends on the adsorption of the activator first and foremost. On adding NaOH to raise the pH, the negative surface charge increases, promoting the adsorption of activator cations. Flotation performance may, on the other hand, decline again in the very high pH range, with the Na^+ ions starting to compete with the Ca^{2+} ions for the mineral-grain surfaces.

Figure 2.64 shows relative abundances of $Ca(OH)_2$, $CaOH^+$ and Ca^{2+} and the total Ca percentage adsorbed on quartz, as well as percentage quartz recoveries obtained using different fatty acids, all vs. the pH. The dissociation constants of $Ca(OH)_2$ and $CaOH^+$ are, respectively,

$$K = \frac{[CaOH^+][OH^-]}{[Ca(OH)_2]} = 2.52 \cdot 10^{-4} \quad (pL = 3.82)$$

and

$$K = \frac{[Ca^{2+}][OH^-]}{[CaOH^+]} = 0.050 \quad (pL = -1.3).$$

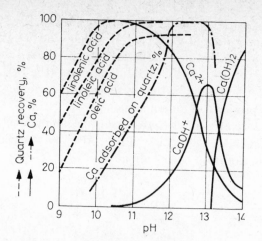

Fig. 2.64. Relative abundances of Ca(OH)$_2$, CaOH$^+$ and Ca^{2+} in a solution, aggregate Ca percentage adsorbed on quartz and quartz recoveries attained using different fatty acids, vs. the pH

In water, hydroxyl ions get attached to the Si atoms and hydrogen ions to the O atoms of the quartz surface, combining to form "compounds" of approximate composition Si(OH)$_4$. In an alkaline pulp, the quartz surface becomes negative,

$$\text{>Si}\begin{smallmatrix}OH\\OH\end{smallmatrix} + 2OH^- \rightleftharpoons \text{>Si}\begin{smallmatrix}O^-\\O^-\end{smallmatrix} + 2H_2O,$$

so that it can adsorb cations. It has a preference for divalent cations which turn its surface charge positive. These cationic activators are adsorbed as hydroxides above all; it is to the site of their hydroxyl radical that the collector anion attaches itself when adsorbed in its turn:

$$\text{>Si}\begin{smallmatrix}O^-\\O^-\end{smallmatrix} + 2CaOH^+ \rightleftharpoons \text{>Si}\begin{smallmatrix}OCaOH\\OCaOH\end{smallmatrix}$$

$$\text{>Si}\begin{smallmatrix}OCaOH\\OCaOH\end{smallmatrix} + 2RCOO^- \rightleftharpoons \text{>Si}\begin{smallmatrix}OCaOOCR\\OCaOOCR\end{smallmatrix} + 2OH^-$$

The greater activity of hydrocarbon chains with double bonds (unsaturated chains) adsorbed on quartz activated with calcium can be interpreted on the hypothesis that the more polar (double-bonded) parts of the hydrocarbon chains also participate actively in surface adsorption, and that the collector ions lie

236

more or less flat on the quartz surface. The density of adsorption of soap ions on activated quartz is invariably less than what is required for the formation of hemimicellae, whereas in haematite, the collector ions adsorbed as counterions at the surfaces of opposite charge do exhibit a propensity to associate and to form hemimicellae. Here, the hydrophilic double bonds reduce the degree of both association and adsorption. On haematite, greater angles of contact are measured than on activated quartz; also, the angle of contact of haematite decreases whereas that of activated quartz increases as the polarity of the hydrocarbon chain increases. In the flotation of iron ores, for example, the presence of unsaturated fatty acids impairs performance; this effect can, however, be offset if the activated quartz is flotated out — by bubble attachment to the unsaturated fatty acid — from beside the depressed iron oxide.

The fact that rutile (TiO_2) flotates better with the less saturated linolenic acid than with linoleic or oleic acid at a pH lower than its own $pK \simeq 6$ (where most of the reagent is in the form of a free acid), whereas a high pH reverses the sequence, may be explained by a similar assumption: at a low pH, the free acid molecules promote the formation of hydrophobic clots of linoleate, whereas at a high pH, only the oleates with their single double bond will clot under conditions under which the more polar linoleates with their three double bonds form no hemimicellae any more.

Quartz activated unintentionally (auto-activated) may be deactivated in different ways, depending on the nature of the activating ion. If activation is due to the adsorption of a base-metal cation (e.g. Cu^{2+}), then deactivation may be achieved by adding CN^-, to form a complex compound with the base metal. If the activator is an alkali earth (Ca, Ba, etc.), it is the concentration of the free ions of this element that has to be lowered in the solution. The dosage of soda ash (sodium carbonate), water glass (sodium silicate) or some alkali phosphate will often help. In other practical cases, tartrates, citrates or certain dyes will prove helpful (Clark 1968; Colombo et al. 1965; Estefan and Malati 1973).

2.2.6.3. To **salt-type minerals,** the collector attaches itself by chemisorption as a rule. The selective flotation of these — using suitable collecting reagents — can be achieved by means of depressants and activators affecting the different minerals more or less selectively. Conditions have to be created under which the chemisorption of the collector is stronger on the mineral to be flotated out than on the other minerals.

Fluorite (CaF_2), for example, is often found together with calcite, barite and quartz. The flotation of fluorite with an oleic acid collector can be promoted by dry-grinding the feed with some oleic acid added. In this way, a concentrate of 98% CaF_2 content was obtained at a recovery of 92%, whereas wet grinding gave 61% CaF_2 content at 51% mineral recovery (or 66% at 29% recovery or 74% at 18%). At the freshly formed, strongly reactive dry mineral surfaces, chemisorption takes place according to the formula

$$CaF_2 + RCOOH \rightarrow (RCOO)FCa + HF.$$

In water, chemisorption is a more complicated process, presumably involving exchange with the chemisorbed OH^- ions or the F^- ions of the surface:

$$CaF_2 + RCOO^- \rightarrow (RCOO)FCa + F^-.$$

Dry grinding turns fluorite, calcite and barite into p-type semiconductors; wet grinding turns barite p-type but fluorite and calcite n-type. In dry grinding,

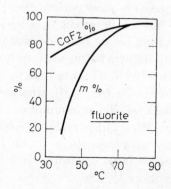

Fig. 2.65. Fluorite recovery, $m\%$, and fluorite content of the concentrate, $CaF_2\%$, vs. the temperature of conditioning with oleic acid

oxygen adsorption and the reduction of the Fermi energy level are more pronounced, resulting in an enhanced adsorption of anionic collectors.

Selective chemisorption is promoted also by raising the temperature of conditioning. Figure 2.65 shows fluorite recovery $m\%$ and the CaF_2 content of the concentrate produced by the flotation of a fluorite–calcite–barite-containing feed, vs. the temperature of conditioning with oleic acid. A fair fluorite recovery and high CaF_2 content can be achieved also by flotation with a polyethylene oxy-alkyl phenol and the polyethylene oxy-ester of some fatty acid.

In the soapy flotation of fluorite, calcite is readily depressed by tannic acid (quebracho). To the differential flotation of apatite in the presence of calcite, short-chain fatty acids and certain aromatic fatty acids lend themselves best: in virtue of their better solubility, their chemisorption to the calcite surface is less strong. In the flotation of calcite with undecylic acid (11C), the depressing effect of different sodium salts decreases in the following sequence: Na_2SiO_3, $Na_2C_2O_4$, $Na_2C_4H_4O_6$, Na_2HPO_4, Na_2CO_3, Na_2CrO_4, Na_2SO_4. With the exception of the carbonate, this coincides with the sequence of solubility of the sodium salts, as is only to be expected in a case of chemisorption.

Above a pH = 12.2, calcite cannot be flotated with sodium oleate; at high pH's, the oleate ions are displaced from the calcite surface by the OH^- ions.

The OH⁻ ion concentration regulates also the relative abundances of the CO_3^{2-} and HCO_3^- ions through the constant of dissociation

$$K = \frac{[CO_3^{2-}][H^+]}{[HCO_3^-]} = 5.6 \cdot 10^{-11} \quad (pK \cong 10.24).$$

Accordingly, changing the pH changes also the concentrations in the solution of the potential-determining ions of calcite (Ca^{2+} and CO_3^{2-}): in fact, if the concentration of negative CO_3^{2-} is high enough, it may even displace the anionic collector from the mineral-grain surface.

From calcite-containing phosphate (apatite) ores, calcite can be flotated out selectively in the pH range 5 to 6 with sodium oleate if the phosphate minerals

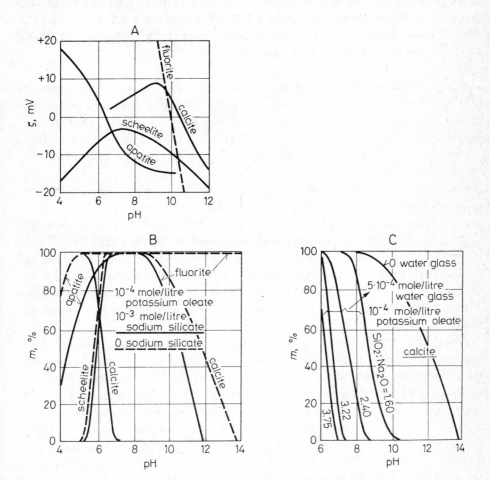

Fig. 2.66. A — zeta potential of some minerals, B — their recoveries on flotation with potassium oleate and water glass, C — recovery of calcite flotated with water glass of different $SiO_2 : Na_2O$ ratios vs. the pH

239

are depressed by means of a mixture of two parts $C_4H_4O_6KNa$ (tartrate) and one part $Al_2(SO_4)_3$ (Smani et al. 1975).

Part A of Fig. 2.66 shows the variation of the zeta potential of calcite, fluorite, apatite and scheelite vs. the pH; Part B shows the recovery vs. the pH of each of these on flotation with 10^{-4} mole potassium oleate and with and without 10^{-3} mole water glass of composition $SiO_2 : Na_2O = 3.22$. Water glass is a strong depressant of calcite and fluorite but a weak one of apatite; it depresses scheelite not at all. Part C shows calcite recovery vs. the pH with the dosage and composition of the water glass as the parameter. Depressive action is the stronger, the higher the $SiO_2 : Na_2O$ ratio in the water glass (i.e., the greater the abundance of colloidal SiO_2). An increased colloidal SiO_2 content — and hence an enhanced depressive action — can be achieved by adding acid to the water glass before dosage (Browning 1964; Buckenham 1963; Clement 1977; Dobiaš 1968; Fuerstenau et al. 1968; Iskra et al. 1973; Prédali 1969; Siebel 1962; Töpfer and Bilsing 1964; Yazan and Schäfer 1966).

2.2.7. Modifiers for other purposes. Chemicals may be added for purposes other than depression or activation. The pH is usually adjusted in practice by dosages of lime (CaO), soda ash (Na_2CO_3), possibly caustic soda (NaOH), sulphuric acid (H_2SO_4) or sulphurous acid (H_2SO_3). Lime is the cheapest alkali; it selectively depresses pyrite and galena into the bargain. Sulphuric acid, the cheapest acid, activates pyrite in turn. By suitably adjusting the pH, the concentrations of the OH^- and H^+ ions or other counter-ions or of other ions having a desirable or undesirable influence on flotation (activators, depressants, reagent-guzzlers, flotation poisons, etc.) can be controlled; given a combination of reagents, flotation performance will be optimal at different pH's for different minerals. If two minerals are floatable using one and the same collector, the critical pH's at which their flotation is just feasible may differ (cf. Fig. 2.53). Likewise, it is at different concentrations of an ion vying for the mineral surface with the collector that the collector will be displaced from the surfaces of different minerals.

A fine film of alien slimes coating a mineral surface is liable to prevent flotation and/or impair concentrate purity. The coating may be due to opposite electric charges on the slimes and the mineral grain. It may, however, adhere quite strongly also close to the isoelectric point. The anions of the pay mineral may even constitute an insoluble precipitate with the cations of the slime mineral. Figure 2.67 shows the recovery of quartz on flotation with 10^{-4} mole dodecyl ammonium acetate, vs. the pH, in the presence of ferric oxide slimes in different concentrations (Aplan and Fuerstenau 1962). Here, the pH is a potential determinant to both minerals: it influences the sign and magnitude of their surface charges. The Fe_2O_3 particles have their isoelectric point in the vicinity of pH $= 8$. With no slimes present, quartz readily flotates above a

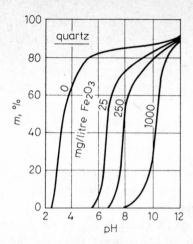

Fig. 2.67. Recovery of quartz flotation with 10^{-4} mole per litre dodecyl ammonium acetate vs. the pH, at different concentrations of iron oxide slimes

pH = 5; as the slimes concentration increases, the onset of quartz flotation moves towards the higher end of the pH range, where both the Fe_2O_3 slimes and the quartz acquire a negative charge. The amine flotation of quartz is not affected at all by kaolinite or bentonite slimes at a pH = 6, but is fully inhibited by goethite slimes. The flotation of particulate goethite with sodium dodecyl sulphate at a pH = 3 is not affected by fine goethite slimes but is impaired by slimes of quartz, kaolinite or bentonite (cf. Table 2.8).

Nor is flotation performance indifferent to the particle size of the slimes. Figure 2.68 shows recovery of quartz, $m\%$, vs. concentration of goethite slimes

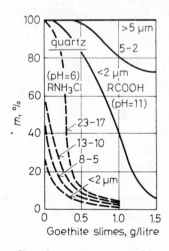

Fig. 2.68. Recovery of quartz flotation, $m\%$, vs. goethite slimes concentration for different slime particle sizes using a cationic and an anionic collector reagent

16

(g/l), for different slimes sizes, using a cationic collector (10^{-4} mole dodecyl ammonium chloride) at a pH = 6 and an anionic collector (10^{-4} mole linoleic acid) at a pH = 11, after activation with 50 mg/l Ca^{2+} (Iwasaki et al. 1960). The cationic flotation of quartz is impeded even by comparatively coarse goethite (23 μm), whereas its anionic flotation is affected by goethite finer than 5 μm only. Cationic flotation, then, is much more sentitive to these slimes than anionic flotation. Slimes impair flotation performance the more, the finer they are.

The flotation of galena with its negative zeta potential is practically unaffected by negatively charged slimes (such as kaolinite or other clay minerals, or gypsum, etc.). Positively charged ones, on the other hand (such as iron oxides, bauxite, fluorite) depress galena almost completely. By changing the pH of the pulp, the charge of these latter slimes can be turned negative (so as to match it with the charge on the galena); this cancels their depressive influence (Gaudin, Fuerstenau and Miaw 1960).

In a general way, fine slime particles with their small mass have a low enough probability of colliding with bubbles; also, even if a collision does take place, their kinetic energy is insufficient to permit them to pierce the water films coating both the bubble and themselves in order to bring about adherence. (This does not hold for very fine bubbles in the process of growing in the solution, which prefer to appear on fine hydrophobic particles of great specific surface.) The adhesion of slimes to large particles, deleterious to flotation as a rule, may be due to a chemical reaction, but more probably to coagulation-flocculation. Even if their weight percent abundance is small, the slimes with their large specific surface can form films on large portions of the surfaces of the coarser-sized particles or bubbles, can adsorb a great deal of reagent, increase the viscosity of the pulp and the persistence of the froth; they are fairly soluble in water, their hydration is rapid, their surface reaction rates are high and their selectivity *vis-à-vis* the reagents is low (Clement 1977; Meloy 1962).

The adhesion of more or less fine alien slimes to the particles, which can be regulated within limits, can, on the other hand, be turned to profit in the concentration of fine slimes: these can sometimes be made to flotate quite well after adherence to suitable carrier minerals. Carriers include conditioned barite, limestone, fluorite, quartz sand, etc., added in particles finer than 40 to 50 μm and approximately in the same weight percentage as the mineral to be flotated out. (For example, by adding 250 kg/t carrier at 20 to 30 weight percent.) The carrier mineral in this process of ultraflotation is fed back into the raw pulp after separation from the slimes (Grounds 1964; Mellgren and Shergold 1966).

The favourable influence on the flotation of fine slimes of bubbles just growing out of the solution is made clear by Fig. 2.69 which shows the outcome (in terms of recovery, $m\%$, and CaF_2 content, $c\%$) of the flotation of a mixture

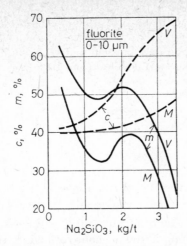

Fig. 2.69. Fluorite content $c\%$ and recovery $m\%$ of a fluorite slimes concentrate (minus-10 μm) vs. water glass dosage in a mechanical cell (M) and a vacuum cell (V)

of minus-10 μm quartz and fluorite in an agitation cell (M) and in a vacuum cell (V), using 2.7 kg/t sodium oleate, 1.0 kg/t soda ash and 30 g/t pine oil, all vs. Na_2SiO_3 dosage.

The performance of the vacuum cell is revealed to be superior also by Table 2.23 which states the beneficiation results of minus-10 μm barite slimes under standard reagent dosages in an agitation cell (M) and a vacuum cell (V), for the entire minus-10 μm material and separately for the minus-5 μm and the 5 to 10 μm fraction. The beneficiation efficiency η of the minus-5 μm fraction was 1.8 times, that of the 5 to 10 μm fraction 1.2 times as high in the vacuum cell as in normal flotation.

The v, m and c parameters obtained on the flotation of minus-10 μm raw barite $(a = 33.3\%\ BaSO_4)$ with 3.7 kg/t sodium oleate and 1.7 kg/t sodium silicate in agitation and vacuum cells are stated in Table 2.24, and so are the values for flotation with 5.0 kg/t sodium oleate and 1.7 kg/t sodium silicate.

Table 2.23. Flotation of fine barite slimes in a mechanical cell (M) and a vacuum cell (V)

%	10—0 μm		10—5 μm		5—0 μm	
	M	V	M	V	M	V
a	33.2	33.1	41.7	37.6	27.1	29.4
b	57.0	57.8	65.4	66.8	46.5	50.7
c	24.9	19.7	29.0	23.1	22.2	17.3
v	25.9	35.2	38.0	33.2	20.2	36.3
m	44.4	61.4	59.5	58.9	34.6	62.5
η	27.8	39.3	32.3	38.8	21.6	39.5

Table 2.24. Flotation of minus-10 μm raw barite in a mechanical cell (*M*) and a vacuum cell (*V*)
(a) using 3.7 kg/t sodium oleate and 1.7 kg/t sodium silicate
(b) using 5.0 kg/t sodium oleate and 1.7 kg/t sodium silicate

		$v\%$	$m\%$	$c\%$			$v\%$	$m\%$	$c\%$
a)	*M*	18.5	30.6	54.4	b)	*M*	28.6	44.2	51.3
	V	24.3	45.7	63.6		*V*	30.4	56.4	61.5

Flocculation is due to van der Waals forces as a rule: it comes about whenever these forces can overcome the repulsion between any two particles of identical surface charge. The repulsion can be enhanced by the dosage of suitable electrolytes. The strong hydrate shells formed on the adsorption of a protective colloid (e.g. starch) may also prevent flocculation. The dispersants most often used to remove or attenuate slimes films include water glass (Na_2SiO_3), soda ash and certain polyphosphates.

Agglomerative flotation is a process that lends itself well to the beneficiation of certain slimes. On the vigorous agitation (at a power input of 30 to 40 kW h/t or so) of a dense pulp (>600 g/l) for a long enough time ($\gtrsim$10 minutes), with large doses (5 to 80 kg/t) of the emulsion of a non-polar oil, the hydrophobic particles can be made to agglomerate with the droplets of oil; the agglomerates float up quasi-instantly after the pulp has been diluted (Fahrenwald 1957; Fayed 1965; Gates 1957; Karjalahti 1972). Performance is determined by the relative magnitudes of the surface tensions a_{sw}, a_{so} and a_{ow} of the solid, aqueous (water) and oleaginous phase. The particle finds its way into the oil if

$$a_{sw} > a_{ow} + a_{so};$$

it remains in the water if

$$a_{so} > a_{ow} + a_{sw},$$

and adheres to the oil–water interface if

$$a_{ow} > a_{sw} + a_{so}.$$

The slime particles adhering to the interface tend to stabilize both oil-in-water and water-in-oil type emulsions. At large enough dosages of oil, a "paste" may form; less oil, on the other hand, tends to constitute oil-stabilized clots of mineral grains, and it is these that adhere to the air bubbles (Mellgren and Shergold 1966).

2.3. THE FROTH

2.3.1. Froth theory. Below a certain critical throughput rate ("volume velocity") q_{cr}, a gas emerging from a capillary of diameter d (or from the pores of a porous plate) into a liquid of surface tension a, density γ and viscosity μ forms bubbles whose diameter,

$$D = \sqrt[3]{\frac{6ad}{\gamma}},$$

is independent of q. The formula is derived by equating the buoyant force $\gamma \pi D^3/6$ acting on the bubble with the surface tension force restraining it at the end of the capillary, πda. In water at 20 °C,

$$D \cong 0.763 \sqrt[3]{d}.$$

Gas emerging from the capillary at a throughput rate q constitutes bubbles to the number

$$z = \frac{6q}{\pi D^3}$$

per unit of time. As q increases, the number of bubbles increases and the spacing between them decreases. At a high enough velocity, the spacing decreases to zero, so that a coalescent string of bubbles is formed, rising at the linear velocity

$$u_b = zD.$$

Inserting $z = u_b/D$ into the above formula, one obtains

$$q = \frac{\pi D^2 u_b}{6};$$

that is, in a string of bubbles, bubble diameter D does depend on the gas throughput rate.

The dimensionless numbers characterizing a bubble in a liquid are the Reynolds number

$$\mathrm{Re} = \frac{u_b D}{\nu},$$

the Froude number

$$\mathrm{Fr} = \frac{u_b^2}{gD},$$

and the Weber number

$$\mathrm{We} = \frac{u_b^2 \gamma D}{ga},$$

where

$$\nu = \frac{\mu g}{\gamma}$$

245

is kinematic viscosity and a is surface tension.

$$K = \frac{Re^4 Fr}{We^3} = \frac{a^2 g^2}{\gamma^3 \nu^4}$$

is a material constant: apart from the acceleration of gravity, it is made up exclusively of the parameters of the liquid. $K = 3.9 \cdot 10^{10}$ for water at 20 °C and 10^{12} for water at 80 °C.

The rise rate of a bubble in water at rest is

$$u_b = \sqrt{\frac{4g}{3c} D \frac{(\gamma - \gamma_l)}{\gamma}} = \sqrt{\frac{4gD}{3c}},$$

where the drag coefficient c is a function of Re, Fr and We (cf. Table 2.25). The shape of the bubble is spherical at (1) and (2), ellipsoidal at (3) and mushroom-like at (4); it rises in the liquid at the velocity u_b. It teeters up in a spiral in case (3) and rises in a straight line in the other three cases.

The relationship between $D' = D/A$ and

$$u_b' = \frac{u_b}{\sqrt{gA}}$$

is shown by Fig. 2.70 to be a linear one $(A = \sqrt{a/\gamma})$.

If the bubbles are small enough, flow may be laminar: in that case,

$$u_b = \frac{D^2 \gamma}{18\mu}.$$

In turbulent flow,

$$u_b \cong 13.7\sqrt{D}.$$

In the zone of transition, velocity decreases as bubble size increases. Flow is laminar as long as Re < 2.

Substitution of the appropriate u_b values gives

$$D = \left(\frac{108\mu g}{\pi\gamma} \right)^{1/4}$$

Table 2.25. Drag coefficient formulae for different ranges of the Reynolds, Weber and Froude numbers

		Drag coefficient c
(1)	Re < 2	24/Re
(2)	Re > 2; We < 3.67	$18.2/Re^{0.682}$
(3)	We = 3.67; Fr < 0.525	0.37 We/Fr
(4)	Fr = 0.525	2.61

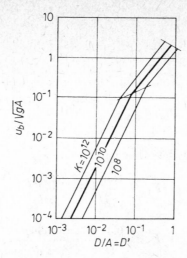

Fig. 2.70. Influence of agitation and aeration: $u_b/\sqrt{gA}$ vs. D/A

and

$$D = \left(\frac{q}{2.28\pi}\right)^{2/5}$$

respectively for the diameter of a string of bubbles in linear and turbulent flow. In water at 20 °C,

$$D \simeq 0.136q^{1/4}$$

and

$$D \simeq 0.455q^{0.4},$$

where D is in cm and q in cm³/s.

The critical throughput rate q_{cr} of the gas flow, where separate bubbles coalesce into strings, can be calculated using the D (independent of q) of the individual bubbles. For example, in water at 20 °C,

$$q_{cr} = 177\, d^{\frac{4}{3}}$$

and

$$q_{cr} = 13.2\, d^{\frac{5}{6}},$$

respectively, with q_{cr} in cm³/s and d in cm.

In all these relationships, throughput rate q refers to a single capillary orifice of diameter d. Such an orifice emits z bubbles per unit of time; these rise at velocity u_b, traversing a column of a water of height $1/u_b$ per unit of time. The number of bubbles simultaneously in the column, then, is z/u_b at any one time; their aggregate surface area is

$$F_1 = \frac{D^2z}{u_b}.$$

247

The substitution of z yields

$$F_1 = \frac{6q}{u_b D}$$

for the aggregate surface area of bubbles in a liquid column of unit height emitted by a single orifice. If bubbles are emitted in strings rather than one by one, then

$$F_1 = \pi D \; ;$$

for separate bubbles, on the other hand,

$$F_1 \simeq \frac{108\mu q}{\gamma D^3} = \frac{243\,\mu q}{\gamma d}$$

in laminar flow and

$$F_1 \simeq \frac{0.439q}{D^{3/2}} = \frac{0.656q}{\sqrt{d}}$$

in turbulent flow. If the single orifice is replaced by a porous plate (a "mat"), the number of whose pores is known, then the surface area of the gas–liquid interface present in a unit of volume is $F = nF_1$.

If an orifice of diameter d emits a bubble into a liquid, the diameter of the bubble equals d initially: it expands only later on to D. For such a bubble to form, an overpressure

$$p_1 = 4\,\frac{a}{d} \; ,$$

equal to capillary pressure, is required. In addition, the emerging bubble must overcome the static head, $p_2 = H\gamma$, of the liquid column of height H above it and also the drag

$$p_3 = \left(\frac{\zeta\gamma}{2g}\right) u^2$$

resisting its passage at velocity

$$u = \frac{4q}{\pi d^2}$$

through the orifice (where ζ is a system coefficient). Total gas pressure required for bubbling is thus

$$p = p_1 + p_2 + p_3 = \frac{4a}{d} + H\gamma + \left(\frac{\zeta\gamma}{2g}\right) u^2.$$

This sum may — especially if the orifice d is small — greatly exceed p_2, the static head in the liquid.

2.3.2. Bubble behaviour. A bubble risen to the surface of a liquid is separated from ambient air by a thin liquid film. Large bubbles, of diameter 5 cm or so, are hemispherical at rest, and their bottom face is flush with the liquid surface;

small bubbles (of a diameter less than about 0.5 mm) are approximately spherical, with their centres approximately flush with the liquid surface. Bubbles of intermediate size at rest at the surface are transitional between a sphere and a hemisphere (Fig. 2.71). A water ring of some thickness forms where the film of the bubble meets the liquid surface.

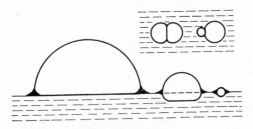

Fig. 2.71. Forms assumed by bubbles of different size at the water surface

The radius of curvature of the interface between two bubbles, which have diameter r_1 and r_2 respectively is

$$R = \frac{r_1 r_2}{r_1 - r_2} \,,$$

the surface is convex as seen from inside the larger bubble (the radii of curvature diverge into that bubble). The pressure difference between the two sides of the curved interface is

$$\Delta p = 4 \, \frac{a}{R}$$

(a is surface tension).

Bubbles of equal size have plane interfaces ($R \to \infty$). A froth made up of bubbles of equal size consequently is polyhedral in its interior. The close-packed polyhedra that can fill out space with a minimum of aggregate surface area are 14-faced (tetrakaidecahedra): six of their faces are equal-sized squares and the remaining eight are equal-sized hexagons of a different size. A real-life froth is made up of irregular polyhedra of between 8 and 18 faces, but 14-faced ones predominate.

The liquid film confining the bubble gradually thins out as liquid seeps out of it, down into the main body of liquid: the bubbles burst sooner or later for this reason if for no other; adjacent bubbles unite their gas spaces, coalescing into a single bubble whose volume equals that of the original ones. (The great curvature at the apices of the polyhedral bubbles generates a capillary suction which makes the film thin more rapidly. Pressure generated by van der Waals forces, varying inversely as the cube of film thickness, has a similar effect.) As the bubbles at the top of the froth burst, their gas spaces unite with the ambient atmosphere. Bubble size gradually increases in the froth from the bottom up, as illustrated by Fig. 2.72 (Gaudin 1957). In the steady state, froth thickness is a constant: the gas liberated by the bursting bubbles at the top equals the gas contained in the bubbles freshly arriving at the bottom. If bubble

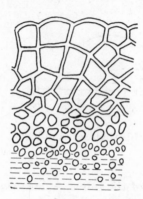

Fig. 2.72. Section of a volume of aerated pulp and polyhedral froth

formation is interrupted, the froth disappears sooner or later. The froth-forming propensity (frother behaviour) of a reagent may be expressed for a given reagent concentration and gas feed rate in terms of froth height or of the time it takes for the froth to disappear after the turning off of the gas feed. If the top of the froth is removed by drainage across a weir or lip, — as is the case in flotation cells, — then it is the gas contained in the overflow that is to be made up by the bubbles arriving from below.

Solutions of proteins tend to constitute very stable froths even in the absence of any solid particles because the bubble walls turn into a fairly tough elastic gel (like the skin on hot milk). Even if no visible skin forms, viscosity is higher in the more or less elastic surface layer than in the interior of the solution. (This surface viscosity is responsible for the frothing e.g. of saponine solutions.) In the absence of surface viscosity (e.g. in a watery solution of alcohol), persistent frothing may be caused by the Marangoni effect; wherever a tear starts in a bubble wall, liquid from the interior is exposed at the surface; having a higher surface tension, it strives to seal ("heal") the tear. This is why a solid may drop through a layer of foam or froth without leaving a hole or causing a discontinuity. A further cause for froth persistence may be the presence of a film of a colloid electrolyte (e.g. soap), with the liquid counter-ions of the film sandwiched between the film's layers of long-chain ions: the electric repulsion of identical charges prevents the films from coming too close together (which is the first stage in the formation of a tear).

Once the critical concentration of micella formation is exceeded, heteropolar hydrocarbons with a propensity to form micellae (e.g. soaps, alkali-sulphates, alkali-sulphonates) tend to give very persistent froths, which is undesirable in flotation practice. Froth stability is increased by hydrophilic colloids but reduced by hydrophobic ones or by non-polar emulsions of oils. (The hydrate layer on a hydrophilic colloid hinders the thinning of the bubble films in the froth.) Froth stability is often affected rather remarkably by even a small change in pH.

The most widespread method of breaking down stable froths is mechanical shattering. Another method involves changing the surface tension of the bubbles by the addition of a suitable liquid (e.g. an alcohol, an ether, ammonia, etc.).

2.3.3. Flow in a bubbly medium. Flow lines, in front of a bubble rising in a liquid at rest (or in the liquid flowing down around a stationary sphere) are shown in Fig. 2.73 under viscous and turbulent conditions (Gaudin 1957). The flow lines behind the sphere are symmetrical to those in front of it in viscous flow, whereas they are highly irregular and very different from those in front in turbulent flow. If the flow contains small particles whose centres of gravity follow the flow lines, those particles will not make contact with the bubble in viscous flow because even the closest flow line passes the equator of the bubble at a comparatively great distance (about equal to its distance, before deflection, from the straight line that passes through the centre of the bubble). In turbulent flow, on the other hand, there is more "pinch": the flow lines approach the bubble much closer. A spherical particle does not make contact with the bubble even then (except if it is rotating), because the pinch of flow lines between particle and bubble pushes the particle outward. If, on the other hand, the particle is angular and rotating, it may hit the bubble with one

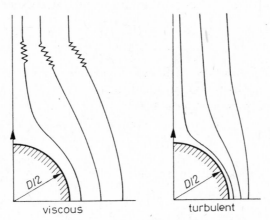

Fig. 2.73. Approximate flow lines in a liquid passing a sphere

of its prominences and the two may adhere together. The maximum likelihood of encounter between bubble and particle by this mechanism is

$$p \simeq \frac{3kx'}{D} .$$

where D is bubble diameter, x' is the diameter of the sphere equal in volume to the particle, and

$$k = \frac{x'' - x'}{x'} = \frac{x''}{x'} - 1$$

is the angularity of the particle (x'' is the diameter of its circumscribed sphere). In the case of a cube of edge length x, e.g.,

$$x' = x \sqrt[3]{\frac{6}{\pi}} = 1.24x$$

and

$$x'' = x \sqrt{3} = 1.73x ;$$

that is,

$$k = \frac{1.73}{1.24} - 1 = 0.40$$

and, e.g., if $\quad D/x = \quad$ 10 $\quad$ 20 $\quad$ 40

(that is, $\quad x'/D = \quad$ 0.124 $\quad$ 0.062 $\quad$ 0.031),

then $\quad p = \quad$ 14.9 $\quad$ 7.4 $\quad$ 3.7%.

If a bubble of diameter D rises through a height h before it attains the bottom of the froth, it sweeps a pulp column

$$\frac{hD^2\pi}{4}$$

which contains a volume of mineral grains to be flotated out

$$\frac{\sigma_f hD^2\pi}{4} ,$$

where σ_f is the volume ratio of floatable particles in the pulp. Let x' be the diameter of the sphere of volume equal to the grain volume; then the number of grains in the pulp swept by the bubble is

$$n = 6\pi D^2 \frac{h\sigma_f}{4\pi x'^3} ,$$

and the maximum possible number of rotating grains of angularity k making contact with the bubble is

$$N = pn = 9kh \frac{\sigma_f D}{2x'^2} .$$

The surface of the bubble, $D^2\pi$, can pick up

$$N' = 2\pi \frac{D^2}{\sqrt{3x'^2}} = 3.62 \left(\frac{D}{x'}\right)^2$$

grains close-packed one layer deep.

$$f = \frac{N}{N'} = 9 \frac{\sqrt{3}}{4\pi} kh \frac{\sigma_f}{D} = 1.24 kh \frac{\sigma_f}{D}$$

states the percentage of the bubble surface that gets covered with mineral grains, captured by the mechanism outlined, before the bubble hits the froth bottom. At $f = 1$, the bubble is fully loaded (fully mineral-lined one layer deep). For example, if $x' = 0.004$ cm, $D = 0.4$ cm, $h = 100$ cm, $k = 0.2$, $\sigma_f = 0.006$, then $N = 13{,}500$, $N' = 36{,}200$ and $f = 0.37$ (Gaudin 1957).

If particles of volume V spinning at angular velocity ω move at a relative velocity $v = v_{\text{fluid}} - v_{\text{particle}}$, the Magnus effect enters into play: it is a force of magnitude

$$M = 2\gamma V \omega v,$$

perpendicular to both the spin axis and the direction of v, where it coincides with ω, the direction of the spin (Fig. 2.74). The water film adhering to a bubble rising next to a particle will spin a particle sinking in the fluid so that it is deflected towards the bubble by the Magnus effect, which thus promotes encounters between bubbles and particles.

Owing to their non-negligible momentum mv, particles moving relative to the fluid deviate from the flow lines which avoid the bubbles: they move in closer to the bubble, closer to their original, undeflected lines of settling, which increases the likelihood of their making contact with the bubbles. If the velocity of the bubble relative to the fluid is too great, the bubbles are deformed: they lose their spherical form and oscillate between an oblate and a prolate spheroidal shape. The solid particles in the pulp surrounding the bubble can follow this vibration less readily than the fluid proper can. Both the expanding girth of the bubble and the suction generated by its subsequent slimming promote encounters with particles. The larger particles with their greater inertia are more prone to succumb to all these effects than the finer ones.

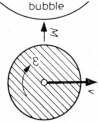

Fig. 2.74. The Magnus effect promotes bubble-particle collisions

Very fine particles, on the other hand, tend to follow the flow lines passing the larger bubbles. Only particles of diameter $2r$ which move on a flow line passing at a distance r or less from the bubble make contact with it. The flow line which passes the bubble equator at a distance r was originally (before its deflection) at a distance of about

$$E = \sqrt{3Rr}$$

from the axial line of the bubble (where R is bubble radius); that is, a rising bubble of radius R will sweep up the particles of radius r found in the fluid column of cross section $\sim E^2\pi$ above it. In a flotation cell of cross sectional (pulp-surface) area F, the probability of encounter per bubble is

$$p = \frac{E^2\pi}{F}.$$

If q is air feed rate to the cell, the number of bubbles formed per unit of time is

$$n = \frac{3q}{4\pi R^3}.$$

If every encounter leads to adherence, and every adhering grain is removed from the cell, then the number N of particles remaining in the pulp varies in time as

$$\frac{dN}{dt} = -pnN$$

or

$$N = N_0 e^{-pnt}.$$

For example, if

$$R = 10^{-1}\ \text{cm}, \quad r = 10^{-4}\ \text{cm}, \quad F = 40\ \text{cm}^2, \quad q = 20\ \text{cm}^3/\text{s},$$

then

$$E = 5.5 \cdot 10^{-2}\ \text{cm}, \quad p = 2.35 \cdot 10^{-4}, \quad n = 4.77 \cdot 10^3\ \text{s}^{-1},$$

$$\frac{dN}{dt} = -1.12 \cdot 10^{-2} N$$

and

$$N = N_0 e^{-1.12 \cdot 10^{-2} t},$$

if t is in seconds, or

$$N = N_0 e^{-0.67 t},$$

if t is in minutes. Since

$$e^{-0.67} = 0.512,$$

the number of fine slime particles left behind in the pulp is approximately halved every minute. More accurately, we have

$N/N_0 =$	0.512	0.262	0.134	0.069	
after	1	2	3	4	minutes,

if every encounter results in adherence and no adhering grain drops back from the froth into the pulp. Thanks to Brownian motion, the probability of collision with and adherence to the liquid–air interfaces of suspended fine slime particles is even higher in the thin liquid films of the bubbles in the froth than in the interior of the pulp. Hence, a greater flotation recovery of fine slimes is to be expected in a pneumatic cell with its thick froth bed than in an agitation cell with its shallower one (Gaudin 1957).

The encounter of a hydrophobic mineral grain with a bubble does not, however, invariably lead to adherence, for which a certain minimum time of contact is needed. At high contact angles or in the case of hydrophobic mineral grains which have fine bubbles newly formed out of the gas-supersaturated water adhering to them, this time may be practically zero, whereas in other cases only some of the floatable grains encountering bubbles will adhere to those; the rest will — owing to the insufficient time of contact — rebound from the bubble into the pulp. This type of elastic rebound is more likely to involve the coarser grains which, on impact, deform the bubble surfaces more than the finer ones (Klassen 1960).

When a bubble and a grain stick together, the water film between them disappears. As soon as the film is thinned to less than about 1 μm, ionic diffusion sets in: some of the collector ions adsorbed by the particle diffuse over to the bubble and, vice versa, some of the frother adsorbed on the bubble passes over to the grain. This phenomenon becomes significant especially in the case of the longer-chain frothers (surfactants, tensids) with their comparatively large molecules: solutions containing these attain equilibrium surface tension only after a longish time. The fact that the dynamic surface tension is higher than the static — owing, among other things, to the diffusion of frother from the bubble to the grain — may increase contact angles and thereby improve flotation performance.

The molecules or ions adsorbed by a bubble may move about on the bubble surface: the flow sweeping the bubble may tend to drag them from its leading to its trailing hemisphere. Concentration will thus become greater on the trailing hemisphere; the result is a diffusion of surfactant (frother) into the solution from the supersaturated trailing hemisphere and from the solution onto the subsaturated leading hemisphere. This generates an electric field about the bubble, in which fine particles ($\lesssim 10$ μm) are moved towards the bubble by a phenomenon resembling electrophoresis. The forces of diffusion and the electrostatic forces act on the molecules of the liquid film also: the film is thinned as a result of the one-sided removal of molecules. At a distance of 0.1 μm or so, van der Waals forces enter into play between the bubble and the grain, resulting in the rapid further thinning and finally the snapping of the liquid film separating them. The rate at which this takes place depends on the viscosity of the liquid first and foremost, but also on the hydrophobia of the mineral grain

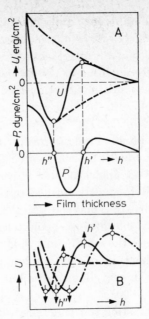

Fig. 2.75. Specific repulsive force P and energy content U vs. film thickness h

surface and the structure of the boundary layer of the bubble (its maximum velocity is about 20 cm/s). Coarser grains have larger areas of contact, and squeezing out the residual liquid film from between them and the bubble takes a longer time. Strength of adherence is a function of the surface area of contact and/or of the length of the three-phase boundary (that is, of the square and/or first power of grain size); the forces that strive to detach the grain from the bubble are proportional to the mass (that is, to the cube of the diameter) of the grain (Derjaguin and Dukhin 1961; Laskowski and Iskra 1970).

Both the bubble and the mineral grain wear a hydrate shell of more or less thickness, attached to them more or less strongly. Hydrophobic grains have a thinner and less strongly bound shell than hydrophilic ones. As a grain moves in close to a bubble (as the water film between them thins out), the free energy

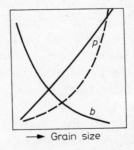

Fig. 2.76. Probability of encounter with a bubble (p) and of adherence to it (b) vs. grain size

U of the film is changed. The phenomenon is illustrated by part A of Fig. 2.75 (Klassen and Mokrousov 1963). U increases up to a point as the film thins, attaining a relative maximum at h'; it then decreases to h'', the thermodynamically stable thickness of the hydrate shell, where U is a minimum. Once it has attained h', film thickness decreases spontaneously to h'' (which is in the 0.1 to 0.01 μm range). The dashed $U = f(h)$ graph refers to extremely hydrophobic grains; the dot-dash one refers to extremely hydrophilic ones. The specific repulsive force P (in dynes per cm^2) is obtained by differentiating U (in ergs per cm^2).

The full curve in Part B of Fig. 2.75 shows the normal $U = f(h)$ graph of some mineral; the dashed curve shows it after the adsorption of a collector; the dot-dash curve shows it after the dosage of a depressant. Even hydrophilic grains with a strongly attached thick hydrate shell may adhere to a bubble, if the two have oppositely charged electric double layers that stick together by Coulomb attraction. The adherence of a hydrophobic grain to a bubble may on the other hand be hindered by a stronger electrical repulsion between identically charged surfaces. (This is the reason for the frequent parallelism between a declining zeta potential and increasing floatability.)

The p curves in Fig. 2.76 illustrate the probability of bubble–grain encounters. One (the full curve) varies approximately linearly as particle size. According to some authors, the variation is quadratic (Tomlinson and Fleming 1963; cf. the other, dashed curve). The b curve illustrates the probability of adherence after an encounter, decreasing with increasing particle size as a result of elastic rebound, of the longer time of contact required, of the stronger detaching forces, etc. The shape and position of the b curve is a function of reagent combination and dosage. The probability of a grain being flotated out is provided by the product, pb, which is small both for too fine grains whose p is small and for too coarse grains whose b is small (Klassen and Makrousov 1963).

2.3.4. Adherence between bubbles and mineral grains.

The mineral grains adhering to a bubble may line the entire bubble surface or only part of it. The small bubbles at the bottom of the froth have a greater aggregate surface than the bubbles of increasing size in the interior or at the top of the froth: the mineral load of the fully lined small bubbles cannot therefore be accommodated on the larger bubbles. Conversely, the bubbles at the top of the froth may be fully lined with mineral grains even if the small bubbles arriving from below do not carry full linings. If the thickness of a full, close-packed lining is x, then bubbles of diameter

$$D = 6x \frac{\delta - \gamma}{\gamma}$$

can float at equilibrium in a fluid of density γ. For a fully lined bubble to rise to the top of the fluid, it must accordingly be larger than D. If the full close-packed lining is made up of spheres of diameter x, rather than of cubes of edge length x, then critical bubble diameter is

$$D = 2\pi x \frac{\delta - \gamma}{\sqrt{3}\,\gamma}.$$

(This is about 0.6 times the critical diameter belonging to a close-packed, intersticeless lining of thickness x.) For example, if $\gamma = 1$, then

$$\frac{D}{x} = 6\frac{\delta - \gamma}{\gamma} = 1.8 \qquad 9.6 \qquad 24 \qquad 39$$

if

$$\delta = 1.3 \qquad\qquad 2.6 \qquad\quad 5 \qquad\quad 7.5.$$

In other words, a bubble of diameter $D = 2$ mm can rise up to the froth bottom if it carries a close-packed lining of coal particles ($\delta = 1.3$) not larger than $x = 1.1$ mm or of grains of galena ($\delta = 7.5$) not larger than about $x = 50\ \mu$m. A relationship of general validity for the critical state is

$$V\gamma = V'(\delta - \gamma),$$

where V is the volume of the bubble and V' is the aggregate volume of the mineral grains of s.g. δ adhering to it, regardless of whether the grains form a full lining or an incomplete one. Raising even a single particle of volume V' requires a bubble volume

$$V = V'\frac{\delta - \gamma}{\gamma}.$$

For example, at $\gamma = 1$, raising a single cube of coal of edge length 1 mm ($\delta = 1.3$) requires a bubble volume $V \geq 0.3$ mm³ (made up of a single bubble of $D \geq 0.83$ mm diameter, or ten bubbles of ≥ 0.38 mm diameter or one hundred bubbles of ≥ 0.18 mm diameter); in a denser pulp ($\gamma = 1.1$), $V \geq 0.182$ mm³ suffices (one bubble of ≥ 0.70 mm diameter, or ten of ≥ 0.33 or one hundred of ≥ 0.15 mm diameter). Raising a galena cube of the same edge length (1 mm) requires at $\gamma = 1$ a bubble of $V \geq 6$ mm³ ($D = 2.25$ mm) (Gaudin 1957).

The mineral load of a bubble is

$$G = \bar{a}A(1 - S),$$

where

$$S = e^{-ckt}$$

or

$$\frac{dS}{dt} = -ckS.$$

Here, the constants a and k are functions of the particles' distribution in the pulp and of their propensity to float out. A is the aggregate surface area of all the bubbles in a unit volume of pulp; S is the unlined fraction of that area; c is the quantity of solids per unit volume of pulp (solids concentration), and t is time. The maximum solids load of the bubbles, G_{max} mg, and their aggregate volume, $V \mu l$, was found to be related by

$$G_{max} = KV^b,$$

where the exponent b was shown by experiment to equal $3/8 = 0.375$ (rather than the theoretical $2/3$ independent of bubble size). This implies that the maximum possible mineral load per unit surface area is greater on a small bubble than on a larger one. The stronger curvature of the smaller bubble results in a denser lining with irregular-shaped grains (King, Hatton and Hulbert 1974).

2.3.5. Other details of froth formation and handling

(A) Figure 2.77 presents, for flotation in a single-cell laboratory device, graphs vs. time t (or, what is the same for flotation in the continuous mode, vs. distance t along the progress of the pulp) of percent mineral lining f_b and f_t for the bubbles at the bottom and top of the froth, respectively, the relative size of the bubbles at the top, D_t, mineral recovery $m\%$ and the rate of flotation, dm/dt. (f_b and dm/dt practically coincide and are therefore not shown separately.)

Pulp vorticity seldom lifts up to the froth bottom the coarser gangue particles of greater settling velocity; these nonadhering coarse particles will (in virtue of their weight) escape from the films between bubbles readily enough. Medium-sized gangue particles, on the other hand, may rise halfway and higher in the froth. These particles' downward slide in the upward-tapering water films separating the polyhedral bubbles is hindered by the pay mineral grains adhering to the bubble walls: these may retain the larger gangue particles by acting somewhat like a screen. Figure 2.78 shows a section of some polyhedral bubbles with almost 100% mineral lining. The hatched (angular) particles are the hydro-

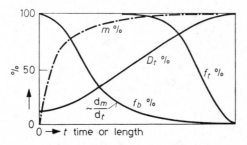

Fig. 2.77. Percent mineral lining of a bubble surface at the bottom (f_b), and top (f_t) of the froth column, relative size of bubbles at the top, D_t, mineral recovery $m\%$ and rate of flotation dm/dt vs. time (or distance along the trajectory of the pulp)

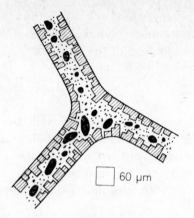

Fig. 2.78. Section of a loaded film in a polyhedral froth

phobic mineral grains (those to be flotated out), whereas the dark rounded ones are undesirable gangue particles entrained into the froth. The fine slimes of the gangue have practically zero settling velocity in the pulp; these will accordingly have the same concentration in the films of the overflowing froth as in the pulp within the cell. Those gangue grains whose backsliding velocity in the froth films is less than the velocity at which the bubbles rise in the froth will not be less abundant in the liquid phase of the overflow froth than in the pulp either. Froth composition can be improved by sprinkling the froth top with clear water: the undesirable slimes content of the films making up the overflowing froth can be efficaciously reduced thereby (Gaudin 1957).

(B) Rather than becoming polyhedral, the bubbles of a watery froth remain more or less deformed spheres: they are separated by thickish walls rather than thin films of pulp. In a watery froth, the rise velocity of the bubbles is less than

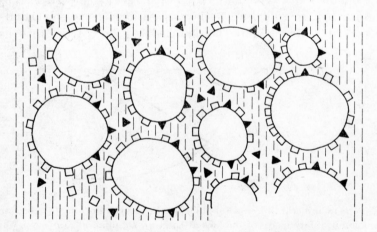

Fig. 2.79. Section of loaded bubbles in a watery froth

the backsliding velocity of the gangue grains but greater than that of the hydrophobic grains. A section through a volume of watery froth is shown in Fig. 2.79. The white rectangles denote hydrophobic grains (e.g. a copper sulphide); the black triangles denote gangue grains. The gangue grains slide down the top half of a bubble to its equator and fall off there: the bottom halves of the bubbles carry no such grains. The hydrophobic grains, on the other hand, slide down the bubble surface as far as its nadir (if there are no other grains there to stop them), and fall off only there if at all. In such cases, then, concentration takes place in the froth proper; the time of retention of the froth in the cell accordingly acquires a great importance. If it is too short, concentrate grade deteriorates; if it is too long, recovery is reduced by the demineralization ("weeping") of the froth.

(C) Froth removal at the right time is important also in the case of polyhedral froths (froths containing little water): the rate of removal must equal the rate of froth formation. Failure to adjust the first cells for the optimum rate of froth removal cannot be made good by increasing the time of flotation (i.e. the number of cells): in the upshot, the selectivity of flotation will suffer and mineral recovery will decline, although weight recovery may increase. Optimum froth removal improves both performance (throughput) and selectivity.

A froth is the more persistent, as a rule, the greater $f\%$, the percentage of mineral-lined bubble surface, and the finer the particles adhering to the bubbles.

Water content in the overflowing froth may vary over a wide range. It tends to be lower in polyhedral froths with a high f. Froths overflowing at the end of a bank of cells tend to be more watery and poorer in pay mineral than those overflowing from the first few cells. Table 2.26 e.g. shows froth composition for a galena ore flotated in a single-cell laboratory device vs. the duration of flotation (Gaudin 1957).

At the bottom of a thicker layer of watery froth, the concentration of minerals adhering to the bubbles does not change abruptly (it roughly equals the concentration in the pulp); starting from there, however, it rises to a maximum at the top of the froth. Figure 2.80 shows Cu contents at different depths in the

Table 2.26. Froth composition of a galena ore vs. retention time in flotation in a single-cell laboratory device

Time, minutes	0—1	1—2	2—4	4—8
Solids in froth, g	102	33	8	6
Water in froth, g	48	49	90	407
Approx. froth dilution, g water per g solids	0.5	1.5	11.2	68
Galena in froth solids, %	96	91	68	43
Volumetric solids content of froth, $\sigma\%$	27	8.5	0.9	0.12

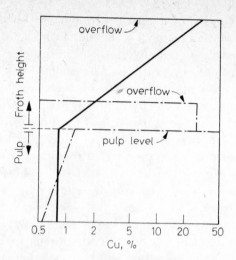

Fig. 2.80. Variation of Cu content in pulp and froth in a pneumatic cell (full line) and an agitation-froth cell (dot-dash line)

pulp and froth, respectively, of a pneumatic cell run with a watery froth and an agitation-type cell run with a polyhedral froth, flotating a sulphide copper ore.

For froth transportation, vertical-shaft pumps lend themselves best, installed so as to suck pulp out of a tank or sump with a sufficient height of pulp in it. Air can escape upward through an aperture in the pump housing next to the shaft. (The suction pipe of horizontal shaft centrifugal pumps tends to be obstructed by the air slug forming there.)

(D) An overpersistent froth can be destroyed by mechanical, thermal or chemical means. Mechanical means include beating the froth, the use of gas or liquid jets, ultrasonic waves (150 dB at 0.7 to 27.5 kcps) or rapid changes of pressure. The thermal method relies on the local heating of the froth (by a hot jet of gas, radiating heat, hot wires or rods), on evaporation, or on the changing of surface tension, viscosity or internal pressure. The most efficient method is the use of anti-frothing reagents. There are good anti-frothers among the alcohols, esters, ethers, phosphates, polyamines, silicones, sulphates and sulphonates. Flotation practice tends to prefer as anti-frothers esters such as ethyl acetate, isoamyl isovalerate or glycerine monostearate (Lindkvist 1973).

(E) The pulp fed to a flotation unit is usually diluted 2 to 5 times. For a pulp carrying rather coarse-grained hard gangue minerals, initial dilution may be less (the input pulp may be thicker) than e.g. in the case of platy gangue minerals. A thicker pulp most often is an advantage: it reduces water demand, increases cell throughput in terms of solids in the pulp and reduces the consumption of reagents (of frothers and pH regulators in particular). In a thicker pulp, however, more solids will be entrained mechanically into the froth, so that the floating mineral fraction will be less clean. Figure 2.81 shows the outcome of flotation of a mixture of 10% galena and 90% granite with a terpineol frother and 25 g/t amyl xanthate as a function of initial dilution h. The curves c and b represent lead contents in the concentrate and tailings; v represents weight recovery; m represents metal recovery and η represents separation efficiency. c and b rise but v and m fall as dilution is increased. Efficiency has a maximum between $h = 4$ and 5. Between $h = 1$ and 2, c and η rise abruptly and v drops just as abruptly. The graphs imply that rougher flotation intended to produce a pre-concentrate should use as thick a pulp as possible, whereas the cleaning of the pre-concentrate should use a dilute one.

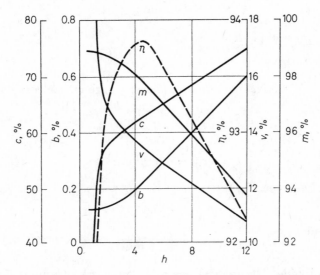

Fig. 2.81. Flotation performance of a galena–granite mixture vs. initial dilution h: v — weight recovery, m — metal recovery, c — the concentrate's Pb content, b — the tailing's Pb content, η — concentration efficiency

2.4. FLOTATION KINETICS

2.4.1. Fundamentals. In steady-state flotation, the feed rate equals the sum of the removal rates of the different outputs. In each of a number of short cells connected in series, froth is flotated out of a pulp whose composition is roughly the same as that of the underflow pulp fed to the next cell. In long single-cell flotation machines, pulp composition changes continuously along the length of the cell; it is identical with the composition of the feed near the feed end and with the composition of the tailings near the outflow end. Froth removal gradually reduces the quantity of pulp left behind in the tank: hence, the throughput rate of pulp gradually decreases from the feed end towards the outflow end.

Let the concentration of some component be c g/l in a pulp volume of V litres. Let the rate of removal of the component in the froth be r g/min. The expression

$$P = \frac{r}{cV} \text{ min}^{-1}$$

is a measure of the specific floatability of the component under the given conditions.

For example, if in a pulp volume $V = 1.6$ l of a raw ore made up of quartz and a copper sulphide, the concentration of quartz (A) is

$$c_A = 190 \text{ g/l},$$

that of the copper sulphide (B) is

$$c_B = 1.05 \text{ g/l},$$

and the rates of removal of the two minerals — given the combination of reagents used — are

$$r_A = 7.2 \text{ g/min}$$

and

$$r_B = 6.0 \text{ g/min},$$

respectively, then specific floatability is

$$P_A = 0.024 \text{ min}^{-1}$$

for quartz and

$$P_B = 3.57 \text{ min}^{-1}$$

for copper sulphide. The relative floatability of the two minerals is the ratio of the two expressions:

$$\Phi = \frac{P_B}{P_A} = 150.$$

The ratio of component concentrations in the overflowing froth (with the gas phase disregarded) vs. the pulp is the degree of concentration of the mineral:

$$M = \frac{c_{\text{froth}}}{c_{\text{pulp}}}.$$

$M = 1$ implies that the mineral is entrained into the froth by the liquid phase, at no change of concentration. The ratio of the degrees of concentration of any two minerals yields the same relative floatability as above:

$$\Phi = \frac{M_B}{M_A}.$$

In the foregoing example, with $c_B = 42$ g/l and $c_A = 50$ g/l in the froth, we had $M_B = 40$ and $M_A = 0.26$ (Gaudin 1957).

If every grain of a mineral had the same surface properties and also the same shape and size, the floatability of that mineral would remain the same from the beginning right to the end of the flotation process. In reality, each of these properties varies from one grain of the mineral to the next, giving rise to differences in floatability as a matter of course. It is the grains of higher floatability that are entrained into the froth first; those of lower floatability get relatively enriched in the pulp. The specific floatability of one and the same mineral thus decreases gradually as the flotation operation proceeds. The situation is further complicated by the presence of intergrown grains.

Increasing the thickness of the froth tends to increase the degree of concentration M of the floatable minerals, without significantly affecting their specific floatabilities P. Increasing frother dosage tends as a rule to increase P (presumably by changing bubble size) while affecting M but slightly. Up to a point, larger doses of collector increase both P and M (and also metal recovery $m\%$), as shown e.g. for galena and potassium ethyl xanthate (KEtX) in Part A of Fig. 2.82. Parts B and C of the figure respectively show the variation of P and M vs. grain size for galena, with collector (KEtX) concentration as the parameter. It is seen that, using e.g. 600 g/t KEtX, P is 0.28 min^{-1} and M is 33 for grains finer than about 4 μm; on the other hand, $P \simeq 0.066x$ and $M \simeq 8x$ for grains coarser than that. The P and M curves are near-parallel at reagent dosages of 600 and 400 g/t: both are linear functions of grain size for particles coarser than 4 or 5 μm. Even at a 400 g/t collector concentration, the probability of adherence between colliding bubbles and grains is clearly almost as high as at the 600 g/t dosage. At collector dosages lower than that, on the other hand, the probability of adherence per encounter decreases rather substantially. (If every collision results in adherence, then the linear variation of specific floatability P vs. grain size x is consistent with the formula

$$p = \frac{D}{3kx'}$$

of encounter probability, which is also linear in x.)

Up to a certain grain size, the specific floatability of the hydrophobic coarser grains is greater, that of the hydrophilic ones is less than that of the finer grains; hence, the relative floatability of hydrophobic vs. hydrophilic grains decreases as grain size decreases. Figure 2.83 shows the selectivity index (S.I.) of an industrial flotation operation treating a galena ore, vs. grain size, x μm. The bottom curve refers to all the galena-containing particles; the top one refers to the pure (liberated) grains of galena. The former has a peak about 30 μm, whereas the latter increases monotonically up to the top end of the range shown (128 μm). The dashed line shows the recovery $m\%$ of quartz grains vs. grain size,

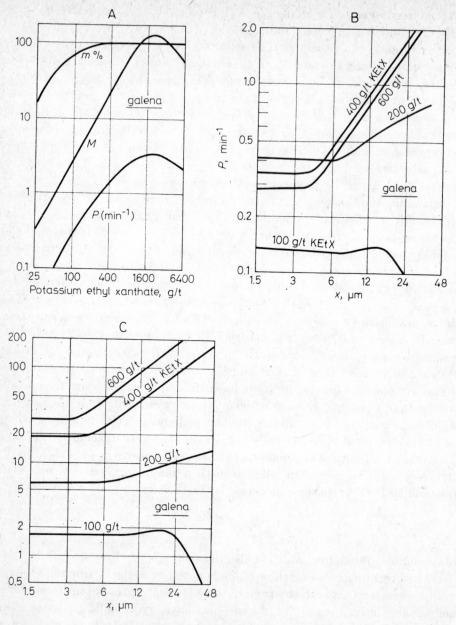

Fig. 2.82. A — Metal recovery *m*%, concentration index *M* and specific floatability *P* vs. collector concentration in galena flotation; variation vs. grain size *x* of *B* — specific floatability *P* and *C* — concentration index *M* at different reagent concentrations in galena flotation

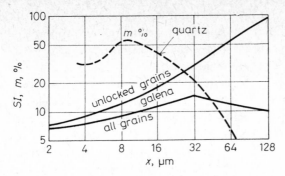

Fig. 2.83. Selectivity index S.I. and metal recovery $m\%$ of galena flotation vs. grain size x

on flotation with 0.6 mg/l dodecyl amine at a pH = 6.7. Quartz grains between 7 and 12 μm size could be flotated out best. Figure 2.84 shows galena recovery $m\%$ vs. grain size x μm for different retention times in a single-cell laboratory flotation machine. The coarser grains with their greater floatability are seen to float out sooner than the finer ones (Gaudin 1957).

The fact that specific floatability P and degree of concentration M are largely independent of particle size in the case of slimes finer than 4 to 5 μm may be due to the propensity of these fine particles to flocculate, so that, in fact, P and M describe the behaviour of the floccules rather than of the individual particles. The poor floatability of fine slimes may be due to several causes. One is their low probability of encounter with bubbles. Another is the capture by their surfaces of ions released by other minerals. Their greater specific surface endows them with a greater propensity to release ions into a solution and to adsorb ions

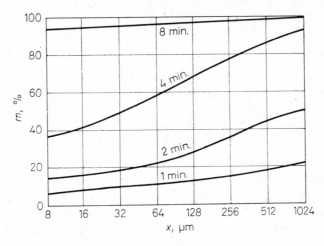

Fig. 2.84. Metal recovery $m\%$ of galena flotation in a laboratory cell vs. grain size x, at different retention times

from it; the surfaces of fine slime particles of different minerals therefore tend to change so that their properties converge (grow more and more uniform). This is one of the reasons why the flotation of a pulp rich in slimes is more difficult than that of a slimeless pulp.

A further cause of the poor floatability of fine pulps may lie in the electric charges carried by the particles and bubbles. If the particles are comparatively large (e.g. plus-10 μm), then the electrostatic repulsion (or attraction) between their electric double layers is negligible against the forces of inertia and viscosity; in the case of fine grains (of 1 μm size or so), however, the electrostatic forces between particles and bubbles may gain the upper hand in preventing or promoting collision and/or adherence. In an aqueous suspension, bubbles of air tend to acquire negative charges; now the adsorption of an anionic collector displaces the surface charge of a mineral grain likewise towards the negative. Cationic reagents, on the other hand, reduce the zeta potential of the mineral if it is negative, and indeed turn it positive if their concentration is high enough. If the charge on the bubble remains negative the while, an electrostatic attraction arises, and the propensity to adhere to the bubbles increases also for the fine slimes (Schuhmann 1942). (Cf. also Section 2.2.7.)

2.4.2. Equations of recovery. The quantity of mineral flotated out of a pulp during a time interval dt may be written up as

$$-V\,dc = r\,dt\,.$$

The substitution

$$r = PcV$$

brings that equation to the form

$$\frac{-dc}{c} = P\,dt\,.$$

That is,

$$\ln c = -Pt + C.$$

If $c = c_0$ at $t = 0$, then the constant term becomes $C = \ln c_0$, whence

$$\ln\left(\frac{c}{c_0}\right) = -Pt\,,$$

provided that all particles of the mineral behave identically (or, at least, that P remains constant throughout the flotation process, independently of t and c). Mineral concentration c in the pulp left behind in the cell is affected also by the rate of water removal in the overflowing froth. This fact was disregarded in the above derivation (which is therefore an approximation at best). In the course of the flotation process, the various chemical, colloid chemical and physical parameters affecting its outcome may change. (For example, the mineral

268

load on the bubbles and the dissolution and precipitation of soluble salts also vary with time, in addition to the shift in specific floatability P from the coarser to the finer grains.) In view of the overlaps between all these changes, it seems unreasonable to assume the formula derived above — or, for that matter, any other formula proposed for the reaction kinetics of flotation (corresponding to this or that equation of reaction kinetics in chemistry) to hold throughout the flotation process: any one of these formulae holds at best for phases of the process, covering brief intervals of time.

The first-order reaction equation

$$\frac{-dc_i}{c_i} = P_i \, dt$$

or

$$\ln\left(\frac{c_i}{c_{i0}}\right) = -P_i t$$

holds separately for each group of grains with identical features (size, shape, etc.) of any given mineral; the behaviour of the mineral aggregate made up of these groups is determined by the superposition of the fractions' different specific floatabilities P_i.

Disregarding the water entrained in the froth, that is, assuming the quantity of pulp (water) in the cell to be a constant, the ratio c/c_0 (the ratio of mineral concentrations) expresses the relation of the quantity of mineral left behind in the cell to the initial quantity. The ratio of the quantity of mineral entrained in the froth to the initial quantity gives the recovery m, suggesting the substitution

$$\frac{c}{c_0} = 1 - m;$$

it results in

$$\ln(1 - m) = -Pt$$

or

$$m = 1 - e^{-Pt}$$

or

$$\ln\left[\frac{1}{1-m}\right] = Pt \, .$$

Both the mineral-concentration c and the mineral residue $(1 - m)$ are exponential functions of time $t : c \to 0$ or $(1 - m) \to 0$ as $t \to \infty$. On the other hand, the halving time belonging to $c = c_0/2$ or $m = 1/2$ is

$$t = \frac{\ln 2}{P} \simeq \frac{0.7}{P}$$

and the time it takes to attain $c = c_0/100$ or $m = 0.99$ is

$$t = \frac{\ln 100}{P} = \frac{4.6}{P} \text{ min}.$$

In a semilog diagram with t linear and c or $(1 - m)$ logarithmic, the time equation is a straight line of slope $- P$.

In possession of the P values of the individual minerals under given conditions of flotation, these formulae can be used to calculate the relative (or percentage) abundances of each mineral left behind in the pulp after a time t. Let e.g. for an ore made up of galena (A), sphalerite (B) and quartz (C),

$$P_A = 1.2, \quad P_B = 0.1, \quad P_C = 0.02 \text{ min}^{-1},$$

and let specific floatability referred to water (D),

$$P_D = 0.04 \text{ min}^{-1};$$

then, after a flotation time $t = 2$ min, the quantities left behind in the pulp will be

$$A = 9.0, \; B = 81.9, \; C = 96.1, \; D = 90.5\%$$

of the starting quantities after $t = 2$ min and

$$A = 0.07, \; B = 55.0, \; C = 88.5, \; D = 74.0\%$$

after $t = 6$ min. Figure 2.85 is a graphic solution of the problem: it permits to read off for any time t the percentage $100 - m\%$ of any mineral (and of water) left behind in the pulp.

In an industrial flotation operation, corresponding t and $100 - m\%$ values will not as a rule fall onto a straight line in the t vs. log $(1 - m)$ net, owing to the presence of intergrown grains as well as to original differences in the chemical nature and behaviour of the grain surfaces, in grain size and shape, to non-uniform reagent concentrations in the solution and to changes in those as flotation proceeds. The grains of greater floatability of any mineral are flotated out soon enough: accordingly, the straight line in the t vs. log $(1 - m)$ net is replaced by a curve of gradually declining slope (Curve I of Fig. 2.86). On the assumption that the input is made up of several fractions, each with a different average floatability P, the curve I can be decomposed into several straight-line segments, each of a different slope P. Line II in the figure is tangent to the gently sloping part of Curve I; Line III joins the plots of the differences ($100 - m\%$) between Curve I and Line II. The slopes of the two lines are, $P_{II} = 0.138$ and $P_{III} = 1.055$. For example, with $100 - m\% = 50$ at $t = 5$ on Line II,

$$-P_{II} = \frac{\ln 0.5}{6} = -0.138,$$

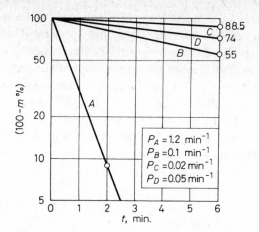

Fig. 2.85. In possession of the specific floatabilities of the minerals in the feed (and of water), the lines *A*, *B*, *C* and *D* can be plotted in a *t* vs. log (1 − *m*) net. The weight percent fractions left behind in the pulp of the individual minerals (and of the water) may be read off at any time *t*

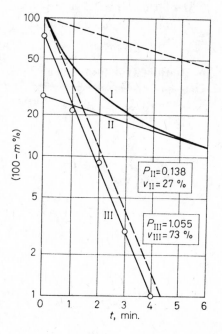

Fig. 2.86. If the plot is curved rather than straight in the *t* vs. log (1 − *m*) net (I), it can be decomposed into lines (II and III) of different slope *P*

and the relative abundance in the feed of the mineral fractions having the average floatabilities so defined read off the ordinate intercepts as $v_{II} = 27\%$ and $v_{III} = 73\%$, respectively. The experimentally determined Curve I could just as well be decomposed into more than two graphs; the only point to be kept in mind is that the slope ($-P$ value) of none of these should be greater than the initial or less than the final slope of Curve I, and that the ordinate intercepts of the graphs must add up to 100% between them.

If a percentage b of the mineral grains will not flotate owing to some surface impurity or some other reason, and the maximum recovery that can be achieved is a (<1), then m is to be replaced by m/a, and c/c_0 by

$$\frac{c - b}{c_0 - b}.$$

It is only if the values of a and b are chosen correctly that the function

$$\ln\left[\frac{c - b}{c_0 - b}\right] = -Pt$$

or

$$\ln\left(1 - \frac{m}{a}\right) = -Pt$$

plots as a straight line in the given net: if a and/or b are wrong, the function deviates from a straight line either upward or downward as t increases.

The exponent n of the general reaction equation

$$R = Pc^n$$

states the "order" of the reaction. It is first-order if $n = 1$:

$$\ln \frac{1}{1 - \dfrac{m}{a}} = Pt$$

or

$$\frac{m}{a} = 1 - e^{-Pt}; \tag{X}$$

it is second-order if $n = 2$:

$$\frac{m}{a} = \frac{Pt}{Pt + \dfrac{1}{a}} \tag{Y}$$

or, rearranged,

$$\frac{t}{m} = \frac{1}{a^2 P} + \frac{t}{a},$$

or with $a = 1$,

$$m = \frac{Pt}{Pt + 1}$$

272

or

$$Pt = \frac{m}{1 - m}, \tag{Z}$$

or

$$\frac{t}{m} = \frac{1}{P} + t.$$

In all the above expressions, mineral recoveries m are used to replace concentrations c.

The second-order reaction equation gives straight-line graphs in ordinary linear t and t/m nets; the graph's ordinate intercept (at $t = 0$) is the reciprocal of corrected floatability a^2P. The floatability ratio

$$\frac{P_1}{P_2}$$

of two minerals of floatability P_1 and P_2 states selectivity of flotation with respect to the two minerals. If,

$$a_1 = a_2 = 1,$$

then the expression

$$\frac{P_1}{P_2} = \frac{m_1(1 - m_2)}{(1 - m_1)m_2}$$

gives the square of the selectivity index S.I.

It has been recommended to apply to flotation kinetics the function

$$Pt = A \ln \frac{m}{1 - m} + (1 - A) \frac{m}{1 - m},$$

which unites a first- and a second-order reaction equation. A is the abundance in the feed of the mineral to be flotated out; the first-order process comes to the fore if A is great and the second-order one if A is small. It has further been recommended to replace Eq. (X) above by

$$\frac{m}{a} = 1 - \frac{(1 - e^{-Pt})}{Pt}$$

and Eq. (Y) above for times $t \gtrsim 6/P$ by

$$\frac{m}{a} = \frac{Pt}{Pt + 1}$$

or

$$\frac{m}{a} = \frac{Pt - 1}{Pt}$$

(Huber-Panu 1965, 1970).

The first-order reaction equation (X) plots in a RR net, whose abscissa is calibrated in log t and its ordinate in

$$\log \log \frac{1}{1 - \dfrac{m}{a}} \, ,$$

as a line of unity slope whose time parameter ("time constant") $1/P$ corresponds to a recovery $m = 63.2\%$ (to $m = 1 - 1/e$).

The distribution parameter p, on the other hand, is not necessarily unity in all cases; if it is not, then the resulting formula of form

$$\frac{m}{a} = 1 - e^{-(Pt)^p}$$

or

$$(Pt)^p = \ln \frac{1}{1 - \dfrac{m}{a}}$$

or

$$P = \frac{- \ln \left(1 - \dfrac{m}{a}\right)^{\frac{1}{p}}}{t}$$

exhibits full analogy with the RR function. Also, instead of the second-order reaction equation (Z), the formula

$$(Pt)^p = \frac{m}{1 - m}$$

or

$$m = \frac{(Pt)^p}{(Pt)^p + 1}$$

is often found to be valid and useful at $p \simeq 1.3$ (Rozgai 1972).

The equation

$$\frac{1 - (1 - m)^{\frac{P'}{P}}}{1 - (1 - m)} = \frac{A(1 - C)}{(1 - A)C}$$

may also be used, where m is pay mineral recovery, and P and P' are, respectively, the floatabilities of the pay and the gangue minerals (their ratio

$$\Phi = \frac{P}{P'}$$

being their relative floatability). A and C are pay mineral contents in the feed and concentrate, respectively (Digre 1960).

The second-order reaction equation was found to hold on flotating pure galena in a Hallimond tube at pH = 9 using 2 mg/l sodium isopropyl xanthate or a mixture of one part galena with nine parts quartz in a Denver laboratory cell at pH = 9 using 20 g/t sodium isopropyl xanthate and 150 g/t Dowfroth 250 brand frother after 10 minutes conditioning. The floatabilities P of the different

Table 2.27. Floatabilities P and long-run recoveries $m\%$ of galena vs. grain size, as established in a Hallimond tube (H) and in a Denver lab cell (D)

Mesh		48	65	100	150	200	270	325	400
x μm		250	175	125	86	63	48	40	<37
H	P	0	1.2	1.5	6.0	12.0	8.4	4.6	0.3
	$m\%$	2	65	72	75	92	99	90	66
D	P	0	0	0.5	1.2	10.0	8.4	7.0	6.0
	$m\%$	0	0	12	38	100	93	90	86
D	P'	0	0	0	0	0.06	0.06	0.20	0.45
	$m\%$	0	0	0.3	0.3	3.0	4.1	8.6	9.2

grain size fractions and their long-run recoveries $m\%$ in the Hallimond tube (H) and the Denver cell (D), respectively, are stated in Table 2.27 (Suwanasing and Salman 1970).

Other authors maintain that the order of the reaction equation is a function of particle size: it is $n = 3.2$ for the coarser particles (250 to 180 μm), declining to $n = 1$ at 60 μm (DeBruyn and Modi 1956; Hukki 1953; Prosser 1969; Schuhmann 1942; Steiner 1970; Tomlinson and Fleming 1963).

2.5. FLOTATION EQUIPMENT

In the flotation operation suitably prepared solid particles dispersed in an aqueous solution — a conditioned pulp — are brought into contact with gas bubbles; the particles attaching themselves to the bubbles are recovered separately from those that remain in the liquid phase. Flotation machines are tanks in which the saturation of the pulp with bubbles and the separation of the two types of particles can be performed at a satisfactory efficiency. A flotation shop may use a single long cell or a bank of a number of identical (short) cells connected in series, each being fed the de-frothed pulp of the cell upstream of it.

2.5.1. Cell types. The different types of flotation cell can be classified most readily according to the mechanism of bubble introduction. There are nine possible ways of generating gas bubbles in a pulp: (1) producing a gas by a chemical reaction; (2) producing steam bubbles by boiling; (3) the cascade method, where a free-falling jet or tumbling body of pulp entrains with it more or less air; (4) the agitation-froth method, where an impeller rotating near the pulp surface beats air into the pulp from the ambient atmosphere; (5) the vacuum method, where a vacuum, created in a suitably sealed space, lifts the pulp above its normal hydrostatic level and makes the air dissolved in it at normal atmospheric pressure separate out at the surfaces of the hydrophobic particles in the form of very fine bubbles; (6) the pressure method, which saturates the pulp with air at a pressure: this air subsequently separates out in the form of very fine bubbles at the surfaces of the hydrophobic grains as the pressure is gradually or abruptly lowered; (7) the cyclone (injector) method, where pulp spinning in a "vortex vessel" disperses into fine bubbles the air introduced into it (or sucked in from the ambient atmosphere); (8) the pneumatic method, where air at a slight pressure is blown in at the bottom of the pulp, through pipes or a mat (a porous sheet); and (9) the subaeration (bottom-impeller) method, in which air at atmospheric pressure or a slight pressure above it is introduced next to an impeller that, rotating at the bottom of the pulp, keeps it in dispersion.

The first three methods, obsolete today, are of purely historic interest. The popularity of the remaining six increases in the approximate order of their enumeration.

Diagrams of some typical cells are shown in Fig. 2.87.

Diagram A shows the MS agitation-froth cell of Minerals Separation Ltd. An impeller rotating in the agitating compartment beats air into the pulp and disperses it thoroughly; it also sucks in settling pulp from the spitzkasten-shaped froth compartment S of the upstream cell. (The bottom of each spitzkasten in connected by a pipe P with the agitating compartment of the next cell.) Providing a large froth surface, this machine is useful for handling feeds rich in the fraction to be flotated out (e.g. coal slurries).

Diagram B shows a vacuum cell. Under a hermetically sealed separator-tank top, a pump attached to pipe P creates a vacuum which lifts suitably conditioned pulp (pulp treated with reagents and saturated with air) into the tank through axial bottom pipe C. Dissolved air thereupon separates out at the surfaces of the hydrophobic mineral grains. Floating froth is driven by a rake into a froth-collecting funnel F. Froth and tailing pulp enter across overflow weirs into "barometric pipes" of appropriate length. Settled-out sand-size waste is also driven by a slowly rotating mechanism towards a (barometric) discharge pipe O.

Diagram C shows the principle of an airlift-type flotation machine using compressed air. Part of the air introduced at the bottom of the airlift is absorbed by the water phase of the pulp: higher up in the riser, the drop of head permits this air to separate out in the form of micro-bubbles on the hydrophobic minerals. The top of the riser is best attached tangentially to a cylindrical vessel operating as a centrifugal froth separator: the fast-spinning pulp in the vessel rapidly separates into froth, collecting axially, and tailings, collecting next to the vessel wall: all this increases the throughput of the device.

Diagram D shows an injector, a device that has gained widespread acceptance for dispersing air in water (pulp) or — operated at pressure — for rapidly saturating water with dissolved air. Abrupt depressurizing by means of a suitable device in an ejector cell generates abundant fine air bubbles separating at the hydrophobic surfaces. Using this type of apparatus, the time needed for the hydrophobic mineral grains to attach themselves to the large bubbles in the machines operating with such can be saved largely or entirely, which greatly increases throughput. Microbubbles separating out on hydrophobic slimes particles in the μm size range will lift these into the froth, without their getting anywhere near the large bubbles.

Diagrams E to I represent pneumatic flotation cells.

The Callow cell (Diagram E) and the MacIntosh cell (Diagram F) are both long single cells (troughs) at the bottom of which air is introduced at a slight pressure in the form of fine bubbles through a mat (a porous sheet). The sloping porous bottom of the Callow cell is made up of a perforated sheet and several layers of canvas. The pores of the canvas are clotted up fast by tailings particles and, in an alkaline medium, by precipitating $Ca(OH)_2$. This drawback is overcome in the MacIntosh cell by the use of a rotor, a perforated pipe slowly rotating near the bottom of a level-bottomed trough. The perforated shell of the rotor is wrapped with canvas or a porous sheet of rubber. In other machines, the pulp at the cell bottom is separated from the compressed-air space by porous bricks.

Designs G and H exploit the airlift principle to keep the pulp in suspension. A header pipe running above the long axis of a long cell has vertical pipes of 1.0 to 2.5 cm dia. branching from it, spaced at 10 to 15 cm intervals, reaching down to the cell bottom between vertical baffles B reaching from one end of the cell to the other. Aerated pulp rising between the baffles collides with the splashboards S under the header (which have a number of apertures open to the ambient atmosphere): it is spattered on collision, so that part of the air that it contains is broken up into small bubbles. Outside the baffles B, pulp moves downward. Pulp introduced at the feed end of the cell thus moves in a double spiral towards the discharge end, where it is discharged across a weir of adjustable height. Froth overflows lips placed lengthwise on either side of the cell. The G type cells (Forrester, Southwestern, Ekof W) are run at a pulp depth of about one metre; the H type (Britannia) cell is run at about 3 m. A greater depth of pulp means a higher pressure at the cell bottom, which brings with it the advantages of the flotation machines using pressure (cf. e.g. Type C above), such as greater throughput, smaller bubbles with fuller mineral linings, and

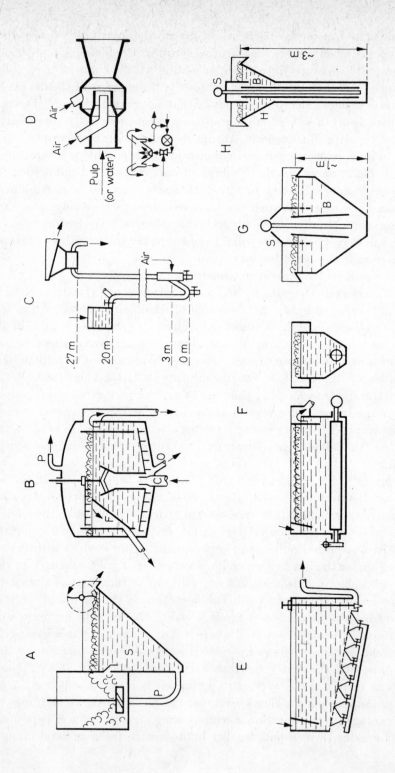

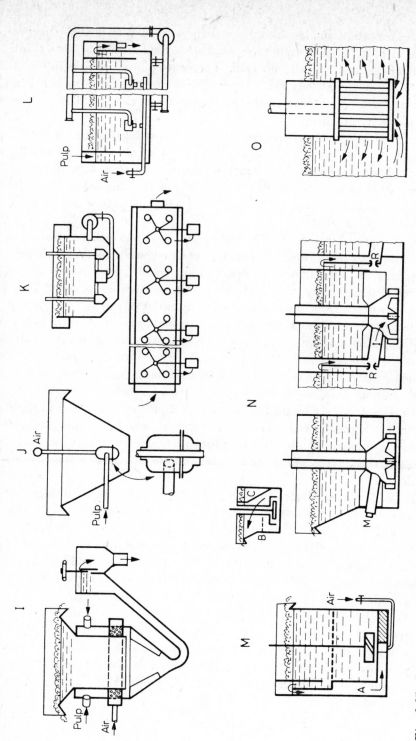

Fig. 2.87. Diagrams of flotation machines. *A* — MS agitation cell, *B* — vacuum cell, *C* — airlift cell, *D* — ejector (with the outline of an injector), *E* to *I* — pneumatic cells (*E* — Callow, *F* — Mac-Intosh, *G* — Forrester [or Ekof], *H* — Britannia, *I* — centrifugal), *J, K, L* — cyclone cells, *M, N, O* — sub-aeration cells (*M* — MS, *N* — Denver [or Fahrenwald], *O* — Wemco [or Fagergren])

hence, a more persistent and less bulky froth. The suction of an airlift in deeper pulp is more vigorous, so that middlings can as a rule be returned to some point of the cell near the feed end without using a separate pump, whereas in the G type cells, with their relatively shallow pulp, middlings do not flow back on their own but must be returned to the feed end by a device installed for the purpose (e.g. a separate airlift).

The cylindrical cell of Diagram I relies on the centrifugal force for better bubble dispersion and greater throughput. Pulp is introduced tangentially into the annulus between two concentric cylinders: air at a slight pressure ($\sim$0.25 gauge at) is introduced in fine bubbles through a ring below the pulp feed. The conical bottom part of the tank is fitted with baffles to break the spin of the pulp (Wilczinski 1972).

Diagrams J, K and L represent different types of cyclone cell. The essential feature of these is a small cylindrical cyclone (vortex vessel). Several such vessels are typically installed 1 to 1.5 m apart in longer cells. Pulp is introduced into each vessel tangentially, at a high speed; air is introduced axially. Pulp spreading out in a fan from the central (bottom) outlet of the vessel contains the air in the form of very fine bubbles. For a satisfactory aeration of the entire bulk of pulp, it is sufficient to make, say, one-third of pulp volume only pass through the vortex vessels. Several vortex vessels (e.g. 2, 4 or 8) may be hooked up to a single pulp pump, either in parallel, in a symmetric arrangement, as in the TA cell made at Tatabánya, Hungary (Diagram K), or in series, as in the Heyl and Patterson cell (Diagram L). In the TA cell, the cyclones suck in their own air from the ambient atmosphere (auto-suction), whereas in the H and P cyclones, air is introduced at a slight pressure (John 1973; Tarján 1947). The cyclones of the Davcra cell are horizontal and are mounted on the outside of the tank.

Diagrams M, N and O illustrate the most widespread types of subaeration cells. Diagram M is the cross section of the MS subaeration cell made by Minerals Separation Ltd. In it, air is blown in at a slight pressure under the impeller. The bottom part of the cell (the aeration space) is separated from the top (froth) space by a damping grille. The tank is double-walled on one side and has a false bottom: pulp entering the space A thus constituted over an adjustable weir is led through a sub-floor feed passage under the impeller of the next cell. (Raising the weir reduces froth height.)

If the impeller shaft is surrounded by a tube reaching down to the impeller (as is the case e.g. in the Denver Sub-A or Fahrenwald cell, Diagram N), and the impeller is run at sufficient speed, it will suck in air through the tube from the ambient atmosphere. For the usual run of pulp heads (1 to 1.2 m), the approximate formula

$$Q = 135D^3 \left(n - \frac{100}{D} \right)$$

holds, where Q litres per minute is the volume of air sucked in, D m is impeller diameter and n rpm is impeller speed. A stationary, inverted-saucer-shaped hood fitted to the bottom of the suction tube surrounding the impeller shaft of the Denver Sub-A cell protects the impeller from silting up during stoppages, so that it can always be restarted rather easily. From the rim of the hood, lugs L reach down into the pulp: between the lugs, pulp and air can pass well-dispersed from the impeller space to the cell bottom. In the space above the hood, pulp vorticity is damped by diagonal baffles. Overflow pulp from the next cell upstream is poured by a gently sloping transfer pipe I onto the impeller. The impeller thus does not have to actually lift the pulp as in the MS cell: this is why Denver cells may be fed a coarser-grained feed. Sanding up of the cell is prevented by a rubber-ringed port R in the bottom of the plate the top of which constitutes the overflow weir. R drains the heavier sand grains collecting at the bottom of the upstream cell direct into pipe I. Pipe M, passing from the impeller space to the outer atmosphere through the front wall of the cell, serves for returning middlings, if required, into one of the upstream cells.

The more recent Denver $D-R$ machine comprises no cells separated by walls reaching down to the bottom: the air tubes surrounding the impeller shafts are sealed at the top (that is, they do not permit autosuction), and the stationary hood has a short cylindrical or conical attachment, open at the top and concentric with the air tube. Generating an inner gyratory system in the pulp, this attachment ensures that the pulp is kept well in suspension. The $D-R$ machine has a greater throughput than the older, Sub-A machine divided up into cells: it is to be preferred in simple flowsheets above all.

Machines resembling the Fahrenwald (Denver Sub-A) with smaller or greater differences include the designs of the Hungarian Jászberényi Aprítógépgyár, or Mechanobr (USSR) or of the VEB Schwermaschinenbau "Ernst Thälmann", Magdeburg (GDR).

Diagram O shows the agitating and air-dispersing unit in the Fagergren (Wemco) cell. It includes two concentric cages made up of vertical pipes or rods. The outer cage is the stator, the inner one is the rotor. The stator carries a standpipe (a cylinder of sheet metal) rising above the pulp surface: it is through this pipe that the rotor sucks in air while it simultaneously lifts up pulp from the space below the stator. (The cell might thus be regarded as an agitation-type device with equal right.) Strong shear between the two cages disperses the air into fine bubbles. The double-cage units can be installed either centrally in each of a bank of series-connected short cells or axially, suitably spaced, in long uncompartmented cells (in the same way e.g. as the vortex vessels in a cyclone cell, Diagram L). A more recent Fagergren mixing-dispersing unit, designated $1+1$, features a rotor that is a single long-ribbed rotating rubber or plastic "star" and a stator that is a rubber shell with apertures, replacing the two cages assembled from numerous steel elements (Reck 1969).

The MS machines require compressed air (that is, an external air compressor). For the Denver and the Fagergren, a source of compressed air is no absolute must; Denver machines may, however, be run on compressed air with the top end of the pipe surrounding the shaft sealed off by means of a stuffing box and the compressed air introduced under it. In that case, impeller speed (and, through it, power draft, wear, etc.) may be optimized independently of the required air feed rate. For returning middlings to some upstream cell of the same bank, Denver cells do not as a rule require a separate pump: the MS may require one, and the Fagergren always does.

Pressure in the pulp is slightly greater in front of an impeller blade than behind it, where vorticity is stronger. Hence, air absorbed at points of higher pressure in a subaeration cell can separate out at the hydrophobic particle surfaces in these pressure shadows.

The optimum running of a flotation shop requires, in addition to eliminating turbulence at the pulp surface, the generation of sufficient volumes of a stable enough froth, etc., as also the optimum design and operation of froth discharge. A rear crowding board C and front baffle B installed as shown in the inset of Diagram N deflect circulation towards the froth overflow lip at a velocity several times as high as pulp velocity along the length of the flotation machine. This permits to reduce the retention time of froth at the pulp surface to a minimum, by driving it rapidly towards the discharge lip and by ensuring its complete removal.

There are many more types of subaeration cell widely used in practice (e.g. Agitair, Boliden FR, etc.) (Fahlström et al. 1970). In the Agitair or Galigher machine, a rotor recalling that of the Fagergren cell is installed at the pulp bottom at the end of a tubular shaft: compressed air is led to the rotor axially down the shaft.

Some of the more recent cells feature two impellers mounted on a single shaft, with blades different as to shape or pitch, or two impellers rotating at different speeds or counterrotating on two concentric shafts; or the impeller rotating at the bottom of the pulp may incorporate an obliquely mounted disk in gyrating motion, resulting in a more efficient pulp transport and air suction (Kellerwessel 1966; Stöhr and von Szantho 1974).

2.5.2. Geometric and hydrodynamic similitude in flotation cells. If x/D, σ and δ/γ are constant, the following dimensionless numbers remain invariant in a subaeration cell:

— the Reynolds number

$$\mathrm{Re} = \varrho \frac{Du}{\mu} = \frac{Du}{\nu}$$

or

$$\mathrm{Re}' = \varrho n \frac{D^2}{\mu} \left(= \varrho D^2 \frac{\omega}{2\mu} = D^2 \frac{\omega}{2\nu} \right).$$

— the Froude number

$$Fr = n^2 \frac{D}{g},$$

— the Weber number

$$We = \varrho n^2 \frac{D^3}{a},$$

— the Archimedes number

$$Ar = D^3 g \frac{\Delta\varrho}{\varrho v^2} = Re^2 \frac{\Delta\varrho}{\varrho Fr},$$

— the expression

$$Z_Q = \frac{Q}{nD^3} \quad \text{and}$$

— the Newton number

$$Ne = (Z_N) = \frac{N}{\varrho n^3 D^5},$$

where

$$\varrho = \frac{\gamma'}{g}$$

is pulp density, and

$$\Delta\varrho = \frac{(\delta - \gamma')}{g};$$

a is surface tension, μ is dynamic viscosity, v is kinematic viscosity, u is the peripheral speed of the impeller of diameter D and speed n, ω is its angular velocity, Q is air feed rate and N is power draft.

The relationship

$$Ne (= Z_N) = K Re^m Fr^p$$

also holds. If the pulp surface is non-turbulent, then $p = 0$, and

$$Ne = K Re^m;$$

if the flow is laminar, then $m = -1$, that is,

$$N = K n^2 D^3 \mu;$$

if it is turbulent, then $m = 0$, that is,

$$N = K n^3 D^5 \varrho.$$

(The constant K is different in each case.) Flow is laminar if

$$Re' = \frac{nD^2}{v} \lesssim 50.$$

Figure 2.88 presents $Ne = f(Re')$ curves for different types of agitation. The energy demand of agitating a liquid and a gas dispersed together is less

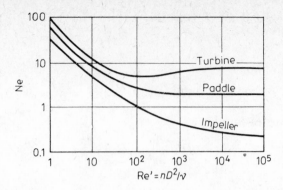

Fig. 2.88. Ne $= f(\mathrm{Re}')$ curves of different agitator designs

than that of agitating the liquid alone. If

$$\frac{D_1}{D_2} = k, \quad \frac{N_1}{N_2} = k^3,$$

then

$$\frac{n_1}{n_2} = k^{-\frac{2}{3}}; \quad \frac{Q_1}{Q_2} = k^{\frac{7}{3}}.$$

At higher Newton numbers, agitation must be stronger to ensure the suspension of the pulp. It is therefore indicated to use a turbine-type agitator. The deflection of the pulp at the cell wall and at the baffles causes wear and loss of energy. Energy consumption per unit of cell volume is a measure of flotation intensity, just as energy consumption per unit of mill volume is a measure of grinding intensity. (In both cases, energy is dissipated in a multitude of ways and lost as heat in the final reckoning.)

Ne and Z_Q are the two most important indicators of hydrodynamic conditions. Q/D^2 varies as air feed rate per unit surface area, Q_1; nD varies as the peripheral speed u of the impeller; that is,

$$Z'_Q = \frac{Q_1}{u}$$

may also be used instead of

$$Z_Q = \frac{Q}{nD^3}$$

as the dimensionless air flow number. This parameter greatly affects concentrate quality. Especially if the feed is a coarse one prone to settling out, the correct matching of Q_1 and u is of great importance. If Q_1 is increased with u kept constant, the power draft N of agitation (that is, Z_N) is reduced, and the coarser particles settle out of suspension. The value of N, on the other hand, is affected also by pulp density ϱ (that is, by solids concentration). That is, if grinding fineness is reduced (the maximum limiting particle size of grinding output is raised), then — with Q_1 and u constant — more of the coarse grains will settle out and the power draft of the impeller will be less. By monitoring the power draft, then, it is possible to adjust the correct air feed rate and also to control the grinding circuit. In order to attain optimum flotation performance (given a comparatively coarse-grained feed), the regulation of impeller speed may also be necessary. The way N and Q (the air feed rate) vary as functions of u, ϱ, H' and Q_z is illustrated by Fig. 2.89. (Q_z is the central pulp flow rate to the impeller.)

The critical impeller speed n_{cr} of geometrically similar mechanical cells of different size (the speed which is just sufficient to keep all particles suspended in the pulp) is characterized by the Reynolds number

$$\mathrm{Re} = K \sqrt{Ar\left(\frac{\sigma x}{D}\right)^{\frac{1}{3}}}$$

and the Froude number

$$\mathrm{Fr} = K'\frac{\Delta\varrho}{\varrho}\left(\frac{\sigma x}{D}\right)^{\frac{1}{3}},$$

where x is particle size. With $\Delta\varrho/\varrho$ and σ unchanged, the critical parameters remain unchanged on changing the cell dimensions if

$$\mathrm{Fr}/\sqrt[3]{x/D} = \mathrm{const.}$$

and

$$\mathrm{Fr} \cong n^2D = \mathrm{const.}$$

If Fr is a constant, then so is Ne $(= Z_Q)$; hence,

$$\mathrm{Ne}\sqrt{\mathrm{Fr}} = \frac{Q}{D^{2.5}\sqrt{g}}$$

is also a constant, and so is

$$\frac{Q}{D^{2.5}} \cong \frac{Q}{F\sqrt{D}}$$

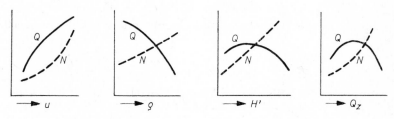

Fig. 2.89. Q and N vs. u, H', ϱ and Q_z — approximate

for hydrodynamically similar cells of different size. (F, the cross sectional area of the cell, roughly equals the pulp surface area.) In non-mechanical -- impeller-less — cells, D is to be replaced by B, the edge of the cell, and

$$\mathrm{Fr} = n^2 \frac{D}{g} = \frac{u^2}{D\pi^2 g}$$

is to be replaced by the quantity modified by the air inflow rate,

$$\mathrm{Fr'} = \frac{Q^2 \varrho}{\varDelta \varrho g B^5} \; .$$

In other words, the relationship

$$\mathrm{Fr'} \simeq \frac{Q^2}{B^5} \simeq \frac{Q}{B^{2.5}} \simeq \frac{Q}{F\sqrt{B}} = \text{const.}$$

is also here the key of transformation from one cell size to another.

The relationship

$$\frac{N}{V\sqrt{D}} = \text{const.}$$

or

$$\frac{N}{V\sqrt{B}} = \text{const.}$$

also holds for the transformation ($V = B^2 H$). If e.g. V is increased by a factor of 10, then D or B increases by a factor of about $\sqrt[3]{V} = \sqrt[3]{10} = 2.16$ only and $\sqrt{D}$ or $\sqrt{B}$ by a factor of 1.47 only: hence, in practice, a transformation based on the relationship

$$\frac{N}{V} = \text{const.}$$

will do (Zlokarnik 1973).

2.5.3. Parameters of the main types of mechanical flotation cells are listed in Table 2.28. The last two columns of the table state the parameters N/V and Fr.

For example, in the Denver and the (large) Agitair and Wemco cells,

$$c = \frac{D}{B} \simeq \qquad 0.50 \qquad 0.64 \qquad 0.25,$$

in that order. $c_1 = b/D$ is about 0.15 for the Denver and about 0.9 for the Wem-co. V and B are related by

$$V = c' B^p,$$

286

Table 2.28. Parameters of some makes of mechanical flotation cell

Make	Designation	B cm	H cm	V m³	Impeller D, cm	Impeller u, m/s	N^* kW	N/V	Fr
Agitair	24	61	76	0.285	31	7.26	1.2	4.2	1.76
	36	92	76	0.64	45	7.26	2.4	3.8	1.21
	48	122	76	1.14	78	7.26	4.2	3.7	0.70
	60	148	76	1.66	95	7.26	6.0	3.6	0.575
	96	244	76	4.50	155	7.26	15.0	3.3	0.35
	120	295	76	6.62	188	7.26	22.0	3.3	0.29
	120A	295	125	10.90	188	7.26	33.0	3.0	0.29
Denver D-R	12	61	76	0.285	28	7.88	0.8	2.8	2.26
(Fahrenwald)	15	68	76	0.34	31	7.82	0.9	2.7	2.04
	18	75	92	0.515	36	7.82	1.4	2.7	1.76
	18sp	88	92	0.71	41	7.82	2.0	2.8	1.54
	21	106	102	1.14	48	7.70	2.5	2.8	1.28
	24	118	102	1.42	56	7.70	4.0	2.8	1.10
	30	153	122	2.85	69	7.70	7.0	2.5	0.89
	200	170	198	5.70	80	7.70	13.8	2.4	0.77
	300	200	215	8.60	96	7.70	20.6	2.4	0.64
Fagergren	36	92	36	0.31	23	7.80	1.8	5.8	2.73
(Wemco)	48	112	48	0.60	28	8.10	3.3	5.5	2.42
	56	142	56	1.14	36	8.50	5.9	5.2	2.07
	66	168	62	1.74	42	8.80	8.8	5.0	1.90
	120	305 × 230	125	8.75	76	9.80	22.0	2.5	1.30
	120	305 × 305	120	11.20	76	9.80	25.0	2.2	1.30
	144	366 × 270	145	14.30	91	10.10	30.0	2.1	1.16
Mechanobr	1	50	55	0.14	20	6.3	0.6	4.3	2.05
	2	60	60	0.24	25	7.0	1.0	4.2	2.02
	3	70	70	0.38	30	7.4	1.3	3.4	1.98
	4	90	85	0.80	35	8.0	2.4	3.0	1.89
	5	110	100	1.35	50	8.5	3.5	2.6	1.49
	6	175	110	3.26	60	8.8	8.0	2.4	1.33
	7	220	125	6.25	75	9.4	15.0	2.4	1.22

	Desig- nation (cm)	EUU (unit cell) V, m³	N, kW	N/V	EUM** for ores V, m³	N, kW	N/V	EUM** for coals V, m³	N, kW	N/V	Weight (tons) $\sim t$
Hungarian	30	0.03	0.15	5.0	0.03	0.15	5.0	—	—	—	0.2
make	50	0.175	0.75	4.3	0.18	0.8	4.5	0.20	0.8	4.0	0.3
(Aprítógép-	60	0.3	1.3	4.3	0.3	1.0	3.3	0.35	1.0	2.9	0.5
gyár, Jász-	80	0.6	2.3	3.8	0.7	2.0	2.9	0.75	2.0	2.6	0.7
berény)	100	1.0	3.1	3.1	1.25	3.0	2.7	1.40	3.1	2.2	1.4
	120	1.8	5.0	2.8	2.0	4.0	2.5	2.25	4.5	2.0	1.6
	140	2.8	7.6	2.7	3.0	7.5	2.5	3.20	6.4	2.0	2.5
	160	4.0	11.0	2.7	4.3	10.0	2.5	4.60	9.0	2.0	2.6

* A motor rating higher by 25% is to be chosen.
** Two-, four- and six-module cells are available.

where the exponent p is in the 2 to 3 range and the coefficient c' in the 0.6 to 1.3 range, with $p = 2.6$ and $c' \cong 0.9$ for rough averages. In the above order, e.g.,

$$p = \qquad 2.6 \qquad\qquad 2.1 \qquad\qquad 2.8.$$

Peripheral impeller speed u is 7.7 m/s in the Denver and 7.3 m/s in the Agitair. (That is, u increases as c and c_1 decrease.) In earlier Wemco cells (made before 1962), u used to be constant at 8.6 m/s; for cells made after 1962, on the other hand, the relationship

$$u \propto D^{0.38}$$

holds. For the Mechanobr cells made in the USSR,

$$u \propto D^{0.3}$$

(for example, $u = 6.3$ m/s at $V = 0.1$ m³ and $u = 9.1$ m/s at $V = 4.5$ m³). The specific parameter $c_2 = N/V$ is least in the Denver cells; its values for the three above-named types of cell relate as

$$\text{Denver : Agitair : Wemco} = 1 : 1.9 : 2.5.$$

c_2 is a constant irrespective of cell size for each of these US-made cell types. In European makes, on the other hand, c_2 decreases as V increases; the relationships

$$c_2 \propto V^{-\frac{1}{3}}$$

or

$$B^{-\frac{p}{3}}$$

hold: in other words,

$$N \propto V^{\frac{2}{3}}$$

(Arbiter et al. 1969; Harris 1974).

There are some large custom-made cylindrical cells of $\sim$20 m³ (3 m dia $\times$ 3 m height) and $\sim$60 m³ (4.3 m dia. $\times$ 4.3 m height) in use (Maxwell cells: converted agitating tanks), especially in rougher flotation.

The Hungarian-made Tatabánya TA cells are welded together out of two-metre modules. The "A" series, of one m² useful cross section, contains one row of vortex (cyclone) vessels; the "B" series, of 2 m² cross section, contains two. In the latter, symmetric clusters of four cyclones are attached to the pressure pipe (or to symmetric branches issuing from it) of a pulp pump delivering 1.5 (3) m³ per minute at 2 to 2.5 gauge at, driven by a 17.5 (30.5) kW motor, and catering to 4 (8) m³ of pulp volume. There is one vortex vessel per m³ of clear (useful) cell volume; hence, cell volume may be stated in terms of the number of vortex vessels also. The largest TA cell currently being made, designated 5/40-B, has five pumps and a useful volume of 40 m³. Installed power is 4.4 or

3.8 kW/m³; effective power draft is about three quarters as much (3.3 to 2.8 kW/m³). The TA cell requires no source of compressed air. Specific cell weight is about 300 kg/m³ (whereas it is in the range from 600 to 1,350 kg/m³ for impeller-type cells) (Tarján 1971).

Where a great deal of froth is being produced (as is the rule with pneumatic cells), it tends to overflow spontaneously. In cells producing little froth, the froth is usually ladled over the tailboard or lip by slowly rotating blades (cf. e.g. Diagram A of Fig. 2.87).

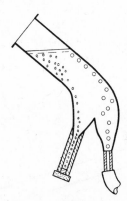

Fig. 2.90. The Hallimond tube

Figure 2.90 illustrates a Hallimond tube. This mini pneumatic cell permits to perform meaningful laboratory flotation tests on samples as small as one gram or less. The bottom part of the tube branches into two capillaries. Bubbles passing through a finely porous filter inset in the upright capillary carry hydrophobic particles to the top of the solution; dropping off the bursting bubbles, these collect in the other, stoppered capillary. No frother must be added to the solution (Wark 1955).

2.5.4. Flotation cell hookups. The duration of each of the usual phases of roughing, cleaning and scavenging flotation and the treatment to which the middlings are to be subjected are determined by cell hookup which therefore has a great influence on flotation performance. The composition of overflowing froth changes gradually from the feed end as flotation proceeds. The composition of the mineral phase in the froth of a bank of cells flotating a pyritic copper sulphide ore in a silicate gangue might vary as in Fig. 2.91. The bold lines in Fig. 2.92 indicate possible hookups of froth-collector launders for a nine-cell bank. Here, Nos 4 to 7 are rougher cells Nos 8 and 9 are scavenger cells and 1 to 3 are cleaner cells. Froth from the rougher cells is returned to Cell 1; froth from the scavenger cells is feed back to Cell 3. By removing stoppers from the froth launders and sealing off certain launder segments, cell hookup can be

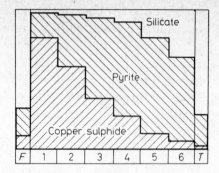

Fig. 2.91. Mineral composition of the froth, feed (F) and tailings (T) of a series-connected cell bank

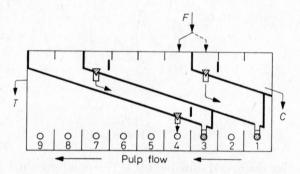

Fig. 2.92. Possible hookups of the froth launders of a flotation bank

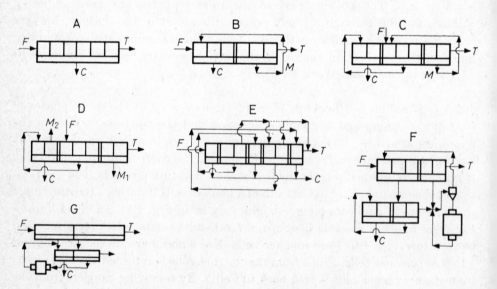

Fig. 2.93. Some of the more frequent flotation flowsheets

altered fairly simply. (For example, by changing the feed pattern in the way shown by the dashed lines, Nos 3 to 6 become roughers, Nos 7 to 9 become scavengers and Nos 1 and 2 become cleaners.)

Flotation middlings include as a rule many hard-to-flotate particles (intergrown, unlocked but of peculiar shape or unusual size, or unlocked but with a surface contamination). Many of these find their way into the comparatively sparse middlings, which of course contains misrouted free ore and gangue particles also. These latter can be taken out of the middlings by a simple repeat flotation (by a direct feedback of middlings into the flotation circuit). Most of the problem grains, however, can be suitably treated only by a re-grinding and subsequent re-flotation of the middlings.

Figure 2.93 presents some of the possible flotation flowsheets. Large flotation shops have a preference for the arrangement shown as diagram G, where the rougher and scavenger banks receive fresh feed only, with no admixtures at any point of either the middling-type froth of downstream cells or the output of one of the cleaner cells. This facilitates the automation and computer control of the process and permits of a more efficacious optimization.

In a differential flotation operation, where a certain number of different concentrates are to be recovered, each of these requires a separate circuit. For example, in the differential flotation of a galena–sphalerite–pyrite ore in a silicate gangue, the sphalerite circuit is usually preceded by the galena circuit and followed by the pyrite circuit. This makes for a fairly complicated flowsheet.

The differential flotation of pay minerals A, B and C with a view to separating them from one another and from the gangue D can be achieved in several ways. It is possible, first of all, to flotate out A, B and C in succession and to let D collect in the tailings. Second, one may separate A, B and C in a single bulk flotation pass from the gangue D, and then split the bulk concentrate by flotating out minerals A + B so that C is left behind in the pulp; finally, A can be flotated out and B left behind. These solutions may be combined e.g. by flotating out A + B with C + D left behind; then A is flotated out while B is depressed and, in another pass, C is flotated out from beside D. If the concentrations of A, B and C in the feed are about equal, it is usual to remove them in succession, but if one is much more abundant than the rest, it is more usual to resort to partial bulk flotation with subsequent separation. The production of a bulk pre-concentrate is indicated also if coarse grinding produces many satisfactorily unlocked gangue grains besides grains of intergrown sulphide minerals.

2.5.5. Dimensioning of flotation apparatus. Cell volume can be calculated starting from the retention time required, as established by flotating the feed conditioned with the suitable reagents in a small (one to five litre) laboratory cell.

Example. If the laboratory test says eight minutes of retention are required for the fair flotation of a galena ore in quartz, how many 2 m³ cells are required to flotate 60 tph of ore? The volume of 60 tons of ore, of s.g. 2.7, is 22 m³; choosing a pulp density of 25 weight percent, hourly pulp throughput is

$$\frac{60 \times 75}{25} + 22 = 200 \text{ m}^3;$$

hence, eight-minute throughput is

$$Q = 200 \cdot \frac{8}{60} = 27 \text{ m}^3$$

of pulp. The fittings within the cell, the froth layer and the bubbles in the pulp take up about one quarter of total cell volume; hence, about three quarters of that volume may be regarded as useful. Effective pulp volume per cell may thus be taken to equal

$$V = 2 \cdot \frac{3}{4} = 1.5 \text{ m}^3.$$

Now since

$$\frac{Q}{V} = \frac{27}{1.5} = 18,$$

we want 18 cells of 2 m³ size to flotate out the galena, given a 25% density pulp. If pulp density may be increased to 30%, then

$$Q = \left(\frac{60 \cdot 70}{30} + 22\right)\frac{8}{60} = 22 \text{ m}^3$$

and

$$\frac{Q}{V} = \frac{22}{1.5} = 14.7;$$

that is, 14 to 15 cells will do. The optimum number of cells in a rougher-plus-scavenger bank is 8 to 16 in the flotation of copper ores, 6 to 8 in pyrite flotation, 6 to 16 for lead and zinc ores, 10 to 20 for fluorite, 4 to 6 for glass sand and 4 to 6 in coal flotation (Kind 1972; Roman 1970).

If the preconcentrate is say, 15 weight% (= 9 tph), with s.g. is 5 and cleaning at pulp density of 12%, requires a retention time of 5 minutes, then, thinking in terms of one m³ cells, we have a useful cell volume

$$V = 0.75 \cdot 1 = 0.75 \text{ m}^3,$$

and

$$\frac{Q}{V} = \frac{\left(\frac{9 \cdot 88}{12} + \frac{9}{5}\right) \times 5}{60 \cdot 0.75} = \frac{5.65}{0.75} = 7.6;$$

that is, eight cells of that size are required. (If 0.5 m³ cells were to be used, then

$$V = 0.5 \cdot 0.75 = 0.375 \text{ m}^3$$

and

$$\frac{Q}{V} = \frac{5.65}{0.375} = 15;$$

that is, fifteen 0.5 m³ cleaner cells would be needed.)

Current practice has a preference for large agitation cells such as the 11 m³ Agitair, the 14 m³ Wemco* or the 8.5 m³ Denver (cf. Table 2.27), equipped with 40 to 50 kW drives. Two D—R 300 Denver cells joined together with the separating wall removed give rise to the "600" mark cell of 17 m³ (Brison and Ellis 1970; Eby 1972). A large cylindrical agitation cell is the 60 m³ Maxwell (4.3 m dia. × 4.3 m height) (Boutin and Wheeler 1967; Mathieu 1972; Maxwell 1972).

2.6. FLOTATION TECHNOLOGY

2.6.1. Nature of run-of-mine product and of mine water. The chain of phenomena affecting the outcome of flotation begins in the mine itself, with the winning of the r.o.m. product. Air and water may cause chemical alteration in the minerals, and the r.o.m. product may be contaminated by various mechanical admixtures.

Chemical alteration of the r.o.m. is the less intense, the drier the mine, the lower the temperature in it, the more silicatic the ore and the shorter the time between winning and introduction into the flotation cell. The chemical alteration of non-ore minerals is not as a rule of a nature or intensity apt to impair flotation behaviour, but the alteration of sulphide ores — especially of copper and polymetallic ones — tends to be fairly rapid and may be intense enough to lower metal contents and recovery in the concentrates by overoxidation and self-activation.

Most of the impurities found in a r.o.m. ore as mechanical admixtures are organic. Wood in various stages of rot tends to be the most abundant of these. It may introduce resin and tannic acid into the ore. Wood shavings may build up in front of the froth overflow, in the tailings weirs, clog up pumps and piping, etc. Most of the lubricants used in the mine and in the crushing and grinding circuit also tend to end up in the flotation cell, in an abundance that vies with the usual concentrations of collectors and frothers. Most lubricants have fatty acids and soaps added to them: these usurp the role of non-selective collectors in flotation.

---

* In 1983 42 m³ Wemco, 60 m³ OK, 70 m³ Dorr—Oliver.

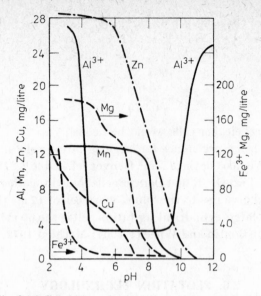

Fig. 2.94. Solubility of metals in mine water vs. the pH

Water used in flotation may also contain a variety of activators, depressants or ions eating up the useful reagents. It may contain harmful concentrations of dissolved salts, excess hydrogen ions, organics (such as tannic acid, humic acids deriving from rotting vegetal debris, lubricants). Figure 2.94 shows the solubility of certain metals in acid mine water as a function of the pH. Fresh water from a lake or river, if it is not being recirculated, tends to be fairly low in alien materials. If, however, fresh water, available in insufficient quantities, is made up with mine water or water recycled from the tailings pond and/or the concentrate, dissolved substances will build up in the circuit. Ca^{2+}, Mg^{2+}, Fe^{2+} and SO_4^{2-} ions tend to be the most abundant, but Na^+ and Cl^- may build up as well. In the flotation of non-ore minerals, carboxylic (fatty-acid type) collectors are frequently used: in that case, calcium and magnesium must be removed (e.g. by the usual method of softening water, by adding soda ash). Iron ions are to be precipitated in the form of ferric hydroxide, using lime. (For example, at a pH = 10, a solution treated with lime retains 10^{-24} g/l Fe^{3+}, and/or 10^{-6} g/l Fe^{2+}, 10^{-7} g/l Pb^{2+}, 10^{-11} g/l Zn^{2+}). The hydrogen ion content (acidity) is also neutralized as a rule by the addition of lime. All these measures are usually required only if the water is being recirculated.

Precipitation of *all* the metals contained in mine waters can be performed in two steps: in the first, Fe and Al are removed by a dosage of lime; in the second, Cu, Zn, Mn, Hg, Cd and As are precipitated by adding sodium sulphide (Na_2S). The formula

$$cC^{+a} + aA^{-c} = C_c A_a \downarrow$$

is valid throughout, where C its the metal cation and A is the (precipitating) anion (OH$^-$ or S^{2-} or HS$^-$). For example,

$$Fe^{3+} + 3OH^- \rightarrow Fe(OH)_3 \downarrow .$$

One may write up the dissociation of water as

$$H^+ + OH^- \rightarrow HOH,$$

whereas for hydrogen disulphide, one has

$$H^+ + S^{2-} \rightarrow HS^-$$

or

$$H^+ + HS^- \rightarrow H_2S.$$

2.6.2. The comminuting circuit is an important stage of the flotation process. This is where the limiting grain sizes and the relative grain sizes of pay and gangue minerals are adjusted. Most often, this is where ore and water first meet, and rapid reactions between the minerals and various alien substances set in.

The limiting grain size of flotation feed is determined first and foremost by the s.g. of the grains to be flotated out and by the sand throughput capacity of the flotation machine. The upper limiting grain size should not exceed 1 to 1.5 mm in the case of coal, 0.2 to 0.3 mm in the case of sulphides, and 0.10 to 0.15 mm in the case of free gold. A dense pulp can flotate coarser grains than a thinner one.

The influence of grain size on flotation performance is illustrated by Fig. 2.95, where m is metal recovery, c is metal content in the concentrate, b is metal content in the tailings, all plotted against grain size x. Poor performance at the fines end is due to the problems connected with slimes flotation; at the coarse end, it is due to unliberated grains above all. The limiting grain size x_{max} (or $x_{80\%}$) of grinding output affects concentration economics also. Metal content

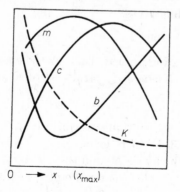

Fig. 2.95. Influence of grain size on flotation performance: m — metal recovery, c — metal content of concentrate, b — metal content of tailings (at some vertical exaggeration); $K = f(x_{max})$ — grinding cost

in the tailings varies according to curve b in the figure, regardless of whether the abscissa is calibrated in x_{max}. It is by confronting this curve with the other curves of Fig. 2.95 — as established by testing the ore to be treated — that the optimum limiting grain size can be determined.

By grinding the feed of rougher flotation to a greater fineness (at the cost of a greater energy input), metal recovery $m\%$ can be improved. The relationship

$$m\% \cong A - Bx_{80\%}$$

provides a fair enough approximation. For porphyry copper ores, e.g., one may assume $A \cong 99.4$, $B \cong 1/30$.

In possession of the Bond coefficient C_3 of the ore, the specific power consumption of grinding,

$$N = C_3 \left(\frac{1}{\sqrt{x}} - \frac{1}{\sqrt{x_0}} \right) \text{ kW h/t},$$

can be calculated for any $x_{80\%}$. For example, if $C_3 = 140$ and $x_0 = 10 \text{ mm} = 10^4 \ \mu\text{m}$, then

$x =$	50	75	100	150	200	250 μm
implies $N =$	18.3	14.7	12.6	10.0	8.5	7.3 kW h/t.

The relationship between the total cost K (owning + depreciation + operating) of grinding and N kW h/t may be assumed to be

$$\frac{K}{K_1} = \left(\frac{N}{N_1} \right)^b,$$

where $b \cong 0.9$ approximately. For example, if at $N = 8.5$ kW h/t, belonging to $x = 200 \ \mu$m, $K_1 = 60$ US cents per ton, then

$x =$	50	75	100	150	200	250 μm

entails the primary grinding costs

$K =$	120	100	87	70	60	52 ¢/t.

Adding the cost of re-grinding prior to cleaning the concentrate (and middling) of rougher flotation, to a fineness $x'_{80\%}$ at a cost of K', total grinding cost

$$\bar{K} = K + K'$$

is obtained as a function of the grain size x of primary grinding output (energy consumption N). The cost K' of re-grinding x to a fineness x' is the greater, the coarser is x (that is, the less is N) and the greater is the concentrate output of rougher flotation (that is, the greater the metal content $a\%$ of the flotation feed).

Let us assume that it is not necessary to re-grind prior to cleaning flotation the rougher concentrate fraction of $\bar{x} = 75 \ \mu$m or less, but it is necessary to

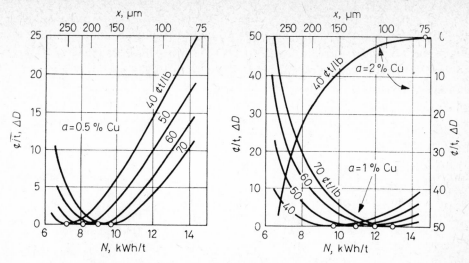

Fig. 2.96. $D = f(N)$ curves of r.o.m. ores of different metal contents $a\%$ Cu, at different metal prices, $\not{e}$/lb Cu

regrind the fraction $x > \bar{x}$ (e.g. to $x'_{80\%} = 50$ μm); in that case, the total-cost graphs $\bar{K} = f(N)$ are approximately straight lines issuing from the point K ($\cong 100$) belonging to $\bar{x}$ (or, in our example, to $\bar{N} = 14.7$ kW h/t). For example, if

$$a = \quad 0.5 \qquad 1.0 \qquad 2.0\% \text{ Cu,}$$

then the $\bar{K}$ value of the lines belonging to these copper contents at $K = 60$ $\not{e}$/t (corresponding to $x = 200$ μm or $N = 8.5$ kW h/t) should be increased by approximately

$$K' = \quad 3.5 \qquad 7.0 \qquad 14.0 \text{ } \not{e}/\text{t;}$$

that is, we have, in the above order,

$$\bar{K} = 63.5 \qquad 67.0 \qquad 74.0 \text{ } \not{e}/\text{t.}$$

Metal recovery in cleaning flotation is less by about 2% as a rule than in the rougher concentrate. If the metal price is known, the ex-mine value P of metal routed into the different concentrates can be calculated (assuming ex-mine metal price per lb to be less by 10 $\not{e}$/lb than the metal-exchange quotation). The optimum grain size x of primary grinding is obtained as the maximum of the difference

$$D = P - \bar{K}.$$

Figure 2.96 shows for an example the curves

$$\Delta D = D_{\max} - D = f(N)$$

for flotation feeds of $a = 0.5$, 1 and 2% Cu content, at different copper prices in $\not{e}$/lb. The $\Delta D = 0$ points (minima) of the curves give the N_{opt} and x_{opt} parameters of optimum grinding, as stated in Table 2.29. A metal price hike of 10 e/lb is seen to raise the admissible power draft of optimum grinding by almost one kW h per ton. The curves further permit to infer also the loss ΔD/ton raw ore incurred by grinding finer or coarser than to the optimum giving the maximum profit.

Table 2.29. N_{opt} and x_{opt} parameters of optimum grinding vs. the copper price, e/lb

cent/lb	$\sim N_{opt}$, kW h/t			$\sim x_{opt}$, μm		
	$a = 0.5$	1	2	0.5	1	2
40	7.1	9.7	14.7	260	160	75
50	8.0	11.0		220	130	
60	8.9	12.1		190	110	
70	9.7	13.0		170	95	

The curves of Fig. 2.96 make the influence of changes in metal price (e/lb Cu) and/or in the metal content of the flotation feed ($a\%$ Cu) easy to see. The profit foregone owing to non-optimum grinding, ΔD, is affected less by a change in metal price than by a proportionate change in metal content. For example, if the metal price changes from 60 e/lb to 50 (or 70) e/lb, but the copper content of the metal is constant at $a = 0.5\%$ Cu, and the grinding parameters are maintained at the old optimum $N = 8.9$ kW h/t and $x = 190$ μm (rather than being changed to the new optimum, $N = 8.0$ [or 9.7] kW h/t and $x = 220$ [or 170] μm, respectively), or if at $a = 1\%$ Cu, N is kept at 12.1 kW h/t and x at 110 μm, which is the optimum at the old metal price of 60 e/lb (instead of being changed to $N = 11.0$ [or 13.0] kW h/t and $x = 130$ [or 95] μm, respectively), then the foregone profit ΔD will be less than about one cent per ton. (The minima of the curves are rather flat.)

If, on the other hand, at a constant metal price of 60 e/lb, it is the metal content of the feed that changes from 0.5 to 1.0% Cu, with the grinding parameters kept constant at $N = 8.9$ kW h/t and $x = 190$ μm (instead of changing them to $N = 12.1$ kW h and $x = 110$ μm), then the foregone profit will be

$$\Delta D = 8 \ e/t.$$

Or, alternatively, if at a metal price of 40 e/lb, grinding is kept at the optimum parameters for $a = 1\%$ Cu ($N = 9.7$ kW h/t and $x = 160$ μm), rather than being adjusted to the optimum $N = 7.1$ kW h/t and $x = 260$ μm belonging to $a = 0.5\%$ Cu (or $N = 14.7$ kW h/t and $x = 75$ μm belonging to $a = 2.0\%$ Cu), the foregone profit will be 6 and 10 e/t, respectively. (The foregone profit is

$$\Delta D = 35 \ c/t$$

if a changes from 0.5 to 2% at a metal price of 40 e/lb !)

Another fairly obvious inference is that total profit may be increased if, instead of blending (homogenizing) the different run-of-mine grades successively extracted from the mine as time proceeds, and feeding them to the flotation shop at a constant rate T tph, one feeds the richer ore at a lower rate $T_1 < T$ tph, grinds it finer and flotates it at a higher metal recovery than the leaner parts of the deposit. The additional profit that can be made in this way is the greater, the more changeable is ore grade (Brison and Campbell 1974).

The granulometry of grinding output depends on the nature of the ore, on the grinding equipment used and on the flowsheet chosen. Minerals differ as to strength and fracture; the minerals that are easier to crush/grind will tend to concentrate in the finer fractions, regardless of the pay mineral grain size to which the circuit is supposed to be adjusted. The grinding circuit includes a wet classifier as a rule; in its overflow, the *de facto* limiting grain size of the heavy mineral is smaller than that of the lighter ones. If an easier fracture coincides with a greater s.g. (as is the case with the pay minerals in most sulphide ores), the mineral thus characterized is likely to get enriched rather substantially in the fines of the flotation feed. It will in that case have a curve similar to the K curve in Fig. 2.95 (with the ordinate calibrated in metal content and the abscissa in particle size). This is why the economic performance of flotation can be improved e.g. by grinding a galena ore in quartz to a comparatively coarse limiting particle size and a gold-bearing pyrite ore disseminated in a softer host rock to the greatest feasible fineness.

The grinding mill is an excellent place for starting chemical reactions. Freshly broken mineral surfaces possess a high reactivity; agitation is strong, and the temperature of the pulp may rise by several degrees during its sojourn in the mill. Sulphide oxidation and exchange reactions between metal ions set in at fast rates; the concentrations of salts dissolved in the pulp rise rapidly. This is why it is indicated to introduce already into the grinding circuit the reagents intended to forestall any effects harmful to flotation (e.g. an alkali cyanide to prevent the activation of sphalerite; hydroxyl ions to neutralize the acid resulting from the oxidation of the sulphides and to precipitate the base metal ions as great consumers of collector reagent, etc.). It is further usual to introduce into the grinding circuit soluble collectors so as to permit them to coat the fresh surfaces of fracture as soon as they are formed, or oleaginous collectors in order to profit by the dispersion and attrition wrought by the motion of the thick pulp.

Coarse-grained sulphides can be flotated out in a cell inserted between the mill and the classifier, keeping in mind that if a floatable particle is overground with no good reason, great deal of poorly floatable fines will form. (Free gold difficult to flotate can be extracted by means of a jig or table inserted into the grinding circuit.)

2.6.3. The flotation operation may be controlled by regulating retention time, temperature, pulp thickness, intensity of agitation or aeration and by the proper choice of cell type and hookup. Reagent quality, dosage and point of introduction are also very important, of course.

(A) *Retention time.* Different ores require different retention times, in view of the different floatability of their minerals. The curve of metal recovery ($m\%$) vs. retention time is logarithmic if floatability P is constant throughout. On the

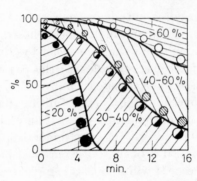

Fig. 2.97. Composition of the froth product of coal flotation vs. retention time

flotation of a fresh sulphide ore in quartz, this curve changes course about 80% metal recovery, often at a retention time of less than one minute, and attains a near-horizontal plateau in as little as 5 to 8 minutes. The fairly steep initial section of the curve flattens out if the limiting grain size, sulphide oxidation intensity or gangue slimes content increases. Maximum recovery out of a hard-to-flotate ore may, on the other hand, require as much as 30 to 60 minutes. The floatability, P min^{-1}, of sulphide ores — using the appropriate reagents — tends to fall between 0.5 and 1 in rougher and cleaner flotation and between 0.05 and 0.1 in scavenging.

Figure 2.97 shows the time-dependent variation of froth composition in coal flotation. The numbers written into the domains indicate ash percentages; the circles next to the curves give an idea of relative particle sizes. It is the medium-sized clean coal particles ($<20\%$ ash) that float out first; coarser clean coal rises into the froth later on (in the 4th to 6th minute according to the diagram), accompanied by medium-sized middling and fine waste. At the end of flotation, coarse intergrown grains and waste rise up, provided there is a sufficiency of collector in the cell (cf. also Fig. 2.91).

Part A of Fig. 2.97 A presents Cu contents in the concentrate (c) and tailings (b) of the rougher flotation of a chalcopyrite ore vs. the duration of the flotation pass. It also presents the metal contents attained on the scavenger flotation of rougher concentrates different as to metal content vs. the number of scavenger passes. Part B of the figure shows the influence of the number of cells operated

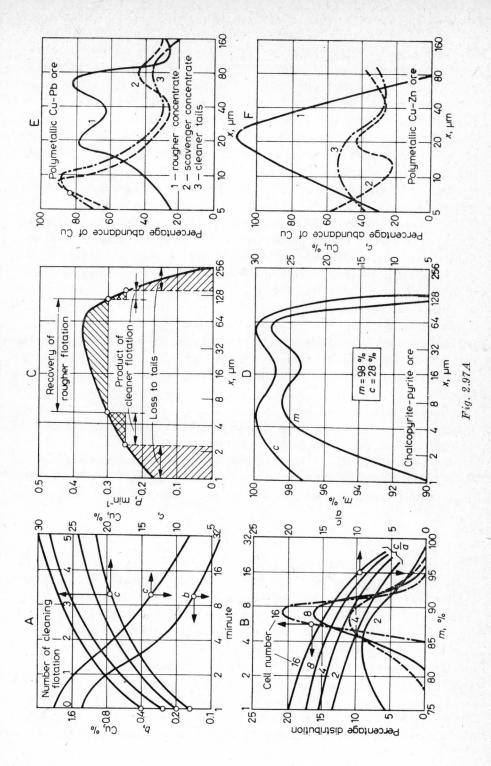

Fig. 2.97A

in series: for a given metal recovery $m\%$, the ratio c/a of metal contents in the concentrate vs. the feed (the r.o.m. ore) increases as the number of cells increases; the fluctuation of the retention time of the particles in the cells decreases. (Retention time is eight minutes for each of the curves in the figure.) Part C presents the floatability P min^{-1} of chalcopyrite particles of different size for a given reagent dosage: it also shows the domains with $P > 0.3$, $P = 0.25$ to 0.3 and $P < 0.25$, the particles belonging to which are routed in their bulk — after a given retention time in flotation — into the rougher and the cleaner concentrate and the tailings, respectively. Part D presents recoveries $m\%$ and metal contents $c\%$ in particles of different size of a concentrate of Cu content $c = 28\%$, won at a metal recovery $m = 28\%$. The curves in Parts E and F of Fig. 2.97A represent the percentage distribution of the metal (copper) content over the particle size fractions in the rougher and cleaner concentrates and in the scavenger tails. In Part A, e.g., which represents a polymetallic Cu–Pb ore, the bulk of the metal content of the rougher concentrate is, in harmony with Part C of the figure, in the particles of 10 to 90 μm size; the cleaner concentrate contains both fine and coarse particles but the intermediate size range is of very low abundance. The tails of the scavenging phase abound in chalcopyrite particles of 5 to 15 μm size above all; the implication is that scavenging flotation did not last long enough; that is why the fine chalcopyrite particles of low floatability could stay behind in the tails (Lindgren 1976).

If the pulp is to be conditioned for a comparatively long time for the purpose of activation or depression, it is simplest to let it pass through a tank of adequate size (or several tanks connected in series).

(B) *Temperature*. Rising temperatures accelerate chemical reactions and promote the dispersion of non-soluble oleaginous reagents. The induction time t of mineral-to-bubble adherence and the temperature T K are related as

$$\log\left(\frac{t_1}{t_2}\right) \cong C\left(\frac{1}{T_1} - \frac{1}{T_2}\right)$$

(Klassen and Mokrousov 1963).

Heating the pulp may greatly improve flotation performance, especially with a fatty acid or a cationic reagent (amine flotation). The melting temperature (cold point) of palmitic acid is at 63 °C; that of oleic acid at 16.3 °C; that of linoleic acid at −5 °C. The collecting action of the first two reagents is therefore largely suppressed in water colder than about 15 °C. Even with soaps readily soluble in water, however, a better performance can be achieved by flotation in a warm pulp. Amine salts are readily, free amine bases rather poorly soluble in cold water. For example, the solubility of Armac T, 0.1% at 20 °C, is a hundred times as great (11%) even at 30 °C. An abrupt improvement of performance can often be achieved by conditioning a dense pulp hot (above

80 °C) prior to roughing or cleaning or before a bulk sulphide or oxide concentrate (e.g. apatite–calcite or scheelite–calcite) is flotated apart. The time of both conditioning and flotation can be reduced considerably, and so can reagent consumption; selectivity is increased also (Hukki 1973).

(C) Pulp density and limiting grain size are interdependent in the overflow of a mechanical classifier. It is fairly easy to thin a pulp of a given limiting grain size by adding water to it, but thickening it requires a separate thickener. The buoyant force acting on the particles is stronger in a denser pulp; for a given dosage, reagent concentration in the liquid phase rises; as a result, reaction rates increase; hence, using a denser pulp, less reagent is required; a smaller cell volume is sufficient, and power draft is reduced; on the other hand, however, the percentage metal content of the concentrate out of a denser pulp tends to be lower for a given metal recovery. The volumetric solids content σ of the feed is usually 10 to 15% in rougher flotation, and half to one-quarter as much in cleaner flotation. Coarser-grained minerals can be flotated in a denser pulp. If, on the other hand, the feed is rich in slimes, a thin pulp should be used. Pulp is to be thinner in a pneumatic than in an agitation cell.

(D) *The influence of agitation and aeration intensity* is illustrated by Parts A and B of Fig. 2.98. Part A shows the recovery $m\%$ of galena grains of different size vs. impeller speed n in a subaeration laboratory cell run in the auto-suction mode (Klassen and Mokrousov 1963). Part B shows the weight G mg of the largest anthracite particles that can just be flotated out, vs. Q cm³/s cm², the air flow rate per square centimetre of pulp surface (or cell cross section) area. The optimum is seen to be between 1 and 1.5 cm³/s cm² (= 0.6 to 0.9 m³/min

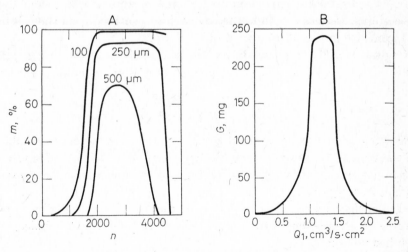

Fig. 2.98. Influence of agitation and aeration. A — Recovery of galena grains of different size vs. impeller speed, n rpm, B — weight G mg of the largest anthracite grains flotated out vs. the air feed rate Q_1

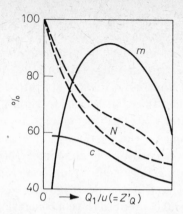

Fig. 2.99. m%, c% and N parameters of a sphalerite concentration operation vs. $Z'_Q = Q_1/u$

m²): a more vigorous aeration entails excessive turbulence which prevents the flotation of coarse particles.

Figure 2.99 is a plot of metal content $c\%$ and metal recovery $m\%$ of an ore concentrate (e.g. ZnS) vs. the dimensionless air throughput number

$$Z'_Q = \frac{Q_1}{u}$$

or

$$Z_Q = \frac{Q}{nD^3}.$$

Power draft N decreases as Z_Q increases, as shown by the dashed curves in the figure. It is especially important to find the optimum of Z_Q when flotating coarse grains. If Z_Q is too high, the coarse grains settle out on the cell bottom or concentrate in the bottom zone of the pulp.

In agitation cells, gas introduced into the pressure shadows generated by agitation gives bubbles whose average diameter next to the pulp surface is

$$D = \frac{ka}{R}\left(\frac{\mu}{n^6\gamma^2\mu_g^3}\right)^{\frac{1}{4}},$$

where k is a constant determined by the system parameters in combination with the volumetric gas content achieved, a is the surface tension of the liquid, γ is its density, μ is its viscosity, R is impeller radius, n is impeller speed and μ_g is gas viscosity.

If the surface tension and viscosity of the liquid are negligible, then gas emerging at a rate q cm³/s from a capillary is dispersed into bubbles, each of which has volume

$$V = \left(\frac{6}{\pi}\right)^{\frac{1}{5}}q^{\frac{6}{5}}/g^{\frac{3}{5}} \simeq 1.14q^{\frac{6}{5}}/g^{\frac{3}{5}} \simeq 0.0183q^{\frac{6}{5}} \text{ cm}^3$$

304

or diameter

$$D = \sqrt{\frac{6V}{\pi}} \simeq 0.33 q^{\frac{2}{5}} \text{ cm},$$

regardless of the diameter d of the capillary. The bubbles detach themselves from the orifice of the capillary when their rise $s = gt^2/2$ due to buoyancy becomes equal to the radius $D/2$ of the bubble of volume $V = qt$. The time this takes is

$$t = \left(\frac{6q}{\pi}\right)^{\frac{1}{5}} / g^{\frac{3}{5}} \text{ s},$$

and the number of bubbles formed per second is

$$z = \frac{1}{t} = g^{\frac{3}{5}} / \left(\frac{6q}{\pi}\right)^{\frac{1}{5}} = 54.5 / q^{\frac{1}{5}}.$$

Average bubble size in a pneumatic cell aerated through a porous sheet (a mat) is about 2 mm as a rule; it is about 1 mm (in the 0.7 to 1.3 mm range) in mechanical (impeller) cells in clear water, and $\sim$0.5 mm (0.2 mm) in the presence of 5 cm^3/m^3 (10 cm^3/m^3) of frother (pine oil). Average bubble size is greater in a pulp than in clear water. The average rise velocity of the bubbles is 16 to 20 cm/s in pneumatic cells, 3 to 4 cm/s in mechanical ones. (In the latter, effective rise velocity is quite low next to the impeller and also immediately below the froth bed, whereas in the middle zone of the pulp and above it — where vorticity is less — it is higher than the average.) (Grainger-Allen 1970.)

The least size of bubbles separating out of water saturated with air as a result of a pressure drop (e.g. in vacuum flotation) can be determined using the formula

$$\Delta P = \frac{2a}{r_{\min}},$$

analogous to the formula of capillary pressure, where a is surface tension, r is bubble radius, and

$$\Delta p = p_g - (p_0 + p_h)$$

is pressure drop. In this latter expression, p_g is the saturation pressure of dissolved air, p_0 is external pressure above the pulp surface and p_h $(= p_2)$ is bydrostatic head under the water. For example, at $a = 70$ dynes per centimetre, a pressure drop

$\Delta p =$	5	10	25	50	100	250	500	760 Torr

gives least bubble diameters

$r_{\min} =$	210	105	42	21	10.5	4.2	2.1	1.4 μm

(Heinisch and von Szantho 1972; Klassen 1960; Konigsmann 1973; Sutherland and Wark 1955).

Bubble size in vacuum flotation is in the 0.1 to 0.5 mm range in practice. Much smaller (8 to 50 μm size) and highly uniform bubbles of hydrogen and/or oxygen may be produced by the electrolytic decomposition of water. In electro-flotation, which holds a great deal of promise especially in the concentration of very fine slimes, the two gases are used together, or separately or mixed with air. The excellent performance of this process, which cannot be reproduced by ordinary flotation techniques, is due to considerable saturation of the pulp with very fine uniform-sized bubbles whose size can be regulated within limits, as well as to the specific chemical action of the hydrogen and/or oxygen gas (Glembotsky et al. 1961).

Theoretically, the creation of z bubbles, each of diameter d (surface area $d^2\pi$ cm^2) requires a work input

$$E_1 = zad^2\pi \text{ erg.}$$

One cubic metre (one million cubic centimetres) of air gives

$$z = \frac{6 \cdot 10^6}{d^3\pi}$$

bubbles of d cm diameter. The theoretical work input required to disperse one m^3 of air is

$$E_1 = \frac{6 \cdot 10^6 a}{d} \text{ erg/m}^3 \simeq 0.06 \frac{a}{d} \text{ mkp/m}^3.$$

For example, if $a = 67$ dynes per centimetre, $E_1 \simeq 4/d$ mkp/m^3: that is,

$$d = \quad 0.2 \qquad 0.02 \qquad 0.002 \text{ cm}$$

implies

$$E_1 \simeq 20 \qquad 200 \qquad 2,000 \text{ mkp/m}^3.$$

If these bubbles are formed in a pulp of depth H and density γ, under a hydrostatic pressure

$$p_2 = H\gamma \text{ m water column} = 10^3 H\gamma \text{ kp/m}^2.$$

then — pV being a constant — air of volume

$$1 + \frac{H\gamma}{10} \text{ m}^3$$

and atmospheric pressure (one atmosphere absolute) has to be compressed to

$$10^3 H\gamma \text{ kp/m}^2$$

to give one m³ of air at depth H. The theoretical work input required is

$$E_2 = 10^3 H \gamma \left(1 + \frac{H\gamma}{10}\right) \quad \text{mkp/m}^3.$$

For example, at $\gamma = 1$,

$$H = \quad 1 \qquad 2 \qquad 4 \qquad 8 \text{ m}$$

implies

$$E_2 = 1{,}100 \quad 2{,}400 \quad 5{,}600 \quad 14{,}400 \text{ mkp/m}^3;$$

at $H = 2$ m and $d = 0.02$ cm, the theoretical work input of creating bubbles of an aggregate volume of 1 m³ is

$$E = E_1 + E_2 = 200 + 2{,}400 = 2{,}600 \text{ mkp/m}^3 = 7 \cdot 10^{-3} \text{ kW h.}$$

It increases strongly as pulp depth H increases and slowly as bubble diameter decreases. For example, using an air throughput

$$10 \text{ m}^3/\text{min} = 600 \text{ m}^3/\text{h,}$$

the theoretical work input will be about 4.2 kW and (reckoning with an efficiency $\eta = 0.7$ to 0.5), power draft will be about 6 to 8 kW. In deep cells (e.g. $H = 8$ m and $d = 0.02$ cm),

$$E \simeq 14{,}600 \text{ mkp/m}^3 \simeq 4 \cdot 10^{-2} \text{ kW h/m}^3,$$

which, at an air input rate of 600 m³/h, corresponds to a theoretical work input of about 24 kW and a power draft of 35 to 45 kW.

The surface area of a bubble of diameter d cm is $d^2\pi$ cm²; its volume is $d^3\pi/6$ cm³. One mole of a surfactant whose molecules are of cross section

$$\sim 20 \text{ Å}^2 = 20 \cdot 10^{-16} \text{ cm}^2$$

can form a full monomolecular lining on

$$\sim 20 N \text{Å}^2 = 20 \cdot 10^{-16} N \simeq 1.2 \cdot 10^9 \text{ cm}^2$$

of bubble surface, the number of bubbles being

$$z = 20 \cdot 10^{-16} \frac{N}{d^2}.$$

Here,

$$N = 6.023 \cdot 10^{23} \text{ mole}^{-1}$$

is the Loschmidt number. That is, assuming full monomolecular linings on the bubbles ($\varphi = 1$),

$$V = 0.4 \qquad 4 \qquad 40 \text{ m}^3/\text{mole}$$

belongs to

$$d = 0.002 \qquad 0.02 \qquad 0.2 \text{ cm.}$$

(If $\varphi < 1$, gas volumes greater by a factor $1/\varphi$ are obtained.)

2.6.4. Reagent consumption is usually stated in practice in grams per tonne of (solid) feed, although for the majority of reagents it would be more to the point to state it in grams per m^3 (or milligrams per litre) of solution (or pulp). The concentration ranges usual in practice, in g/t (solid) units, are 10 to 120 for frothers, 25 to 1,200 for collectors, 250 to 5,000 for pH regulators, 25 to 500 for depressants, 250 to 1,000 for activators and 25 to 250 g/t for deactivators.

It is an important rule never to add any reagent over and above the exact optimum dose required. Using the correct dosage of cyanide, e.g., chalcopyrite can be separated from pyrite; chalcopyrite will float out with a xanthate, whereas pyrite will stay behind. On the other hand, too little cyanide does not provide sufficient selectivity, whereas too much of it depresses both minerals. Each reagent and combination of reagents has its optimum dosage, a function of many variables; finding it is still more of an art than a science. Rules of thumb of general applicability are: (1) Optimum doses increase as grinding fineness increases. (Frothers are an exception. Frother dosage may be kept constant; it may in fact be preferable to reduce it.) (2) After de-sliming a feed, less is required of all the reagents that exert their action at the mineral-grain surfaces. (3) Less reagent is required in a denser pulp. (4) The optimum dosage of a reagent may change if the type of flotation machine, the point, timing or physical means of reagent introduction are changed.

The method of reagent feeding depends on the nature of the reagent, on its solubility in water and physical consistency. Solid reagents that are not readily soluble in water such as lime, thiocarbanilide, etc., are usually introduced into the grinding mill. They may also be added in the form of an aqueous slurry (a frequent choice e.g. in the case of slaked lime). Compounds readily soluble in water (e.g. xanthates, cyanides, etc.) can be added in the form of an aqueous solution of the right concentration. Oils may be added as they are, or as emulsions.

Powders of solid reagents may be added by means of a slowly moving feeder passing under a small hopper. Dosage may be regulated by raising or lowering the hatch in the hopper aperture or by changing feeder speed. Aqueous solutions may be added by means of cups mounted on the rim of a disk dipping into the solution ("disk-and-cup feeder"). Dosage may be regulated by adjusting disk speed or changing the number and/or size of the cups. Oleaginous liquids may be added in the same way or making use of their viscosity. [From the coating adhering to a rotating disk dipping into the oil, a scraper ("finger") scrapes off a narrow band ("pulley-and-finger feeder"). Dosage may be regulated by adjusting disk speed or the position or width of the scraper.] Fluids may be added also making use of hydrostatic pressure, as in the constant-head feeders of Fig. 2.100. Here, hydrostatic head h at the capillary orifice remains a constant regardless of the head of liquid in the tank. Dosage may be regulated by adjusting h or changing the orifice.

The sequence of addition of the different reagents is also essential, especially if they are miscible. For example, the activation of sphalerite with copper sulphate must be completed before any xanthate is added, as otherwise the copper ions in the solution will consume the xanthate ions and the sphalerite will not be activated. Feeding a collector in several small doses into successive cells will often make for a purer concentrate. In the surface sulphidization of base metal

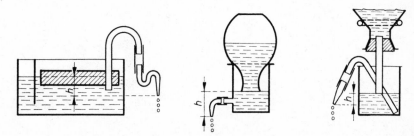

Fig. 2.100. Home-made constant-head reagent feeders for the feeding of liquid reagents (solutions or oils)

oxides, the alkali sulphide is invariably to be added in small doses, as it will depress any sulphides present if added in excess. Fatty acids (e.g. oleic acid) solidify in a cold pulp. This hazard can be forestalled by adding them in the form of an emulsion. The partial sulphonation (sulphatization) of the fatty acid also ensures its ready dispersibility.

Collector concentration (of, say, xanthate, aerofloat, oleic acid, etc.) can be monitored continuously in the pulp feed or in the tailing underflow either direct or after extraction, by one of the methods of spectrophotometry, photometry, polarography, colorimetry or gas chromatography. Oxygen concentration in the pulp can be measured by polarography or by titration. The progress of reactions of oxidation or reduction may be monitored by measuring the redox potential (e.g. in the form of the voltage between a platinum and a calomel electrode). The pH in the pulp or in its filtrate can be measured e.g. using glass electrodes, or by titration or by following the change of colour of liphan paper.

2.7. EXAMPLES OF FLOTATION

Table 2.30 lists usual flotation reagents for some minerals, enumerated in the ABC order of their principal chemical constituents.

2.7.1. Base metal sulphides (and certain base metal oxides after surface sulphidization) can be flotated with thiols. Xanthates and aerofloats are used most frequently. A combination of several collectors is often to be preferred (e.g. ethyl and amyl xanthate for copper sulphides, isopropyl and amyl xanthate

Table 2.30. Usual flotation reagents of some minerals

Element	Mineral	δ	Modifiers			Collector	Frother
			depressants	activator	other		
Al	alunite	2.7	much V		WG	O, R708	CA, A
	bauxite	2.5	P		NaOH, P, Pa	O, R801, 825	A
	feldspars	2.5		HF	HF	Am	PO, A
	kaolinite	2.6	P		WG	Am	PO
	corundum	4.0	much acid		NaOH	O and salts	PO, A
	cryolite	2.4		CuSO$_4$	Or	O and salts	A
	kyanite	3.6			NaOH, Aes	FA and salts R825	PO, A
As	arsenopyrite	6.0	NaCN, lime	CuSO$_4$	SA, WG	X(2-5C)	PO
Au	gold	17.5	NaCN, lime	R404	SA	X, Aer	CA, PO
B	borax	1.7		BaCl$_2$, Pb(NO$_3$)$_2$	An, Sta, D, Qu	FA	An, Xy, Py
Ba	barite	4.5	AlCl$_3$, FeCl$_2$	Pb(NO$_3$)$_2$	WG, SA, Ci, Aes	O and salts, Su	PO, CA
Be	beryl	2.7	SuA	Pb(NO$_3$)$_2$	HF	Am, O and salts, R825	
C	graphite	2.0	Sta, R600 —		SA, WG	Pa, FO	PO, A
	coal	1.4	Ta, Qu		WG	FO, Pa, Cr	PO, CA
	shale	2.4	R600—			FO, PA	PO, A
Ce	monazite	5.1	strong acid		SA, WG	O, FA and salts	PO
Co	cobalt oxides	4.5		Pho	WG, SA	X, FA and salts	PO, A
Cr	chromite			Pho	NaOH, SA, Fl	R800 —, FA, Am	PO, FO
Cu	copper	8.8	NaCN		WG, lime	X, Aer	PO
	copper oxides		Qu	Pho	WG, SA, NA$_2$S	FA and salts, X	PO, DF, CA
	copper sulphides		NaCN		SA, lime	X, Aer	PO
F	fluorite	3.2	Qu, K$_2$Cr$_2$O$_7$		WG, SuA	O, FA, R825	PO
Fe	iron oxides		Ta, P	CuSO$_4$	SuA	R801, 825, O	PO, FO
	iron sulphides		NaCN, lime		SuA	X	PO
Hg	cinnabar	8.1	WG			X(5C)	PO
Li	micas	3.1	glue, sta, HF	Pb(NO$_3$)$_2$	SuA	Am, R825	PO, CA
	spodumene	3.1	Sta, D		Aes	O, R825	PO
Mg	brucite	2.4	Ta		P	X	PO
	magnesite	3.1				O and salts	PO
	talc	2.8	Sta, glue		P	Am, R825	PO, Pa

		pH	Modifiers			Collectors	Frothers
Mn	pyrolusite	4.7	P, Qu		WG, SA	FA and salts	PO, Pa
	rhodochrosite	4.0	D		WG, SA, NaOH	R708	PO
Mo	molybdenite	4.8			Po	Aer, X	PO
Nb	pyrochlore	4.3				FA and salts	PO
Ni	pentlandite	4.8	lime	$CuSO_4$	WG, alkali	X(5C)	PO
P	apatite	3.1	HF		NaOH, SA	FA and salts	PO
	phosphate	3.2			NaOH	FA	PO
Pb	anglesite	6.3	Na_2S, P, $CuSO_4$		SA	R404, X, Aer	PO, CA
	cerussite	6.5	Na_2S, $CuSO_4$		SA	X, R404, Aer	PO, CA
	galena	7.5	$K_2Cr_2O_7$		SA, WG	Aer, X	PO
Sb	antimonite	4.7	NaCN, much alk.	$CuSO_4$	SA, WG	X(2—4C)	PO
U	carnotite	4.1		$Pb(NO_3)_2$	SA, WG	FA	PO, CA
	pechblende	7.2		$FeCL_3$		FA, Am	PO
V	descloizite	6.0	Ca-ion	soft water	SA	X	A
	vanadinite	7.0	lime	soft water	WG, SA	X(2 + 5C)	Me
W	scheelite	6.0	much WG, Qu		WG, SA, Aes	O and FA salts	PO
	wolframite	7.3		$Pb(NO_3)_2$	WG, SA	FA	PO, CA
Zn	smithsonite	4.3		Na_2S	SA, WG	FA, Am	PO
	sphalerite	4.1	NaCN, $ZnSO_4$ $NaHSO_3$, SO_2	$CuSO_4$	lime	X	PO

Modifiers: Aes: aerosol, An: aniline, Ci: citric acid, Ta: tannic acid, D: dextrin, Fl: fluosilicate, Pho: phospho- Mo and W acids, Sta: starch, SuA: sulphuric acid, Or: orthotoluidine, P: polyphosphate, Pa: paraffin, Po: polysulphides, Qu: quebracho, SA: soda ash, WG: water glass.

Collectors: Aer: aerofloat, Am: amine, FO: fuel oil, Cr: creosote, O: oleic acid, Pa: paraffin, R: Cyanamid reagent, Su: higher alcohol sulphates, FA: fatty acids, X: xanthate

Frothers: A: higher alcohols, An: aniline, PO: pine oil, DF: diesel fuel, CA: cresylic acid, Me: methyl isobutyl carbinol, Pa: paraffin, Py: piridine, Xy: xilidine.

311

for galena, xanthate and oleic acid for sulphides with oxidized surfaces, etc.) (Prasad and Rao 1970).

Pyrite, a mineral that frequently accompanies copper sulphides, can be depressed with lime (at a pH > 10). Alkali cyanides are also useful depressants of pyrite. The vigorous aeration of the pulp (during conditioning or in the grinding mill) may also be sufficient to oxidize the surfaces of certain pyrites and thereby to reduce their floatability. Depressed pyrite can subsequently be floated out either after surface sulphidization with an alkali sulphide in an alkaline pulp or after acidizing the pulp (to a pH < 6 using sulphuric acid), e.g. with butyl xanthate as a collector.

In the flotation of polymetallic complex lead-zinc sulphides, soluble salts of zinc, alkali cyanides, alkali sulphides and/or alkali sulphites are used to depress sphalerite from beside galena. Most often, zinc sulphate and sodium cyanide are used in combination, in a pH range from 7 to 10. In order to increase the pH, weak bases (soda ash or sodium phosphate) are usually added. Lime should be dosed with special care because in too high a concentration it will depress galena also. After flotating out the galena using e.g. soda ash, zinc sulphate, sodium cyanide, ethyl xanthate and pine oil, the sphalerite is activated, by means e.g. of copper sulphate, at a high pH (9 to 11) adjusted with lime, in order to forestall the contamination of the sphalerite concentrate with the well-nigh omnipresent pyrite.

At Gyöngyösoroszi in Hungary, a polymetallic galena–sphalerite–chalcopyrite–pyrite ore containing approximately 1% Pb, 0.1–0.2% Cu, 3% Zn, 6% pyrite, 1–2 g/t Au, 30–40 g/t Ag is subjected to differential flotation. The veins are in a pyroxene andesite, with quartz, and kaolinite as the principal gangue minerals. The ore is comminuted to minus-20 mm in a jaw crusher and two Symons cones; from the 4 to 20 mm screen fraction, the light fraction is removed in a preconcentration pass in a FeSi dense medium, and the minus-1 mm fraction is de-slimed in a hydrocyclone. The 1 to 4 mm fraction, the de-slimed underflow of the cyclone and the 4 to 20 mm sink fraction of the dense-medium cone separator are ground to 95% minus-0.2 mm in three ball mills in circuit with a classifier. The pulp is after conditioning flotated differentially in Denver type cells.

The reagents used in the flotation of galena plus chalcopyrite at a pH of 7.5 to 8.3 are water glass (250–700 g/t), sodium cyanide (30–90 g/t), zinc sulphate (90–100 g/t), sodium ethyl xanthate (70 g/t); the reagents used in the flotation of sphalerite are lime (to adjust a pH of 9 to 9.3), copper sulphate (750–850 g/t) and sodium ethyl xanthate (200 g/t); in pyrite flotation, sodium ethyl xanthate is used, and the pulp is adjusted after thickening in a hydrocyclone to a pH in the 6.6 to 7.5 range by the addition of mine water (pH = 5.5). The frother is Flotol B (50 g/t in all). Metal balances for a copper-rich and a normal-run ore are shown in Table 2.31.

Table 2.31. Weight recovery, metal content and metal recovery of the concentrates of a copper-rich and a normal-run ore won at Gyöngyösoroszi, Hungary

Product	Copper-rich ore				Normal-run ore			
	weight %	Pb%	Cu%	Zn%	weight%	Pb%	Cu%	Zn%
R.o.m. ore	100.0	0.98	0.18	2.92	100.0	1.02	0.12	2.98
D.M. tailings	18.0	0.15	0.02	0.75	25.0	0.17	0.04	0.95
Hydrocyclone overflow	1.2	0.35	0.04	1.35	1.4	0.48	0.04	1.56
Flotation feed	80.8	1.18	0.22	3.47	73.6	1.32		3.70
Galena concentration	1.95	44.50	5.90	5.70	1.67	53.20	2.80	5.40
Sphalerite concentration	4.35	0.6	0.78	50.69	4.10	0.65	0.82	53.3
Pyrite concentration	3.50	0.2	0.10	1.20	3.4	0.3	0.10	1.3
Flotation tailings	71.0	0.07	0.05	0.54	64.43	0.07	0.04	0.61

Metal recoveries %								
R.o.m. ore		100.0	100.0	100.0		100.0	100.0	100.0
D.M. talinings		2.5	2.0	4.6		4.2	8.3	8.0
Hydrocyclone overflow		0.4	0.3	0.5		0.7	0.5	0.7
Flotation feed		97.1	97.7	94.9		95.1	91.2	91.3
Pb concentration		88.5	63.7	3.8		87.1	39.1	3.2
Zn concentration		2.6	19.0	75.5		2.6	27.5	73.3
Pyrite concentration		0.7	1.7	1.5		1.0	2.5	1.5
Flotation tailings		4.2	13.3	14.1		4.4	22.1	13.3

In the separation of lead and copper sulphides, it is usual to depress galena by means of bichromate ($Cr_2O_7^{2-}$) or of starch and sulphurous acid. Fine-grained galena misrouted into the copper concentrate can be recovered using a weak anionic or cationic collector after oxidizing the collector coating by means e.g. of hypochlorite.

The separation of copper and zinc sulphides, especially if the former belongs to the more soluble group of secondary copper sulphides (such as chalcocite, bornite, etc.), is somewhat difficult owing to the high state of activation of the sphalerite. In such cases, sphalerite can be depressed out of the bulk concentrate by great doses of CN^- and Zn^{2+} ions; alternatively, copper minerals can be depressed using ferrocyanide ions.

Some copper ores contain small amounts ($\approx 0.02\%$) of molybdenite which flotates up into the froth concentrate. It can be separated by repeated cleaning flotation, after depressing the copper sulphide with an organic colloid or with hypochlorite (at a pH of 7.8 to 8.0), with ferrocyanide (in an alkaline medium) or phosphorus pentasulphide, or after the oxidative roasting of the concentrate (Papin 1955; Shirley et al. 1967; Wie and Fuerstenau 1974).

Prior to the differential flotation of a bulk concentrate of base metal sulphides, the adsorbed collector can be displaced from the grain surfaces by means of sodium sulphide. Selectivity of separation may be improved by the dosage of CN⁻ or ferrous sulphate. (Ferrous sulphate permits to regulate oxygen concentration in the pulp and, through it, the degree of surface oxidation of the individual sulphides.)

2.7.2. Flotation of non-sulphide minerals. The most widely used anionic collectors are fatty acids and soaps, but cationic reagents are also used. It is possible to win high-purity concentrates using specific collectors and depressants — possibly after carefully adjusting the pH and all the other factors influencing flotation performance. Non-sulphide minerals may be grouped into base metal oxides, polar non-ores, non-silicates and silicates of alkali earths. Inert (non-polar) minerals (coals) will be discussed separately.

2.7.2.1. Base metal oxides. The oxidation of lead-zinc sulphide ores tends to give rise to highly complex ores. Galena alters into anglesite, cerussite, pyromorphite, mimetesite, lead jarosite, etc.; sphalerite turns into oxidic zinc minerals (calamine, smithsonite) and soluble salts. The sulphide core of the original mineral may be conserved within an oxidized shell of varying thickness. After unlocking, such ores give grains of sulphides and oxides mixed together. The oxidized base-metal minerals left behind after the flotation of the sulphides can — after surface sulphidization — be flotated out together rather readily, using a strong thiol collector (e.g. amyl xanthate). Cerussite can be flotated with amyl xanthate even without sulphidization. Smithsonite (dry bone ore) and the zinc silicate minerals (willemite, calamine) can be flotated without sulphidization using cationic amines (especially the higher, 16C to 18C primary aliphatic ones). Mixtures of amines (>12C) and xanthates are also used as collectors, possibly in combination with solvents, emulsifiers or organic colloids (starch, tannin, lignin sulphate, etc.). These are added to the pulp in order to regulate froth quality or to minimize the harmful effects of fine slimes.

Copper oxides or carbonates (malachite, azurite) can be flotated readily with sulphydryl collectors after sulphidization or with sulphonated fatty acids without sulphidization. The LPF (leaching–precipitation–flotation) process may also use a xanthate collector to flotate copper oxides dissolved in a sulphuric acid solution and to win metallic copper by cementation with iron powder (Last et al. 1957).

Of the iron and manganese minerals, the carbonates (siderite and rhodochrosite) can be flotated readily enough as a rule using fatty acids in combination with the usual reagents of gangue depression (water glass, organic colloids). Of the oxides and hydroxides, those of massive, crystalline texture (pyrolusite, psilomelane, haematite, magnetite) also flotate readily enough with fatty acids or kerosene sulphonates, but the earthy, soft varieties (wad, limonite) are very hard to flotate and then only at high reagent consumptions.

For very muddy manganese ores, agglomerating flotation at very high dosages of emulsified reagents may help. For example, a dosage of 4.2 kg of SO_2

(sulphurous acid) with a reagent emulsion of 71 kg diesel fuel, 34 kg tall oil and 4.3 kg sodium alkyl-aryl sulphonate ("oronite") per ton and a four-stage after-cleaning gave a concentrate containing 40% Mn at a Mn recovery of 80% out of a complex secondary sedimentary ore (wad). Treatment with sulphurous acid makes Mn ions pass into solution, where they constitute with the fatty acids of the tall oil manganese soaps which precipitate onto the activated mineral surfaces. The emulsion is broken as a result, and the liberated diesel fuel can coat the surfaces lined with the manganese soap. Mechanical agitation results in the agglomeration of the grains, the size of the clots being determined by the third component of the emulsion (the oronite). The process of conditioning requires different retention times and power inputs (30 to 40 kW h per ton!) depending on the fineness of the ore. Heating improves performance (Gates 1957).

Problematic manganese or iron ores can be flotated in an alkaline pulp using cation-active collectors (long-chain primary aliphatic amines) after the addition of colloids. In a different approach, the gangue minerals are flotated out after depressing the Mn or Fe mineral. In view of the removal by cationic flotation of a silicate or quartz gangue, the iron oxides are readily depressed using starch (dextrin). A pH adjusted to within 8 and 9 by means of soda ash gives the best results. On flotation with anionic collectors, Ca and Mg salts reduce iron recovery greatly; they activate the quartz, however. Unsaturated fatty acids (at pH's above 11) are fair collectors for quartz activated with Ca and saturated ones for iron oxides (cf. also Section 2.2.3.2). Quartz can be flotated out of muddy iron ores also, where the flotation of the iron oxides would be greatly hindered by the mud and slimes. A muddy haematite ore can likewise be flotated fairly well using a suitably prepared emulsion of one part tall oil and two to four parts of a non-polar oil (in which case no micellae will form) (Chang et al. 1953; Dolotova et al. 1968; Erck 1961; Iwasaki and Lai 1965; Kihlstedt 1957).

Uranium minerals accompanied by silicate gangue minerals can be flotated at high recoveries as a rule, using fatty acids, a kerosene sulphonate or the emulsion of a long-chain fatty acid with a hydrocarbon solvent (e.g. one part stearic acid, one part sodium oleate and 1.2 part kerosene in 100 parts water) in the presence of suitable depressants (e.g. water glass in an alkaline medium, sodium silicofluoride in an acid one). In the flotation of secondary uranium minerals (phosphates, vanadates), dithiocarbamates ($RNHCSS^-$) have proved most useful (straight-chain 8C to 12C monoalkyl compounds above all). The addition of Zn, Pb or Cu salts improves recovery and shortens the time required for the operation. The presence of limonite, limestone or kaolin impairs recovery and the U content of the concentrate since these minerals are also activated by the dithiocarbamate and the metal salts (Butler and Morris 1956; Jude and Trătilă 1973; Light et al. 1962; Marabini and Rinelli 1973; Mariacher 1956).

2.7.2.2. Flotation of polar non-ores. Of these non-metallic minerals, fluorite, calcite, barite and apatite can be flotated fairly readily as a rule using fatty acids or alkyl sulphonates. Often, however, two or more of these minerals, hardly different as to surface properties, occur together. Separating them is a much harder task.

Part A of Fig. 2.101 shows the contact angles $\vartheta°$ of some non-ore minerals vs. dodecyl amine concentration. Part B shows the influence of water glass on fluorite and calcite. Curves 1 show percent water glass adsorption; Curves 2 show percent oleic acid adsorption; Curves 3 show recovery $m\%$, all vs. water glass concentration c. The full curves refer to fluorite, the dashed ones to calcite. Water glass is vigorously adsorbed by both minerals, hindering oleic acid adsorption, but fluorite recovery increases nevertheless (Eigeles 1957). When using a fatty-acid collector, calcite can be depressed, besides water glass, also by means of aluminium salts, tannic acid and/or starch (Yazan and Schäfer 1966).

Fluorite is readily flotated also with a water-soluble mixture of the mono- and diesters of alcoholic phosphoric fatty acid which constitute poorly soluble Ca and Ba salts. If a certain reagent concentration is exceeded, barite also will flotate out: still higher concentrations activate quartz also. In the presence of this reagent, water glass to depress quartz is superfluous and in fact harmful (Siebel 1962).

Flotation of barite in the presence of the waste minerals limonite, quartz and silicates using sodium oleate has its optimum at a water glass dosage of 300 g/t or so: true, more water glass gives a purer concentrate, but at the cost of a much reduced $BaSO_4$ recovery. The best activator of barite is lead acetate. Good

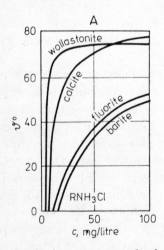
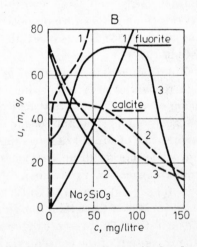

Fig. 2.101. A — contact angles ϑ of some non-ore minerals vs. collector (dodecyl ammonium chloride) concentration, B — recovery $m\%$ and reagent adsorption u (water glass — 1 and oleic acid — 2) of fluorite and calcite vs. water glass concentration

specific collectors of barite include alkali sulphonates (in the pH range from 9.5 to 11) or mixtures of the sodium salts of medium-length fatty acids with even numbers of C atoms (e.g. caprylic acid, 10C, and lauric acid, 12C, mixed in the proportions 7 : 3). Sodium taurate is another good barite collector. Celestite ($SrSO_4$) and certain lithium minerals (amblygonite, spodumene) also flotate well with taurates.

From barite and fluorite in a silicate gangue one can extract a bulk barite–fluorite concentrate using oleic acid in an alkaline medium (pH = 9 to 10, adjusted by means of NaOH); barite can then be depressed in an acid pulp (pH = 4.6 to 4.8). The critical pH at which flotation ceases is 5.2 for barite and 3.8 to 4.2 for fluorite, depending on the prior dosage of alkali. (A concentrate containing 98% CaF and 0.6% $BaSO_4$ was thus obtained at a fluorite recovery of 83%, out of a pulp warmed to 45 °C.) Barite can be depressed from beside fluorite also by means of sodium lignin sulphonate, potassium bichromate or starch. Citric acid e.g. in combination with a sodium lauryl sulphonate collector depresses fluorite while activating barite. (Starting with a fluorite "ore" of 10% barite content, a $BaSO_4$ concentrate of 91% was obtained at 94% barite recovery and then a 99% CaF_2 concentrate at 90% fluorite recovery, using 80 g/t citric acid, 200 g/t sodium lauryl sulphonate and 200 g/t sodium silicate in the first step and 120 g/t sodium bichromate, 300 g/t sodium silicate, 420 g/t oleic acid, 45 g/t sulphuric acid and 10 g/t pine oil in the second step.)

Apatites and phosphorites can after de-sliming be separated from quartz and silicates by flotation at a pH of 8.9 or so using a carboxylate (e.g. a di-olefinic unsaturated 18C acid), fuel oil and water glass. As in any fatty-acid type flotation, water quality is essential: the sum of the Ca^{2+}, Mg^{2+}, Al^{3+} and Fe^{3+} ion concentrations should be less than about 17 ppm. "Inverse" flotation can be achieved by means of cation-active collectors (Abeidu 1973; Browning and Rampacek 1964; Dobiaš 1968; Töpfer and Bilsing 1964; Yazan and Schäfer 1966).

The components of sands made up of quartz, feldspar and mica can be separated after a close adjustment of the pH, using a cationic or anionic collector and special modifiers. The surface charge of the minerals to be separated plays a decisive role here: it may be regulated by additions of electrolytes. Without activation, the zero-charge point of quartz is in the pH range from 1.5 and 3.7; that of the different iron oxides in the pH range from 6.5 to 8.5; between the two ranges, anionic collectors are selectively adsorbed by the iron oxides and cationic ones by quartz (Gaudin and Fuerstenau 1955; Iwasaki and Lai 1965; Kind 1970).

The flotation of quartz with one of the collectors octadecyl amine or dimethyl lauryl benzyl ammonium chloride is promoted by additions of citric acid, oxalic acid and disodium phosphate. Barium chloride depresses quartz activated with citric acid (DeBruyn and Agar 1962).

In Hungary, a quartz sand at Fehérvárcsurgó, containing 96 to 97 percent SiO; and 0.4 to 0.5 percent Fe_2O_3 is improved by flotation to glass-making grade (0.025 to 0.05% Fe_2O_3). The plus-0.65 mm fraction (5 to 15 weight%) of the r.o.m. sand is removed in a wet trommel screen; the minus-0.08 mm fraction (10 weight% or so) is removed in a hydrocyclone prior to flotation. The heavy-mineral impurities (leucoxene, magnetite, ilmenite, haematite, rutile, zircon, epidote) are then flotated out in combination with repeated passes of attrition and hydrocycloning. The pulp of 450 g/l density is conditioned for 5 min with a 500 to 700 g/t sulphonate soap collector and, after thinning, flotated with 20 g/t Flotanol C frother. The froth product, 7 to 10 weight percent, is rejected.

Micas can be flotated out of a pulp weakly acidized with sulphuric acid using cationic collectors of 8C or so chain length. The accompanying silicates can be depressed by means of aluminium sulphate.

In flotation with dodecyl amine and pine oil, feldspars float better than quartz at a low pH; in the medium pH range (5 to 10), the floatabilities of the two minerals are about equally fair; about a $pH > 10$, they are equally poor. Fluorides activate the feldspars but not the quartz. As a rule, then, quartz can be flotated with amines out of an alkaline pulp, feldspars out of a pulp acidized by means of hydrogen fluoride. For example, out of a pulp acidized with sulphuric acid, the mica can be flotated out first with amines; then the iron-containing heavy minerals can be won with sulphonates plus fuel oil and a frother out of a likewise acid medium; the feldspars can be recovered last with amines plus fuel oil and a frother after activation with hydrogen fluoride; quartz is left behind in the pulp.

Prior scrubbing (attrition) of the raw pulp and possibly also the washing out of the finest slimes may have a significant influence upon the removal of iron-mineral impurities and on the separation of quartz from the feldspars.

2.7.2.3. Coal flotation. Hard coals are among the non-polar substances endowed with a native floatability. Coals are made up by chemical bonds between the elements C, H, S, O and N and physical bonds between the compounds so made up, moisture and inorganic ash. The hydrocarbon compounds participating in the makeup of young brown (sub-bituminous) coals carry oxygen-containing radicals (OH, COOH, etc.) which make them hydrophilic. These humic acids gradually pass into neutral humins as coalification proceeds: the oxygen-containing hydrophilic radicals gradually disappear, to be replaced by hydrophobic ones ($CH_3 \ldots C_nH_m$). The native floatability of coals in different stages of coalification keeps step with these changes. It is maximum in the readily caking coking coals (gas and prime coking coals) and decreases again at still higher grades of coalification (low-volatile steam coal, anthracite) in which the strongly hydrophobic hydrocarbon compounds are replaced once again by less hydrophobic ones (which contain less than optimum numbers of hydrogen atoms and stand closer to graphite: cf. Table 2.32).

If strongly hydrophobic hydrocarbon compounds are predominant at the surface of a coal particle, then the native contact angle of the particle is great and it is possible to flotate it without a collector (using a frother only). Assuming the compounds at the fresh surfaces of fraction of the coal particles to

Table 2.32. Approximate compositions of different coal grades

	Moisture content, %	Carbon content, %, ash- and moisture-free basis	Volatiles content, %
Lignite	30—50	70	55
Young brown coal	18—32 }		
Older brown coal	12—20 }	60—75	50—60
High-volatile steam	6—15	70—85	40—50
Gas		{ 84—88	{ 29—40
Prime coking	3—6	{ 88—92	{ 17—30
Low-volatile steam		{ 90—93	{ 9—23
Anthracite	2—3	92—95	3—10

represent the average composition of the coal, their contact angles (that is, the floatability of the coal) can be inferred with some accuracy.

A measure M_f of coal floatability is given by the formula

$$M_f \cong 0.26\,C + (2 - 0.05\,H)H - (0.26 - 0.005n)n - 25,$$

where C and H are, respectively, the percentage carbon and hydrogen content of the coal on a moisture- and ash-free basis and n is the moisture content of the r.o.m. coal (Sun 1954). If M_f is positive, then the coal is floatable in practice and has a measurable contact angle,

$$\vartheta^\circ \cong 7M_f$$

approximately. The reagent concentration, R kg/t (three parts kerosene plus two parts frother) required for a recovery of about 90% of the inflammable components relates to M_f approximately as

$$\log R \cong 0.7 - 0.25M_f \,.$$

Even in one and the same coal seam, the different petrographic constituents of coal (vitrain, clarain, durain, fusain) usually differ as to chemical composition: as a result, their floatabilities differ also (cf. Table 2.33 and Sun 1954).

The floatability of a coal particle is the greater, the greater the percentage of its surface made up of clean coal (more accurately, of hydrophobic hydrocarbon compounds) and the less is its mass. As ash content increases, both factors change adversely for flotation: the surface with a propensity to adhere to air bubbles decreases and the weight of the particle increases. As particle size decreases, the specific surface (surface area per unit weight) increases: hence, finer particles tend as a rule to be more floatable than coarser ones, for a given ash content.

In order to enhance the native floatability and increase the contact angle of coals, it is usual to add as collectors non-polar hydrocarbons (crude petroleum or the products of its refining: kerosene, diesel fuel; or brown coal tars or tar distillation products). Collector oils that are non-polar in their entire bulk will not adhere to the polar minerals but will coat the aero- and oleophilic surfaces endowed with contact angles, increasing those angles and substantially reducing the time of adherence to the bubbles. The sequence of floatability of different types of coal is not upset as a rule by the adhesion of the collector oil: the higher, notably, the measure of floatability M_f, or the native contact angle, the greater is adsorptivity towards oil and the less is wettability by water.

Collector oils are water-insoluble and reluctant to disperse. Oil droplets dispersed in water by strong shaking do not constitute a stable emulsion: after the cessation of shaking, they rise to the surface. In such systems, some particles are coated more thickly than is good for them, whereas others receive no collector at all. This is why it is preferable to emulsify the collector oil first in a suitable liquid and to introduce it in the form of a stable emulsion. Reagent consumption is substantially reduced thereby, recovery is increased and concentrate purity is improved. For example, the flotation for three minutes of minus-0.42 mm raw coal with 45 g/t pine oil and 200 g/t paraffin oil at a pH = 7.7 gave

| coal recoveries of | 27 | 51 | 56% |

using non-emulsified paraffin oil and

| | 81 | 82 | 83% |

using ultrasonically emulsified paraffin oil, after conditioning for

| | 0 | 1 | 2 |

minutes (Sun et al. 1966).

Most of the proprietary makes of packaged coal-flotating reagents available are emulsions of kerosene or diesel fuel in primary and secondary alcohols or 5C to 10C monocarbonic acids (the optimum being between 6C and 8C), where the alcohol or carbonic acid is the frother. (Non-frothing emulsifiers may, however, also be used to prepare the collector-oil emulsion if it is desired to introduce the frother separately from the collector.) Sulphonated kerosene may be used as a collector-cum-frother reagent. Heavy xylenols derived as by-products of semi-coke making, natural or synthetic pine oil products and methyl isobutyl

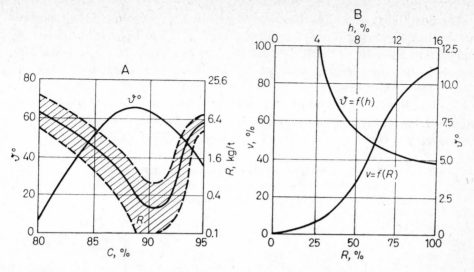

Fig. 2.102. A — native contact angle ϑ and reagent dosage R kg/t required for optimum (90%) recovery in the flotation of coal, vs. the carbon content C% of clean coal; *B* — coal recovery v% vs. reagent dosage R and contact angle vs. ash content h%

carbinol (MIBC) are also among the favoured frothers of coal flotation (Horsley 1951/52).

Part A of Fig. 2.102 presents the native contact angle $\vartheta°$ of ash-free vitrain and the optimum reagent dosage R kg/t (two parts creosote mixed with one part cresylic acid) giving 90% recovery vs. the carbon content of clean coal (Horsley 1951/52). Part B of the figure shows recovery v% (or m%) vs. R% (with the dosage R required to obtain the optimum recovery of about $m = 90$% taken as 100%) and the native contact angle $\vartheta°$ vs. ash content h% (Klassen 1960).

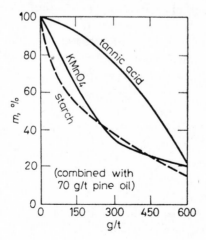

Fig. 2.103. Decline of coal recovery m% as a function of increasing depressant dosage

The floatability of coal particles is reduced by the oxidation of their surfaces or by their acquiring films of hydrophilic colloids. Coal-particle surfaces are oxidized to a greater or smaller extent by simple exposure to air, but oxidizing agents (potassium permanganate, potassium bichromate, nitric acid, ferric sulphate) affect them even more. Some organic compounds such as starch, albumin, glue, humic acid, tannic acid, etc. are also useful depressants of coal. Figure 2.103 shows coal recovery obtained using various depressants, referred to recovery without a depressant, vs. reagent dosage in g/t.

Table 2.33. Weight percent outputs of the first, middle and last third of a bank of coal flotation machines and their petrographic composition

Section	Weight %	$V\%$	$D\%$	$F\%$	$m\%$		
					V	D	F
1	65	80	1	19	99	2	55
2	30	2	70	28	1	85	38
3	5	2	65	33	0	13	7
	100	53	25	22	100	100	100

Depressants are selective, more or less. Organic colloids tend to reduce the floatability of fusain more as a rule than that of vitrain or durain. Oxidizers, on the other hand, usually depress vitrain more than fusain because the latter contains comparatively less reoxidizable humin. Differential coal flotation (that is, the separation to a greater or smaller of vitrain, the preferred coking component, from indifferent durain, and from fusain, which is harmful to coking) can thus be achieved by the proper choice and dosage of reagents.

Table 2.33 presents the relative weight percentages of the froth products of a given raw coal treated with a given combination of basic reagents, without modifiers, emerging from the first, middle and last third of a bank of cells, the vitrain–durain–fusain composition of their organic fraction (V–D–F) and the percentages ($m\%$) of the different outputs (Klassen and Mokrousov 1963).

Pyrite contained in coal can be depressed with lime, an alkali cyanide, calcium chloride (at a pH > 8.5), Fe^{3+}, Al^{3+} or Cr^{3+} chloride, ferrous or ferric sulphate (in the pH range 4.5 to 7, these metal ions form positively charged colloids even with small quantities of NaOH), or copper sulphate in the pH range 5.5 to 8.0. Soda ash, permanganate, caustic soda, sodium sulphite are used more seldom to depress pyrite in coal, but gelatine, starch and glue also enter into consideration for the purpose.

In an acid medium, pyrite contained in ores can be flotated readily with ethyl xanthate, whereas porous "coal pyrite" (pyrite contained in coal) will flotate poorly, even though its xanthate adsorption, increasing as the pH decreases, is about twice as much as that of "ore pyrite". In an alkaline medium, on the other hand, the coal pyrite can be flotated more readily than the ore pyrite. For example, on feeding potassium ethyl xanthate at a $pH = 6$ in concentrations

| 0 | 10 | 20 | 40 | 75 g/t, |

recoveries were

| 2 | 18 | 35 | 40 | 72% |

for coal pyrite and

| 1 | 87 | 94 | 96 | 99% |

for ore pyrite; at a $pH = 10$, they were

| 20(!) | 20 | 23 | 34 | 42% |

for coal pyrite and zero throughout for ore pyrite (Chernosky and Lyon 1972).

In Part A of Fig. 2.104, the dashed curve shows average sulphur contents $c_S\%$ for the clean-coal curve obtained by the gravity analysis of a given coal; the full curves state sulphur contents for the froth products obtained on rougher flotation, roughing plus cleaning and roughing plus double cleaning, respectively, vs. weight recovery, $v\%$. For example, clean coal of one percent S content can be obtained at $v = 40\%$ on single cleaning, and at $v = 80\%$ on double cleaning. Without cleaning, no froth product containing one per cent sulphur

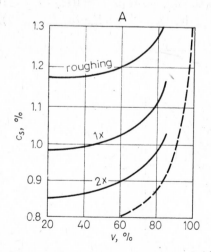 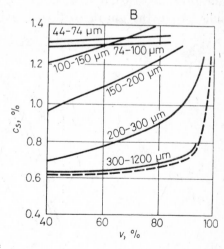

Fig. 2.104. Sulphur content $c_S\%$ A — of different coal concentrates obtained by concentration by gravity and flotation, and B — of their different grain size fractions vs. weight recovery

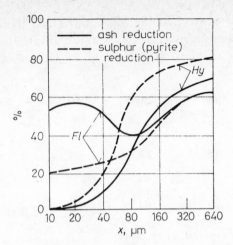

Fig. 2.105. Reduction of pyrite and ash content achieved by flotation (*Fl*) and hydrocycloning (*Hy*), vs. grain size

or less can at all be gained from this coal. (The sharper gravity separation of the
coal, on the other hand, gave such a product at about 90% weight recovery.)

Part B of Fig. 2.104 presents the sulphur content c_S% of the different grain
size fractions in the froth product vs. weight recovery v%. The dashed curve
has been obtained by gravity analysis also in this case. It coincides practically
with the c_S% curve of the plus-300 μm fraction of the flotation product.

Figure 2.105 presents percentage reductions of ash and sulphur (pyrite) content as a result of flotation (*Fl*) and hydrocycloning (*Hy*), respectively, vs.
grain size x. As to ash reduction, the two methods give approximately identical
results above 100 μm or so (hydrocycloning has a slight edge on flotation),

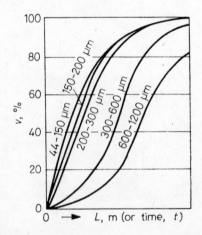

Fig. 2.106. Recoveries of different grain size fractions of clean coal vs. retention time *t*
(or length of displacement along the flotation machine)

whereas under 100 μm, flotation clearly gives a superior performance. For pyrite (sulphur) reduction, hydrocycloning is to be preferred above 50 μm and flotation under that limit.

The outcome of coal flotation is affected, in addition to the nature of the coal and to the reagent combination and dosage used, also by the grain size distribution of the coal, its maximum grain size, slimes content, pulp density, the pH, cell hookup, etc.

Cumulative weight percentage $v\%$ of clean coal particles of different size flotated out vs. length L along the bank of cells (or vs. time t) is presented for one specific case in Fig. 2.106.

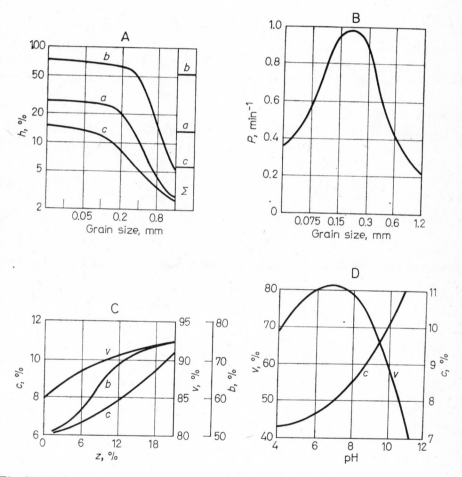

Fig. 2.107. A — ash content of a coal slurry (a) and its flotation products (b and c) vs. grain size, B — specific floatability of coal P vs. grain size, C — weight recovery $v\%$ and average ash content $c\%$ of the products (b and c) vs. pulp density $z\%$, D — average ash content c and weight recovery $v\%$ of a flotation product of coal vs. the pH

Both in the froth product and in the flotation residue, coarser particles are lower in ash than finer ones: this is why grains coarser than e.g. 0.5 to 0.6 mm are often screened out of the flotation feed or out of the tailings. Part A of Fig. 2.107 shows for an example ash contents vs. grain size for a coarse-grained raw-coal slurry (a) and of its two flotation products (b and c). Part B of the figure shows specific floatability P min^{-1} vs. grain size: a maximum for the 150 to 300 μm fraction, floatability decreases abruptly on either side of that grain size class. For a given combination of feed and reagents, Part C and Part D of Fig. 2.107 show the influence of pulp density and that of the pH on weight recovery $v\%$ and ash content of the products (froth product c and tailings b). The $z\%$ pulp density on the abscissa in Part C is weight percent of solid grains. In coal flotation practice, the usual range of this parameter is 3 to 20%: it is between 10 to 14% for minus-300 μm feeds containing less than 25% minus-75 μm material. The flotation performance of coarser (0.5 mm) feeds containing little slimes (minus-60 μm material) is quite fair also at pulp densities about 20%; very fine-grained pulps, on the other hand, require strong dilution ($z = 3$ to 5%), entailing great water and reagent consumptions. Pulp density in the downstream cells tends to be much lower than in the cells close to the feed end.

By Part D of Fig. 2.107, weight recovery is highest in a neutral pulp (in the vicinity of pH = 7); froth product purity deteriorates abruptly in an alkaline and less so in an acid medium. In the vicinity of pH = 7, coal particles have a weak negative charge; the H$^+$ ions which they adsorb in a slightly acid pulp reduce the charge to zero and raise surface hydrophobia to a maximum. Coal

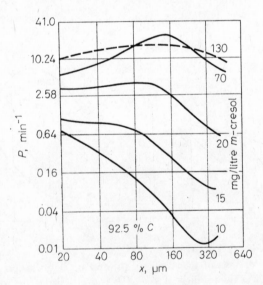

Fig. 2.108. Floatability P vs. grain size at different reagent concentrations in coal flotation

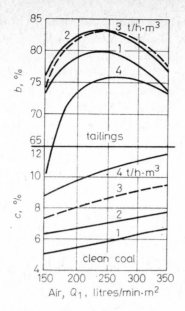

Fig. 2.109. Ash content of coal flotation products at a given retention time, vs. Q_1 litre/minute×sq.m, at different throughputs t/h · m³

particle surfaces acquire a positive charge in a strongly acid pulp and a negative one (by adsorbing OH^- ions) in an alkaline one; both reduce hydrophobia.

Figure 2.108 presents the floatability P of clean coal particles of 92.5% carbon content vs. particle size x at different concentrations of m-cresol. Besides grain size, floatability is affected by ash content also (in addition to the influence of reagent combination and dosage, pulp density, aeration, etc.). Table 2.34 states as an example the weight percentages s and ash contents h of different grain size fractions of a coal of 85% carbon content (on an ash-free basis) at 2.2 kg/t reagent dosage and $z = 9\%$ pulp density. The two last columns of the table list the recoveries $m\%$ of the fractions routed into the froth product of the individual grain size classes and their specific floatabilities P min⁻¹. The 125 to 250-μm class which had the highest ash content had the least floatability and, conversely, the plus-500 μm class, lowest in ash, had the greatest, in the case of this particular coal.

Other research revealed that in a mat-type cell (a cell with a porous bottom plate), floatability P varies — up to a certain point of saturation — as the aggregate surface area of the bubbles passing through the cell per unit of time. Saturation sets in at about 10 volume% air in the pulp: above it, the froth height increases abruptly. In the more widely used impeller-type (subaeration) cells, optimum air feed rate is about 30 volume percent at 0.9 mm average bubble diameter.

327

Figure 2.109 shows the variation of ash content in the tailings ($b\%$) and the froth product ($c\%$) for a time of 3.5 minutes flotation at different throughput rates per m³ of useful cell volume, t/h · m³, vs. air feed rate Q_1 per m² of cell surface area, l/min · m². The cleanest tailings ($b = 82.5\%$) were obtained in the throughput rate range of 2 to 3 t/h · m³ at an air feed rate of about 225 l/min · m² (the ash content of the resulting clean coal product being 7 to 8% in that case) (Brown 1956, 1962).

Table 2.34. Weight recovery $s\%$, ash content $h\%$, coal recovery $m\%$ and floatability P of the grain size fractions of a coal flotation feed and its products

85%C, $z = 9\%$ $R = 2.2$ kg/t	Feed		Clean coal		Waste		$m\%$	P min^{-1}
	$s\%$	$h\%$	$s\%$	$h\%$	$s\%$	$h\%$		
$+500\ \mu$m	19.5	5.1	18.1	2.1	1.4	45.9	93	0.55
250—500 μm	23.6	22.1	17.7	6.3	5.9	71.0	75	0.34
125—250 μm	17.1	36.1	10.6	12.8	6.5	75.0	62	0.22
—125 μm	39.8	32.9	26.7	14.1	13.1	70.0	67	0.29
	100.0	25.6	73.1	9.1	26.9	70.2	73.1	

Table 2.35. Influence of different variables on the pilot-plant flotation of six types of coal

	1		2		3		4		5		6	
Raw coal —420 μm:	22 $a\%$	41 $i\%$	11 $a\%$	40 $i\%$	20 $a\%$	24 $i\%$	14 $a\%$	31 $i\%$	28 $a\%$	17 $i\%$	15 $a\%$	19 $i\%$
Clean coal	$v\%$	$c\%$	$v\%$	$c\%$	$v\%$	$c\%$	$v\%$	$c\%$	$v\%$	$c\%$	$v\%$	$c\%$
<35%—44 μm	33.0	11.6	74.5	7.9	78.4	9.9	77.3	8.3	66.6	10.4	76.2	5.8
>35%—44 μm	33.6	11.5	70.2	8.4	73.0	11.9	74.6	9.6	67.3	11.4	70.9	7.5
Impeller 900	33.4	11.6	74.4	8.1	76.0	11.0	78.0	9.0	68.4	10.9	76.9	6.7
speed, rpm 1100	31.3	11.5	70.4	8.2	75.4	10.9	74.0	8.6	65.5	10.8	70.2	6.7
Retention 1 min.	19.7	11.8	58.3	7.8	66.0	10.5	65.4	8.4	56.2	10.4	63.2	6.7
time 2 min.	32.9	11.5	75.4	8.5	78.2	11.3	78.9	9.3	71.8	11.5	79.4	7.0
3 min.	48.8	11.5	82.8	8.2	81.9	10.9	83.3	9.3	73.2	10.9	79.2	6.4
MIBC 125 g/t	24.0	11.2	71.9	7.6	77.1	10.3	72.8	8.0	64.2	9.3	73.9	6.1
250 g/t	36.3	11.6	73.0	8.3	76.0	11.0	78.6	9.2	68.2	10.8	75.5	6.9
500 g/t	40.0	11.9	72.2	8.6	74.5	11.5	76.8	9.9	68.7	12.7	73.2	7.0
Air feed 0.3 scfm	11.2	10.4	57.9	7.1	62.3	9.4	61.5	7.8	59.7	8.9	62.0	5.8
rate 1.0 scfm	31.8	11.2	74.0	8.2	77.4	11.2	78.7	9.1	68.6	10.7	76.2	6.7
2.0 scfm	54.6	13.0	85.8	9.2	87.4	12.1	88.3	10.2	72.7	13.1	84.6	7.5
Solids content, 5%	35.0	10.9	75.2	7.5	78.6	9.1	76.7	7.9	64.1	7.4	70.0	5.4
weight % 10%	35.1	11.5	74.7	8.1	78.2	11.0	80.4	9.3	67.2	10.3	78.0	6.5
15%	30.8	12.1	68.1	8.8	70.9	12.9	70.7	10.0	69.1	14.7	67.4	8.1

($i\%$: volatile content on ash- and moisture-free basis.)

Table 2.35 shows the outcome of flotating hard coals in a pilot-plant-scale four-cell Fagergren machine using a methyl isobutyl carbinol (MIBC) reagent.

Longer retention times and a more vigorous aeration increase recovery and selectivity (more precisely, the v/c parameter), whereas a higher slimes content, higher impeller speed, greater reagent concentration and greater pulp density affect the quantity and quality of the froth product adversely. The v/c ratio increases in the succession 1-5-3-4-2-6 (in terms of the numbering of raw coals in the table): it is more favourable for the low-ash coals (Nos 4, 2 and 6) than for the high-ash ones.

Relative energy requirement is lowered (the v/N ratio is increased) as retention time, reagent dosage, air throughput and pulp density increase but is greatly raised by increasing impeller speed. Slimes content does not affect v/N at all significantly.

Table 2.36. Comparison of optimum outcome of pilot-plant flotation with flotation in a lab cell and the washing curve of a gravity-analysis run

	a%	i%	Const. v%	c%			Const. c%	v%		
				pilot	lab.	grav. an.		pilot	lab.	grav. an.
1	22	41	81.2	13.3	9.6	8.8	13.3	81.2	90.0	90.5
2	11	40	82.4	7.7	6.4	4.8	7.7	82.4	92.5	93.2
3	20	24	78.1	8.4	6.8	7.0	8.4	78.1	85.5	83.5
4	14	31	75.8	7.8	7.4	4.2	7.8	75.8	82.0	89.2
5	28	17	71.0	5.3	5.2	4.8	5.3	71.0	72.0	72.0
6	15	19	74.6	4.4	4.2	2.6	4.4	74.6	78.0	85.3

Table 2.36 shows varying ash contents $c\%$ at constant weight recovery (yield) $v\%$ and varying yields $v\%$ at constant ash contents $c\%$ for the above six coals, as obtained (1) in the pilot-scale Fagergren machine, (2) in a 0.5 litre laboratory cell and (3) by means of heavy-liquid gravity analysis. The outcome of flotation in the lab cell is much closer to that of the pilot-scale flotation test than to the values derived from the washing curves of the gravity analysis (Cavallaro 1970).

2.8. LITERATURE ON FLOTATION

ABEIDU, A. M.: Selective depressions of calcite from fluorite. *Trans. IMM* 1973, C49—C50.
ADAM, N. K.: *The Physics and Chemistry of Surfaces.* (3rd ed.) Oxford University Press, New York 1941.
ADDISON, C. C.: The properties of freshly-formed surfaces. *J. Chem. Soc.* 1945, 98—106.
APLAN, F. F.—D. W. FUERSTENAU: Principles of nonmetallic mineral flotation. *Froth Flotation 50th Anniv. Volume, AIME,* New York 1962, 170—214.
ARBITER, N.—C. C. HARRIS: Flotation machines. *Froth Flotation 50th Anniv. Volume, AIME,* New York 1962, 347—364.

ARBITER, N.—J. STEININGER: Hydrodynamics of flotation machines. 6. *IMPC*, Cannes 1963, 595—605.

ARBITER, N.—N. L. WEISS: Design of flotation cells and circuits. *Trans. AIME* 1970, 340—347.

ARBITER, N.—C. C. HARRIS—R. F. YAP: Hydrodynamics of flotation cells. *Trans. AIME* 1969, 134—148.

BARTELL, F. E.—J. W. SHEPARD: Surface roughness as related to hysteresis of contact angles. *J. Phys. Chemistry* 1953, 211—215, 455—463.

BLAKE, R. A.: Effect of partial removal of xanthate collector on size of material floated. *Trans. AIME, SME* 1972, 39—42.

BOGDANOV, O. S. (et al.): Hydroxamic acids as collectors in the flotation of wolframite, cassiterite and pyrochlore. *IMPC*, London 1973.

BOUTIN, P.—D. A. WHEELER: Column flotation. *Mining World* 1967 March, 47—50.

BRISON, R. J.—R. A. CAMPBELL: Optimizing grinding and regrinding capacity in mill design. *Trans. AIME, SME* 1974, 239—245.

BRISON, R. J.—H. G. ELLIS: Large flotation cells. *Min. Congr. J.* 1970 Jan., 50—54.

BROWN, D. J.: Fundamentals of froth flotation. *Chem. & Proc. Engng* 1956, 201—205.

BROWN, D. J.: Coal flotation. *Froth Flotation 50th Anniv. Volume* 1962, 518—538.

BROWN, D. J.—H. G. SMITH: Continuous laboratory flotation testing of coal. *Symp. Coal Prep.*, Leeds 1952, 179—190.

BROWNING, J. S.—C. RAMPACEK: Flotation of complex barite-fluorspar ores. 7. *IMPC*, New York 1964, 221—226.

BRUCHHOLD, C.: *Der Flotationsprozess.* Verlag J. Springer, Berlin 1927.

BUCKENHAM, M. H.—J. M. W. MACKENZIE: Fatty acids as flotation collectors for calcite. *Trans. AIME* 1961, 450—454.

BUCKENHAM, M. H.—J. H. SCHULMAN: Molecular associations in flotation. *Trans. AIME* 1963, 1—6.

BUSHELL, C. H. G.—C. J. KRAUSS—G. BROWN: Some reasons for selectivity in copper activation of minerals. *Can. M. M. Bull.* 1961, 244—251.

BUTLER, J. N.—R. J. MORRIS: Flotation or secondary uranium minerals. *Min. Engng* 1956, 1008—1011.

CARTA, M. (et al.): The influence of the surface energy structure of minerals on electric separation and flotation. 9. *IMPC*, Praha 1970, 47—57.

CARTA, M. (et al.): Improvement in electric separation and flotation by modification of energy levels in surface layers. *IMPC*, London 1973.

CAVALLARO, J. A.: Operating variables in coal flotation. *Min. Congr. J.* 1970 Sept., 49—57.

CHANG, C. S.—S. R. B. COOKE—R. O. HUCH: Starches and starch products as depressants in amine flotation of iron ore. *Min. Engng* 1953, 1282—1286.

CHERNOSKY, F. J.—F. M. LYON: Comparison of the flotation and adsorption characteristics of ore and coal-pyrite with ethyl xanthate. *Trans. AIME* 1972, 11—14.

CLARK, S. W.—S. R. B. COOKE: Adsorption of calcium, magnesium and sodium ion by quartz. *Trans. AIME* 1968, 334—341.

CLEMENT, M.: Probleme der Flotation feiner Schlämme. *Erzmetall* 1977, 447—454.

CLEMENT, M.—K. BRENNECKE—J. BONJER: Untersuchungen über das Flotationsverhalten nichtsulfidischer schwerlöslicher Minerale wie Schwerspat, Coelestin und Flußspat. *Erzmetall* 1973, 225—229.

CLEMENT, M.—H. HARMS—H. M. TRÖNDLE: Über das Flotationsverhalten verschiedener Mineralarten unter besonderer Berücksichtigung der Kornfeinheit. 9. *IMPC*, Praha 1970, 179—187.

COLOMBO, A. F.—R. T. SORENSEN—D. W. FROMMER: Calcium ion measurements provide insights to anionic flotation of silica. *Trans. AIME* 1965, 100—109.

DEBRUYN, P. L.: Flotation of quartz by cationic collectors. *Min. Engng* 1955, 291—296.

DEBRUYN, P. L.—G. E. AGAR: Surface chemistry of flotation. *Froth Flotation 50th Anniv. Volume* 1962, 91—138.

DEBRUYN, P. L.—H. J. MODI: Particle size and flotation rate of quartz. *Min. Engng* 1956, 415—419.

DEBRUYN, P. L.—J. T. G. OVERBECK—R. SCHUHMANN: Flotation and the Gibbs adsorption equation. *Min. Engng* 1954, 519—523.

DERJAGUIN, B. V.—S. S. DUKHIN: Theory of flotation of small and medium-size particles. *Trans. IMM* 1961, 221—246.

DIGRE, M.: Separation factor analysis for mineral dressing processes. *IMPC*, London 1960, 999—1012.

DOBIAŠ, B.: Beitrag zur Theorie der Flotation von nichtsulfidischen Mineralen. *Freib. Fh. A335* 1965, 7—20.

DOBIAŠ, B.: Flotierbarkeit und elektrokinetische Eigenschaften von Flußspat und Schwerspat. *Erzmetall* 1968, 275—281.

DOLOTOVA, I. A. (et al.): Processing techniques and equipment for beneficiation of manganese ores. 8. *IMPC*, Leningrad 1968, E8.

DU RIETZ, C.: Chemisorption of collectors in flotation. 9. *IMPC*, Cagliari 1975, 375—403.

EBY, J. G.: Wemco large-capacity flotation cells. *CIM Bull.* 1972 Feb., 50—55.

EIGELES, M. A.: Selective flotation of non-sulphide minerals. *IMDC*, Stockholm 1957, 591—609.

ERCK, L. J.: Flotation of iron ore. *Froth Flotation 50th Anniv. Volume*, Colorado 1961 July, Vol. 56, No. 3, 387—416.

ERSKINE, R. T.: Trends in bulk handling of reagents at Brunswick Mining and Smelting. *Can. Min. J.* 1970 June, 79—83.

ESTEFAN, S. F.—M. A. MALATI: Activation of oleate flotation of quartz by alkaline-earth ions. *Trans. IMM* 1973, C237—C240.

EVANS, R. C.: *Einführung in die Kristallchemie.* I. A. Barth Verlag, Leipzig 1954.

FAHLSTRÖM, P. D. (et al.): Boliden FR flotation machine; why and how it has been developed. *World Mining* 1970 May, 67—71.

FAHRENWALD, A. W.: Emulsion flotation. *Min. Congr. J.* 1957, 72—74.

FAYED, L. A. M.: Ölflotation feinstkörniger Mineralen. *AT* 1965, 374—378.

FINKELNBURG, W.: *Einführung in die Atomphysik.* Springer Verlag, Berlin—Göttingen—Heidelberg 1964.

FUERSTENAU, M. C. (ed.): Froth Flotation 50th Anniversary Volume. *MIMMPE*, New York 1962.

FUERSTENAU, M. C. (et al.): The influence of sodium silicate in nonmetallic flotation systems. *Trans. AIME* 1968, 319—323.

FUERSTENAU, D. W.—M. C. FUERSTENAU: Ionic size in flotation collection of alkali halides. *Min. Engng* 1956, 302—307.

GATES, E. H.: Agglomeration flotation of manganese ore. *Min. Engng* 1957, 1368—1372.

GAUDIN, A. M.: *Flotation.* (2nd ed.) McGraw Hill, New York 1957. (1st ed. in 1932.)

GAUDIN, A. M.—F. W. BLOECHER: Concerning the adsorption of dodecylamine on quartz. *Trans. AIME* 1950, 499—505.

GAUDIN, A. M.—D. W. FUERSTENAU: Quartz flotation with anionic collectors. *Min. Engng* 1955, 66—72.

GAUDIN, A. M.—D. W. FUERSTENAU: Quartz flotation with cationic collectors. *Min. Engng* 1955, 958—962.

GAUDIN, A. M.—P. L. DeBRUYN—O. MELLGREN: Adsorption of ethyl xanthane on pyrite. *Min. Engng* 1956, 65—70.

GAUDIN, A. M.—D. W. FUERSTENAU—H. L. MIAW: Slime-coating in galena flotation. *Trans. AIME* 1960, 668—671. (Or: *Can. M. M. Bull.* 1960, 960—963.)

GLEMBOTSKY, V. A. (et al.): Selective separation of fine mineral slimes using the method of electric flotation. 11. *IMPC*, Cagliari 1961, Paper 20.

GLEMBOTSKY, V. A.—V. I. KLASSEN—I. N. PLAKSIN: *Flotatsiya.* Gosgeotekhizdat, Moscow 1961.

GORODETSKY, M. I. (et al.): Increase in flotation recovery of porphyry copper ores of the Balkash concentrator. 10. *IMPC*, London 1973, 42.

GRAINGER-ALLEN, T. J. N.: Bubble generation in froth flotation machines. *Trans. IMM* 1970, C15—C22.

GRANVILLE, A.—N. P. FINKELSTEIN—S. A. ALLISON: Review of reactions in the flotation systems galena-xanthate-oxygen. *Trans. IMM* 1972, C1—C30.

GROUNDS, A.: Fine-particle treatment by ultraflotation. *Mine & Quarry Engng* 1964, 128—133.

HARRIS, C. C.: Impeller speed, air and powder requirements in flotation machine scale-up. *Int. J. Min. Proc.* 1974, 51—64.

HARRIS, C. C.—V. LEPETIC: Flotation cell design. *Min. Engng* 1966 Sept., 67—72.

HEINISCH, R.—E. VON SZANTHO: Über den Zusammenhang zwischen der Luftblasengrösse und der Korngrösse des Feststoffes bei der Injektor-Flotation. *AT* 1972, 365—372, 551—560.

HOFMANN, H.—P. LENGLER: Zur Kinetik der Flotation des Meggener Erzes. *Erzmetall* 1969, 234—238.

HORSLEY, R. M.: Oily collectors in coal flotation. *Trans. IME* 1951/52, 868—894.

HUBER-PANU, J.: Beitrag zur Theorie der Flotationskinetik. *Freib. Fh. A335* 1965, 159—169.

HUBER-PANU, J.: Beitrag betreffend Gleichungen und Methoden zur Berechnung der Flotationsergebnisse. *Rudy* 1970 (3—4), 123—132.

HUKKI, R. T.: Measurement and evaluation of the rate of flotation as a function of particle size. *Trans. AIME* 1953, 1122—1123.

HUKKI, R. T.: Hot flotation improves selectivity and raises mineral recoveries. *World Mining* 1973 March, 60—63.

ISKRA, J.—C. GUTIÉRREZ—J. A. KITCHENER: Influence of quebracho on the flotation of fluorite, calcite, hematite and quartz with oleate as collector. *Trans. IMM* 1973, C73—C78.

IWASAKI, I. (et al.): Flotation characteristics of goethite. *BuMines RI 5593* 1960.

IWASAKI, I. (et al.): Iron wash ore slimes — some mineralogical and flotation characteristics. *Trans. AIME* 1962, 97—108.

IWASAKI, I.—R. W. LAI: Starches and starch products as depressants in soap flotation of activated silica from iron ores. *Trans. AIME* 1965, 364—371.

JOHN, P.: Zur Entwicklung der rührerlosen Flotationszellen. *AT* 1964, 532—543.

JOHN, P.: Zum Entwicklungsstand der rührerlosen Flotation. *AT* 1973, 156—161.

JUDE, E.—N. TRĂTILĂ: Recovery of uranium compounds in mine water by ion flotation. 10. *IMPC*, London 1973, 25.

KARJALAHTI, K.: Factors affecting the conditioning of an apatite ore for agglomeration flotation. *Trans. IMM* 1972, C219—C226.

KELLERWESSEL, H.—P. ZAHR: Die Entwicklung von Rührwerks-Flotationsmaschinen in der Steinkohlen-Aufbereitung. *AT* 1966, 560—571.

KELLOGG, H.—H. VASQUEZ-ROSAS: Amine flotation of sphalerite-galena ores. *Trans. AIME* 1946, 476—504.

KIHLSTEDT, P. G.: Flotation of hematite ores with tall oil emulsions. *IMDC*, Stockholm 1957, 559—576.

KIND, P.: Erzeugung von Glassandqualitäten mit Hilfe der Flotation. *Erzmetall* 1970, 199—205.

KIND, P.: Einige Gesichtspunkte zur Auslegung von Flotationsanlagen unter Berücksichtung von Zellen grosser Leistung. *AT* 1972, 140—146.

KING, R. P.—T. A. HATTON—D. G. HULBERT: Bubble loading during flotation. *Trans. IMM* 1974, C112—C114.

KLASSEN, V. I.: Theoretical basis of flotation by gas precipitation. *IMPC*, London 1960, 309—322.

KLASSEN, V. I.—V. A. MOKROUSOV: *An introduction to the theory of flotation.* Butterworth and Co. Publ. Ltd., London 1963.

KLEBER, W.: *Einführung in die Kristallographie.* VEB Verlag Technik, Berlin 1956.

KLYMOWSKY, I. B.: Effect of dissolved oxygen in sulphide flotation. *Canad. Mining J.* 1973 June, 51—52.

KLYMOWSKI, I. B.—T. SALMAN: The role of oxygen in xanthate flotation of galena, pyrite and chalcopyrite. *CIM Bull.* 1970, 683—688.

KONIGSMANN, K. V.: Aeration in plant practice. *Canad. Mining J.* 1973 June, 52—53.

KRÖGER, C.—E. BADE: Anreicherung der Gefügebestandteile der Steinkohle durch Flotation. *Glückauf* 1960, 741—747.

KÜHLWEIN, F. L.: Fusitabscheidung durch selektive Kohlenflotation. *Glückauf* 1934, 245—252, 275—277.

LARSEN and ROSS: *E/MJ* 1976 Feb., 94—96.

LASKOWSKI, J.—J. ISKRA: Role of capillary effects in bubble-particle collision in flotation. *Trans. IMM* 1970, C6—C10.

LAST, A. W.—J. L. STEVENS—L. EATON, Jr.: L—P—F treatment of Ray ore. *Min. Engng* 1957, 1236—1238.

LEPETIC, V. M.: Flotation of chalcopyrite without collector after dry, autogenous grinding. *CIM Bull.* 1974 June, 71—77.

LIGHT, D. E. (et al.): The flotation of radioactive minerals. *Can. M. M. Bull.* 1962, 30—34.

LIN, I. J.: CMC of flotation reagents and its relation to HLB. *Trans. AIME* 1971, 225—227.

LINDGREN, E.: Aspects of flotation circuit design. *Concentrates* 1976, No. 1, 6—10.

LINDKVIST, L.: Froth pumping. *CIM Bull.* 1973 Jan., 69—72.

MARABINI, A. M.—G. RINELLI: Flotation of pitchblende with a chelating agent and fuel oil. *Trans. IMM* 1973, C225—C228.

MARIACHER, B. C.: Preconcentration of primary uranium ores by flotation. *Min. Engng* 1956, 1006—1007.

MATHIEU, G. I.: Comparison of flotation column with conventional flotation for concentration of a molybdenum ore. *CIM Bull.* 1972 May, 41—45.

MAXWELL, J. R.: Large flotation cells in Opemiska concentrator. *Trans. AIME* 1972, 95—98.

MAYER, E. W.—H. SCHRANZ: *Flotation.* Verlag S. Hirzel, Leipzig 1931.

MCHARDY, J.—T. SALMAN: Some aspects of the surface chemistry of talc flotation. *Trans. IMM* 1974 March, C25—C29.

MELLGREN, O. (et al.): Thermochemical measurements in flotation research. 10. *IMPC*, London 1973, 21.

MELLGREN, O.—S. L. LWAKATARE: Desorption of xanthate ions from galena with sodium sulphide. *Trans. IMM* 1968, C101—C104.

MELLGREN, O.—H. L. SHERGOLD: Method for recovering ultrafine mineral particles by extraction with an organic phase. *Trans. IMM* 1966, C267—C268.

MELOY, T. P.: The treatment of fine particles during flotation. *Froth Flotation 50th Anniv. Volume,* 1962, 247—257.

MODI, H. J.—D. W. FUERSTENAU: Flotation of corundum — An electrochemical interpretation. *Trans. AIME* 1960, 381—387.

NEUNHOEFFER, O.: *Grundlagen der Schwimmaufbereitung.* Th. Steinkopf, Dresden und Leipzig 1948.

PANU, I. H.: Matematische Beziehungen für die Durchlaufflotation in Mehrzellenmaschinen. *AT* 1967, 465—469.

PAPIN, J. E.: Flotation of molybdenite at the Morenci concentrator. *Min. Engng* 1955, 145—147.

PETERSEN, W.: *Schwimmaufbereitung.* Verlag Th. Steinkopf, Dresden und Leipzig 1936.

PLAKSIN, I. N.: Interaction of minerals with gases and reagents in flotation. *Trans. AIME* 1959, 319—324.

PLAKSIN, I. N.: Study of superficial layers of flotation reagents on minerals and the influence of the structure of minerals on their interaction with reagents. *IMPC,* London 1960, 253—268.

PLAKSIN, I. N. (et al.): Microradiographic study of the action of flotation reagents. *Bull. IMM* 1957 Oct., 1—7.

PLAKSIN, I. N.—R. S. SHAFEYEV—V. A. CHANTURIA: Relation between energy structure of mineral crystals and their flotation properties. 8. *IMPC,* Leningrad 1968, S—3.

POPE, M. I.—D. I. SUTTON: Collector adsorption during froth flotation. *Powder Technology* 1972 Jan., 101—104.

PRASAD, M. S.—S. R. RAO: Studies on mixed collectors with special reference to xanthate-dixanthogen system. 9. *IMPC* 1970, 157—165.

PRÉDALI, J. J.: Flotation of carbonates with salts of fatty acids; role of pH and the alkyl chain. *Trans. IMM* 1969, C140—C147.

PRÉDALI, J. J.—J. M. CASES: Thermodynamics of the adsorption of collectors. 10. *IMPC,* London 1973, 33.

PROSSER, A. P.: Influence of mineralogical factors on the rates of chemical reaction of minerals. *Min. Proc. & Extr. Met. 9. CMMC,* London 1969, 59—79.

PROSSER, A. P.—J. R. D. KIWIA: Observations on the flotation of soluble salts. *Trans. IMM* 1969, C237—C238.

PUSCH, G.: Die selektive Flotation von Kupferkies und Bleiglanz unter Verwendung des kationaktiven Sammlers Tetracylpyridiniumbromid. *Bergakademie* 1965, 750—753.

RABONE, P.: *Flotation plant practice.* Min. Publ. Ltd., London 1957. (1st ed. in 1936.)

READ, A. D.—R. M. MANSER: Surface polarizability and flotation: study of the effect of cation type on the oleate flotation of three orthosilicates. *Trans. IMM* 1972, C69—C78.

RECK, W. H.—P. KIND: Neuere Entwicklungen der Wemco-Flotationzelle. *AT* 1969, 699—704.

ROGERS, J.: Flotation of soluble salts. *Bull. IMM* 1958 June, 439—452.

ROGERS, J.: Principles of sulphide mineral flotation. *Froth Flotation 50th Anniv. Volume* 1962, 139—169.

ROMAN, R. J.: Large flotation cells — Selection of the proper size and number. *Min. Congr. J.* 1970 June, 56—59.

ROMAN, R. J.—M. C. FUERSTENAU—D. C. SEIDEL: Mechanism of soluble salt flotation. Part I—II. *Trans. AIME* 1968, 56—64, 64—70.

Rozgai, S.: Ein Beitrag zur Untersuchung der Flotationskinetik. *AT* 1972, 226—231.

Samoilov, O. J.: *Struktur der wässrigen Elektrolytlösungen.* B. G. Teubner Verlagsgesellschaft, Leipzig 1961.

Schoefield, I. (et al.): The kinetic theory of surface films. *Proc. Roy. Soc.* 1925, 55—77; 1926, 167—177.

Schubert, H.: Zum gegenwärtigen Stand der Setztheorie. *Bergakademie* 1964, 748—755.

Schumann, R.: Flotation kinetics. I. Methods for steady-state study of flotation problems. *J. Phys. Chem.* 1942, 981—990.

Shirley, J. F. et al.: Recovery of molybdenite at Toquepala. *Min. Engng* 1967, Sept., 73—79.

Siebel, J.: Beitrag zur Flotation des Flußspates, ein Vergleich verschiedener Reagenten-Kombinationen. *Erzmetall* 1962, 303—309.

Siedler, Ph.—G. Sandstede—H. Frank: Über die Anhängigkeit der Flottierbarkeit von Mineralien vom Bedeckungsgrad ihrer Oberfläche mit Sammlerionen. *Erzmetall* 1962, 293—299.

Singewald, A.: Zum gegenwärtigen Stand der Erkenntnisse in der Salzflotation. *Chem. Ing. Techn.* 1961, 376—393, 558—572, 676—688.

Smani, M. S.—P. Blazy—J. M. Cases: Beneficiation of sedimentary Moroccan phosphate ores. *Trans. SME, AIME* 1975, 168—182.

Spurný, J.—R. Dobiaš: Der Einfluss des Zeta-Potentialwertes auf die Adhesion der Mineralteilchen zur Luftblase bei der Flotation. *3rd Int. Congr. Surface Activity*, Main 1960, 421—429.

Steiner, H. J.: Über die Anwendbarkeit der Flotationskinetik auf praktische Problemstellungen. 9. *IMPC*, Praha 1970, 209—213.

Steiner, H. J.: Kinetic aspects of the flotation behaviour of locked particles. 10. *IMPC*, London 1973, 37.

Stöhr, R.—E. von Szantho: Über den Einfluss der Rührerbauart auf den Flotationsprozess. *AT* 1974, 1—15.

Sun, S. C.: Hypothesis for different flotabilities of coals, carbons and hydrocarbon minerals. *Min. Engng* 1954, 67—75.

Sun, S. C.—L. Y. Tu—E. Ackerman: Mineral flotation with ultrasonically emulsified collecting reagents. *Min. Engng* 1966, 656—660.

Sutherland, K. L.—I. W. Wark: *Principles of flotation.* Austr. Inst. Min. & Met., Melbourne 1955.

Suwanasing, P.—T. Salman: Particle size in flotation studies. *Canad. Min. J.* 1970 Dec., 55—62.

Tarján, G.: A flotációs ásványszemek úszásának, szemnagyságának és határszögének elméleti vizsgálata. (Theoretical investigation into the floating, particle size and angle of contact of flotable mineral particles.) *Bányászati és Kohászati Lapok* 1947.

Tarján, G.: A Tatabányán kifejlesztett TA-celláról. (On the TA cell, developed at Tatabánya, Hungary.) *Műszaki és Közgazdasági Közlemények* 1971, 196—200.

Tomlinson, H. S.—M. G. Fleming: Flotation rate studies. 6. *IMPC*, Cannes 1963, 563—573.

Töpfer, E.—U. Bilsing: Selektive Schwerspatflotation bei hohen Schwerspatgehalten in der Aufgabe. *Freib. Fh. A314* 1964, 25—39.

Usul, A. H.—R. Tolun: Electrochemical study of the pyrite-oxygen-xanthate system. *Int. J. Min. Proc.* 1974, 135—140.

Van Lierde, A.: Effects of acrylate polymers on the sulphidization flotation of copper, lead and zinc oxide ores associated with a carbonate gangue. *Trans. IMM* 1972, C204—C212.

WARK, I. W.: *Principles of Flotation*. Austr. Inst. Min. Met., Melbourne 1955. (1st ed. in 1938.)

WIE, J. M.—D. W. FUERSTENAU: The effect of dextrin on surface properties and the flotation of molybdenite. *Int. J. Min. Proc.* 1974, 17—32.

WILCZINSKI, P.: Erfahrungen und Betriebsergebnisse mit einer neuen rührerlosen Flotationszelle. *Erzmetall* 1972, 108—111.

WOLF, K. L.: *Physik und Chemie der Grenzflächen. Bd. 1.* Springer Verlag, Berlin—Göttingen—Heidelberg 1957.

WOODCOCK, J. T.—M. H. JONES: Oxygen concentrations, redox potentials, xanthate residuals and other parameters in flotation plant pulps. *Min. Proc. & Extr. Met. 9. CMMC*, London 1969, 439—468.

ZLOKARNIK, M.: Ähnlichkeitstheoretische Kriterien zur Dimensionierung von Flotationszellen. *Erzmetall* 1973, 107—113.

YAZAN, A.—H. G. SCHÄFER: Untersuchungen über den Einfluss von Stärkearten auf die Flotation der Mineralien Flußspat, Schwerspat und Kalkspat mit Ölsäure, *Aachener Bl.* 1966 July, 1—69.

3. MAGNETIC SEPARATION

3.1. FUNDAMENTALS

3.1.1. Magnetic force, permeability, susceptibility. Magnetic force emanates from the north (N) and south (S) poles of a magnet: the forces residing in the two poles are equal. Like poles repel, unlike poles attract one another. The force of repulsion/attraction is expressed by the formula

$$P = \frac{km^2}{r^2},$$

where m denotes pole strength ("magnetic mass"), r is pole separation (distance between the poles), and k is a coefficient of proportionality. In the cgs system of units, P is in dynes; pole strength $m = r\sqrt{P}$ has dimension $cm^{3/2} g^{1/2} s$, and

$$k = 1/\mu,$$

where μ is the permeability of the medium.

The magnetic moment of a magnet of pole strength m whose poles are separated by a distance l is

$$M = ml.$$

Let a magnetic north pole of strength m_1 be situated in the proximity of such a magnet, as shown in Fig. 3.1. This pole is attracted by S with a force

$$P_S = \frac{kmm_1}{r_S^2}$$

and repelled by N with a force

$$P_N = \frac{kmm_1}{r_N^2}.$$

The resultant P of the two force vectors $P_N + P_S$ provides the direction and magnitude of the magnetic force acting in the point of space where m_1 is situated:

$$P = kmm_1 \left(\frac{1}{r_S^2} + \frac{1}{r_N^2} \right).$$

With $m_1 = 1$, P provides the field intensity (or "field" for short):

$$H = \frac{P}{m_1} = km \left(\frac{1}{r_S^2} + \frac{1}{r_N^2} \right).$$

In the SI units, the unit of field intensity is A/m, in connection with the fact that the field (or field intensity) in the interior of a solenoid of n turns and

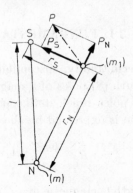

Fig. 3.1. Force vectors acting on a north pole of strength m_1 placed in the field of a magnet of moment ml

length l in which a current of i amperes (A) is passing is

$$H = \frac{ni}{l}.$$

In practice, field intensity is still often stated in oersteds (Oe):

$$1 \text{ Oe} = \frac{1,000}{4\pi} \text{ A/m} = 79.557 \text{ A/m}.$$

The dimension of field intensity in cgs units is $\text{cm}^{-1/2}\,\text{g}^{1/2}\,\text{s}^{-1}$.

The lines of force of the field are conceived as emerging from the north pole of the magnet and re-entering its south pole. In the magnet proper, they are envisaged as running from the south to the north pole. A magnet exerts some force on any body placed in its field. For a majority of materials, however, this force is very weak and can only be demonstrated by the most painstaking measurements. Materials fall into two large groups according as they are attracted or repelled by magnets. The former are called paramagnetic; the latter, diamagnetic. Paramagnetic substances concentrate magnetic lines of force into themselves: they are pushed by the magnetic field in the direction of higher field intensity. Diamagnetic materials on the other hand expel lines of force from themselves and are pushed by the field to where field intensity is less. The diamagnetic force is too weak to be useful in magnetic separation. The

338

paramagnetic force, on the other hand, is often strong enough to permit the separation in industrial practice of minerals different as to magnetic permeability.

If at a given point of a magnetic field, field intensity is H in air or water (more precisely, in a vacuum; air is very weakly paramagnetic, whereas water is very weakly diamagnetic), but B in some other material, then the material in question is endowed with a magnetic permeability

$$\mu = \frac{B}{H}.$$

B is termed flux density or magnetic induction: it is of the same dimension as field intensity H, whence μ is a dimensionless number. In the SI system of units, the induction constant (permeability) of vacuum is

$$\mu_0 = \frac{4\pi}{10^7} \frac{V\,s}{A\,m} = \frac{4\pi}{10^7} \frac{N}{A^2} = \frac{1.257}{10^6} \text{ henry/metre},$$

and the dimension of flux density

$$B = \mu_0 \mu H$$

is

$$V\,s/m^2 = \text{weber}/m^2 \ (Wb/m^2),$$

where

$$10^{-8}\,Wb = 1 \text{ maxwell (1 M)}.$$

In practice, flux density is still often stated in gauss units:

$$1 \text{ gauss} = 10^{-4}\,V\,s/m^2.$$

To one gauss of flux density belongs one oersted of field intensity:

$$H = \frac{1 \text{ gauss}}{\mu_0} = (10^{-4}\,V\,s/m^2) \left(\frac{10^7}{4\pi}\,A\,m/V\,s\right) = \frac{1,000}{4\pi}\,A/m,$$

whereas the flux density belonging to one A/m field intensity is

$$B = (4\pi \cdot 10^{-7}\,V\,s/A\,m) \cdot 1\,A/m = 4\pi \cdot 10^{-7}\,V\,s/m^2.$$

When placed in a magnetic field, a permeable-paramagnetic body is temporarily turned into a magnet of pole strength m' by the lines of force that it concentrates in itself. If the force-line pattern prevailing before the insertion of the paramagnetic body is subtracted from the one prevailing after it, the residue resembles the field of a bar magnet: its south pole is by definition where the lines of force enter and its north pole is where the lines of force emerge. The magnetic moment of the paramagnetic body so placed is

$$M' = m'l;$$

its magnetization (magnetic moment per unit of volume) is

$$I = \frac{M'}{V} = \frac{lm'}{Sl} = \frac{m'}{S},$$

where V is the volume of the body, S is its cross section and l is the separation of its poles (the equivalent length of the body). The dimension of magnetization I is likewise the same as that of field intensity: the ratio of the two,

$$\varkappa = \frac{I}{H}$$

as exemplified by the magnetic moment of a body of volume 1 cm³ at a field intensity of one Oe, is called the magnetic susceptibility, another dimensionless number. The relationship between magnetic permeability and susceptibility is

$$\mu = 1 + 4\pi\varkappa$$

or

$$\varkappa = \frac{\mu - 1}{4\pi}$$

in the cgs system and

$$\mu = 1 + \varkappa$$

or

$$\varkappa = \mu - 1$$

in the SI system. One has

$$I > 0, \ \varkappa > 0, \ \mu > 1$$

for paramagnetic bodies and

$$I < 0, \ \varkappa < 0, \ \mu < 1$$

for diamagnetic ones (as exemplified by bismuth, antimony, carbon, etc.)

In any magnetizable body placed in a field of intensity H, an "effective field"

$$H' = H - H_B$$

is generated, where

$$H_B = CI$$

is the "countervailing field", the body's own field, which acts against the external magnetizing field. C is a form coefficient. It is, in SI units, $C \simeq 1$ for a very thin disc ($l/\sqrt{S} \to 0$), $C \simeq 0$ for a very long rod ($l/\sqrt{S} \to \infty$) and $C \simeq 1/3$ for a sphere ($l/\sqrt{S} \simeq 1$). For the usual ore-particle shapes ($l/\sqrt{S}$ about 1.5 to 2), C tends to fall between 0.15 and 0.25. Furthermore, if

$l/\sqrt{S} =$	1	3	6	10, then
$C \simeq$	0.33	0.10	0.05	0.02 for an ellipsoid.

340

Table 3.1. Symbols, denominations and mutual transformation coefficients of magnetic units in the cgs and SI systems of units

Quantity	Symbol	cgs	SI	cgs → SI
Induction	B	Gauss	Weber/m² = tesla (T)	10^{-4}
Field intensity	H	Oersted	ampere-turn/m	$10^3/4\pi = 79.56$
Permeability	μ	Gauss/Oersted	henry/m	$4\pi \cdot 10^{-6} = 12.56 \cdot 10^{-6}$
Magnetic flux	Φ	Maxwell	Weber	10^{-8}
Magnetomotive force	MMF	Gilbert	ampere-turn	$10/4\pi = 79.56 \cdot 10^{-2}$
Reluctance	R	Gilbert/Maxwell	ampere-turn/Weber	$1/4\pi = 79.56 \cdot 10^{-3}$
Permanence	P	Maxwell/Gilbert	Weber/ampere-turn	$4\pi \cdot 10^{-9} = 12.56 \cdot 10^{-9}$
Susceptibility	$\varkappa$	$(\mu - 1)/4\pi$	$\mu - 1$	$4\pi = 12.56$
Mass suscepti- bility	χ	$\varkappa/\varrho$	$\varkappa/\varrho$	$4\pi = 12.56$

We also have   at $l/\sqrt{S} = 3$ $= 6$
for an ellipsoid, $C = 0.103$ 0.051
for a cylinder, $C = 0.086$ 0.037
for a prism of base 1×1, $C = 0.083$ 0.036
for a prism of base 1×4, $C = 0.075$ 0.032.

Volume susceptibility is

$$\varkappa_0 = \frac{I}{H}$$

for the "solid" and

$$\varkappa = \frac{I}{H'},$$

or the "body". The two are related by

$$\varkappa_0 = \frac{\varkappa}{1 + C\varkappa}.$$

For weakly magnetic materials, $\varkappa$ is small and

$$\varkappa_0 \cong \varkappa.$$

Specific susceptibility (susceptibility per unit mass) of a material is

$$\chi = \frac{\varkappa}{\varrho}.$$

Its dimension is the inverse of the dimension of density ϱ. Of the paramagnetic materials ($\chi > 0$), it is usual to consider non-magnetic those with

$$\chi \lessapprox 200 \cdot 10^{-6},$$

341

Table 3.2. Approximate specific susceptibilities χ cm³/g of some minerals (in cgs system)

Mineral	δ	$\sim\chi \cdot 10^6$
Sulphides		
Arsenopyrite	6.0	280—500
Galena	7.5	—4.5
Chalcopyrite	4.2	90—360
Marcasite	4.9	14
Pyrite	5.0	8—13
Pyrrhotite	4.6	$(2-10) \cdot 10^4$
Oxides		
Franklinite	5.15	$(6-70) \cdot 10^3$
Haematite	5.1	100—2,600
Ilmenite	4.75	$(1-10) \cdot 10^3$
Cassiterite	7.0	160
Corundum	4.0	500—900
Chrome spinel	4.45	700—1,700
Lepidocrocite	3.8	500—4,500
Limonite	3.8	65—650
Manganite	5.17	$(3-175) \cdot 10^5$
Maghemite	5.0	$(5-160) \cdot 10^4$
Magnetite	4.3	900—1,500
Pyrolusite	4.8	350
Psilomelane	4.2	800
Rutile	4.2	26
Carbonates		
Dolomite	2.85	4—16
Calcite	2.71	—4.6
Magnesite	3.05	8—46
Malachite	4.0	110
Rhodochrosite	3.5	1,400
Siderite	3.85	1,050—1,800
Sulphates, tungstates, phosphates		
Apatite	3.2	—3.1
Barite	4.5	0
Fluorspar	3.1	50
Monacite	5.1	150
Wolframite	7.4	400
Silicates		
Almandite	4.0	400—700
Andradite	3.85	1,050—2,300
Augite	3.3	500—1,000
Biotite	2.9	300—500

Table 3.2 (continued)

Mineral	δ	$\sim\chi \cdot 10^6$
Zircon	4.7	$-2-+9$
Phlogopite	2.8	800
Grossularite	3.3	150
Hornblende	3.2	$400-3{,}800$
Kaolinite	2.6	25
Chlorite	2.9	100
Quartz	2.65	-7.5
Muscovite	2.9	45
Olivine	3.3	3,800
Serpentine	3.3	$45-900$
Talc	2.7	40
Topaz	3.5	-5

weakly magnetic those with

$$\chi \sim 200 \text{ to } 7{,}500 \cdot 10^{-6},$$

medium-magnetic those with

$$\chi \sim 7{,}500 \text{ to } 38{,}000 \cdot 10^{-6},$$

and strongly magnetic or ferromagnetic those with

$$\chi \gtrsim 38{,}000 \cdot 10^{-6}.$$

(In the cgs system, the corresponding χ values (cm^3/g or m^3/t or dm^3/kg) are less by a factor of 4π). Ferromagnetic minerals include magnetite, $FeO \cdot Fe_2O_3$, maghemite, $\gamma\text{-}Fe_2O_3$, some ferrites, $RO\ Fe_2O_3$ [where R is a bivalent ion such as Mn, Ca, Mg — cf. e.g. franklinite, $(Zn, Fe, Mn)O \cdot (Fe, Mn)_2O_3$, ilmenite, $FeO \cdot TiO_2$, chromite, $FeO \cdot Cr_2O_3$, pyrrhotite, $Fe_{11}S_{12}$]. Ferromagnetic metals include iron, nickel, cobalt and many of their alloys and compounds (Derkatsch 1960; Grimsehl 1961; Schubert 1967).

For the separation of strongly magnetic minerals, a field intensity of

$$H \lesssim 1500 \text{ Oe } (\simeq 1200 \text{ A/cm})$$

should be sufficient: medium-magnetic ones tend to require 3,000 to 6,000 Oe: weakly magnetic ones require 6,000 to 25,000 Oe (about 4,800 to 20,000 A/cm).

Informative-approximative specific susceptibilities of some minerals are presented in Table 3.2: volume susceptibilities of some pure materials are listed in Table 3.3; both refer to room temperature. Diamagnetics include coal and the sulphates of Ca, Al and Mg (with specific susceptibilities of about $-4 \cdot 10^{-6}$ to $-7 \cdot 10^{-6}$ SI units); paramagnetics include iron sulphates ($\chi \simeq 500 \cdot 10^{-6}$ to $900 \cdot 10^{-6}$) shale ($\chi \simeq 400 \cdot 10^{-6}$ to $500 \cdot 10^{-6}$), clay and sandstone ($\chi \simeq 200 \cdot 10^{-6}$ to $300 \cdot 10^{-6}$).

A	—19.6	$Cu(OH)_2$	+1,170
Ag	—19.5	CuS	—2.0
AgCl	—49	$CuSO_4$	+1,330
$AgNO_3$	—45.7	$CuSO_4 \cdot 5H_2O$	+1,460
Al	+16.5	Fe	ferrous
Al_2O_3	—37	$FeCl_3$	+13,450
$Al(SO_4)_3$	—93	$FeCO_3$	+11,300
As	—23	FeO	+7,200
As_2S_3	—70	FeS	+1,074
Au	—28	$FeSO_4$	+10,200
$AuCl_3$	—112	$FeSO_4 \cdot 7H_2O$	+11,200
B	—6.7	H_2	—3.98
Ba	+20.6	HCl	—22.6
$BaCO_3$	—58.9	HF	—9.3
$BaSO_4$	—71.3	H_2O	—12.97
Be	—9	HNO_3	—19.9
BeO	—11.9	H_3PO_4	—43
$BeSO_4$	—37	H_2S	—25.5
Bi	—280.1	H_2SO_4	—39.8
Bi_2S_3	—123	Hg	—33.44
Br_2	—56.4	HgCl	—52
C	—6	$HgCl_2$	—82
CO_2	—21	$HgCrO_4$	—12.5
Ca	+40	Hg_2CrO_4	—63
CaF_2	—28	$Hg_2(OH)_2$	—100
$CaCO_3$	—38.2	HgS	—55.4
CaO	—15	Hg_2SO_4	—123
$Ca(OH)_2$	—22	J	—88.7
$CaSO_4$	—49.7	K	+20.8
$CaSO_4 \cdot 2H_2O$	—74	KBr	—49.1
Cd	—19.8	KCl	—39
$CdCO_3$	—46.7	Mg	+13.1
CdS	—50	$MgCl_2$	—47.4
$CdSO_4$	—59.2	$MgCO_3$	—32.4
Ce	+2,450	MgO	—10.2
CeO_2	+26	Mg(OH)	—22.1
Ce_2S_3	+5,080	$MgSO_4$	—50
$CeSO_4$	+37	$MgSO_4 \cdot 7H_2O$	—135.7
Cl_2	—40.5	Mn	+529
Cr	+180	$MnCO_3$	+11,400
Cr_2O_3	+1,960	MnO_2	+2,280
$Cr_2(SO_4)_3$	+11,800	Mn_2O_3	+14,100
Cu	—5.46	$Mn(OH)_2$	+13,500
CuO_1	—40	MnS	+5,630
$CuON_2$	+1,080	$MnSO_4$	+13,660
CuCN	—24	$MnSO_4 \cdot 5H_2O$	+14,700
Cu_2O	—20	Mo	+89

Table 3.3 (continued)

N_2	−12		$SrSO_4$	− 57.9
NH_3	−17		Ta	+154
NH_4Cl	−36.7		Te	− 39.5
NH_4OH	−31.5		$TeCl_2$	− 94
Ni	ferrous		Th	+132
K_2CO_3	−59		Ti	+153
$K_2Cr_2O_7$	+29.4		$TiCl_3$	+1,110
$K_2Fe(CN)_6$	+2,290		$TiCl_4$	−54
$K_4Fe(CN)_6$	−130		TiO_2	+5.9
$KMnO_4$	+20		Ti_2O_3	+125
KNO_3	−33.7		Tl	− 50.9
K_2SO_4	−67		Tl_2O_3	+76
Li	+14.2		$TlCl_2$	57.8
NiS	+190		U	+409
$NiSO_4$	+4,005		UCl_4	+3,680
O_2	+3,449		UO_2	+2,360
Os	+9.9		UO_3	+128
P	−20.8		$U(SO_4)_2$	+31
Pd	+567.4		V	+255
Pt	+201.9		W	+59
$PtCl_4$	−93		WO_2	+57
S	−15		WO_3	−15.8
Se	−25		Zn	−11.4
Sn	+3.1		$ZnCl_2$	−65
$SnCl_2$	−69		$ZnCO_3$	−34
SnO	−19		$Zn(OH)_2$	−67
SnO_2	−41		$ZnSO_4$	−45
Sr	+92		$ZnSO_4 \cdot 7H_2O$	−143
$SrCO_3$	−47		ZnS	−25
SrO_2	−32.3		Zr	+122
Sr(OH)	−40		ZrO_2	−13.8

The magnetic susceptibility of pyrite and of the other coal contaminants with a s. g. higher than about 2.8 tends to increase even on gentle heating in an oxidizing atmosphere, as illustrated by the figures in Table 3.2. In the case referred to, both pyrite and ash could after gentle heating be removed successfully from the coal by means of a high-intensity magnetic separator. Performance on a minus-2 mm coal with and without thermal pre-treatment is presented in Table 3.4 (Monostory 1974).

It is to be pointed out in connection with Table 3.1 that χ (or $\varkappa$ or μ) is no material constant in minerals: it is greatly influenced by mechanical impurities adhering to the grain and even more so by alien substances dissolved in the lattice. For example, in the case of sphalerite–marmatite, susceptibility increases as the isomorphic Fe content of the zinc sulphide:

$$Fe = 0.8 \quad 4.5 \quad 12 \quad 15\%$$
$$\varkappa \cong 37 \quad 400 \quad 650 \quad 2,800 \cdot 10^{-6},$$

whereas $\varkappa = -25 \cdot 10^{-6}$ for pure ZnS. Grain size and the size of the crystalloids making up the grains also play a role, and so does the intensity of the field in which $\varkappa$ or μ is being determined. In ferromagnetic materials, any change of field intensity induces a marked change of permeability. In such materials, flux density B as a function of field intensity H varies as shown in Part A of Fig. 3.2. ($\mu = B/H$ is the slope of the line connecting the point of the B curve at abscissa H with the origin.)

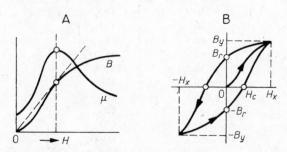

Fig. 3.2. A — Permeability μ and flux density (induction) B vs. field intensity H in a ferromagnetic substance. B — Hysteresis loop showing remanence B_r and coercive force H_c

Table 3.4. Removal of pyrite and ash by magnetic separation, with and without preheating

	$v\%$	Without preheating				With preheating			
		60	70	80	100	60	70	80	100
Pyrite	$c\%$	2.1	2.2	3.1	4.0	0.4	0.5	1.1	4.0
	$b\%$	7.1	8.2	7.1	?	9.4	12.1	15.6	?
	$m\%$	32	38	62	100	6	9	22	100
Ash	$c\%$	10	11	15	26	11	13	17	30
	$b\%$	50	61	70	81	68	75	77	82
	$m\%$	23	30	46	100	22	30	45	100

As field intensity is increased from 0 to H_x, flux density B in a ferromagnetic substance (cf. Part B of Fig. 3.2) increases from 0 to B_y. On switching off the fields, B does not return to zero along this "virgin curve": a remanence (remanent induction, retentivity) B_r is left behind, which can be eliminated only by applying a coercive force $-H_c$ opposed to the original field. On repeatedly varying the field from $+H_x$ to $-H_x$ and back again, a closed induction curve can be plotted; it is called the hysteresis loop of the substance. The loss on hysteresis, the energy converted into heat while the ferromagnetic material is taken through a single cycle of magnetization, is proportional to the area enclosed by the loop. Ferromagnetic materials differ greatly as to remanence and coercivity (coercive force). For example, natural magnetites tend to have a weak coercive force but a strong remanence, whereas the magnetites formed by the roasting of other iron minerals (siderite, haematite, goethite, pyrite, etc.) have a remanence in the same range as the natural magnetites but also a strong coercive force. (The coercive force varies as the specific surface, all other things being equal.)

A particle placed into a homogeneous magnetic field is exposed to a pure torque, whereas in an inhomogeneous field a translating ("tractive") force will also act upon it.

If the intensity of an inhomogeneous field varies in space as dH/dr, with grad H denoting the spatial rate of change in the direction in which it is greatest, then the mechanical force acting upon the particle is

$$P = \mu_0 \left(\frac{\varkappa}{1 + C\varkappa} - \varkappa_m \right) VH \text{ grad } H,$$

where

$$\mu_0 = 4\pi \cdot 10^{-7} \text{ V s/A m}$$

is the constant of induction, $\varkappa$ and $\varkappa_m$ are the volume susceptibility of the mineral and of the medium, respectively, V is the volume of the grain, H is field intensity with the mineral grain removed, and C is a form factor which is in the 0.15 to 0.25 (SI) range for most mineral grains. The P formula stated above is valid whenever H grad H may be considered constant within the particle (i.e. whenever the particle is small enough). If

$$\varkappa_m \to 0$$

and the grains are weakly paramagnetic:

$$1 + C\varkappa \to 1,$$

then the formula simplifies to

$$P = \mu_0 \varkappa VH \text{ grad } H$$

(at 20 °C, $\varkappa_m$ equals $0.36 \cdot 10^{-6}$ for air and $-13 \cdot 10^{-6}$ for water). The formula furnishes P in newtons (N) if V is in m³ and H in A/m and grad H are in A/m²; the formula

$$P = 10^{-1} \mu_0 \varkappa VH \text{ grad } H$$

furnishes P in dynes if V is in cm³ and μ_0, H and grad H are as above.

If $\varkappa$ is great enough, then

$$\frac{\varkappa}{1 + C\varkappa} - \varkappa_m \cong \frac{1}{C}$$

347

and

$$P = 10^{-1} \left[\frac{\mu_0}{C}\right] V H \text{ grad } H \text{ dynes.}$$

That is, for strongly magnetic substances — such as magnetite or maghemite among the minerals — magnetic attraction is a function of C, V and H grad H only and is practically independent of susceptibility $\varkappa$.

The specific magnetic force acting upon one gram of the particle,

$$p = \frac{\mu_0 \varkappa V H \text{ grad } H}{V \varrho} = \mu_0 \varkappa H \text{ grad } H,$$

is of dimension acceleration. The magnetic force referred to $\chi = 1$ cm³/g specific susceptibility is specific magnetic field intensity

$$p' = \mu_0 H \text{ grad } H \text{ N/m}^3.$$

(A p' value greater by a factor of 10 is obtained on using Oe²/cm or dyne/cm³ units.)

If the magnetic force has to overcome gravity only, it must satisfy the condition

$$p \geq g.$$

Taking e.g. a particle of specific susceptibility

$$\chi = 200 \cdot 10^{-6} \text{ cm}^3/g$$

the specific field intensity satisfying this condition is

$$p' \geq \mu_0 H \text{ grad } H \geq \frac{10g}{\chi} = \frac{10 \cdot 981}{200 \cdot 10^{-6}} \simeq 50 \cdot 10^6 \text{ Oe}^2/\text{cm} \text{ or } \text{dynes/m}^3,$$

implying that a great H and a great grad H are required; grad H, of course, is itself a function of H. For example, if

$$\frac{\text{grad } H}{H} = \qquad \frac{1}{2} \qquad \frac{1}{4} \qquad \frac{1}{8}$$
$$\text{then} \qquad 10{,}000 \quad 14{,}000 \quad 20{,}000 \text{ Oe}$$

(or higher) is the average field intensity that must prevail in the air gap where separation takes place. At $\chi = 38{,}000 \cdot 10^{-6}$,

$$p' \simeq 26 \cdot 10^4 \text{ Oe}^2/\text{cm},$$

and if, say,

$$\frac{\text{grad } H}{H} = \frac{1}{2}.$$

then the condition $p = g$ is satisfied by an average field intensity of about 720 Oe; if p is to exceed g, p' must be that much greater. Low-intensity industrial separators used to handle strongly magnetic minerals tend to operate in the vicinity of

$$p' \lesssim 2 \cdot 10^4 \text{ to } 6 \cdot 10^4 \text{ dynes/cm}^3$$

or

$$H < 800 \text{ to } 1{,}600 \text{ Oe} \simeq 650 \text{ to } 1{,}300 \text{ A/cm}.$$

High-intensity separators used to handle weakly magnetic materials tend to operate at

$$p' \simeq 1.6 \cdot 10^6 \text{ to } 10^7 \text{ dynes/cm}^3$$

and

$$H = 6{,}000\text{--}25{,}000 \text{ Oe} \simeq 4{,}800\text{--}20{,}000 \text{ A/cm};$$

they will serve in the 10 mm to 20 μm particle size range.

3.1.2. Field inhomogeneity. A great enough inhomogeneity (a strong enough gradient grad H) is ensured by appropriate pole piece design. The comparatively weak fields of 800 to 1,600 Oe used in the separation of strongly magnetic materials are usually generated by open multipole systems, with poles of alternating polarity in a planar or arcuate arrangement (Fig. 3.3). Figure 3.4 illustrates the variation of field intensity (in Oe or gauss) and of

$$p' = \mu_0 H \text{ grad } H \text{ Oe}^2/\text{cm}$$

vs. distance r from the pole. Fields of 6,000 to 25,000 Oe suited for the separation of weakly magnetic materials are generated by means of opposed poles forming closed line-of-force patterns. These arrangements include flat or shallow-groove pole pieces faced by one or several wedge-shaped ones, or deeply grooved soft iron pole pieces or pole pieces made up of soft iron lamellae alternating with diamagnetic ones. Such arrangements pinch the lines of force (make them converge). Some of the basic types are shown in Fig. 3.5.

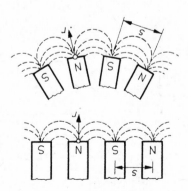

Fig. 3.3. Low-intensity "open", plane or arcuate multipole arrangements

In the pole arrangement according to Fig. 3.3 field intensity as a function of distance r from the pole varies as

$$H_r = H_0 \, e^{-r \, dH/dr},$$

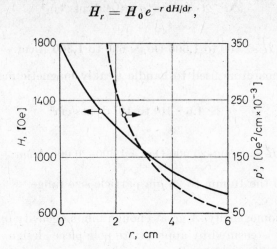

Fig. 3.4. H Oe and p' Oe²/cm vs. separation from the pole(s), r cm

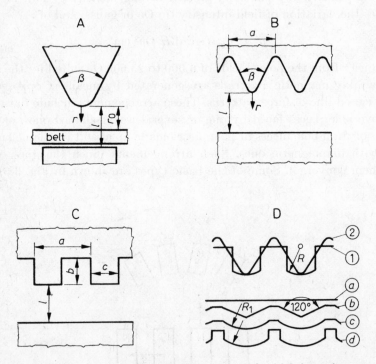

Fig. 3.5. A, B, C, D — some basic pole-piece designs for high-intensity systems with closed line-of-force patterns

where H_0 is field intensity next to the pole. At a fair estimate,

$$\mathrm{d}H/\mathrm{d}r \; (= \operatorname{grad} H) \simeq \frac{\pi}{s},$$

where s is the distance between poles of alternate polarity. It is best to have

$$s \geq \pi(x_{\max} + 2r_0),$$

where $x_{\max}$ is the maximum grain size to be handled and r_0 is the separation of the particle stream from the poles.

In the pole arrangement according to Part A of Fig. 3.5 (a flat pole piece facing a single wedge-shaped one), the field is inhomogeneous everywhere in the space between the pole pieces. The separation of the feed stream (which is carried e.g. on a belt) from the apex of the wedge-shaped pole piece should be

$$r_0 \geq 2x_{\max} - 0.5x_{\min}.$$

In a multi-apex arrangement (as in Parts B and C of Fig. 3.5), the field is practically smooth already at a distance $r \simeq a/2$: hence, the ore to be separated is to be passed through the field as close to the wedge-shaped or grooved pole pieces as possible.

Figure 3.6 is a plot of field intensity H Oe vs. distance r and of p' Oe²/cm vs. distance r_0 from the pole apices, for the pole arrangement in Part B of Fig. 3.5, for a given number of ampere-turns and a given pole spacing. Pole spacing a should be

$$a \geq 4r_0 \simeq 6x_{\max} - 2x_{\min}$$

for a bottom-feed (pick-up type) and

$$a \geq 4r_0 \simeq 2x_{\max} - 2x_{\min}$$

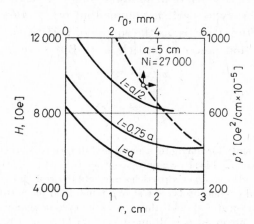

Fig. 3.6. H and p' vs. r for the pole-piece design in Part B of Fig. 3.5

351

for a top-feed (holding-type) arrangement.* In other words, as $x_{min} \to 0$, one may choose

$$a \geq 4r_0 \cong 6x_{max},$$

that is,

$$r_0 \cong 1.5x_{max}$$

for bottom-feed (pick-up type) separators and

$$a \cong 4r_0 \cong 2x_{max},$$

that is,

$$r_0 \cong 0.5x_{max}$$

for top-feed (holding-type) separators.

Part D of Fig. 3.5 shows various combinations of grooved pole pieces with a radius of curvature R (denoted 1) and wedge-shaped ones (denoted 2) on the one hand and of plane pole pieces (denoted a), flat ribbing with a 120° aperture angle (denoted b), and grooved pole pieces (denoted c and d) with a radius of curvature R_1, on the other. Field intensity distribution is different for each combination. The zones where field intensity exceeds a given p' (e.g. $300 \cdot 10^5$ Oe^2/cm) for a given ampere-turn excitation of the electromagnet are shown in Fig. 3.7 for various pole piece combinations (1-a, 2-a and 1-d). By changing pole piece configuration, then, both the magnitude and the pinch of the magnetic field can be changed quite substantially (Derkatsch 1960).

The magnetic attraction exerted upon a particle equals the product of specific magnetic force

$$p = \chi p' = \mu_0 \chi H \text{ grad } H$$

and particle mass. Now mass at a given s.g. varies as volume, that is, as the third power of particle size. Magnetic attraction is opposed by a variety of external forces including gravity, the momentum of the particle (its mass into its velocity), inter-particle friction, adhesive forces, fluid resistance, etc. Some of these forces also vary as particle volume, but others vary as the particle's surface or cross section (that is, as the square of particle size) or indeed as its circumference (the first power of particle size). But since

$$x > x^2 > x^3$$

for small particles and

$$x < x^2 < x^3$$

* Feeding arrangements for magnetic separators fall into two broad types. In the top-feed or holding type, the feed is strewn onto a surface backed by a strong magnetic pinch field which holds on to the magnetic particles and lets the rest slide or roll or be washed off; in the bottom-feed or pick-up type, a strong pinch field picks the magnetic particles out of a feed stream below it and holds them fast against a moving or stationary collector surface by which they are eventually dropped as the field is cut or weakened in one way or another.

352

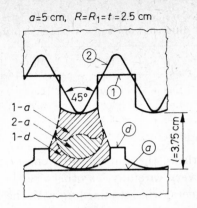

$a = 5$ cm, $R = R_1 = t = 2.5$ cm

Fig. 3.7. Domains where $p' = \mu_0 H$ grad H exceeds $30 \cdot 10^6$ Oe²/cm for three pole-piece combinations as shown in Part D of Fig. 3.5

for large ones, the strength of the magnetic forces relative to the mechanical ones tends to be different for different particle sizes, with the magnetic force gaining the upper hand as particle size increases. Moreover, the distance of a particle's centre of gravity from the pole as it passes through a magnetic field is also a function of its size. Hence, the magnetic force p' perceived in the field will also differ from one particle to the next.

All this implies that the successful separation of weakly magnetic minerals may require the close sizing of the feed beforehand; performance on fine feeds (minus-0.5 mm, say) may, however, be unsatisfactory nevertheless (a large percentage of the magnetic particles may get misrouted into the tailing fraction).

For a pole piece arrangement as shown in Part B of Fig. 3.5 and pick-up type feeding of plus-0.1, minus-3 mm ore, the p' and H_0 values calculated for different specific susceptibilities χ on the assumption of a specific magnetic-force condition

$$p = 1{,}200 \text{ dynes/gram}$$

are given in Table 3.5. The particles of 3 and 0.1 mm size are seen to differ rather widely in H_0 over the specific susceptibility ranges from $7{,}500 \cdot 10^{-6}$ to $1{,}200 \cdot 10^{-6}$ cm³/g and from $1{,}200 \cdot 10^6$ to $400 \cdot 10^{-6}$ cm³/g: such particles separate easily and well. On the other hand, for the specific susceptibility ranges (in 10^{-6} cm³/g)

| 1,200 to 600 | 600 to 400 | 400 to 200 |

the H_0 differential (in 10^3 Oe) between small and large grains is fairly small at

| 5.12 to 5.70 | 7.24 to 7.76 | 9.85 to 9.90; |

Table 3.5. Connection between p' and H_0 at a specific magnetic force $p = 1,200$ dynes per gram, at different values of specific susceptibilities, χ

$\chi \cdot 10^6$ cm³/g (SI)	7,500	1,200	600	400	200
$p' \cdot 10^{-6}$ Oe²/cm	1.6	1.0	2.0	30	60
$H_0 \cdot 10^{-3}$ Oe $\begin{cases}3 \text{ mm} \\ 0.1 \text{ mm}\end{cases}$	1.62 2.05	4.03 5.12	5.70 7.24	7.76 8.85	9.90 12.53

that is, in separating them, the ampere-turns on the electromagnet must be selected and adjusted very carefully, as otherwise the 3-mm particles of the lower-susceptibility mineral will get mixed up with the 0.1-mm particles of the higher-susceptibility mineral (either in the concentrate or in the tailings).

In a top-feed (holding-type) operation, if the feed stream is just one particle deep, the situation is reversed: it is the centres of gravity of the smaller particles that pass closer by the poles; that is, it is these that experience a stronger magnetic field p'. In this case, attractive force per unit of volume,

$$p = \chi p',$$

will be the greater, the smaller the particle, all other conditions being equal. For example, in an open-field drum separator with a pole piece arrangement as in Fig. 3.3 (top), the specific attractive force p dyne/gram acting on a unit weight of magnetite and on intergrown grains of different Fe contents was found to vary vs. particle size (p vs. x if Fe = const.) as shown in Fig. 3.8. For grains

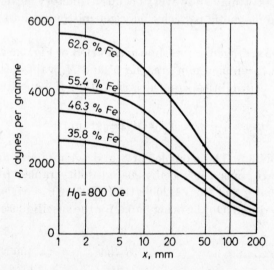

Fig. 3.8. Specific magnetic force p vs. grain size x in a drum separator of field intensity $H_0 = 800$ Oe handling magnetite intergrown with impurities, with the percentage Fe content of the particles as the parameter

different as to particle size but identical as to specific susceptibility (iron content), specific magnetic attraction p can be made near-uniform in a top-feed separator if the finer grains are layered onto the coarser ones. (If the magnetic separator is the drive pulley of an endless belt, then such an arrangement of the particles on the belt can be achieved simply enough, by using a feed chute down which the feed stream slides opposite to the direction of belt motion: falling further, the coarser grains constitute the bottom layer on the belt. Using such a feed arrangement, the Fe content of the concentrate could be increased by 8% [from 50 to 58%] and its Fe recovery by 20% against a random-distribution feed on handling a minus-6 mm magnetite ore.)

In separating paramagnetic minerals of high susceptibility or, indeed, ferromagnetic minerals from weakly magnetic or non-magnetic ones, it is not as a rule necessary to close-size the feed prior to separation, as the difference in magnetic attraction between the two groups will be greater by several orders of magnitude than the difference in the countervailing mechanical forces.

In such a setup, the separation of finer grains will be hampered more by the tendency of such grains to aggregate (clot) under the influence of their mutual (induced) magnetic attraction, and by the risk that the clots so formed will entrap waste grains also. Clots of paramagnetic minerals whose remanence is very small will of course fall apart quite readily after leaving the field, — so that their cleaning separation in a second device may yield a satisfactory product, — but clots of ferromagnetic grains which do possess a remanence must be demagnetized prior to such cleaning separation.

The separation of strongly magnetic minerals prone to clotting is usually performed in a device with an open arrangement of alternating poles. This makes the magnetic grains and clots tilt and spin on successive reversals of polarity, a process that creates numerous opportunities for the rearrangement of the clots and for the shaking-out of the non-magnetic particles entrapped in them. It is indicated to use alternating poles especially in the separation of minerals weak in coercive force. (With minerals of strong coercivity, this method may turn out to be less than economical because the repolarization of the particles whose turning into the field is blocked results in a hysteresis loss which translates into a greater power consumption.)

In a coarse-grained, well-sized feed, no waste grains will be entrapped, partly because in that case the feed stream tends to be one or two particles deep at most and partly because coarse grains will not clot up tightly enough to prevent the odd heavy non-magnetic particle from dropping out.

In a wet separator — where fluid friction is relatively strong — the magnetic particles are slower to move towards the pinch in the field: accordingly, the likelihood of non-magnetic grains being entangled in a magnetic clot is less than in a dry separator. (Magnetic clotting may incidentally be put to good use in the concentration of fine-grained ferromagnetic slurries: the clots of high susceptibility can be separated from the non-clotting low-susceptibility grains e.g. in a wet classifier.)

The retention time of the feed stream in the field is very short, often a fraction of a second only, with field intensity varying all the time. The routing of a particle into the concentrate or tailing fraction is greatly influenced, in addition to the magnetic attraction to which it is exposed, also by its own mechan-

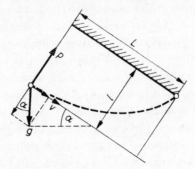

Fig. 3.9. Trajectory (dotted curve) of a particle arriving in a magnetic field of specific force p at an angle of incidence α

ical momentum: from a slower-moving stream, more particles of lower susceptibility will be routed into the concentrate.

If, in terms of the notation of Fig. 3.9, a particle entering a field of length L at a distance l from the pole piece, at a velocity v that includes an angle α with the horizontal, then the average specific magnetic force intensity acting upon it will be

$$p = \mu_0 \chi H \operatorname{grad} H.$$

For the case that magnetic attraction lifts the particle exactly by l over a travel L taking a time t, one may write up

$$l = \frac{p - g \cos \alpha}{2} t^2$$

and

$$L = \frac{gt^2}{2} \sin \alpha + vt;$$

the two yield the relationship

$$p \geq g \cos \alpha + \frac{l}{L^2} [v^2 + Lg \sin \alpha + v \sqrt{v^2 + 2Lg \sin \alpha}].$$

For example, the magnetic force required to route the grain into the concentrate is furnished by

$$p \geq g + \frac{2lv^2}{L^2}$$

356

for $\alpha = 0°$ and by

$$p \geq \frac{lg}{L}$$

for $a = 90°$ and $v = 0$ (Derkatsch 1960).

In a drum separator of radius R and peripheral velocity v, the grains are exposed in addition to the gravity force g and the specific magnetic force p also to a centrifugal acceleration v^2/R. Figure 3.10 shows that — if the coefficient of friction

$$f = \tan \varrho$$

is great so that the particle does not slip on the drum surface — the condition

$$S \geq g \sin \alpha$$

holds, where

$$S = \left(p - \frac{v^2}{R} + g \cos \alpha \right) f$$

is friction. Hence

$$p = \mu_0 \chi H \operatorname{grad} H \geq \frac{v^2}{R} - g \cos \alpha + \frac{g \sin \alpha}{\tan \varrho} = \frac{v^2}{R} + \frac{g \sin (a - \varrho)}{\sin \varrho} .$$

The maximum of p is furnished by the condition

$$\frac{dp}{d\alpha} = 0;$$

it is found to occur at

$$\alpha_{\text{crit}} = 90° + \varrho,$$

where

$$p_{\text{max}} \geq \frac{v^2}{R} + \frac{g}{\sin \varrho} ,$$

or

$$v \leq \sqrt{R \left(p_{\text{max}} - \frac{g}{\sin \varrho} \right)} .$$

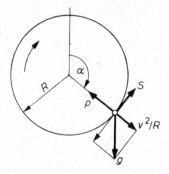

Fig. 3.10. Forces acting on a particle pinned to a rotating magnetized drum

If $\alpha = 90°$, then

$$p \geq \frac{v^2}{R} + \frac{g}{\tan \varrho},$$

or

$$v \leq \sqrt{R \left(p_{90°} - \frac{g}{\tan \varrho} \right)}.$$

The specific magnetic force p needed to pin a particle to a drum of radius $R = 10$ cm at different peripheral velocities and angles of friction ϱ vs. angular position $\alpha°$ on the drum shell is plotted in Fig. 3.11. The force is seen to rise steeply as the angle increases from zero to between 110 and 120°, to attain 2 to 5 times the acceleration of gravity, $g = 981$ cm/s²; it decreases beyond that angle. The figure (and the formulae) further reveal that the higher the friction coefficient, the less of a magnetic force is required to pin the magnetized particles to the drum. The drum shell should accordingly be somewhat rough rather than quite smooth.

The specific susceptibility χ of weakly magnetic minerals being low, pinning those to the drum requires a very strong field. For example, if $\chi \leq 1{,}000 \cdot 10^{-6}$ cm³/g, then even $p \simeq g \simeq 1{,}000$ dynes/gram requires a

$$p' \geq 10^7 \text{ Oe}^2/\text{cm},$$

and if p is to exceed g by a factor of two to five, field intensity also must be multiplied by 2 to 5 ! It is no simple task to generate such a field, especially an

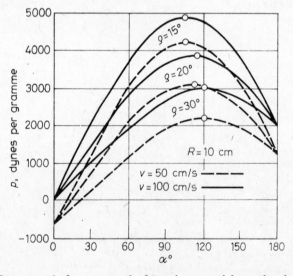

Fig. 3.11. Specific magnetic force p required to pin a particle to the shell of a drum vs. position angle α on the shell, for a drum of radius $R = 10$ cm rotating at peripheral velocity v, at friction angles $\varrho = 15°$, 20° and 30° (friction coefficients $f = 0.27$, 0.36 and 0.58)

extensive one. This is why it is best to carry out the entire separation near the top of the drum (at $\alpha \leq 45°$), where less of a field is required than in the bottom part of the drum (at $\alpha \geq 90°$). Induced-roll separators used to separate weakly magnetic minerals should therefore have pole pieces shaped according to the full rather than the dashed line in Fig. 3.12. In drum separators used to separate strongly magnetic minerals with a high χ, on the other hand, the magnetic field is often directed at the bottom part of the drum because even the higher p

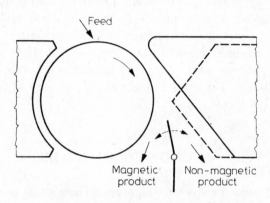

Fig. 3.12. Pole-piece design for induced-roll separators

required there is easily provided by a comparatively weak magnetic field. (For example, at or above $\chi = 50,000 \cdot 10^{-6}$ cm^3/g, the p' belonging to $p \simeq g \simeq$ $\simeq 1,000$ cm/s^2 is

$$p' \leq 2 \cdot 10^5 \text{ Oe}^2/\text{cm.})$$

It is usual to energize magnetic separators with d.c., although a.c.-excited electromagnets can also be used to separate certain ferromagnetic minerals. Instead of electromagnets, permanent magnets made of special alloys have become increasingly popular recently. Alloys appropriate for the purpose include alni (Al—Ni) and alnico (Al—Ni—Co[—Cu]), silmanal (Ag—Mn—Al), sendust (Fe—Si—Al), barium ferrite, $BaO \cdot 6Fe_2O_3$ and other ferrites (on a Mn—Zn or Ni—Zn base among others). The general ferrite formula is

$$RO \cdot Fe_2O_3,$$

where R is a divalent metal, Ni, Mg, Mn, Cu, Fe, Zn or Cd (Baran 1973). One great advantage of permanent magnets is that they consume no power; no d.c. supply has to be provided and power failures will not cut off the field. This is particularly welcome in the reconditioning of magnetic dense media (magnetite or FeSi), where a power failure in the electromagnets' circuit may result in a loss of medium solid (Derkatsch 1960; Schubert 1967; Sheahan 1958).

3.1.3. Magnetohydrostatic separation.

An attractive force directed towards the convergence of the lines of force acts upon a paramagnetic or ferromagnetic fluid placed into a magnetic field. If the field vector, H grad H, is collinear with the gravity field vector, then the fluid perceives per unit of volume a total force

$$F = \gamma + \chi H \text{ grad } H.$$

H, grad H and χ may be changed by changing the excitation of the electromagnet, pole design and/or the concentration of the magnetic fluid. The fluid used in this process of magnetohydrostatic separation may be e.g. $FeCl_3$ or $MnSO_4$ or $MnCl_2$ or a ferromagnetic colloid (a "ferrofluid"). Magnetic fluids giving rise to very strong forces can be prepared using the aqueous solutions of the rare earths (Er, Tb, Dy, Ho, etc.). The equivalent density of the medium may attain even 10 or 20 g/cm^2.

3.2. ROASTING TO MAGNETIZE

Certain non-magnetic or weakly magnetic minerals can be turned strongly magnetic by roasting (heat treatment) under carefully controlled conditions. Magnetizing roasting affects the chemical composition and crystalline structure of the minerals: it is therefore more of a metallurgical than a straightforward mineral-processing operation.

Roasting weakly magnetic iron oxides in a reducing atmosphere may transform them into a ferrous-ferric oxide ($Fe_3O_4 = FeO \cdot Fe_2O_3$, an artificial magnetite) or into a ferromagnetic iron oxide ($\gamma - Fe_2O_3$, maghemite).

Reactions between iron oxides e.g. in a $CO - CO_2$ gas mixture (with no solid C present) may include the following:

$$3Fe_2O_3 + CO \rightleftarrows 2Fe_3O_4 + CO_2 + 25.1 \text{ kJ}$$

$$Fe_3O_4 + CO \rightleftarrows 3FeO + CO_2 + 26.4 \text{ kJ}$$

$$FeO + CO \rightleftarrows Fe + CO_2 + 14.2 \text{ kJ}$$

$$Fe_3O_4 + 4CO \rightleftarrows 3Fe + 4CO_2 + 16.5 \text{ kJ}.$$

The direction in which the reaction actually proceeds is determined by the temperature and by the CO/CO_2 ratio in the gas. Part A of Fig. 3.13 presents equilibrium diagrams, with full lines for a CO/CO_2 atmosphere and with dashed lines for a H_2/H_2O atmosphere. The diagrams divide up space into areas in which metallic iron (Fe), ferrous oxide (FeO), ferrous-ferric oxide (Fe_3O_4) and ferric oxide (Fe_2O_3) are at equilibrium with the gas phase. Clearly, the transformation of Fe_2O_3 into Fe_3O_4 (according to the first equation) will take

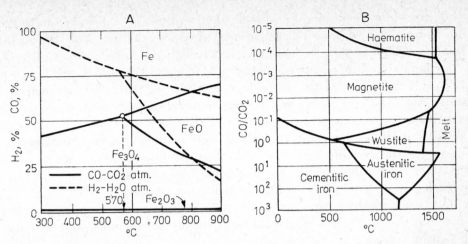

Fig. 3.13. A — Equilibrium domains of iron and its oxides in CO/CO_2 and H_2/H_2O atmospheres, *B* — idem, in a CO/CO_2 atmosphere, as a function of the CO/CO_2 ratio

place even on heating to a dark glow in both atmospheres, even if CO (or H_2) is present in quite small quantities only. The

$$\text{haematite } (Fe_2O_3) \rightleftarrows \text{magnetite } (Fe_3O_4)$$

phase boundary almost coincides with the axis of abscissae at CO contents ranging from 0 to 0.3% or H_2 contents ranging from 0.1 to 0.3% between 300 and 900 °C. At temperatures below 570 °C (the wustite point), at high concentrations of CO, ferromagnetic Fe_3O_4 is turned into even more strongly magnetic metallic iron. At temperatures above the wustite point, in the middle CO concentration range, the figure shows low-susceptibility paramagnetic FeO to be the phase at equilibrium. In reality, the solid phases Fe_3O_4, FeO and Fe are soluble in one another within limits: hence, in the domain marked "FeO", a weakly magnetic solid solution of FeO and Fe_3O_4 (the wustite phase) will form. The higher the solution in FeO, the lower its susceptibility.

Part B of Fig. 3.13 shows the equilibrium domains of magnetite, wustite, cementite and austenite in the CO/CO_2-ratio-vs.-temperature space.

The direction in which the reaction proceeds is determined, as pointed out above, by temperature and the CO/CO_2 ratio in the gas mixture. This does not, however, mean that the reactions are instantaneous and complete: in fact, they tend to be somewhat sluggish, and equilibrium is practically never reached in some of them.

Figure 3.13 and the reactions presented in connection therewith refer to pure iron oxides free of contaminations and impurities. Actual iron ores, on the other hand, tend to contain a variety of impurities (SiO_2, CaO, MgO, Al_2O_3, etc.), chemically bound or intergrown in a wide range of proportions. These affect the reducibility of iron oxide in a variety of ways: they impair it if the iron

361

oxide combines chemically with the accessory phases or is dissolved in those. An essentially analogous phenomenon is revealed by Part A of Fig. 3.13: Fe_3O_4 formed, according to the figure, next to the axis of abscissae out of Fe_2O_3 is further reduced to wustite e.g. between 33 to 60% CO at 700 °C and between 22 to 70% CO at 900 °C, the reason for the shift being that, at higher temperatures, Fe_3O_4 and FeO, more soluble in one another, have a greater propensity to constitute the solid solution wustite and therefore reducibility to metallic Fe is less). Higher temperatures will, on the one hand, shorten the time required to attain equilibrium, — thereby furthering reduction, — whereas, on the other, they will promote the mixing and mutual dissolution of impurities in each other, thereby hampering the reduction process.

Whether a roasting temperature about or above the wustite point (570 °C) should be chosen depends on the nature of the ore; it can and should be determined by testing.

Cooling in air turns the Fe_3O_4 formed on the roasting of an iron ore into strongly magnetic γ-Fe_2O_3 (maghemite). The process is quite easy to realize in the case of some ores (e.g. limonites with their high rates of reaction) but much less so in the case of some others. The essential thing is to let the wustite formed on roasting cool in an oxygenless atmosphere down to 450 °C; and below that temperature air must be admitted in order to let the charge oxidize, because above the critical temperature of 450 °C low-susceptibility α-ferric oxide (haematite) will form in air instead of the ferromagnetic gamma variant. This oxidation is an exothermic process, which renders close temperature control on the cooling of the roasted ore somewhat tricky. The susceptibility of γ-ferric oxide may be higher even than that of magnetite. Moreover, being higher in oxygen (as a result of the full reoxidation of its entire Fe content), it is preferred to magnetite in the blast furnace burden.

If siderite is heated in the absence of air, it decomposes into ferrous oxide and carbon dioxide according to the equation

$$FeCO_3 \rightarrow FeO + CO_2 - 54.4 \text{ kJ.}$$

The process is irreversible: higher temperatures will merely accelerate the reduction. The decomposition of pure iron carbonate will begin in the vicinity of 300 °C. The sideritic ore of Rudabánya, Hungary, starts decomposing at about 400 °C; most vehement about 540 °C, the reaction terminates altogether at 565 °C (that is, below the wustite point). The FeO produced is unstable: in an oxygenless space, it decomposes into Fe_3O_4 and metallic iron according to the equation

$$4FeO = Fe_3O_4 + Fe.$$

The metallic iron is subsequently oxidized to Fe_3O_4 by the CO_2 resulting from the decomposition of the carbonate.

Some authors prefer the formula

$$3FeO + CO_2 \rightleftharpoons Fe_3O_4 + CO -26.4 \text{ kJ}$$

for the process. This is a reversible reaction; its reversal is a function of temperature (it proceeds leftward when the temperature rises, and vice versa, as implied by Fig. 3.13).

On heating a mixture of oxide- and carbonate-type iron ores in the absence of air, dissociation according to

$$FeCO_3 \rightarrow FeO + CO_2$$

produces FeO which is then oxidized by carbon dioxide according to the formula

$$3FeO + CO_2 = Fe_3O_4 + CO.$$

The CO produced by the latter reaction reduces the oxide ore heated together with the carbonate ore according to

$$3Fe_2O_3 + CO = 2Fe_3O_4 + CO_2.$$

The three reactions may be combined into

$$FeCO_3 + Fe_2O_3 = Fe_3O_4 + CO_2.$$

The formation of ferromagnetic Fe_3O_4 can proceed to completion only if the shares of carbonate and oxide in the ore mix correspond to the molecular proportions

$$FeCO_3 : Fe_2O_3 = 115.8 : 159.7 = 1 : 1.38.$$

Rudabánya siderite ore contains more or less limonite: by facilitating the reduction of the ore mixture, this mineral is beneficial to the process of magnetic roasting.

Artificial magnetites resulting from magnetizing roasting tend to have about the same susceptibility and remanence as natural magnetites but their coercive force tends to be stronger, the reason being that coercivity varies as specific surface: now the thermal shock of roasting and the change in lattice structure tend to shatter the particles' interiors, which results in a considerable increase of internal surface. This is also why artificial magnetites tend to be so much more fragile and friable. Accordingly, concentrates of roasted ores must often be compacted (sintered or pelletized) before being fed to the blast furnace. Intergrown grains in a roasted ore, on the other hand, have a greater propensity to separate along the phase interfaces, which reduces the cost of their comminution (if applicable) and metallurgical processing as compared with natural magnetites (their porosity permits them to be reduced faster and more easily in the blast furnace). (Cavanagh and Last 1961; Davis 1937; DeVaney 1952; Gagyi-Pálfy et al. 1963; Kirchberg 1952; Luyken and Kraeber 1934; Meiler 1964; Tarján and Vécsey 1956.)

3.3. MAGNETIC SEPARATORS

These devices can be classified in a variety of ways. They are dry or wet according to the medium chosen; low- or high-intensity according as the minerals to be separated are strongly or weakly magnetic: bottom-feed (pickup-type) or top-feed (holding-type) according to the mode of introduction of the material to be separated. Design features, the mode of feed introduction and product takeoff further permit the distinction of belt, drum, roll, disk, ring, etc. separators, separators with stationary and/or moving magnets, etc. (Derkatsch 1960; Sheahan 1958; Tarján and Vécsey 1956; Weisbeck 1962).

Low-intensity dry separators used to handle strongly magnetic materials typically have a field intensity in the 800 to 1,200 Oe range at the separating surface: low-intensity wet separators have 600 to 800 Oe at a distance of about 5 cm from the separating surface; the high-intensity separators used to handle weakly magnetic minerals may attain 25,000 Oe next to the separating surface. Diagrams of low- and high-intensity dry and wet separators are presented in Fig. 3.14 and Fig. 3.18, respectively.

Diagrams 1 to 7 in Fig. 3.14 represent drum separators. No. 1 is a West German make, No. 2 is Canadian (Cavanagh), No. 3 is Finnish (Laurila), No. 4 is Swedish (Mörtsell): all four are of the dry type. Nos 5 to 7 are wet drum separators: No. 5 is of the concurrent, No. 6 of the countercurrent, No. 7 of the semi-countercurrent type. The spikes of the rotating roll at top right in Diagram No. 3 remove concentrate from the drum surface by means of the strong magnetic pinch field that they produce. The drum proper is non-magnetic in each case. In its interior, a bank of magnets, stationary (Diagrams 1, 4, 5, 6, 7) or rotating (Diagrams 2 and 3) is mounted, with adjacent magnets having opposite polarity. The rotating-magnet type is suited for the separation of fine powders above all (e.g. minus-50 μm), because the magnetic particles in these powders tend to stick together to form chains and strings which start rotating end for end between the poles (they thus acquire a proper motion relative to the drum also !). The length of a string depends on the susceptibility of the material and its grain size, on field intensity and frequency of field reversal. In a device with stationary magnets, field reversal frequency is a function of pole spacing and drum speed, whereas in a device with rotating magnets, it is a function of the speed differential between the magnets and the drum. High frequencies reduce string length and thereby make it easier for the strings to drop the waste particles entrapped in them (Kihlsted and Sköld 1960; Laurila 1954; Pearce 1962; Runolinna 1957).

Speed (peripheral velocity) is chosen to be inversely proportional to particle size. It is about 0.8 to 1 m/s in the separation of large lumps (50 to 200 mm) and 5 to 10 m/s typically for fine-grained dry feeds. Drum diameter (D) is in the 30 to 90 cm range. Drum length (L) is a function of the required throughput rate (20 to 180 cm). For the designs shown in Diagrams 2 to 4, approximate throughput per square metre of drum plan area ($D \times L$) is 15 to 25 m³/h of fine dust or 20 to 35 m³/h of a coarse feed. In the design shown as Diagram 1, throughput per field is about 5 t/h for a coarse feed and about 0.2 t/h for a minus-1 mm feed (Derkatsch 1960; DeVaney 1960; Roche and Crockett 1933).

The concurrent wet separator of Diagram 5 furnishes at a higher recovery and less drum wear a cleaner concentrate containing less water than the counter-current separator of Diagram 6. The latter, however, has the advantages of

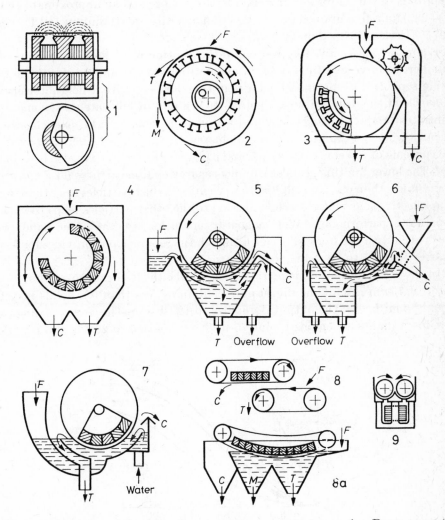

Fig. 3.14. Diagrams of low-intensity magnetic separator types. *1* — Drum separator with cam-shaped poles, *2* — Cavanagh, *3* — Laurila, *4* — Mörtsell type drum separator, *5* — concurrent, *6* — countercurrent, *7* — semi-countercurrent wet drum separator, *8* — dry belt separator, *8/a* — wet belt (Crockett) separator, *9* — magnetic log washer

rapid concentrate removal (concentrate travel is confined to a short arc on the drum), the ability to handle feeds rich in magnetic particles and less of a sensitivity to fluctuations in feed volume. As a further advantage, concentrate is taken off on the feed side. The advantages of the two designs are united in the semi-countercurrent separator of Diagram 7. For the concentration of magnetite ores by means of a single unassisted drum separator, the concurrent design is more popular. Per metre of length of the most widespread drum, which has 75 cm diameter, throughput at a water consumption of 2 to 2.5 m³/t is an approximate 40 t/h for a coarse (minus-15 mm) ore and an approximate 10 t/h ($\pm 50\%$) for a fine-grained (minus-2 mm) magnetite ore (Hamilton and Twichell 1971; Hawker 1972; Suleski 1972).

Figure 3.15 is a plot of Fe content in the limiting particles of separation of a number of close-sized fractions of a magnetite ore vs. drum speed, using a dry drum separator of 60 cm diameter (e.g. the Mörtsell) with a field intensity of 1,000 Oe at the drum surface. Figure 3.16 is a plot of Fe contents of some concentrates produced using a dry and a wet drum separator vs. particle size x, also showing a section of the granulometry curve $S_F\%$ of each. The average Fe contents of the concentrates (57 and 67%, respectively) have also been plotted. The lower limiting grain size of dry-separating fine particles (at a moisture content less than one per cent !) is 10 to 20 μm: for dust particles finer than that, non-selective (e.g. electrostatic) adhesion to the other particles tends to impair separation performance. Wet magnetic separation, on the other hand, will work even with the finest of feeds, although the separation it provides for feeds coarser than 75 to 80 μm is not so sharp.

In the regenerating of magnetic dense media, the feed rate to a drum separator of 75 cm dia. of the dilute pulp containing less than 5% solids may be about 60 m³/h · m; the output is about 9 to 12 t/h · m. The corresponding values for a dia. of 90 cm are about 75 m³/h · m and 15 to 20 t/h · m. (Cf. also

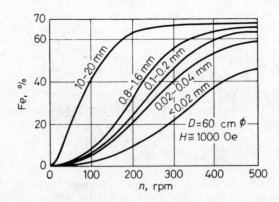

Fig. 3.15. Separation Fe content of sized magnetite fractions vs. drum speed, in a dry drum separator of field intensity $H = 1,000$ Oe

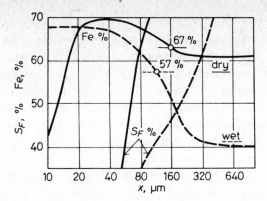

Fig. 3.16. Fe content vs. particle size of concentrates produced by dry and wet magnetic separation, respectively

Section 1.3.3.) Figure 3.17 shows magnetic medium-solid loss in the tailings vs. pulp feed rate. The parameter, z, is weight percent magnetic solids content in the pulp: the magnetic fraction is 70 to 95% of total solids. For example, if $z = 20$ weight percent and $\delta \simeq 5$ (magnetite), then $\sigma \simeq 5.5$ to 7.5%; if $\delta \simeq 6.8$ (FeSi), then $\sigma \simeq 4.1$ to 5.6% (Bronkala 1963).

In the concentration of magnetite ores, the separation of a middling fraction may be justified. This can be achieved either by letting the feed pass through a gradually intensifying field or by letting the concentrate pass through a gradually (or, possibly, abruptly) weakening one. Field intensity can be adjusted by changing ampere-turns on successive poles or their distance from the material stream. An example for the latter case is presented in Diagram 2 of Fig.

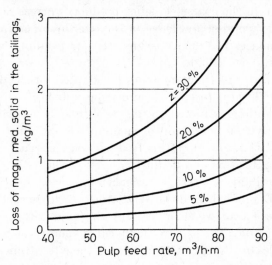

Fig. 3.17. Loss of magnetic medium solid into the tailings vs. pulp feed rate, with z weight percent magnetic content in the pulp, as the parameter

367

3.14, where the rotating magnet bank is mounted eccentrically within the drum. In another solution, two drum separators of the type in Diagram 4 are installed side by side and the preconcentrate of the first separator (of stronger excitation and/or less peripheral velocity) is split into a middlings and a concentrate by the second (of weaker field and/or higher peripheral velocity).

Diagram 8 of Fig. 3.14 shows a dry belt separator suited for the separation of minus-15 mm feeds. The lower belt which carries the feed into the field moves slower than the upper one: the magnetic particles picked up by the upper belt will thus always find empty space on it.

Diagram 8/a of Fig. 3.14 represents the Crockett submerged-band wet separator, earlier a fairly widespread type. It has a multi-hopper tank with the feed chute at one end. The successive hoppers produce a tailing, a middling and a concentrate. (Two products suffice in dense-medium reconditioning.) An endless belt is immersed into the tank: it passes at a speed of about one m/s in front of a bank of 20 poles whose strength decreases downstream. Throughput is a sensitive function of feed particle size and concentrate yield. For one metre of belt width, a typical output is 50 t/h for minus-2.5 mm magnetite ore and between 20 to 30 t/h for minus-0.3 mm magnetite ore. Belt width varies in the 0.2 to 1.4 m range. Power draft per metre of belt width is about 4 kW (d.c.) for the excitation and 3 to 4 kW for the mechanisms of operation.

Diagram 9 of Fig. 3.14 is the cross section of the magnetic log washer. This is basically an Akins classifier, the helical-screw conveyors of which are made of some non-magnetic metal (e.g. bronze or manganese steel), and which has a bank of electromagnets fitted underneath the tank. The magnetic field makes the magnetic particles in the pulp clot and settle down at the bottom: these clots are removed in the coarse classifier product, whereas non-magnetic particles remain in suspension and leave in the overflow. The finer the feed, the better is performance. The device is unsuited for handling magnetite ores of plus-0.3 mm grain size (Wade 1922).

The drum separator of Diagram 1 can be adapted for the dry separation of medium-susceptibility materials by mounting soft-iron hoops on its outer surface, in front of the pole pieces: the edges of these hoops will pinch the lines of force sufficiently to retain grains of medium susceptibility. Output is about 0.1 to 0.2 t/h per hoop: upper limiting feed particle size is about 5 mm. A painstaking prior classification and de-dusting is required.

Medium-susceptibility materials can also be sorted using the pole piece arrangement in Diagram 1, in drum separators on whose shell axial non-magnetic bars (made e.g. of wood or bronze) alternate with magnetizable ones (made e.g. of soft iron). The soft-iron bars carry spikes which brush the north and the south poles in alternation (or approach them to within a fine clearance). Magnetized by induction, the soft iron bars create a strong pinch field at their outer edges, strong enough to separate medium-magnetic minerals (of specific susceptibility $\chi = 600 \cdot 10^{-6}$ to $3{,}000 \cdot 10^{-6}$ cm³/g), although the device is used most often to concentrate lumpy magnetite ores between 25 and 50 mm size (Cavanagh and Williams 1957; Derkatsch 1960).

Figure 3.18 presents the diagrams of some high-intensity magnetic separators used to handle weakly magnetic minerals. Diagram 1 is a dry cross-belt separator (the Wetherill); Diagrams 2 and 3 respectively represent the Rapid and Rapidity disk separators. Diagrams 4 and 5 show induced-roll separators (with top — holding-type — feed in the first and bottom — pick-up type — feed in the second); Diagram 6 shows a wet ring separator (the Ullrich), whereas Nos 7 to 13 refer to various induced-roll separators.

Under the strong horseshoe electromagnet or electromagnets of the cross-belt separator (Diagram 1), the closure of the magnetic circuit is ensured by soft iron keeper bridges. (In Diagram 1, the keeper also carries an excitation winding.) The upper pole pieces are wedge-shaped: those of the keeper (or lower magnet) are flat. Ore is fed onto a belt moving lengthwise between the poles: the cross belts (shown in cross section in bold line) prevent the magnetic particles from reaching the upper pole pieces when they are caught up from the lengthwise belt by the field pinch. Operation is hampered by abundant ferromagnetic matter (e.g. magnetite, pyrrhotite or iron filings) in the feed: these are attracted strongly enough even by the leakage flux of the magnets to bypass the cross belts and to be picked up by the pole pieces on which they build up into a ragged beard. This can be prevented by adding a first, auxiliary pole, an open one with no counter-pole (as shown dashed in Diagram 1). The field of this pole is much weaker, which permits the ferromagnetic particles to be picked up by its cross belt in orderly fashion. The field intensity of the successive poles increases downstream, so that successive cross belts remove products of decreasing susceptibility. (Field intensity can be increased by increasing the excitation [ampere-turns] on the successive magnets and/or by reducing the clearance between the feed belt and the upper pole pieces). Typical feed belt speed is between 0.25 and 0.5 m/s for weakly magnetic feeds and between 0.5 and 1.5 m/s for medium-magnetic ones. The upper limiting grain size of the feed is 2 to 3 mm for weakly magnetic materials; it may be greater for medium-magnetic materials. Throughput is approximately proportional to particle size: at one mm size, it is 0.3 to 0.6 t/h per decimetre (10 centimetres) of feed belt width. That width should not exceed 4 to 5 dm in a low weight-recovery operation: it should be even less in high weight-recovery cases to prevent the fractions picked up by the cross belts from crowding material off the feed belt.

Disk separators operate in much the same way as the cross-belt separator. In Diagram 2, Fig. 3.18, flat-pole electromagnets are mounted inside the loop of an endless conveyor belt. (The belt may be replaced by a shaking feeder of the link-belt type.) Susceptible grains are attracted by the pinch fields of the rotating soft-iron disks installed above the belt, the bottom faces of which have sharp wedge-shaped rims. The polarity of the disks reverses twice per turn: at a point approximately perpendicular to the excited poles (that is, to the belt), there is a neutral zone where the induced magnetization of the disk drops to zero, so that the particles picked up by it can drop off. The Rapidity device (Diagram 3) has two feed belts running in opposite directions: the neutral zone is between the two belts. The disks rotate so as to follow the motion of the band on either side. The bands can thus be run at higher speed, resulting in greater throughput, than in a Rapid (or a cross-belt) separator where the disk rim (or cross belt) taking away the susceptible particles moves crosswise to the feed belt.

Two induced-roll separators are shown next: that of Diagram 4 is of the top-feed (holding) type whereas that of Diagram 5 is of the bottom-feed (pick-up) type. The roll, made up of alternate permeable and impermeable sheets (say, soft iron and bronze) as shown in Diagram 4, rotates with a certain clearance between the poles of a strong electromagnet. The sheets may be replaced by sharp-rimmed disks strung up side by side, as in Diagram 5. In another design, a roll, permeable in its entirety, is provided with triangular (wedge-shaped) or square grooves around its girth. The rims of the disks or the lands between the grooves concentrate strong pinch fields. The roll is thus provided with a number of secondary (induced) poles. The strength of these poles varies as the roll rotates: twice per turn, the roll field is magnetically neutralized (repolarized).

Dry induced-roll separators permit the efficient handling of weakly magnetic minerals down to a lower limiting grain size of about 20 to 40 μm. The upper limiting grain size is about 3 to 5 mm in bottom-feed (pick-up) roll separators but may be much larger than that in top-feed (holding-type) ones: 15 to 70 mm, depending on the susceptibility of the mineral to be concentrated and on pole design. (Of course, a fair performance presupposes an adequate prior classification.) Typically, roll length is between 0.8 to 1.5 m, roll diameter between 10 and 25 cm; peripheral velocity is in the 0.4 to 1.0 m/s range. Frequently, two or three top-fed rolls are installed one below another; each roll is fed the waste of the roll above it for cleaning.

Throughput per metre of roll length is a sensitive function of particle size and of susceptibility. For example, in a top-fed roll of 15 cm diameter, 0.5 to 1 mm size quartz sand was "deferrified" ($a = 0.025\%$, $c = 0.016\%$ Fe_2O_3) at a rate of 0.5 to 0.7 t/h · m. A martitic-haematitic iron ore ($a = 43\%$, $b = 14\%$, $c = 56\%$ Fe; $v = 69\%$, $m = 90\%$) was concentrated on a 25 cm dia. roll (with a pole design as in Diagram 4) at an output of 12 to 15 t/h · m if sized to within 10 and 35 mm and at an output of 15 to 20 t/h · m if sized to within 10 and 70 mm. At a roll diameter of 10 cm, excitation requires about 2.5 kW and the drive about 1.5 kW per metre of roll length; for a roll of 25 cm diameter, the two are equal at about 4.5 kW to each. A bottom-fed 15 cm dia.

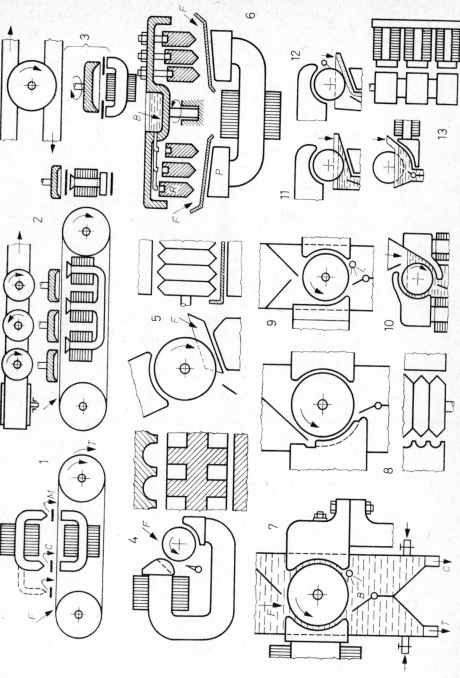

Fig. 3.18. Diagrams of high-intensity magnetic separator types. *1* — cross-belt (Wetherill), *2* — Rapid, *3* — Rapidity disk separator, *4* and *5* — induced-roll dry types: *4* — top-feed (holding-type), *5* — bottom-feed (pick-up-type), *6* — Ullrich ring separator, *7* to *13* — top-, side- and bottom-feed induced-roll wet separators

induced-roll separator (consuming 1.5 + 2.2 kW/m) handling a minus-5 mm martitic-haematitic iron ore at

peripheral velocity	60	95	cm/s
had a throughput of	2.5 to 3.5	4 to 5	t/h · m

with $a = 58\%$, $b = 36\%$, $c = 60\%$ Fe, $v = 91\%$ and $m = 94\%$; the same machine, handling a minus-3 mm manganese ore at 95 cm/s peripheral velocity gave a throughput of about 2.5 t/h · m with $a = 16\%$, $b = 7\%$, $c = 39\%$ Mn, $v = 28\%$ and $m = 68\%$ (Derkatsch 1960; Henčl 1963; Monostory 1974; Neumann 1964; Wada et al. 1964).

The essential features of a high-intensity wet ring separator (the Ullrich) are shown in Diagram 6 of Fig. 3.18. An even number (4 or 6) of flat primary poles of alternating polarity (P) is arranged in a circle. Rotating above them, there is a table from which depend several (3 to 6) soft-iron rings (R) with sharp bottom edges. The table features a water basin (B) which feeds a trickle of water to each of the rings. Pulp is fed into the magnetic fields through stationary launders installed above each of the flat primary pole pieces. The magnetic particles contained in the pulp are picked up by the pinch fields converging on the sharp rims of the soft-iron rings; since the water trickling down the rings bridges the air gap, the pick-up does not have to overcome the surface tension of water. This is important because, for fine particles, the force needed to overcome surface tension is several times the force of gravity. For example, the specific magnetic force p required to overcome both gravity and the resistance of the water surface is

$p =$	980	2,200	11,000	46,000 dynes/gram
for grain sizes $x =$	2.5	1.5	0.5	0.2 mm.

Now $\dfrac{p - g_0}{g} =$	0.2	1.4	10.2	45.2

for grains of s.g. $\delta = 4.5$, for which $g_0 = 760$ dynes/gram. In their rotation, the rings pass through neutral zones in between poles: there, the trickle of water can wash off the captured particles. The clearance between rings and primary poles decreases in the direction of pulp flow: for the innermost ring, it should equal twice the upper limiting particle size to be handled. The particles in the pulp thus enter fields of increasing intensity, so that rings placed further inwards pick up products of weaker and weaker susceptibility. The throughput of the ring separator is 0.1 to 0.2 t/h per primary pole when handling a weakly magnetic fine-grained feed, greater when handling a coarser-grained or higher-susceptibility feed. Ullrich (1941) suggested a throughput per primary pole of 0.3 to 0.5 t/h for a weakly magnetic minus-10 mm feed, 0.4 to 0.6 t/h for a strongly magnetic fine-grained feed and 1.0 to 1.2 t/h for a coarse (minus-50 mm) feed (Ullrich 1941).

Diagrams 7 to 13 of Fig. 3.18 represent wet induced-roll separators. Diagram 7 is a pure top-feed type: Nos 8 to 10 are side-feed designs, approaching bottom feed more and more, whereas Nos 11 to 13 are pure bottom-feed. (Whether the feed is to be regarded as top or bottom type is decided by the position of the narrowest working clearance.) Typical roll diameter is 15 cm; roll length is about 80 cm; peripheral velocity is in the 0.5 to 0.6 m/s range. (The single exception is No. 13, where roll diameter is 27 to 30 cm to provide a large iron cross section, on account of the magnetic circuit being closed through the roll.)

The rolls of Nos 7 to 9 are entirely immersed in the pulp in a closed housing. In No. 10, it is the pole pieces that constitute two opposite walls of the pulp tank. In Nos 11 and 13, only the bottom of the roll dips into the pulp to a greater or smaller depth; in No. 12, the roll just touches the pulp flowing down under it; a water spray directed at the side of the roll closes any air gap that may form between pulp and roll. In the case of the fully immersed roll, a flow of fresh water keeps solid particles out of the clearance between roll and counter-pole. The hoppers in which the tailings and the concentrate collect at the bottom of the separator tank are also provided with regulated flows of wash water (as shown in Diagram 7): the adjustment of total wash-water flow permits to regulate the flow rate through the working clearance, whereas adjusting wash flows separately permits to control the routing and rate of flow of water in the clearance between the roll and adjustable baffle B, and thereby to enhance the purity of the one or the other product (Horst and Dyrenforth 1971).

Similarly to the dry machines, wet separators can be fed coarser material when top-fed than when bottom-fed (up to about 8 mm in the first case vs. 3 mm in the second). The throughput of the top-fed type is accordingly greater. For example, throughput per metre of roll length was found to be:

	Mn%				
	a	b	c	$v\%$	$m\%$

in the top-fed separator of Diagram 7, for a 0.2 to 5 mm manganese ore,

$\sim$2.5 t/h · m	at 27	6	39 Mn	64	92

for a minus-3 mm manganese ore

$\sim$0.2 t/h · m	at 21	8	41 Mn	39	77

in the side-fed type of Diagram 8, for a minus-3 mm manganese ore,

1.5 to 2.0 t/h · m	at 18	6	37 Mn	39	63

in the side-fed type of Diagram 9, for the same ore,

$\sim$1.6 t/h · m	at 18	12	38 Mn	23	50

in the bottom-fed type of Diagram 11, for the same ore,

1.2 to 1.5 t/h · m	at 18	10	30 Mn	40	67

(Derkatsch 1960).

A design suited for the separation of low-susceptibility pulps is the Carpco (Jones) separator, a ring-shaped tank made of perforated plate and filled with pieces of some highly susceptible material (e.g. small soft-iron balls). The tank rotates between the poles of strong electromagnets (20,000 Oe or so). The susceptible particles of the pulp fed in between pole pieces get caught by the magnetized filling, whereas any non-magnetic particles can flow straight through the matrix. The magnetic concentrate can be washed out from the matrix where the ring tank in its rotation emerges from between the poles (Carpenter 1964; Lawver and Carpenter 1965). The Jones separators made by Humboldt WEDAG and Ferro-Magnetics Ltd. of Montreal employ the same operating principles, except that the magnetic lines of force in the matrix are tangential in the ring itself (while they are perpendicular to the Carpco device). Some of these machines are designed for very high throughputs, up to 130 t/h.

Another type of wet Jones separator permits the concentration of weakly and medium-magnetic fine pulps (e.g. of haematite, garnet, biotite, etc.) down to very fine particle sizes, possibly even 1 μm. It features wedge-shaped passages between vertically grooved sheets of iron. The particles of low or medium susceptibility are caught in the strong magnetic pinch fields thus formed, while the non-magnetic part of the pulp flows off. After a feed period of about 2 s, the feed stream is interrupted and the middling-type particles are washed off by a pulsating jet (for 1.5 s). For another 0.5 s, the energizing current is cut off and a high-pressure jet is applied to wash the concentrate off the sheets. In each phase, the outflow is led to a different hopper. Power draft is only about 3 kW h per ton.

The Jones separator has been put to good use in the concentration of certain magnetically susceptible uranium minerals. These are, in decreasing order of susceptibility, brannerite, monazite, uraninite, pitchblende and uranothorite. For example, a r.o.m. ore ground to 35% minus-44 μm, containing 0.18% U_3O_8, could be enriched in a Jones separator to a U_3O_8 content of $c = 2.37\%$ ($v = 5.3\%$, $m = 68.9\%$). Another uranium ore, ground to 60% minus-44 μm, gave $a = 0.07\%$, $c = 1.04\%$ U_3O_8, $v = 4.3\%$, $m = 61.5\%$ (Jones 1964; Stone 1965, 1971; Vogeno 1971; Wenz 1973).

The dry devices most widespread in practice are top-fed induced rolls, but ring and cross-belt type dry separators are also encountered with some frequency. High-intensity separators are less suited for wet concentration owing to the hydrodynamic effect (greater drag) of the water, the hydrophilic particles' resistance to being lifted out of the water (which is to be avoided if possible at the point of separation!) and the diamagnetic nature of the medium (water). Even though the magnetic force acting upon a particle is greater in a diamagnetic medium, the ratio of magnetic forces acting upon particles of different susceptibility is less: the sharpness of separation is impaired thereby.

Industrial (Jones) high-intensity wet separators are employed e.g. in the production of high-purity iron oxides used in ferrite manufacturing or in the direct-reduction processes of ferrous metallurgy, e.g. to win a concentrate containing 67.5% Fe at an iron recovery of 95% out of Brazilian itabirite (where 28 Jones-WEDAG devices of 120 t/h throughput each are installed), in the removal of impurities from kaolin, talc and similar materials, from concentrates of cassiterite and scheelite, etc.

The minimum magnetic field intensity (in 10^3 gauss units), required to win different para- and ferromagnetic minerals in the interstices of the matrix of a high-intensity wet separator, is given below.

0.1 magnetite,
1 ferberite, pyrrhotite,
2 martite,
3 maghemite, franklinite,
4 serpentine,
8 ilmenite, itabirite,
10 siderite, chromite, biotite,
11 olivine (fayalite), xenotite,
12 columbite, davidite, garnet, pyrochlore, staurolite, tantalite, wolframite,
13 ankerite, bastnaesite, haematite,
14 apatite, braunite, epidote, monazite, renierite,
15 alabandite, goethite, ilmeno-rutile, muscovite, pyrolusite, rhodochrosite, rhodonite,
16 euxenite, hornblende, limonite, samarskite, turmaline,
18 uraninite,
20 chrysocolla.

For the separation of ferromagnetic materials, a.c.-excited magnets may also be used. (They are unsuited for circuits separating lower-susceptibility minerals because generating a given field with a.c. requires more power, on account of the eddy-current and hysteresis losses in the core, which rapidly increase as field intensity increases.) Pole pieces have to be built up of lamellae of thin transformer sheet, carefully insulated between them as the eddy currents would otherwise heat up the pole body quite considerably even over a short period of operation (Mordey 1922).

An a.c. separator used to handle low-coercive-force ferromagnetic materials (e.g. natural magnetites) may for example carry a winding recalling the stator of a three-phase induction motor unfolded into a plane or an arcuate surface, with the pole pieces shaped so as to suit the purpose of separation. The strong pinch field of the "rotating current" (the "Drehstrom" of German terminology) scans the unfolded surface fifty times per second (provided mains frequency is

50 cps) and, making the magnetic particles spin, carries them to the non-magnetic sheet facing the poles (Eketorp 1951).

The separation of high-coercive-force ferromagnetic materials from non-magnetic (or low-coercive-force magnetic) materials can be achieved by means of an a.c. electromagnet excited to a field intensity less than the coercive force of the ferromagnetics in question. The feed is made to pass beforehand through the field of a d.c.-excited magnet, in order to endow the ferromagnetics with a remanence. Passing into the a.c.-excited field, the minerals whose coercive force exceeds the peak intensity of the a.c.-excited field are not repolarized (although their remanence is weakened), whereas those particles whose remanence is less than the field intensity are repolarized twice per period. The repolarized particles will be attracted by the a.c.-excited electromagnet throughout, whereas the particles of stronger remanence are alternately attracted and repelled. These latter will therefore vibrate in the field, turning end for end as pole polarity changes. Their vibration permits them to slide or saltate off a plane inclined so as to retain the non-magnetic or low-coercivity particles. The a.c. device may be designed e.g. as a drum separator: the feed is introduced at a point of the drum where its slope is not yet sufficient for the non-magnetic particles (or the low-coercivity particles pinned to the shell) to slide off but great enough for the vibrating high-coercivity particles to saltate off the drum rotating in the opposite direction.

The remanence of a highly magnetic pre-concentrate or middling must be cancelled prior to its introduction into a cleaner separator, so as to let the clots of particles re-form and release the non-magnetic particles entrapped in them. Clotting in a reconditioned magnetic dense medium must also be eliminated before reintroduction into the static separating tank. (In a D.M. hydrocyclone, shear is sufficient as a rule to disentangle the magnetic clots even without prior demagnetization.) Demagnetization can be achieved e.g. by introducing the pulp or the dry ore into a non-magnetic pipe surrounded by an a.c.-excited winding whose number of turns decreases (gradually or stepwise) in the downstream direction. As the a.c.-excited field fades out, the hysteresis loop contracts, and the remanence of the particles also fades out till it disappears in the end (Benson et al. 1968).

Electromagnets or strong permanent magnets are frequently mounted as guard magnets upstream of comminution equipment (stone crushers) so as to pick tramp iron out of the feed. For the purpose, a magnetic drum is often installed as the head pulley of the feed belt conveyor. In other arrangements, a strong magnet is mounted at some other strategic point above the feed stream, to pick tramp iron out of the feed layer. (Manganese steel being non-magnetic, its removal must be achieved by some other means, e.g. using a suitable metal detector.)

3.4. LITERATURE ON MAGNETIC SEPARATION

BARAN, W.: Magnetwerkstoffe und Magnetfelder. *AT* 1973, 440—442.

BENSON, W. H.—J. A. BARTNIK—G. D. ROSE: Demagnetizing coils and magnetic floccu-
lators used in magnetite beneficiation. *Min. Engng* 1968 Aug., 58—61.

BRONKALA, W. J.: How to select wet magnetic separators for heavy media plants. *E/MJ*
1963 Dec., 98—102.

CARPENTER, J. H.: Carpco-Amax high intensity wet magnetic separator. 7. *IMPC*, New
York 1964, 399—404.

CAVANAGH, P. E.—E. W. WILLIAMS: Dry magnetic concentration. *Can. M. M. Bull.*
1957, 326—332.

CAVANAGH, R. L.—A. J. LAST: Experimental and commercial magnetite roasting. *Can.
M. M. Bull.* 1961, 615—622.

DAVIS, E. W.: Magnetic roasting of iron ore. *Univ. Minn. Mines Exp. Sta. Bull.* 13, 1937.

DERKATSCH, V. G.: *Die magnetische Aufbereitung schwachmagnetischer Erze.* VEB Deutscher Verlag für Grundstoffindustrie, Leipzig 1960.

DEVANEY, F. D.: Magnetic roasting of lean ores. *Min. Engng* 1952, 1219—1223.

DEVANEY, F. D.: New developments in the magnetic concentration of iron ores. *IMPC*,
London 1960, 675—688.

EKETORP, B.: Three-phase a.c. can improve fine size magnetic separation. *E/MJ* 1951
Oct., 82—84.

GAGYI-PÁLFFY, A.—G. PÁLFY—A. HALÁSZ: The treatment of siderites in Hungary and
the recovery of their barite and copper content. 6. *IMPC*, Cannes 1963, 469—482.

GRIMSEHL, I.: *Lehrbuch der Physik. Bd. 2: Elektromagnetisches Feld.* 15. Auflage, B. G.
Teubner, Leipzig 1961.

HAMILTON, A. W.—E. S. TWICHELL: High-gradient wet-drum separators optimize the
use of magnetic energy. *E/MJ* 1971 Sep., 142—143.

HAWKER, T. G.: Choosing a wet drum separator. *Australian Mining* 1972 Feb., 78—79.

HENČL, V.: Complex treatment of Slovakian siderites. 6. *IMPC*, Cannes 1963, 483—
499.

HENČL, V. (et al.): New high-intensity magnetic separator for treatment for fine fraction
of weakly magnetic materials. 9. *IMPC*, Praha 1970, 69—77.

HORST, W. E.—W. P. DYRENFORTH: Wet high-intensity magnetic separation of industrial
minerals. *Min. Engng* 1971 March, 57—59.

JONES, G. H.: The separation of strongly magnetic particles, particularly those of small
dimension. 7. *IMPC*, New York 1964, 405—413.

JONES, G. H.—W. J. D. STONE: Wet magnetic separator for feebly magnetic minerals.
IMPC, London 1960, 717—743.

KIHLSTED, P. G.—B. SKÖLD: Concentration of magnetite ores with dry magnetic separators of the Mörtsell-Sala type. *IMPC*, London 1960, 691—704.

KIRCHBERG, H.: Magnetisierendes Rösten von Eisenerzen. *Metallurgie und Giessereitechnik*
1952, 424—427.

LAURILA, E.: Magnetscheider mit Dauermagneten zur trockenen Aufbereitung feinver-
teilter starkmagnetischer Eisenerze. *Stahl und Eisen* 1954, 1659—1661.

LAWVER, J. E.—J. H. CARPENTER: Wet magnetic separation of oxidized semitaconites.
Min. Engng 1965 Sept., 87—91.

LUYKEN, W.—L. KRAEBER: Über das Verhalten des Spateisensteins bei der Röstung.
Stahl und Eisen 1934, 361—364.

MEILER, H.: Untersuchungen zur magnetisierenden Röstung und Magnetscheidung fein-
verwachsener Eisenerze. *AT* 1964, 413—420.

MONOSTORY, F. P.: Trennung schwachmagnetischer Stoffe in Starkfeldscheidern. *AT* 1974, 86—92.

MONOSTORY, F. P.—W. PICKHARDT—W. SIMONIS—E. VON SZANTHO: Das Abscheiden von Pyrit aus Kohlenstaub im elektrischen und im magnetischen Feld. *AT* 1970, 207—220, 599—614.

MORDEY, W. M.: The concentration of minerals by means of alternate electric currents. *Min. Mag.* 1922, 333—334.

NEUMANN, K.: Starkfeldmagnetscheidung von Eisenerzen. *Erzmetall* 1964, 401—406.

NEUMANN, K.: Magnetic separation — an expert reviews current procedures for high intensity magnetic separation. *E/MJ* 1964 July, 88—90.

PALASVIRTA, O. E.: High-intensity magnetic separation of iron ores. *Min. Engng* 1959, 1244—1248.

PEARCE, M. O.: Low-intensity dry magnetic concentration. *Can. M. M. Bull.* 1962, 571—579.

REINBOTH, H.: *Technologie und Anwendung magnetischer Werkstoffe.* VEB Verlag Technik, Berlin 1958.

ROCHE, H. M.—R. E. CROCKETT: Magnetic separation, an up-to-date mill. *E/MJ* 1933, 273—277.

RUNOLINNA, O.: Dry magnetic separation of finely ground magnetite. *IMPC*, Stockholm 1957, 255—284.

SCHUBERT, H.: Zum gegenwärtigen Entwicklungsstand der Starkfeldmagnetscheidung. *Bergakademie* 1966, 479—484.

SCHUBERT, H.: *Aufbereitung fester mineralischer Rohstoffe. Bd. II.* VEB Deutscher Verlag für Grundstoffindustrie, Leipzig 1967.

SHEAHAN, P. M.: Magnetic separation — Basic principles and their practical application. *Proc. Austr. Inst. Min. Met.* 1958, 135—159.

STONE, W. J. D.: Application of the Jones wet magnetic separator to the beneficiation of iron ore. *Can. M. M. Bull.* 1961, 677—686.

STONE, W. J. D.: Effect of variable adjustments on separation in the Jones magnetic separator. *Mine Quarry* 1964, 202—211.

STONE, W. J. D.: Wet magnetic separation of industrial minerals. *Can. M. M. Bull.* 1965, 1288—1291.

STONE, W. J. D.: Base metals and high-intensity wet magnetic separation. *Can. Mining J.* 1971 June, 56—62.

SULESKI, J.: New magnets and tank designs for wet magnetic drum separators. *World Mining* 1972 Apr., 60—61, 89.

TARJÁN, G.—B. VÉCSEY: *A vasércek és a nagyolvasztó elegyének előkészítése. Vaskohászati Enciklopédia IV.* (Preparation of iron ores and of blast furnace burdens. Encyclopedia of Ferrous Metallurgy IV.) Akadémiai Kiadó, Budapest 1956.

TENPAS, E. J.: Magnetic separators — types and applications. *Rock Prod.* 1971 Apr., 88—90.

ULLRICH, G. S.: Elektromagnetische Scheider. *Z. VDI, Beihefte Verfahrenstechnik* 1941, 63—69.

VOGENO, W.: Ein neuer Starkfeld-Nass-Magnetscheider. *AT* 1971, 482—483.

WADA, M.—M. MAJIMA—A. OHBA: Laboratory hot high-intensity, induced-roll magnetic separator and its application. 7. *IMPC*, New York 1964, 391—398.

WADE, H. H.: Magnetic log washer in iron-ore concentration. *E/MJ* 1922, 769—771.

WEISBECK, O.: Magnetscheider mit starkem Magnetfeld. *AT* 1962, 400—418.

WENZ, L.—W. H. ZABEL: Die Aufbereitung schwach magnetisierbarer Eisenerze durch nasse Starkfeld-Magnetscheidung. *AT* 1973, 142—149.

378

4. ELECTRICAL SEPARATION

4.1. FUNDAMENTALS

The principles of electrical separation are related in many respects to those of magnetic separation. An electrically charged body is surrounded by an electrostatic field, just as a body endowed with a magnetic charge is surrounded by a magnetic field. There is an analogy between the behaviour of electric charges (masses) and the behaviour of magnetic charges (masses), and also between the phenomena observed in electrostatic and magnetic fields. The only essential difference is that, whereas magnetism, as far as our current physical knowledge goes, does not exist in the form of monopoles (separate, independent north and south poles), electric charge does exist in two forms, positive and negative. Apart from that, the phenomena and definitions of magnetism as presented in Chapter 3 on magnetic separation have full analogs in the electrostatic field (like poles repel, unlike poles attract one another; the force between poles varies inversely as the square of pole separation; line-of-force patterns are identical, and the charging of bodies by induction/polarization takes place in much the same way as in the magnetic field). The counterpart of magnetic permeability μ in an electric insulator is the dielectric constant, inductive capacity or permittivity ε. The dielectric constant of air (more strictly speaking, of empty space) is unity; that of water varies as

$$
\begin{array}{cccc}
& 80.37 & 78.54 & 34.59 \\
\text{with temperature } T = & 20 & 25 & 200\ °\text{C}.
\end{array}
$$

The dielectric constants of some pure inorganic and organic liquids are listed in Table 4.1. By mixing miscible organic liquids, the dielectric constant of the mix can be adjusted to any desired value intermediate between those of the pure liquids.

Of the minerals, most silicates, phosphates and carbonates are non-conductors (electric insulators or dielectrics): their dielectric constants range from 3 to 10 $\left(\varepsilon = \dfrac{C_a}{C_0}\right)$. Some minerals' dielectric constants are in the range usually termed "middling" (between 10 and 80) (Juhász 1973). Table 4.2 lists some minerals in the order of increasing dielectric constants.

Table 4.1. Permittivities (dielectric constants) of pure liquids

Liquid	ε	°C	Liquid	ε	°C	Liquid	ε	°C
Hydrazine (N_2H_4)	52.9	20	n-butyl alcohol	17.1	25	Bromoform	4.39	20
Ammonia (NH_3)	16.9	25	n-amyl alcohol	13.9	25	Chloroform	4.81	20
Sulphur dioxide (SO_2)	14.1	20	m-cresol	11.8	25	Linolenic acid	2.71	20
Hydrochlore acid (HCl)	4.6	28	o-cresol	11.5	25	Carbon disul-	2.64	20
Sulphur trioxide (SO_3)	3.1	18	Dichlorethane	10.65	20	phide		
Formic acid	58.5	16	Phenol	9.78	60	Oleic acid	2.46	20
Glycol	37.7	25	Aniline	6.89	20	Benzene	2.28	20
Nitrobenzene	35.74	20	o-toluidine	6.34	18	Carbon tetra-	2.24	20
Methyl alcohol	33.62	20	Acetic acid	6.15	20	chloride		
Ethyl alcohol	24.3	25	Chlorobenzene	5.71	20	Cyclohexane	2.02	20
n-propyl alcohol	20.1	25	Bromobensene	5.40	25			

Table 4.2. Permittivities (dielectric constants) of some minerals and rocks

Mineral/rock	ε	Mineral/rock	ε	Mineral/rock	ε
Native sulphur	3.6	Talcum	9.3	Diamond	16.5—5.5
Quartz	4.3	Biotite	9.3	Galena	17.9
Sylvite	5.0	Apatite	9.5—7.4	Cerussite	18.6
Gypsum	5.7	Smithsonite	9.5	Cuprite	20
Limestone	6.1	Muscovite	10.0	Cassiterite	24
Anhydrite	6.6	Bauxite	10.8	Haematite	25
Beryl	7.0—6.1	Chromite	11.0	Anatasae	31
Malachite	7.2	Kaolinite	11.2	Zincite	33
Fluorspar	7.4	Antimonite	11.2	Pyrite	35
Sphalerite	7.8	Barite	11.4	Ilmenite	36
Dolomite	8.0—6.8	Zircon	12.0	Pyromorphite	39
Monazite	8.0	Wolframite	13.0	Tetrahedrite	80
Calcite	8.5—8.0	Anglesite	14.3	Rutile	170—86

The group of conductors and semiconductors ($\varepsilon > 81$) in the mineral realm includes the native metals (Au, Ag, Cu, Bi), graphite, some metal sulphides (e.g. chalcopyrite) and metal oxides (e.g. rutile, manganite, etc.). The dielectric constant of a good conductor is infinite to all practical intents and purposes.

Whether a substance will behave as a conductor or an insulator or something in between is determined by the mobility of its electrons or ions. In the interior or at the surface of a good conductor, the electrons of the metallic bonds constitute an electron cloud: these electrons can move at considerable speed when exposed to an electric field. In the interior or at the surface of an insulator, on the other hand, there are no free electrons, but only more or less strongly bound ions whose mobility is minute: their displacement in an electric field therefore takes a comparatively long time. Semiconductors combine ionic and electronic conduction. The charge carriers in an n-type semiconductor are electrons; in a p-type one, they are holes (empty electron positions with the electron missing from them) (Finkelnburg 1964). An increase of temperature reduces conductivity in a conductor but increases it in a semiconductor or insulator (Fraas 1950).

The conductivity of minerals covers a very broad range. The parameter called volume conductivity (the reciprocal of the resistance, measured in ohms, of a cube of edge length one cm, unit $\Omega^{-1}\,cm^{-1}$), is about

	$\sim 10^6$		for native copper
10	to	10^4	for pyrite
200	to	500	for galena
1	to	10^3	for graphite
10	to	10^{-7}	for most metal sulphides and metal oxides
10^{-14}	to	10^{-19}	for non-metallics (quartz, calcite, mica, rock salt, diamond, etc.).

In terms of volume conductivity, semiconductors and insulators separate some-what arbitrarily at about $10^{-6}\,\Omega^{-1}\,cm^{-1}$.

Charge density is on the order of 10^{22} elementary charges per cubic centimetre in metals, 10^{13} to 10^{18} in semiconductors and negligible in insulators. In electrolytes, it may attain up to 10^{16} per cubic centimetre.

Coulomb's Law states repulsion or attraction between two poles q_1 and q_2 (according as they are like or unlike) to be

$$P = \frac{q_1 q_2}{4\pi\,\varepsilon_0\,r^2}.$$

In the SI system, P is in newtons if q_1 and q_2 are in coulombs, r is in metres, and

$$\varepsilon_0 = \frac{10^7}{4\pi c_0} = 8.854 \cdot 10^{-12}\ \text{A s/V m}\quad \text{(or farads per metre)}$$

(where ε_0 is the permittivity [dielectric constant] of empty space). Here,

$$c_0 = \frac{1}{\sqrt{\varepsilon_0\mu_0}} = 2.997 \cdot 10^8\ \text{m/s}$$

is the speed of light in empty space.

Electric field intensity at the point where the charge q_1 resides is

$$E = \frac{P}{q_1} = \frac{q_2}{4\pi\varepsilon_0 r^2}\ \text{N/As or V/m.}$$

The (homogeneous) field between two plane plates, spaced one metre apart, with a potential of one volt across them, has unity intensity: it exerts a force of one newton upon a point charge of one ampere-second (As or coulomb).

Both force P and field intensity E are vector quantities. Just as in magnetics, the field can be illustrated by means of the line-of-force convention: field intensity varies as line-of-force density. Lines of force emerge from positive charges and end in negative ones; they are parallel and equidistant in a homogeneous field, but divergent, convergent or nonequidistant in an inhomogeneous one.

A plane plate carrying a charge Q/A exerts a force

$$P = \frac{qQ}{2\varepsilon_0 A}$$

upon a point charge q. (A is the surface area of the plate, Q is the charge impressed on it.) The force acting on a point charge q situated between two plane plates of equal size carrying equal but opposite charges Q/A is

$$P = \frac{qQ}{\varepsilon_0 A};$$

the homogeneous field between the plates has intensity

$$E = \frac{Q}{\varepsilon_0 A}.$$

The field being homogeneous, the force that it exerts upon q does not depend on q's position or on its separation from the plates.

A body endowed with a charge Q acquires a potential (voltage) U with respect to its uncharged surroundings:

$$Q = CU,$$

where C is called the capacitance. Its unit is the farad:

$$[C] = 1 \text{ F} = 1 \text{ A s/V}.$$

The capacitance of a plane plate condenser (capacitor) is

$$C = \frac{\varepsilon_0 A}{l},$$

where A is plate surface area and l is plate separation. The capacitance of a sphere of radius R is

$$C = 4\pi\varepsilon_0 R.$$

Placing a dielectric (a non-conductor) into the "empty" space between the plates of a capacitor will change its capacitance. If it was

$$Q_0 = C_0 U$$

prior to the insertion of the dielectric, to become

$$Q_a = C_a U$$

thereafter, then

$$\varepsilon = \frac{C_a}{C_0},$$

where ε is again the dielectric constant or permittivity of the dielectric. It is unity in empty space and $\varepsilon = 1.00059$ in air at 0 °C and a pressure of 760 Torr. The permittivities of most minerals fall between 5 and 25.

To charge a capacitor with a dielectric between its plates to the same potential as a vacuum-insulated one, more of a charge, $Q > Q_0$, is required.

$$Q = \varepsilon Q_0 = \frac{\varepsilon \varepsilon_0 AU}{l} = \varepsilon \varepsilon_0 AE.$$

On the insertion of a dielectric between the plates of a capacitor with a field intensity E_0 between them, field intensity decreases to

$$E = E_0/\varepsilon.$$

Since field intensity is proportional to charge density Q/A on the plates, and since the insertion of the dielectric does not change the overall charge distribution, we may infer that the surfaces of the dielectric facing the plates of the capacitor must have acquired by polarization equal and opposite charges

$$S = \frac{Q'}{A},$$

which maintain the relationship

$$E = \frac{E_0}{\varepsilon} = \frac{(Q - Q')}{A \varepsilon_0}.$$

In other words,

$$S = \frac{Q'}{A} = \frac{Q}{A} - \varepsilon_0 E = D - \varepsilon_0 E = \varepsilon_0(\varepsilon - 1) E.$$

Here,

$$D = \frac{Q}{A} = \varepsilon \varepsilon_0 E$$

is called electric displacement or induction; S is called dielectric polarization and $\varepsilon - 1$ is called dielectric susceptibility. D corresponds to flux density B, E to field intensity H of magnetism, ε corresponds to magnetic permeability μ and $\varepsilon - 1$ to magnetic susceptibility $\varkappa$.

A point charge q placed opposite a plane metal plate that is grounded (connected to earth) induces an equal and opposite charge $-q$ in the plate (by expelling from it a charge equal and identical to itself through the earth lead). The situation is the same as if a mirror charge $-q$ equal and opposite to p were situated on the far side of the plate, symmetrically to q. The attraction exerted

383

by the sheet equals in direction and magnitude the attraction that would be exerted by the hypothetical mirror charge $-q$, situated at twice the distance. Coulomb's Law states the force of attraction to be

$$P = \frac{q^2}{4\pi\varepsilon_0(2l)^2},$$

where l is the separation of the point charge from the sheet (Fraas 1962; Grimsehl 1961; Kirchberg and Schickel 1968; Olofinsky 1962, 1973; Ralston 1961; Schubert 1967; Stieler 1960).

4.1.1. Inductive, conductive and frictional charges. Solids can be endowed with a surface charge in a variety of ways.

In the field of an electrically charged electrode, a particle acquires polarization by *induction*: it becomes a dipole whose end facing the electrode is charged unlike the electrode and whose opposite end is charged like it. The induced moment M of the dipole, that is, the mechanical force that the electrostatic field exerts upon it, is

$$M = k\varepsilon_0 \frac{\varepsilon - 1}{\varepsilon + 2} x^3 E \operatorname{grad} E.$$

The polarizability of a particle (M/E, or dipole moment per unit field intensity) varies as dipole volume (as the cube of particle size x) and as the dielectric constant ε: it is greater for larger and/or conductive particles than for smaller and/or non-conductive ones. The coefficient k is a function of the medium and of particle shape (cf. Table 4.3).

The electrostatic force acting upon a particle is a function of its polarizability: hence, electrostatic separation performance is influenced not only by material constitution (dielectric constant, conductivity, etc.) but also by the size and shape of the particle. In an inhomogeneous (pinched) field converging towards a charged electrode, a polarized particle is invariably attracted by the electrode because, of the two induced poles of the particle the like one is situated farther from the electrode than the unlike one. (In a homogeneous field, a particle is exposed to a torque only.)

Conduction. Particles entering into direct contact with a charged conductor (e.g. a metal sheet) acquire charge by conduction. Charge transfer is practically instantaneous if the particle is a conductor but somewhat sluggish if it is an insulator; very good insulators can acquire practically no charge at all in this way. The charge impressed upon the particle will of course have the same sign as the charge upon the conductor from which it is derived. Conductors touching a grounded conductor lose their charge rapidly; insulators lose it slowly or not at all.

384

A particle in contact with a grounded electrode (a metal sheet) in an electro-static field acquires a charge

$$Q = C_p U,$$

where C_p is the capacitance of the particle and U is the potential difference between the electrodes.

Every particle has a total resistance R_p which is made up of its internal (body) resistance, its surface resistance and its contact resistance. The sum total of these is a function of temperature, field intensity and, indeed, also of the prehistory of the particle (of the films absorbed by it or adhering to it), etc.

Consider an electric model of the particle in which its resistance R_p and capacitance C_p are connected in series, with a potential difference U across them. Then,

$$iR_p + \frac{Q}{C_p} = U,$$

where

$$i = \frac{\mathrm{d}Q}{\mathrm{d}t}$$

is the current flowing in the circuit. Solving and rearranging these equations gives, if $Q = 0$ at $t = 0$,

$$Q = C_p U(1 - e^{-t/R_p C_p}).$$

That is, charge Q at instant t is a function of C_p and R_p. The product $R_p C_p$ is called the time constant of the circuit: it equals the time $t_{63\%}$ in which the particle can be charged to 63% of its final (infinite-time) charge. The formula is analogous in a way to the Rosin–Rammler (RR) grain size distribution function.

The energy of the electrons at the surface of body can be characterized in terms of their Fermi energy levels. If two objects are rubbed together, the one with the higher Fermi level will lose electrons to the one with the lower level. As a result, a *frictional or contact-potential* charge arises in each of the two objects (von Szantho 1949). Such a charge remains in place on dry non-con-ductors or poor conductors. By Coehn's Rule, it is that substance whose dielec-tric constant is greater which is turned positive by rubbing. (A greater dielectric constant implies stronger polarization, which in turn implies a greater propen-sity to hive off electrons.) The maximum charge density that can be generated by rubbing should in principle be about

$$\sim 15 \cdot 10^{-6}(\varepsilon_1 - \varepsilon_2) \text{ A s/m}^2$$

but is limited in actual fact by the breakdown of air as an insulator at any charge density greater than about

$$\sim 22.6 \cdot 10^{-6} \text{ A s/m}^2.$$

Whenever a particle touches a solid surface, a contact potential builds up on it. In normal circumstances, contact between any pair of the materials listed below will endow the one preceding the other with a positive charge:

serpentine — asbestos — topaz — mica — glass — calcite —
— barite — quartz — magnesium — lead — gypsum — zinc —
— beryl — sphalerite — magnetite — galena — pyrite —
— molybdenite — copper — antimony — antimonite—
— silver — sulphur — rubber.

The magnitude and sign of the charge acquired by a mineral on contact with some other material is a function partly of the consistency and state of the mineral surface and partly of the nature and state of the other body (e.g. a feeder plate). Deliberate or fortuitous changes in the nature or consistency of one or both surfaces will affect the magnitude and possibly even the polarity of the contact potential and, naturally, also the amount of charge transferred by conduction. For example, an oxide film formed on the feeder plate, an alteration of the mineral grains' surfaces by means of reagents, an adsorbed film of water or water vapour is likely to affect, more or less, the outcome of electrostatic separation at the charge densities referred to so far (Fraas 1950; Sun et al. 1950).

In a fluidized bed, the particles dancing about collide with or rub against each other and the container wall at frequent intervals. Of the mineral phases making up the bed, one or several may acquire enough of a contact potential to stick strongly enough to a grounded metal rod repeatedly plunged into the bed: and can be removed from the bed by that means (Burgess et al. 1970; Inculet and Bergougnou 1973; John 1967).

Electric conduction, that is, the mobility of electrons in an electric field, is a function, among other things, of field intensity and of time. A strong enough field may breakdown an insulator (may turn it conductive). The breakdown voltage may differ according as the potential impressed on the insulator is positive or negative.

If the frictional charge on a particle is greater than and opposite in sign to its conductive charge, the particle will be attracted by a grounded metal plate charged by induction, and repelled by the charging electrode, whose charge is opposite to that of the plate. If the charge on the electrode is of the same sign as the frictional charge on the particle, and is gradually increased, the inductive charge on the grounded metal plate will also increase gradually, and so will the conductive charge on the particles that are in contact with it: first cancelling the frictional charge, the electrode then imparts to the particles a resultant charge of the same sign as its own. Once this charge has attained a certain magnitude, the particle will be repelled by the plate: it will behave like a conducting mineral which, on account of its identical charge, would also be repelled by the plate. If on the other hand the electrode is charged so that the conductive charge on the particle is identical in sign with its frictional charge, then the two reinforce one another; as a result, the plate will repel the particle even at a lower charge density on the electrode. A mineral particle is called positive (or negative) reversible according as its frictional charge is positive (or negative).

For example, when concentrating a diamondiferous feed, the conductive grains contained in it (magnetite, limonite, ilmenite, etc.) are repelled by a grounded rotating metal roll when the electrode is charged positive, while the diamonds proper, as well as staurolite, tourmaline, quartz, etc., behave as insulators. Now when the electrode is charged negative, staurolite, tourmaline and quartz continue as insulators, whereas the diamonds together with the other conductors (ilmenite, limonite, etc.) are repelled by the grounded roll (Linari-Linholm 1950, 1958, 1964).

Let a mineral grain acquire against a feeder sheet a frictional charge Z and a conductive charge KV, where V is the potential difference between the sheet and the electrode and K is a constant depending on the conductivity of the mineral. For reversible minerals, $Z \neq 0$, and the electrode voltages needed respectively to attract and to repel the particle are separated by

$$V_{\text{crit}} = \frac{Z}{K}.$$

If K is small (that is, the mineral is a poor conductor), then V_{crit} tends to be very high (it may be several hundred kV).

4.1.2. Ion bombardment in a corona-discharge field.

The charges that can be transferred by induction, conduction or friction (and other means not enumerated before, such as pyroelectric charging by heating or piezoelectric charging by pressure) are greatly exceeded by those that can be impressed on both conductors and non-conductors by ion bombardment in a corona discharge. The small charges discussed above, which give rise to weak enough electric forces, arise in electrostatic fields in the stricter sense; a corona discharge, on the other hand, is a stream of gas ions which charges by convection any body within the discharge field to the same polarity as that of the corona electrode, but to a much stronger potential than any of those discussed so far. This is why it is usual to call the fields thus generated electrodynamic, in contradistinction to the electrostatic fields in the strict sense: the process itself is termed electrodynamic separation by corona-discharge ionization.

On increasing the voltage on a charging electrode beyond what is called the corona voltage, a gas discharge called a corona will form on it: as the electrode ionizes the air surrounding it, a strong ion stream (an "electric wind") arises, transferring charge from the electrode to the surrounding bodies without the benefit of any metallic conductor. Any particle in the way of the ion stream first acquires a polarization: the gas ions then adhere to the unlike-charged end of the particle. As a result, the particle acquires a net charge identical with that of the corona electrode. The maximum charge that can be imparted in this way is

$$q_0 = kFE_i,$$

where F m^2 is the surface area of the particle (proportional to the square of particle size x), E_i V/m is ionic field intensity (voltage drop per unit separation)

Table 4.3. Charge coefficient k as a function of form factor $l/\sqrt{S}$ and permittivity ε

$l/\sqrt{S}$	$\sim k$	
	$\varepsilon \to \infty$	$\varepsilon = 5$
5	36.2	27.15
1	3.0	2.15
0	0.67	0.53

and the coefficient k is a function of the dielectric constants of medium and particle and also of particle shape. Approximative k values are presented in Table 4.3. The $l/\sqrt{S}$ value of 5 refers to elongate particles; 1 refers to rounded and 0 to flattish ones. $\varepsilon \to \infty$ for conductors and $\varepsilon \cong 5$ for the sort of insulator that is encountered among minerals.

Falling free in a corona-discharge field an elongate particle can acquire a much greater maximum charge than a flattish, tabular one of the same surface area F. Conducting particles acquire a slightly greater charge than poor conductors or insulators: the charge (the k coefficient) varies as the expression

$$1 + 2\frac{(\varepsilon - 1)}{(\varepsilon + 2)}.$$

A spherical particle of dielectric constant $\varepsilon = 4$ to 5, of diameter $x = 1$ μm will capture some 100 elementary (electron) charges in a typical corona field of intensity $E_i = 2$ to 3 kV/cm. On grains larger than that, the number of captured charges varies as x^2 (meaning about 10^4 at $x = 10$ μm, about 10^6 at $x = 100$ μm, etc.). On particles smaller than 1 μm, on the other hand, the number of captured elementary charges varies as x (being e.g. about 10 at $x = 0.1$ μm).

The maximum charge that can be achieved by ionic bombardment in a corona field is

$$q_0 = k_1 x^2 E;$$

now, particle weight being

$$G = k_2 x^3 \delta,$$

the ratio of the two,

$$\frac{q_0}{G} = \frac{k_3 E}{x \delta},$$

varies inversely as particle size.

A particle making contact with a grounded conductor in the corona field will lose its charge if it is a fair conductor and retain it if it is a poor one. The residual charge would be zero on an ideal conductor and q_0 on an ideal insulator. On a non-ideal, real-life particle, a non-zero conductivity and a continuous make-up flux of ions from the corona electrode combine to create a state of equilibrium, resulting in a charge $q < q_0$. In the final reckoning, any particle exposed to ionic bombardment, regardless of whether it is a conductor or an insulator, acquires on contact with the grounded sheet a charge opposite to the sheet's, but its q will be greater if it is an insulator. Conditions are outlined in Fig. 4.1. On the grounded sheet, the equilibrium charge on the particle exposed to a corona flux is

$$q_i = q_0(A - \sqrt{A^2 - 1}),$$

where

$$A = 1 + K/B.$$

K is a function of corona field geometry and B is the "discharge constant" of the particle. At a fair approximation,

$$K/B = 10^{14}/R,$$

where R is the equivalent total resistance of the particle. (For fair conductors, R is close to zero, and so is q_i; K/B tends to infinity.)

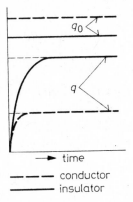

Fig. 4.1. Comparison of electric charge of particles of conducting and insulating materials when floating in the field of a corona electrode (q_0) and when in contact with a grounded sheet (q)

389

Charge q_0 on a particle in the corona field, prior to contact with the grounded sheet, is greater on a conducting particle than on an insulating one. On contact, it drops to q, which is, conversely, greater on the insulating particle than on the conducting one.

When, after their exposure to ionic bombardment, the particles escaping therefrom enter the purely static field of a grounded metal sheet or cylinder, those made up of an insulating substance will undergo practically no change,

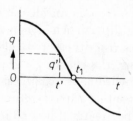

Fig. 4.2. Change of the charge on a particle of a conducting material in contact with a grounded sheet when passing from an ionic into a static field

but the better conductors will lose their charge gradually and will, after some time, be recharged oppositely by the grounded sheet (cf. Fig. 4.2). The time t_1 it takes to repolarize a particle is a function, among other things, of its shape: it is less for flattish particles — whose area of contact with the grounded sheet tends to be greater — than for elongate ones. Even a time $t' < t_1$, however, suffices to reduce the charge on the particle, opposite to that of the sheet, to a value q' weak enough for the external forces acting on the particle (gravity, centrifugal force, etc.) to overcome electric attraction and to detach it from the sheet.

Charge varies in time as

$$q = q_f - (q_f - q_i) e^{-Kt}$$

or

$$q = -q_f + (q_f + q_i) e^{-Kt},$$

where q_f is the final charge that the particle can acquire as $t \to \infty$ by contact with the grounded sheet or drum in the absence of ionic bombardment; q_i is the (initial) charge on the particle when it enters the static field (at $t = 0$), and K is a constant proportional to the ratio of conductivity to capacitance. Now

$$\frac{dq}{dt} = -(q_f + q_i) K e^{-Kt},$$

and

$$\frac{dq}{dK} = -(q_f + q_i) t e^{-Kt},$$

390

that is, the charge will change at a faster rate if q_f and q_i are increased (the electrode voltage is augmented): doing so tends to improve the sharpness of separation.

Electric attraction (the force P_e) varies as the square of particle size: the detaching forces P_c (centrifugal and gravitational) vary as its cube. Hence, if for a particle of given size of a given mineral,

$$\frac{P_e}{P_c} = \frac{k'}{x} = 1,$$

then
$$P_e < P_c$$

will hold for any particle larger than that and

$$P_e > P_c$$

for any smaller particle of the same mineral. If the minerals to be separated differ greatly as to conductivity (e.g., a conductor such as pyrite is to be separated from an insulator such as quartz), then even the smallest conducting particle will lose its charge and drop off the grounded sheet or drum before even the largest insulating particle can drop off. In such situations, a fair separation can be achieved at a comparatively low electrode voltage (1 kV, say) (Barthelemy 1960, 1961; Fraas 1962; Mukai et al. 1967; Ralston 1961; Schickel 1963; Williams 1956).

4.1.3. Interrelationships between the parameters of electric separation.
If the purpose of the operation is the winning of a clean concentrate, then the splitter separating the product hoppers is to be adjusted so that the thrown product (the concentrate) contain no misrouted particles. This means that some of the particles that do belong into the concentrate will be misrouted into the tailing (or middling) fraction instead. They can be recovered by feeding the fraction in question to another separating device (or to the same one for a second pass). Let the recovery of conductive particles in the first-pass concentrate (that is, the probability of a conductive particle's being routed into the concentrate) be p: then the probability of its being misrouted is $1 - p$. The second, third, . . . n-th pass leads to the probabilities

$$m = (1 - p)^2, \ (1 - p)^3 \ldots (1 - p)^n$$

of a conductive particle being misrouted;

$$k = p(1 - p), \ p(1 - p)^2, \ \ldots, \ p(1 - p)^{n-1}$$

are, in turn, the probabilities of its being properly routed into the concentrate. In other words,

$$\frac{k_{n+1}}{k_n} = \frac{p(1 - p)^n}{p(1 - p)^{n-1}} = 1 - p$$

and
$$\log k_n = n \log (1 - p).$$

Plotting the results in a coordinate system calibrated in n and $\log k_n$, a straight line of slope
$$\log (1 - p)$$
is obtained. On plotting the expression
$$K_n = ak_n = ap(1 - p)^{n-1}$$
(where a is the abundance of the conductive mineral in the r.o.m. ore) in a system of coordinates calibrated in n and $\log K_n$, the line retains its slope of $\log (1 - p)$ throughout provided $a \sim 100\%$, that is, provided a practically monomineralic aggregate, e.g. the residue of a concentrate produced by separation is being repeatedly re-run: on the other hand, the plot deviates upward from a straight line at higher values of n if $a < 100\%$, meaning that the feed contains other minerals as well. In such a case, the deviation between the straight line of slope $\log (1 - p)$ drawn through the initial section of the plot of actual test data and the rest of the plot is a measure of the abundance of the undesired mineral in the concentrate (of the probability of its getting misrouted there under the given conditions of separation). The probability p of a given mineral being routed into the concentrate, all other things being equal, varies with electrode voltage (V) as
$$p = A \log V - B,$$
where A and B are constants.

Not all the particles finding their way into the concentrate describe the same trajectory: after being thrown by the grounded drum, they will impinge upon a horizontal plate at different distances s. Their abundance S varies with distance s as
$$S \cong Ce^{-ks},$$
where $s > s_0$, and s_0 belongs to the maximal abundance S_0. C and k are constants. In other words, in a coordinate system calibrated in s and $\log S$, the plot will give a straight line, more or less. The relationship between throw distance s and charge q on the particle is approximately a linear one:
$$q \cong as + b.$$

Charge distribution on the thrown particles is approximately lognormal: that is, it gives a bell curve in a system of coordinates logarithmic in q, or a straight line in the Kolmogorov net, whose ordinate is calibrated in the normal distribution of cumulative particle abundance s_F (with the abundances 2, 9, 25, 50, 75, 91 and 98 percent being equidistant) and whose abscissa axis is logarithmic in q.

392

Current emitted by the corona electrode is in the microampere range: particle charge varies as the current. Using a bare corona electrode, the charge q_i on a particle, opposite in sign to that of the grounded roll, will be the greater, — and hence, their adhesion to the roll the stronger, — the stronger the emission of ion current. A plot of the recovery of any conductive mineral in a Kolmogorov net whose abscissa is calibrated in the logarithm of the current will again be a straight line.

The relationship of mineral recovery $m\%$ vs. mineral (metal) content $c\%$ in a coordinate system, both of whose axes are calibrated in the normal distribution, is an approximate straight line as a rule, as shown for some minerals in Fig. 4.3 (Johnson 1943). (The minerals occurring in the ore are in bracket.)

Surface conductivity K in a non-conducting mineral depends, all other things being equal, on the relative humidity of ambient air, φ, as

$$\log K = a\varphi + b,$$

where a and b are material constants. The sign and magnitude of the contact potential is a function also of relative humidity. For example, the frictional charge acquired by feldspar on a sheet of aluminium is negative up to $\varphi \lesssim 20\%$ and positive above it; the change over is at $\varphi \cong 40\%$ for quartz.

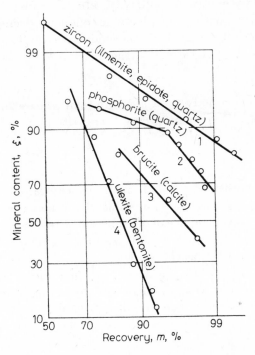

Fig. 4.3. Mineral abundance vs. mineral recovery in the concentrate of an electrical separation operation for some mineral combinations

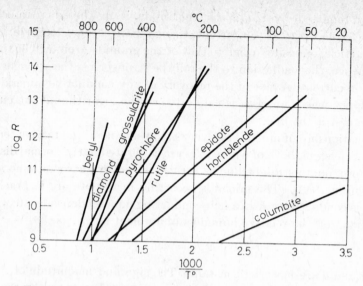

Fig. 4.4. Resistivity R vs. temperature T for some minerals

Each of the electric properties exploited in electrical separation (conductivity, the contact potential, permittivity, etc.) is a function of temperature, more or less. The conductivity of a metallic conductor decreases as its temperature increases; in contrast, that of semiconductors and ionic conductors (such as most minerals are) decreases. For these latter, the formula

$$K = K_0 e^{-k/T}$$

holds, where K is conductivity at absolute temperature T, and K_0 and k are material constants. The equation may be rewritten as

$$\log R = A + \frac{B}{T},$$

where $R = 1/K$ is resistivity and A and B are constants. Figure 4.4 presents resistivity vs. temperature for some minerals. Minerals whose resisitivity at room temperature is very high can often be separated successfully at high temperatures, provided the resistivity of one of the minerals to be separated is decreased sufficiently by heating to let it acquire a great enough charge by conduction (without ion bombardment), in which case it is thrown away by the grounded drum, just as a fair conductor would be (Carta et al. 1970, 1973; Fraas 1950, 1962; Lawver 1960; Olofinsky 1962; Parks et al. 1966; Ralston 1961).

4.1.4. The influence of heating (roasting), of the medium's dielectric constant, of particle size and shape. Resistivity R in a mineral that counts as a conductor (e.g. in a separator with a corona and static electrode at about 28 kV) is less than 10^{11} as a rule; that of a poor conductor usually exceeds 10^{13}. Brief heating (for one minute or so) reduces resistivity; a more protracted roasting (for 15 min or so) may work more or less profound changes in the material, affecting thereby the relative abundance of particles thrown by the roll (fair conductors) vs. those adhering to it (non-conductors), especially in a static (corona-less) field where the polarity of the electrode is not irrelevant.

Minerals are listed hereunder according to their electric separation behaviour before and after roasting.

Poor conductors at ~ 50 °C, $\gtrsim 99\%$ of which adheres to a grounded roll at a corona and static-electrode voltage of 28 kV, which retain this property even on roasting for 15 min in air at 800 °C: actinolite, albite, amblygonite, anhydrite, apatite, beryl, diopside, enstatite, fluorspar, gypsum, hexagonite, kyanite, lepidomelane, magnesite, microcline (monazite 90%), olivine, pyroxene, scheelite, smaragdite, spodumene, scapolite, tourmaline (zircon $\sim 94\%$).

Fair conductors at ~ 50 °C, $\sim 99\%$ of which is thrown by the grounded roll at a corona/static electrode voltage of 28 kV: acmite, cassiterite, chromite, columbite, franklinite, haematite, ilmenite, ilvaite, magnetite, migrine, pyrochlore, samarskite, spinel, struverite, vonsenite, wulfenite.

The underscored minerals do not (in the 0.2 to 0.4 mm grain size range) lose this property even on roasting for 15 min in air at 800 °C.

Table 4.4 presents the behaviour of certain minerals in the 0.2 to 0.4 mm grain size range after Fraas (1956).

Field intensity close to the grounded counter-electrode can at a given charge or voltage on the charging electrode be increased by inserting some material of higher dielectric constant in the path of the lines of force. If two materials, distinguished by subscripts 1 and 2, respectively have dielectric constants ε_1 and ε_2 and thickness d_1 and d_2 (where $d = d_1 + d_2$ is the separation of the charging electrode from the counter-electrode), field intensity in the two materials is E_1 and E_2 volt/cm and electrode potential is U volts, then

$$U = E_1 d_1 + E_2 d_2 = E_1 \left(d_1 + \frac{d_2 \varepsilon_1}{\varepsilon_2} \right) = E_1 \frac{\varepsilon_2 d_1 + \varepsilon_1 d_2}{\varepsilon_2},$$

that is,

$$E_1 = \frac{U \varepsilon_2}{\varepsilon_2 d_1 + \varepsilon_1 d_2}$$

and, by analogy,

$$E_2 = \frac{U \varepsilon_1}{\varepsilon_2 d_1 + \varepsilon_1 d_2}.$$

For instance, using a piece of bakelite of thickness $d_1 = 2.5$ cm and of dielectric constant $\varepsilon_1 = 5.5$ so that the width of the remaining air gap ($\varepsilon_2 = 1$) is $d_2 = 1.5$

Table 4.4. Electrical separation performance on some minerals before and after heat for a given separator design

Mineral	Corona- and stat. el. 28 kV heating for one min at °C				
0.2—0.4 mm	50	100	200	400	600
Actinolite				1	30
Albite				5	72
Almandite			1	92	
Andradite, yellow		1	9	60	99
Andradite, black	22	34	53	70	81
Anglesite				3	22
Anhydrite				5	68
Apatite				1	42
Augite	93	95	97		
Beryl, white				1	42
Beryl, green				15	95
Biotite				5	20
Carnotite		3	70	98	
Cerussite			5	95	
Chromite		92	93	95	
Cryolite		1	23	98	
Enstatite				5	60
Epidote	4	8	34	80	
Euxenite			16	51	56
Fluorspar			2	16	86
Glauconite		36	48	70	93
Glaukophane			5	62	80
Grossularite			2	47	95
Gypsum					2
Halite			1	32	80
Hornblende	50	66	89	98	
Kyanite				4	67
Limonite			3	27	66
Magnesite				1	54
Microcline				5	84
Monazite	9	10	14	19	18
Nepheline			9	27	73
Olivine				10	68
Pyrope			1	65	95
Pyroxene				5	80
Quartz				4	25
Rhodochrosite			5	92	
Rhodolite			1	99	
Rhodonite			1	91	
Rutile	62	67	77	93	
Scheelite				5	30
Serpentine	95		98		
Siderite		3	47	96	

treatment. Percentage of conductive fraction (fraction thrown by the grounded roll) and setting, in air (A) and hydrogen (H)

Electrode(s) at 30 kV corona- plus stat. °C					Cooled to 100 °C after heating for 15 min to °C Stat. el. only charged +/—				
0	400	600	800		0	200	400	600	800
				A	57/12	57/11	51/10	58/8	53/6
				A	44/11	47/14	48/11	52/4	45/5
1	1	40	87	A	25/45	25/32	39/7	60/45	60/50
				A	2/16	5/28	13/3	25/3	15
				A	30/43	28/47	32/19	36/15	25/9
				A	10/14	13/17	32/2	31/2	28/3
10	83	89	80	A	54/35	65/18	78/40	70/32	65/48
87	91	92	98	A	87/68	79/68	82/66	82/66	79/7
1	85	89	61	A	18/22	14/19	66/62	70/67	65/60
				H	40/18	50/22	42/22	38/9	68/6
4	4	1	1						
2	1	1	51	A	52/29	34/18	38/5	46/5	45/2
56	70	76	14	A	90/12	91/11	85/6	82/8	67/7
1	1	1	1						
1	1	2	20	A	4/7	5/12	27/1	29/3	34/1
				A	25/9	45/11	38/4	60/4	
85	92	96	95	A	76/62	71/60	71/59	58/28	48/28
83	9	14	9	A	60/60	30/35	52/42	50/20	68/50
				A	33/42	32/42	31/34	33/36	
				A	38/10	31/12	39/6	44/4	60/
				A	33/17	34/14	64/1	66/2	57/2
2	3	3	2	A	8/20	10/19	20/5	28/6	28/
				H	13/31	7/33	9/24	28/14	21/24
				A	46/7	58/6	46/4	51/4	57/5
1	39	99	98	A	43/4	45/3	63/26	82/73	75/53
				A	34/10	38/18	12/24	50/15	49/13
95	21	1	1	A	43/32	62/66	32/70	40/5	62/12
3	75	88	94						

Mineral	Corona- and stat. el. 28 kV heating for one min. at °C				
0.2—0.4 mm	50	100	200	400	600
Smithsonite			1	53	
Spodumene			1	10	85
Staurolite			1	92	
Turmaline				1	4
Willemite			1	41	66
Zircone	6	6	6	8	24

cm, field intensity is

$$E_1 = \frac{U}{1 \cdot 2.5 + 5.5 \cdot 1.5} = 0.372 \frac{U}{4} \mathrm{V/cm}$$

in the bakelite and

$$E_2 = \frac{5.5U}{1 \cdot 2.5 + 5.5 \cdot 1.5} = 2.046 \frac{U}{4} \mathrm{V/cm}$$

in the air. Before the insertion of the bakelite strip, field strength was

$$E_0 = \frac{U}{4} \mathrm{V/cm}.$$

The lines of force emerging from the strip of bakelite are approximately perpendicular to its surface; field pinch is further increased thereby (Linari-Linholm 1958).

Particle size and shape have a great influence on electrical separation performance. Flat grains (e.g. flakes of mica) or elongate ones (e.g. fibres of asbestos) are readily separated in an electrostatic separator from roundish or angular ones. In fact, such separators can even be used to sort asbestos fibres by length, or to size hard-to-screen materials such as ground glass (Plaksin and Olofinsky 1962).

The mass forces G acting on a particle whose three principal dimensions are ax, bx and x (where $a < b < 1$) vary as particle volume:

$$G = k_1 x^3 (ab);$$

the electrostatic forces E vary as particle surface:

$$E = k_2 x^2 \cdot 2(a + b + ab);$$

for fine enough grains, fluid friction K varies as the Stokes diameter, the cube root of the product of the three principal dimensions:

$$K = k_3 x (ab)^{1/3}.$$

398

Table 4.4 (continued)

Electrode(s) at 30 kV corona- plus stat. °C				Cooled to 100 °C after heating for 15 min to °C Stat. el. only charged +/—					
0	400	600	800	0		200	400	600	800
10	11	12	31	A	4/4	4/10	13/4	20/10	56/60
1	1	70	98	A	7/14	7/10	36/3	53/17	53/41
				H	10/10	8/20	10/15	39/12	60/30
10	7	6	12						

The ratios of the pairs of forces as defined above are

$$\frac{K}{G} = \frac{C_1}{x^2(ab)^{2/3}},$$

$$\frac{E}{G} = \frac{2C_2}{x}\left(1 + \frac{1}{a} + \frac{1}{b}\right)$$

and

$$\frac{E}{K} = 2C_3/x(ab)^{2/3}\left(1 + \frac{1}{a} + \frac{1}{b}\right),$$

where

$$C_1 = \frac{k_3}{k_1}; \quad C_2 = \frac{k_2}{k_1}; \quad C_3 = \frac{k_2}{k_3},$$

and

$$C_1 = \frac{C_2}{C_3}.$$

E/K varies directly and E/G inversely as the first power of particle dimension x; K/G varies inversely as the square of x. In other words, given a certain $a : b$ ratio, electrical separation is more sensitive to the variation of the principal dimension x than elutriation or pneumatic classification is.

Table 4.5. Force ratios (fluid friction K, mass force G and electrostatic force E)

Particle shape	K/G	E/G	E/K
Cubic $a=b=1$	C_1/x^2	$6C_2/x$	$6C_2x/C_1$
Flat $b = 1, a \ll 1$	$C_1/x^2a^{2/3}$	$2C_2(1 + 2a)/ax$	$2C_2x(1 + 2a)/C_1a^{1/3}$
Acicular, fibrous $a = b \ll 1$	$C_1/x^2a^{4/3}$	$2C_2(2 + a)/ax$	$2C_2x(2 + a)a^{1/3}/C_1$

Table 4.6. Multipliers referring the force ratios

	$a =$	1	0.5	0.25	0.1
K/G	$1/a^{2/3}$	1	1.59	2.53	4.65
	$1/a^{4/3}$	1	2.52	6.41	21.6
E/G	$1 + 2a/3a$	1	1.33	2.0	4.0
	$(2 + a)3a$	1	1.66	3.0	7.0
E/K	$1 + 2a/3a^{1/3}$	1	0.84	0.795	0.862
	$(2 + a)a^{1/3}$	1	0.661	0.471	0.324

Force ratios for near-cubic particles ($a \simeq b \simeq 1$), flat ones ($b \simeq 1$, $a \ll 1$) and acicular ones ($a \simeq b \ll 1$) are listed in Table 4.5. Multipliers referring those to the values for the cube are presented in Table 4.6 for different values of a. Given a certain major dimension x, the E/K ratio is seen to decrease monotonically for acicular grains (e.g. antimony, asbestos, etc.) as a decreases; to decrease slightly for lamellar minerals if $a \gtrsim 0.05$ (with the minimum of 0.795 belonging to $a = 0.25$) and to increase if $a < 0.05$. In other words, given a certain principal dimension x, very thin lamellae (e.g. flakes of mica) can be separated more sharply by electrical separation than by elutriation or pneumatic classification; it is the other way round with thicker lamellae and acicular grains.

It is an obvious inference from the way grain size affects separation performance that electric-separator feeds must be close-sized as otherwise sizing in the separator may entirely override separation by material properties. (Placer deposits tend to be fairly close-sized in their natural state: the electrical separation of such deposits tends to give very fair results.) Maximum limiting feed particle size is a function of s.g.: it is 5 to 6 mm for coals, 2 to 3 mm for materials having a s.g. about 3, and close to 1 mm for heavier ones. The presence of particles finer than 50 to 60 μm tends to impair separation performance. These should therefore be removed from the feed as completely as feasible.

4.2. ELECTRIC SEPARATORS

4.2.1. Electrodynamic (corona-electrode) separators usually incorporate rotating rolls, but the device taking the feed into the field may just as well be a belt or rotating disk. A typical roll arrangement is shown as Part A of Fig. 4.5. The corona electrode I is usually backed up by an adjustable static electrode S. Electrode voltage is typically in the 20 to 40 kV range, but may be as low as 10 kV or as high as 70 in extreme cases. The electrodes may be displaced relative both to one another and to the grounded roll. The corona electrode is a in Table 4.5 to those of the cube, for different a values

0.05	0.025	0.01	0.001	0.0001	
7.40	11.7	21.6	100	465	flat
54.6	137.5	465	100,000	216,000	acic.
7.34	14.0	34.0	334	3,333	flat
13.66	27.0	67.0	667	6,667	acic.
0.996	1.17	1.58	3.34	7.18	flat
0.252	0.197	0.144	0.067	0.031	acic.

thin filament as a rule, whereas the static electrode is typically a metal cylinder (possibly in a dielectric sheath) or a curved metal sheet. Part B of Fig. 4.5 shows some of the more usual arrangements.

When the electric field between electrodes and roll is not switched on, the particles are thrown into a narrow "gravity zone" by the roll of radius R rotating at angular velocity ω. That the gravity zone has any width at all is due to the different air resistances of different particles. The splitter separating the concentrate C from the middlings M is to be adjusted flush with the throw-zone edge farther from the roll: the splitter separating the middlings from the tailings T is to be adjusted for minimum pay mineral loss. In order to be routed with certainty into the concentrate, a particle must be a fair conductor, repolarized while still above the roll axis (inside the angle α, or within a time t).

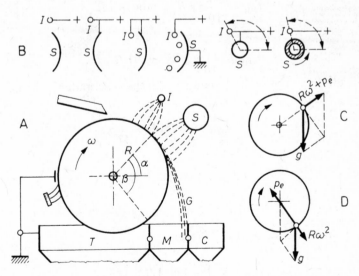

Fig. 4.5. A — rotating-roll corona-electrode separator; B — some alternatives for the relative arrangement of corona electrode I and static electrode S; C and D — forces acting on the particles on the roll

401

Electric repulsion helps to throw such particles beyond the gravity zone. The tailings will contain those poorish conductors whose charge does not, along the arc β (during the time t'), decrease to a value q' low enough to let gravity and the centrifugal force detach them from the roll. β begins where the fields of the two electrodes intersect and ends at the middlings-vs.-tailings splitter. The centrifugal force is 6 to 10 times the force of gravity at typical roll speeds. The critical times t and t' of routing fair conductors into the concentrate and poor ones into the tailings are obtained by introducing

$$\omega = \frac{\alpha}{t}$$

and

$$\omega' = \frac{\beta}{t'} \, ,$$

respectively, into the formula

$$R\omega^2 = mg \quad (m = 6 \text{ to } 10).$$

For example, if

$$R\omega^2 = 10\,g \simeq 10,000 \text{ cm/s}^2 \quad \left(\text{that is, } \omega = \frac{100}{\sqrt{R}} \right)$$

and

$$\alpha = 45^\circ = \frac{\pi}{4} = 0.78, \quad \beta \simeq 90^\circ = \frac{\pi}{2} = 1.57,$$

then

$$t_{\text{crit}} = \frac{\alpha}{100} \sqrt{R} = 0.0078 \sqrt{R}$$

and

$$t'_{\text{crit}} = \frac{\beta}{100} \sqrt{R} = 0.0157 \sqrt{R} \, .$$

The usual roll diameter $2R = 15$ cm gives in the case under scrutiny the critical times

$$t_{\text{crit}} = 0.0214 \simeq \frac{1}{47} \text{s}$$

and

$$t'_{\text{crit}} = 0.043 \simeq \frac{1}{23} \text{s}.$$

If

$$R\omega^2 \simeq 6g \simeq 6,000,$$

the critical times are longer by a factor

$$\sqrt{\frac{10}{6}} = 1.3.$$

Usual roll lengths are in the 1.5 to 2.5 m range.

The times t' and t can be determined experimentally for different minerals in a given field. For example, $t' < 1/50$ s for the conductive minerals of certain river-bank and beach placers such as rutile, cassiterite, columbite, chromite, tantalite, etc. This means that such minerals can be separated fairly well using a high-speed roll of diameter $2R = 15$ cm at

$$v = R\omega = \sqrt{10g\,R} \simeq 2.75 \text{ m/s}; \quad n = 350 \text{ rpm}.$$

For some iron oxides, t' is in the 1/10 to 1/20 s range: a fair enough separation of these requires a lower roll speed and/or a greater diameter. If reducing the rotor speed would reduce throughput to an undesirable degree, a greater roll diameter is to be chosen. For example, if

$$R\omega^2 \simeq 10g,$$

$$t' = \frac{1}{15} = 0.066 \text{ s},$$

$$\beta = \frac{\pi}{22},$$

then

$$R > \left(\frac{0.066}{0.0157}\right)^2 = 18 \text{ cm},$$

that is, a roll of diameter 36 cm or greater is to be chosen: it is to be run at a peripheral velocity of 4.25 m/s (at a speed of $n = 225$ rpm). If

$$R\omega^2 \simeq 6g$$

is satisfactory, then a rotor radius $R \geq 11$ cm and a peripheral velocity $v \geq 2.57$ m/s (a speed of $n \geq 223$ rpm) are adequate. For example, on concentrating a haematitic iron ore containing 38% Fe, recoveries were as follows:

	concentrate	middlings	tailings	Σ
haematite %	56	43	1	100
waste %	1	10	89	100.

The balance of the forces acting upon a mineral grain is shown in Fig. 4.5 (Part C: for a conductor, Part D: for a non-conductor). The resultant of the three forces — gravity, the centrifugal force and the electric force — is tangential to the rotor at the point of equilibrium. The radial component points inward to the roll axis above that point and outward into the air below it. At the point of equilibrium, the particle is thrown away tangentially by the roll, at a velocity $v = R\omega$ (provided friction is great enough to forestall the particle's sliding on the roll).

4.2.2. Electrostatic separators. Electric forces are much weaker in an electrostatic field (a field in which there is no corona electrode and hence no ion stream). The diagram of a static roll separator is obtained simply by leaving the corona electrode *I* off the drawing in Part A of Fig. 4.5. When touching the grounded roll, conducting particles polarized in the field lose that part of their charge which is of the same polarity as the charging electrode. They lose it at

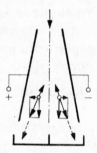

Fig. 4.6. Diagram of an electrostatic chamber separator

a slower or faster rate, depending on their conductivity and on the contact resistance set up: in contrast, they retain as much of their charge of opposite polarity as matches the induced charge density on the grounded roll. Such particles are accordingly repelled by the grounded roll and attracted by the charging electrode, depending on the magnitude of their charge, on field intensity and field pinch. Poorly conducting particles remain, on the other hand, electric dipoles on the grounded roll: they are attracted by the charging electrode's inhomogeneous field only (the pinch field converging towards that electrode). The field being largely homogeneous next to the roll surface, attraction is negligible for poorly conducting particles. If the particles handled differ sufficiently as to volume conductivity and/or permittivity, they will be thrown to different distances by the roll, despite the weakness of the electric forces in operation.

Figure 4.6 is the diagram of a chamber separator.

Electrostatic (coronaless) separation lends itself first and foremost to the separation of non-conducting minerals, provided the charges acquired by those differ as to polarity or at least as to magnitude. Some of the mineral grains falling in a field between grounded plates and high-voltage electrodes facing them are repelled by the electrodes; others are attracted by them or repelled to a different extent.

(This type of separation falls by the wayside in an electrodynamic separator, where ionic bombardment builds up a much stronger charge than the inductive, conductive and/or frictional charges on the particle taken together, and makes all non-conducting particles stick to the grounded sheet without exception.)

404

The grounded sheet of the static separator may be replaced by a series of chutes or rotating rolls in a cascade arrangement. In machines of this type, the charging electrodes are also rotating rolls as a rule; they are mounted relatively close to the grounded rolls. Sharp edges or spikes, or small electrode cross sections, each of which may give rise to a corona even at comparatively low voltages, are to be avoided in these designs.

Using such a machine, quartz e.g. can be separated from practically every other non-conducting mineral (feldspar, barite, apatite). For example, a limestone containing 1.9% SiO could be separated into a product containing 0.3% SiO_2 and one containing 21.7%. However, numerous factors may impair separation performance by modifying the rather weak electric effects arising in such a setup. For example, the feed must be totally dry (in quite a few cases, the temperature and humidity of ambient air have been known to affect performance); surface contaminations have to be removed (salt left behind by a brine such as sea water has to be washed off with fresh water and the feed must then be dried prior to separation). In other cases, pre-treatment with suitable reagents may endow minerals with properties permitting their successful electrostatic separation (Howe and Pope 1970).

The conductivity of minerals increases with relative humidity. The vapours and fumes of a variety of organic substances (pine-tar oil, kerosene, gasolene, turpentine, acetic acid, cresylic acid, benzoic acid, etc.) and inorganic ones (hydrogen fluoride, nitric acid, etc.) can also affect the electric behaviour of some minerals more or less strongly. Similar changes — some of them selective — can be brought about by treating the minerals with aqueous solutions of various electrolytes (salts, acids, bases — e.g. sodium oleate, rock salt, etc.) and drying them out subsequently. Whether a mineral behaves as a poor or fair conductor in a given electrostatic field is a function — as pointed out above — of temperature and of its thermal prehistory, other things being equal. Quartz for one has two points of transition (at 60 and 130 °C) within the usual temperature range of heat driers: both transitions affect its throw trajectory in the electrostatic field. This thermal transition process exhibits a hysteresis in function of time and of grain size: in quite a few cases, it will adversely affect product purity and recovery. (In such cases, drying should be by warm air of carefully controlled temperature, and any local overheating should be avoided.)

A phosphorite ore containing quartz, for example, heated to 206 °C and separated at different temperatures (between 29 and 160 °C), gave a phosphorite concentrate containing about 50% SiO_2 close to the transition temperature of 60 °C and only 4.3% at the optimum temperature, although the feed abounded in intergrown grains and grain aggregates. In the separation of limestones or of feldspars containing quartz or in the removal of base-metal oxides from glass sand, performance will also be affected by temperature. For example, in an operation run at the optimum temperature, about 90% of the base-metal oxides could be removed in 7 (to 15) weight percent tailings, reducing the base-metal oxide content of the concentrate to 0.027 (and 0.003)%.

The high-voltage supply of the electrodes involves as a rule the step-up transformation of the mains a.c. voltage and its rectification using a selenium, silicon, mercury vapour, vacuum tube or mechanical rectifier. (The latter incorporates a synchronous motor driven by the mains voltage; keyed to its shaft, there is an insulating disk with conductive bands around its rim: these connect the transformer's high-voltage terminals to the electrode during those intervals of time when the voltage across them is high enough. The charging electrode thus receives a pulsating d.c. supply. [The other pole is grounded.] Such a mechanical rectifier, then, is essentially a pole-changer-cum-chopper run in phase with the mains voltage.)

4.3. LOW-VOLTAGE SEPARATION BY DIELECTROPHORESIS

Particles finer than about 0.2 mm and different as to permittivity can be separated by dielectrophoresis in an electric field generated by low-voltage (e.g. 220 V) d.c. or a.c. in a medium intermediate as to permittivity between the minerals to be separated. If the field is inhomogeneous (convergent in some direction), then — in full analogy with the behaviour of paramagnetic and diamagnetic materials in a magnetic pinch field — the particles whose permittivity exceeds that of the medium move to where the lines of force converge, and vice versa. For example, in a field between two concentric cylindrical electrodes, the lines of force converge towards the inner cylinder. Field inhomogeneity may be enhanced by providing the shell of the inner cylinder with grooves, rubs or rows of spikes. The concentric cylinders may be replaced by plane plates provided with spikes. In such an arrangement, the particles of greater permittivity are attracted by the spikes: those of lower permittivity remain dispersed in the medium. The most likely choice for the medium of separation is a mixture of organic liquids. Water, by turning the medium conductive, frustrates this type of separation.

Between two concentric cylinders, ER, the product of radius R and field intensity E, is a constant. A particle of volume V perceives a force

$$F = - \frac{KVE^2}{R} = - KV \frac{(E_0 R_0)^2}{R^3},$$

where E_0 is the (known) field intensity at the radius R_0 and

$$K = \frac{3\varepsilon'(\varepsilon - \varepsilon')}{4\pi(\varepsilon + 2\varepsilon')},$$

406

where ε is the permittivity of the particle and ε' is that of the medium. In air, $\varepsilon' = 1$, and K is small: accordingly, the force P will also be weak. Hence, air is unsuited as a medium of dielectric industrial separation.

In air ($\varepsilon > \varepsilon'$), every electrically neutral particle will move towards the inner cylinder because, when a neutral particle is polarized in an electric field, each of its sides acquires a charge unlike that of the electrode facing it. Now, owing to field pinch, the inner electrode with its closer-spaced lines of force will attract the particle more strongly. Electrode polarity is irrelevant in this situation, so that a.c. may be used. An electrically charged particle will move towards a given (unlike) pole only if the poles are fed a d.c. voltage (in the phenomenon called electrophoresis), and will only vibrate (if anything) in an a.c. field.

Fine slimes do not have to be removed from the feed either in dielectrophoresis or electrophoresis.

Neither process has so far been realized on an industrial scale, although electrophoresis has long been used in the laboratory for the fractionation of colloids and charged macromolecules. Given a porous membrane (e.g. of clay), water moves through the membrane towards the cathode whereas the clay particles, which acquire a negative charge in water, move towards the anode. On a metal electrode immersed as the cathode in a clay suspension, a film of clear water develops, forestalling the adhesion of clay. This principle is exploited in the dewatering of pulps containing some solid particles, e.g. in the separation of water and silicate impurities or in the purification and dewatering of clay. A continuous process analogous to the operation of a filter press may be set up making use of the phenomenon of electroosmosis, in which an electric potential makes a solution seep through a stationary colloid membrane.

4.4 MAGNETOHYDRODYNAMIC SEPARATION

A magnetic field and an electric current perpendicular to it in a suspension of solid particles in water that is made conductive by the addition of some electrolyte together give rise to a magnetohydrodynamic (MHD) effect, provided the electric conductivity and permittivity of the particles differ from those of the fluid. The MHD (Lorentz) force arising per unit of liquid volume is

$$F = \mu H i = B i.$$

Here, μ is magnetic permeability, H is magnetic field intensity, $B = \mu H$ is magnetic flux density, and i is the electric current perpendicular to the magnetic field. Assume that the magnetic lines of force pass e.g. horizontally from left to right, and the current moves in a horizontal conductor perpendicular to the magnetic lines of force (in the spectator's line of sight, away from him);

then, by the "right-hand" or "corkscrew" rule, the force acting on the conductor is downward, like the force of gravity. If one of the two fields (the magnetic field or the current in the conductor) is reversed, then so is the direction of the MHD force (but not if both the fields are reversed simultaneously). A MHD force arises in exactly the same way if the conductor is a liquid (an electrolyte). Hence, in the setup described, pressure p_0 in a liquid at rest is determined jointly by its s.g.

$$\gamma = g\varrho$$

due to gravity and the MHD force $F = Bi$,

$$P_0 = \gamma \pm Bi.$$

The MHD effect will, then, increase or decrease the pressure in the liquid depending on the relative orientation of the vectors i and B.

The force increasing or decreasing the buoyancy γ acting upon a spherical particle of volume V is

$$F = 1.5iBV \frac{e' - e}{2e' + e},$$

where e' is the conductivity of the liquid and e is that of the particle. If $e' \gg e$ (for example, if a coal particle of conductivity $e = 10^{-7}$ ohm^{-1} cm^{-1}) is immersed in an electrolyte of conductivity $e' = 10^{-1}$ ohm^{-1} cm^{-1}, the MHD force arising is

$$F = 0.75iBV.$$

The formula may be rewritten to read

$$F = 1.5iHV \left(\frac{\Delta e}{2e} + \frac{\Delta \mu}{2\mu} \right)$$

or

$$F = 1.5iHV \left(\frac{\Delta \varepsilon}{2\varepsilon} + \frac{\Delta \mu}{2\mu} \right),$$

where e is the conductivity, μ is the magnetic permeability and ε the permittivity of the solid particle, and $\Delta e, \Delta \mu$ and $\Delta \varepsilon$ are the deviations of those from the analogous parameters of the liquid.

The "relevant" s.g. of a conductive liquid (of an electrolyte) can, then, be changed by the MHD force: it can be increased or decreased without affecting the viscosity of the fluid (provided it is not overly pressure-dependent). This may be helpful in the separation of fine particles by s.g. For example, the relevant s.g. of a rock salt solution of s.g. $\gamma = 1.15$ (at which effective separation takes place) can be increased to $\gamma' = 1.62$ by a current density $i = 3.1$ A/cm^2 and a magnetic flux density $B = 0.27$ Wb/m^2. The current flowing in the separator may be a.c. if the electromagnet is excited synchronously with the same current. The electrolytic effect of a.c. is negligible whereas, using d.c., chlorine gas will be released by a rock salt solution (Andres 1967; Madai 1970; Schenk 1967).

4.5. SEPARATION OF LUMPY FEEDS BY ELECTRIC CONDUCTIVITY

The idea exploited is that, on impressing a voltage on a lump, a current depending on its conductivity will pass through it: this will be either sufficient or not to open a trap door used to split the feed stream. This arrangement permits the mechanization of hand cobbing.

4.6. LITERATURE ON ELECTRICAL SEPARATION

ANDRES, U. C. (et al.): Magnetohydrodynamische Schwimm/Sinksscheidung feinkörniger Materialien. *Freib. Fh. A415* 1967, 57—63.

BARTHELEMY, R. E.: How high tension electrostatic separation recovers iron ore. *E/MJ* 1958 Dec., 87—91.

BARTHELEMY, R. E.: Modern theory of the electrical high tension process. *Min. Congr. J.* 1961 March, 55—59.

BARTHELEMY, R. E.—R. G. MORA: Electrical high-tension minerals beneficiation. Principles and technical aspects. *IMDC*, London 1960, 757—773.

BULLOCK, H. L.: Quartz gangue or mineral: The effect of temperature on its electrostatic separation. *Trans. AIME* 1968, 367—371.

BULLOCK, H. L.: How temperature affects electrostatic separation of quartz. *Min. Engng* 1969 Aug., 80.

BURGESS, I.—I. INCULET—M. A. BERGOUGNOU: Electrostatic beneficiation of coal in fluidized beds. *CIM Bull.* 1970, 383—385.

CARTA, M. (et al.): The influence of the surface energy structure of minerals on electric separation and flotation. 9. *IMPC*, Praha 1970, 47—57.

CARTA, M. (et al.): Improvement in electric separation and flotation by modification of energy levels in surface layers. 10. *IMPC*, London 1973.

DYRENFORTH, P.—J. E. LAWVER: Beneficiation of iron ore by electrical methods. 9. *IMPC*, Praha 1970, III, 49—55.

FINKELNBURG, W.: *Einführung in die Atomphysik.* Springer Verlag, Berlin—Göttingen—Heidelberg 1964.

FRAAS, F.: Contact potential in electrostatic separation. *Bu. Mines RI 3667* 1942.

FRAAS, F.: Conductance electrostatic separation with convective charging. *Trans. AIME* 1950, 1041—1043.

FRAAS, F.: Effect of temperature on the electrostatic separation of minerals. *Bu. Mines RI 5213* 1956.

FRAAS, F.: Electrostatic separation of granular materials. *Bu. Mines RI 603* 1962.

FRAAS, F.—O. C. RALSTON: The electrostatic separation of several industrial minerals. *Trans. AIME* 1949, 240—251.

GRIMSEHL, I.: *Lehrbuch der Physik. Bd. 2: Elektromagnetisches Feld.* B. G. Teubner Verlagsgesellschaft, Leipzig 1961.

HATFIELD, H. S.: Dielectric separation. *Trans. IMM* 1924, 335—342, 350—370.

HOLMAN, B. W.—S. J. R. C. SHEPHARD: Dielectric mineral separation. *Trans. IMM* 1924, 343—349.

HOWE, T. M.—M. I. POPE: The effect of conditioning agents on the surface conductivity of powders, in relation to electrostatic separation. 9. *IMPC*, Praha 1970, 59—66.

HUDSON, S. B.: Electrostatic separation. *RDMD*, London 1953, 335—348.

INCULET, I. I.—M. A. BERGOUGNOU: Electrostatic beneficiation of fine material particles in a fluidized bed. 10. *IMPC*, London 1973, 11.

JOHN, H. W. P.: Die Anwendung der Wirbelschichttechnik bei der elektrostatischen Gesteinaufbereitung. *Industrie der Steine und Erden* 1967, 258—267.

JOHNSON, H. B.: Electrostatic separation. *E/MJ* 1938 Sept., 42—45; Oct., 42—43; Dec., 41—45.

JOHNSON, H B.: Recovery of valuable minerals by electrostatic separation. *Chem. Met. Eng.* 1943 Nov., 130—133.

JUHÁSZ, Z.: Agyagásványok dielektromos állandója. (Dielectric constant of clay minerals.) *Földtani Közlöny* 1973, Nos 3—4, 301—323.

KIRCHBERG, H.: Elektrische Aufbereitung. *Bergakademie* 1963, 506—511.

KIRCHBERG, H.—A. SCHICKEL: Ein Beitrag zur quantitativen Verständnis der Scheidung in elektrostatischen Feldern. 8. *IMPC*, Leningrad 1968.

LAWVER, J. E.: Fundamentals of the electrostatic concentration of minerals. *Min. Mag.* 1960 Jan., 20—27, 33.

LENHART, W. B.: Rare mineral recovery in the main business. *Rock Prod.* 1956 July, 92—94.

LINARI-LINHOLM, A. A.: Recovery of diamonds by elctrostatic separation. *J. Chem. Met. Min. Soc. S. Afr.* 1950 Oct., 131—157.

LINARI-LINHOLM, A. A.: Neue Aufbereitungsverfahren im Diamantbergbau. *Bergbauwiss.* 1958, 166—175.

LINARI-LINHOLM, A. A.: Elektrostatisches Trennen von Diamanten mit schweren Begleit- mineralen. *AT* 1964, 447—451.

MADAI, E.: Grundlagen der magnetohydrodynamischen Scheidung. *Bergakademie* 1970, 606—609.

MUKAI, S.—T. WAKAMATSU—Y. SHIDA—T. ISHIKAWA: Study on the electrostatic con- centration of low ash coal in corona discharge field. *Trans. AIME* 1967, 205—213.

OLOFINSKY, N. F.: *Elektricheskiye metody obogashcheniya.* Gosgortekhizdat, Moscow 1962.

OLOFINSKY, N. F. (et al.): Application of electrical methods of separation to close sizing of finely dispersed mineral particles. 10. *IMPC*, London 1973, 40.

PARKS, G. A.—B. K. JINDAL—J. ANDERSON: Temperature and humidity in electrical separation of oxide minerals. *Trans. AIME* 1966, 451—457.

PLAKSIN, I. N.—N. F. OLOFINSKY: Dedusting and classifying minerals in the fine-size range with corona-type separators. *Bull. IMM* 1960, 613—626.

PLAKSIN, I. N.—N. F. OLOFINSKY: Elektrische Aufbereitung von Mineralen mit Faser- Textur (am Beispiel von Chrysotil-Asbesthaufwerken). *Freib. Fh. A255* 1962, 151—156.

PLAKSIN, I. N.—N. F. OLOFINSKY: Review of electrical separation methods in mineral technology. *Trans. IMM* 1966, C57—C64.

POHL, H. A.—L. P. SCHWAR: Particle separation by non-uniform electric fields in liquid dielectrics, batch methods. *J. Electrochem. Soc.* 1960, 383—385.

RALSTON, O. C.: *Electrostatic separation of mixed granular solids.* Elsevier, Amsterdam— London—New York 1961.

SCHENK, G. W.: Magnetohydrodynamisches Scheidungsverfahren, eine neue Möglichkeit für die Aufbereitung feinkörniger Steinkohlen. *AT* 1967, 447—454.

SCHICKEL, A.: Entwicklung und betrieblicher Einsatz eines Fünfwalzenkoronascheiders. *Freib. Fh. A269* 1963, 49—58.

SCHUBERT, H.: *Aufbereitung fester mineralischer Rohstoffe*. VEB Deutscher Verlag für Grundstoffindustrie, Leipzig 1967.

SCHUBERT, H.: Zu den Grundlegenden stofflicher Trennungen in elektrischer Feldern. *Verfahrenstechnik* 1967, 31—35.

STIELER, A.: Sortierung von mineralischen Rohstoffen im elektrischen Feld. *AT* 1960, 474—480.

STIELER, A.: Neuere Entwicklungen auf dem Gebiet der elektrostatischen Aufbereitung. *Erzmetall* 1966, 410—417.

SUN, S. C.—J. D. MORGAN—R. F. Wesner: Mineral particles in electrostatic separation. *Trans. AIME* 1950, 369—373.

SZANTHO, E. VON: Über die elektrischen Ladungen feinkörniger Stoffe bei Rieseln. *Bergbauarchiv* 1949, No. 10, 192—210.

SZANTHO, E. VON—H. HILDEBRAND: Untersuchungen über die elektrische Leitfähigkeit von Mineralen und deren Ablenkung am Elektro-Walzenscheider. *AT* 1965, 637—645.

WILLIAMS, A. E.: High tension separation of minerals. *Min. Mag.* 1956 Aug., 75—81.

5. OTHER PROCESSES OF CONCENTRATION

The most important processes, those turning in a fair and economically viable performance when applied to the r.o.m. products of a wide range of deposits, were described in the previous chapters. In addition to these, there are many processes of minor importance, applicable only locally, or to certain special combinations of minerals. In principle, differences in any physical property may serve as a basis for the successful separation of minerals. Some of these processes of a narrower range of application will be described below, partly after Cavanagh and Last (1965), Collier et al. (1973), Funkemeyer (1968), Iohn (1970), Revnitzev and Dimitriev (1964), Stumpf (1970) and Yourovsky et al. (1962).

5.1. PROCESSES RELATED TO FLOTATION

Hydrophobic-aerophilic minerals are at the same time also oleophilic, meaning that they will adhere to oils and fats. Metal sulphides adhere better to a wet sheet of rubber than gangue minerals: this property is helpful in vanner separation.

5.1.1. Selective adhesion to oil. The selective adhesion to oil of mineral grains having a non-zero contact angle can be exploited to granulate pay minerals (to let them form clusters on oil droplets — cf. Part A of Fig. 2.13 which can then be separated from the ungranulated ingredients. (Farnand 1969; Meadus et al. 1968; Mellgren and Shergold 1966; Mular and Puddington 1968; Shergold and Mellgren 1970; Siriani et al. 1968; Sparks et al. 1971).

On mixing a pulp containing one or more pay (oleophilic) minerals with oil about sufficient to fill out the interstices of the pay mineral grains, the droplets of oil get laden with mineral grains: they will either settle to the bottom or can be skimmed off the top of the pulp if they are light enough to float up (bulk-oil flotation). The droplets forming in a coal slurry treated in a similar fashion with crude petroleum or a spent lubricating oil will tend to float up. In the Convertol process, 2 to 10 weight percent (referred to the solids present) of practically valueless spent lube or tar is vigorously kneaded together with

412

a coal slurry containing 40 to 50 weight percent solids: this mass is then dispersed by dilution with water. The watery phase of the emulsion so obtained, together with the waste slimes suspended in it, is separated on a screen centrifuge of 0.2 to 0.3 mm aperture size or on a vibrating screen plus a settling centrifuge from the oily granules of coal particles that are agglomerated by phase inversion and thus retained on the screen. The process gives favourable results for coking coals in particular, what with the waste lube being turned into valuable organic compounds in the course of coking (Brisse and Morris 1958; Götte and Schäfer 1960; Lemke 1954; Müschenborn 1952).

In addition to oil, more or less air may also adhere to the hydrophobic coal particles: the quantity of air so trapped depends on the mode of mixing and on the design of the equipment used. The more air there is, the lighter the granules (spherules) formed by the association of mineral, oil and air will be. If the pulp is fed to a table and shaken/strirred in a thin sheet, the oily granules will float up to the top of the sheet and leave through the outlet for the light product (table flotation), whereas the unclustered "sand" fraction, protected by the ribbing from the wash, will leave it as heavy-product. In such a setup, table (or skin or film) flotation may be used to separate feeds much coarser than the upper limiting particle size of froth flotation. By treating the thick pulp with suitable modifying reagents before introducing the collector and the non-polar oil (crude petroleum, diesel fuel, etc.), the surfaces of most mineral species can be turned oleophilic-aerophilic or hydrophilic as required, just as in froth flotation.

A recent version of the Convertol process, called OLIFLOC, which, as suggested by the name, is flocculation by means of an oil, has been successfully used in the concentration of fine coal pulps (e.g. less than about 60 μm).

5.1.2. Adhesion to grease. Minerals with a non-zero contact angle will adhere not only to liquid oils but also to fats, greases and bitumens, i.e. to hydrocarbons solid or plastic at room temperature. The effect is exploited on an industrial scale in the final recovery of diamonds in Southern Africa. A pre-concentrate obtained by gravity concentration is fed to a symmetrically shaken (or stationary) sheet (table) coated with grease (grease table). The diamonds will stick to the table whereas the minerals accompanying them will not (Loftus et al. 1970).

If one of two co-rotating rolls coated with foam rubber is saturated with bitumen, the non-polar particles will adhere to it and can subsequently be removed by means of a scraper. The other particles remain on the other roll and drop off it as it rotates. Also in this case, mineral surfaces may be rendered polar or non-polar as desired using appropriate collectors and modifiers, just as in flotation. The upper limiting size of the particles that can be separated in this way is 2 to 3 cm (Bierbrauer 1937).

5.1.3. Selective flocculation. Long-chain polymers as flocculating agents often act selectively on different minerals: they may tend to flocculate one mineral of a pair but not the other. The flocculated fraction can be separated either by decantation or by gentle flotation in a cell that will not break up the floccules.

Using the right dispersing agent (calgon, water glass, NaF, NaCl, Na_2S, NaOH, Na-pyrophosphate, Na-hexametaphosphate, ammonia, etc.) and flocculating agent (polyacrylamide, polyacrylonitrile, polysaccharides, starch, polyethylene oxide, carboxy methyl cellulose, etc.), it is possible to achieve the selective flocculation of one of the components in a mineral mixture (e.g. haematite, pyrite, sphalerite, smithsonite, galena, limonite, calcite, apatite, talc, kaolin, coal, etc.) while the other component (silicate, quartz, clay, shale, etc.) remains in suspension (or vice versa) The flocculated grains can be separated from the dispersed ones using bubbles (by flotation — cf. granulating or agglomerating flotation) or without bubbles, by settling (decantation).

The longer or shorter polymer chains get adsorbed on the surface of the slime particles either directly, or by the intermediary of a hydrogen bond that they form with the free part of a chain already adsorbed. Polymer bonds tend to be confined largely to between free particles and particles already hung with one or several polymer molecules (or possibly to between the latter only). In other words, flocculation requires the prior adsorption of polymer molecules on some at least of the particles. The role of electric charges is secondary. For example, quartz, calcite or microcline can be flocculated with polyacrylamide even if their zeta potential remains negative (at 25 to 30 mV) after the adsorption of the polymer. If there is too great a like charge on the particles and the polymer chains, it will of course hinder adsorption, inter-particle collisions and the formation of polymer bonds: conversely, polymers of unlike charge get adsorbed more strongly on the grains than polymers of like charge or uncharged ones. The adsorption of non-ionic (uncharged) polymers may be hindered by strong hydrolysis or (if the particles are charged negative) by too high a pH.

The bonding itself may be different according to the chemical nature of the mineral surface and of the functional radical of the polymer. Unhydrolysed polymers establish hydrogen bonds between their own NH_2 or OH radicals and the OH radicals, if any, of the mineral surface or adhere by multiple dipolar attraction to ionic mineral lattices. Hydrolysed polymers possessing a carboxylate or sulfonate radical can be adsorbed by hydrogen bonding or by chemisorption (the constitution of ionic bonds or complex radicals) if the lattices of the particles incorporate multi-valent cations.

Run-of-the-mill weakly hydrolysing polymers tend to bring about dispersion rather than flocculation if the concentration or the molecular weight of the polymer is too great. In the first case, adsorption becomes so complete that too few free positions remain on the particle surface at which to establish inter-

414

particle polymer bonding; in the second, the long chains will enter into physical interaction with one another rather than with the mineral particles.

Part A of Fig. 5.1 presents for an example the percentage abundance vs. the pH of the ionic form (COO⁻) and the non-ionic form (COOH) of a polyacrylate in aqueous solution. Half-and-half distribution occurs at $pH = 4.8$: it is the

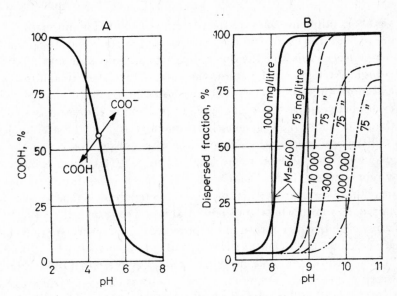

Fig. 5.1. A — Percentage abundance of the ionized and un-ionized fractions of a polyacrylate in aqueous solution, *B* — percentage dispersed fraction in a dolomite suspension

ionic fraction that is more abundant at higher pH values and vice versa. The abundance of the non-ionic fraction is, e.g., about 95% at $pH = 3$ and about 2% at $pH = 7$. At low pH values, the un-ionized carboxyl radicals of the polymer molecules have a propensity to constitute intra-chain hydrogen bonds kinking the chain. At high pH values, the negatively charged carboxylate radicals repel one another: as a result, the chain straightens out. The viscosity of the solution increases as the abundance of the ionic fraction.

Part B of Fig. 5.1 presents as a function of the pH the percentage fraction of a dolomite suspension dispersed by dosages of polyacrylamides of different molecular weight M. The dosages are shown against the curves in mg/l units. The suspension is seen to shift over from the flocculated to the dispersed state within quite a narrow pH interval: the interval in question is displaced towards the higher pH range by higher molecular weights and towards the lower pH range by greater concentrations. For the solutions shown, the molecular weights

$$M = 5,400 \qquad 10,000 \qquad 300,000 \qquad 1,000,000$$

correspond to acrylic acid concentrations of

$$22 \qquad 24 \qquad 40 \qquad 60\%$$

respectively: the viscosity of the solutions is

$$0.13 \qquad 0.4 \qquad 10 \qquad 50 \text{ poises.}$$

In a weakly alkaline medium (in the pH range 7 to 8), dolomite retains a low negative zeta potential even after the adsorption of the polymer: the probability for the distended chains and the dolomite particles to collide and to stick together is high. At higher pH values, the zeta potential of dolomite is fairly high both before and after adsorption; electrostatic repulsion hinders collision and adhesion between particles and polymer molecules: the result is dispersion rather than flocculation. A longer-chain polymer (one of greater molecular weight) will have a longer segment left free after adsorption on the particle. This segment can be adhered to by some more particles, even though those mutually repel one another: this increases the propensity to flocculate. As a result, dispersion takes a higher pH, at which electric repulsion also is stronger. (For example, dolomite whose zeta potential is -10 mV at pH $= 7$ in the absence of any acrylate gets charged in the presence of a polyacrylate of molecular weight $M = 5{,}400$ to -31 mV at pH $= 7$ and to -55 mV at pH $= 10$.) Above a pH $= 11.5$, on the other hand, flocculation may occur again if the compression of the electric double layer reduces the zeta potential sufficiently. For example, at a pH $= 11.8$, and polymer concentrations of

$$310 \qquad 285 \qquad 265 \qquad 250 \qquad 185 \text{ g/t,}$$

$$100 \qquad 47 \qquad 10 \qquad 6 \qquad 2\%$$

of the dolomite in suspension was found to be dispersed.

The ratio

$$R = \frac{Y}{X}$$

(where Y g/t is the polymer concentration which gives rise to 50% dispersion and X g/t is the polymer concentration which maximizes adsorption) is practically independent of the specific surface F m²/g of the solid phase (since both Y and X are linear functions of F) but increases as the molecular weight M of the polymers. It is, moreover, a sensitive function of the pH. The

$$R = f(\text{pH})$$

curves of some acrylates of different molecular weight M acting on dolomite suspensions are shown in Fig. 5.2. The curves refer to the concentration Y: flocculation occurs below and dispersion above them. For example, at a pH $= 10.5$

$$R = \qquad 19 \qquad\qquad 28 \qquad\qquad 69\%$$

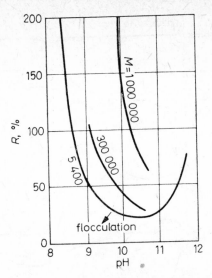

Fig. 5.2. Ratio R of polymer concentration giving 50% dispersion to polymer concentration giving maximum adsorption vs. the pH on the dosage of polyacrylamides different as to molecular weight M

if

$$M = 5,400 \qquad 300,000 \qquad 1,000,000.$$

The polymer with $M = 5,400$ will cause the dolomite suspension to disperse in the 9.5 to 11.2 pH range even at low R values (that is, with little of the polymer adsorbed). $R = 100\%$ at pH $= 8.7$, meaning that the adhesion of the polymer chains results in a full coating of the particles. Dispersion may persist within a very narrow pH range below 8.7 also (even though $R > 100\%$ there), owing to the greater viscosity of the liquid caused by an abundance of unadsorbed polymer chains in the solution. Above a pH $= 11$, the R required to bring about dispersion increases again because the compression of the electric double layers on the particles results in a reduced electric repulsion (zeta potential), entailing an increased propensity to flocculate (van Lierde 1974).

Figure 5.3 presents as examples the behaviour of the gangue minerals quartz and calcite, of smithsonite ($ZnCO_3$) and of the metal sulphides sphalerite, pyrite and galena (ZnS, FeS_2 and PbS) vs. the pH at different concentrations of different flocculants (non-ionic: Separan NP 10, a polyacrylamide; anionic: Aerofloc R 550, a hydrolysed polyacrylonitrile, and Hercules CMC, a carboxy methyl cellulose; and cationic: Nalco 600, an ethylene diamine polymer). The ordinate axis is calibrated in the flocculating effect

$$P_f\% = 100 \left(\frac{c_0 - c_f}{c_0} \right),$$

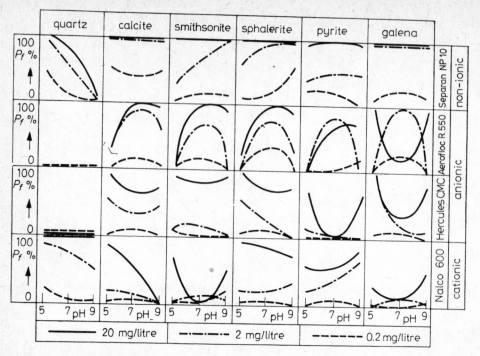

Fig. 5.3. Flocculation of different minerals vs. the pH on the dosage of different flocculants

obtained by adding the flocculant in a calibrated flask to a suspension of $\sigma = 10$ to 15%: after settling for a pre-determined span of time (80 to 180 s), 60% of the contents, is siphoned off and its solids content is determined: c_f is the solids content obtained with the flocculant added; c_0 is the solids content obtained with no flocculant (Bischoff 1960; Friend et al. 1973; Špaldon 1960; Usoni et al. 1968; Yarar and Kitchener 1970).

A fair separation of a minus-20 μm haematite-plus-silicate pulp could be achieved by adding to it a sodium hexametaphosphate dispersant and a large-molecule polyacrylamide plus sodium polyacrylate as a flocculant. Selectivity was greatly influenced by the addition of a NaF or NaCl electrolyte (Read 1971).

Selective flocculation will work with coal slurries also. Protective colloids such as water glass, sodium citrite, tannic acid, etc. selectively adsorbed by the waste particles will stabilize those and prevent their flocculation while the coal particles in the slurry are flocculated e.g. by methacrylic acid or the polymers of methacrylates. Separating the two phases by decantation (in a pulp thickener) gave in certain situations (including industrial scale operations) a performance that was not inferior to that of flotation. The volume and composition of concentrate and waste could be influenced by varying reagent dosage both as to quantity and composition (Volšický et al. 1967).

418

5.1.4. Amalgamation. The ancient way of winning native gold by means of liquid mercury is sometimes classed as a metallurgical operation in which the gold, dissolving in the mercury, forms a gold-and-mercury alloy (an amalgam). Amalgamation, however, is in fact an operation of concentration relying on adhesion, analogous to the processes based on adhesion between mineral grains and oil or air: the winning of gold with mercury does not require the reaction between the two metals to run its full course, being based as it is on their simple propensity to undergo that reaction (as expressed by the fact that gold is wetted by mercury, in analogy with the "wetting" of certain mineral grains by an oil or by air). The essential thing is that the total surface energy of the system decreases when the gold–water and mercury–water interfaces are replaced by a common gold–mercury interface.

It follows at once that the propensity of native gold to amalgamate depends first and foremost on the state of the gold and mercury surfaces, just as, in flotation, the process is determined by the nature of the mineral grains and by the state of the air–water interface. Similarly, certain substances may, in full analogy to the activating, collecting and depressing agents of flotation, promote or hinder the adhesion between gold and mercury. The mercury phase of amalgamation may be a liquid added to the charge in an amalgamating barrel (a tumbling mill) or a layer of amalgam formed on a sheet of copper in plate amalgamation. At intervals, the gold amalgam is removed with hard rubber scrapers from the amalgamating plates: it is then strained through chamois or pressed out in a press. Mercury is subsequently expelled by distillation at the temperature of cherry-red glow. Amalgamation can be used to handle ores containing what is called free gold (native gold in comparatively coarse particles). It will not work with ores in which native gold constitutes a fine-grained impregnation or in which gold is in the telluride or some other compound form.

5.2. CONCENTRATION BY OPTICAL PROPERTIES

It is based on differences in the colour or sheen of the minerals to be separated.

5.2.1. Hand sorting or hand picking. This ancient method which is still going strong in certain situations is low on investment and energy cost but high on live-labour input. It may be preferred where the task to be performed is a simple one and labour is cheap. A stationary sorting surface may be used but it is better to let the surface move slowly (at a speed of 0.15 to 0.3 m/s) and take away the lumps left on it. The moving devices used are sorting belts or revolving picking tables. In practice, the method is confined to lumps larger than 4 to 7 cm because costs rise steeply as lump size decreases (the number of particles making up an aggregate of given weight varies inversely as the cube of particle size!). The weight of the lumps sets an upper limit, in combination with the fact that intergrowths are the more probable, the larger the lumps. The limiting lump size is accordingly about 25 to 30 cm.

From the feed aggregate, sized by screening beforehand, the picker always removes the less abundant fraction, be it the pay mineral or the waste. Lighting should be uniform and suitable for enhancing optical contrast between the materials to be separated. Where artificial light has to be used, daylight lamps are to be preferred. Lumps are often wetted prior to sorting (e.g. as a by-product of wet screening) because an adhesive water film tends to enliven colours and intensify the sheen of ore minerals. Some minerals (willemite, fluorspar, etc.) exhibit fluorescence in ultraviolet light, which permits them to be picked out easily from among the other minerals.

In the Hungarian coal mines, it is usual to hand-pick lump coal (plus-8 to 10 cm), but stove and egg coal (4 to 8 cm) is also being hand-picked here and there. The device most often used for the purpose is an apron conveyor made up of screen elements. Its horizontal sorting section is followed by an inclined discharge section of variable inclination which permits the lumps to be discharged direct into rail cars. A sheet steel box is fixed to every other link in order to hold back the coal on the inclined discharge section. Every other one of these boxes has a raised rear wall which sweeps the small lumps passed by the screen links back to a collector bin. The articulations may be provided with rollers, but the conveyor may simply be borne by its chain links sliding in rails made of appropriate steel profiles, without benefit of any rollers. The picking and conveying section are most often vertically above and parallel to the railroad rails. (If the picking section is orientated differently — e.g. at right angles to the conveying section — two belts are required, but no sheet-metal boxes are needed on the picking section.)

Lumps of intergrown coal and waste are most often broken up on the grid of the conveyor by a cobber using a hammer who grabs the lump by its waste part. If intergrown lumps are abundant, they are taken off the belt and broken up by machine. The picked-off lumps of waste (and the intergrown ones also if that is the system) are thrown either direct into mine cars or into chutes with mine cars below them. It is best for the cobber to throw lumps of smaller size (8 cm or so) away from him, whereas he will prefer to lift the heavier ones toward himself even if the is picking with one hand only.

Feed rate is a function of belt width (not more than 1.2 to 1.5 m in the case of two-sided picking) and belt speed (0.15 to 0.3 m/s). The feed must be spread so as to be no more than one lump deep. The more abundant the material to be removed, the more pickers are required and the longer must the picking section be. Pickers must be placed 1.5 to 1.8 m apart in order not to hamper one another. The average output of one picker per eight-hour shift — under favourable conditions — is provided by the rule-of-thumb formulas

$$Q \simeq 0.03x^2$$

or

$$Q \simeq \frac{x - 3.5}{2} \, (\pm 40\%),$$

where x cm is average lump size and Q is the handling rate of the picked-off product, in compact m³ per shift. The total operating cost (that is, the total cost without investment and depreciation charges) of picking should be estimated at twice the wage bill if x exceeds 10 cm and at half again the wage bill if x is 5 to 6 cm (Chapman 1951/52; Lorbach 1953; Osterlow 1960).

5.2.2. Photocell sorting. In an automated version of hand picking the human eye is replaced by a photocell, the brain by suitable relays and automatisms and the hand by a compressed-air or mechanical device (e.g. a trap door). The photocell senses the difference in reflectivity or colour between different minerals: the electric pulse generated in the photocell circuit is amplified to actuate the sorting mechanism (Brand 1969; French 1968; Pierson 1964; Newman and Whelan 1953; Slotemaker 1964; Stewart 1967; Turall and Porter 1952; Wyman 1969).

In the Sortex sorter, light reflected by the particles freely falling in the optical space of the device is projected by three or four mirrors onto photocells which measure the relevant properties of the reflected light. Particles whose sheen or colour deviates from a certain standard change the voltage in the circuit of one or more of the photocells: suitably amplified, this voltage signal triggers a compressed-air blast from a nozzle installed somewhat below the optical space. The blast kicks the particle thus pinpointed out of its free-fall trajectory. By placing suitable filters in front of the mirrors, the device can be adapted to the separation, at adjustable sensitivity levels, of feeds of a wide range of compositions (Balint 1966; Hintikka and Balint 1971).

Feed lumps are arranged in a single file on a high-speed conveyor. Speed may be, say, 8 lumps per second if lump size is 8 to 12 cm. Assuming a lump to weigh 2 kg on average, throughput is $8 \times 2 \times 3{,}600$ kg per hour $\simeq 58$ tph. This is reduced to 14.5 tph if lumps are half the size (5 cm, 0.25 kg) and feed rate is to 16 lumps per s.

X-ray irradiation brings out a strong visible fluorescence in diamonds. On this basis, diamonds can be separated from non-fluorescent minerals by photocell sorting. The usual lower limiting particle size of the operation is 3 mm or so (Linari-Linholm 1960).

In other installations, photocells are arranged in pairs: one unit is sensitized to red, the other to blue light. The sorting mechanism is triggered by the ratio or difference of the two pulses. This permits to sense difference in colour, sheen or hue between lumps of rock (e.g. limestone and dolomite), irrespective of lighting intensity.

Optical (photocell) sorting can be economical down to a much lower limiting size (about 5 mm) than hand picking. Prior sizing and de-dusting of the feed is a must.

5.3. CONCENTRATION RELYING ON OTHER TYPES OF RADIATION SENSORS

Photocells measure electromagnetic radiation, the bulk of which is within the visible range. Other detectors are sensitive to non-visible electromagnetic radiation (infra-red, ultraviolet, X-ray, etc.) or to particle radiation (alpha beta rays).

Devices designed for the sorting of uranium minerals depend for their operation on the natural radioactivity of the pay mineral. Their sensor is a Geiger-Müller or scintillation counter which, by the intermediary of a suitable electronic amplifier, actuates a mechanism (e.g. a trap valve, a movable baffle, a bat hitting the lump, a compressed-air blast, etc.) that separates lumps different as to radiation.

When a body is irradiated with low-energy gamma rays, the radiation reflected by it varies in intensity as the atomic number of the chemical elements making it up. A device based on this principle permits e.g. to determine the ash content of coals. The signals of the scintillation detector that measures the level of reflected radiation may be used to operate a sorting device that will separate high-ash lumps from low-ash ones. The thulium-170 isotope may e.g. serve as a source providing low-energy radiation.

Higher-density materials absorb X-rays more than lower-density ones. A radiation of initial intensity I_0 having passed through a layer of thickness x of a given material has intensity

$$I = I_0 e^{-\mu x};$$

the X-ray absorption coefficient μ, e.g., for lumps of coal and shale of different s.g. irradiated by X-rays is

$$\mu = 0.5 \quad 1.0 \quad 1.7 \quad 4.6$$

for a s.g.

$$\delta = 1.2 \quad 1.8 \quad 2.2 \quad 2.8$$

(Jenkinson et al. 1973).

Minerals may be endowed with induced radioactivity (e.g. by neutron bombardment in a reactor). The intensity of induced radiation is different for different minerals, and so is its percentage makeup out of alpha, beta and gamma rays (Ramdohr 1963).

422

Minerals and rocks are listed below according to the induced gamma radiation intensity of their key chemical elements.

Strong induced gamma radiation:

Al   (garnet, bauxite, potassium feldspar, chlorite),
Mn   (psilomelane, rhodonite, wolframite, rhodochrosite, pyrolusite),
V   (carnotite),
Ag   (pyrargyrite, proustite),
Cu   (chrysocolla, chalcocite, azurite, chalcopyrite, malachite, bornite, tetra-
     hedrite, stannite, enargite),
Ca   (apatite, fluorspar, calcite, calcium feldspar, dolomite, scheelite, gypsum),
Hg   (cinnabar),
Co   (smaltite),
F

Middling induced gamma radiation:
Cl   (rock salt),
W   (ferberite),
Sn   (cassiterite),
As   (arsenopyrite),
Na

Weak induced gamma radiation:
Zn   (smithsonite, sphalerite, zincite),
Sb   (antimonite),
Mg   (magnesite),
Ba   (barite),
Ni   (garnierite)

Negligible induced gamma radiation:
Cr   (chromite),
S   (pyrrhotite, galena, pyrite),
O   (quartz, cerussite, siderite, magnetite, haematite),
K
H

Every body emits infra-red radiation. The maximum intensity of infra-red emission is at different temperatures for different materials. Emission intensity can be measured by means of suitable detectors which can thus be used to separate materials different as to infra-red emission. In industrial practice, devices depending on this effect are used in the separation of asbestos. Fibres dropping through a flame acquire a greater surface temperature and emit infra-red radiation of shorter wavelength than pieces of parent rock.

5.4. METHODS EXPLOITING DIFFERENCES IN THERMAL BEHAVIOUR

5.4.1. Concentration based on the absorption of radiant heat. Different minerals absorb radiant heat differently. Those absorbing a great deal of heat will, after irradiation with infra-red waves, stick to a rubber conveyor belt coated with a material that is solid at room temperature but softens at a slightly higher temperature (e.g. bitumen or a suitable resin). The optimum wavelength of the infra-red radiation to be used is different for different mineral combinations. For removing anhydrite and dolomite from beside rock salt, e.g., a wavelength of about 1 μm was found most suitable.

Let us mention as a curiosity that lumps of metal sulphides (e.g. chalcocite) strewn on snow will, with their better thermal conductivity and absorption of sunlight, cause it to melt more and will therefore sink deeper in it (indeed, traverse it sooner) than gangue minerals such as silicates, barite, etc.; the gangue minerals can therefore be shovelled off at intervals with the top layer of snow and thus separated from the sulphides which can be collected when all the snow has melted.

5.4.2. Concentration by differences in thermal expansion and thermal conductivity. Minerals or crystal aggregates combining a low thermal conductivity with strong thermal expansion are comminuted by decrepitation upon abrupt heating or cooling. If a r.o.m. ore contains minerals with a marked decrepitation property (e.g. barite, fluorite, spodumene, etc.) in combination with minerals which decrepitate weakly or not at all, then a suitable heat treatment of the screen fractions of the r.o.m. material will shatter one group of minerals and leave the other unaffected. The resulting product can be separated by screening (Kirchberg 1937).

In a mineral having two or more allotropes, passage through the critical changeover temperature may greatly reduce the mineral grains' strength and increase their propensity to decrepitate. For example, trigonal beta quartz changes into hexagonal alpha quartz at 575 °C; at this temperature, both the unit crystallographic cell and the thermal expansion of the mineral take an abrupt change.

5.5. SEPARATION BY DIFFERENCES IN MECHANICAL PROPERTIES

Minerals differ widely as to hardness (resistance to wear), plasticity, ductility, crushing strength and resistance to weathering. Based on scratchability, the Mohs scale of hardness used by mineralogists is in fact a measure of resistance to wear; the scales used by metallurgists (the Brinell, Vickers and Rockwell hardness) are in fact measures of ductility.

Feeding a mixture of minerals different as to wearing resistance to a suitable mill where attrition is the principal comminuting effect, the less hard mineral is ground to a dust while the particles of the harder one remain more or less unworn. For example, the softer component of a diamonds-plus-quartz or a quartz-plus-barite combination will be ground to a pulp in a wet tumbling mill filled with small balls and/or flintstones, whereas the harder component emerges from the mill without suffering any significant comminution. The two phases can be separated subsequently, e.g. by screening or in a classifier. (In the quartz-plus-barite case, the barite, ground to a fine powder, forms a dense-medium suspension in the mill in which the quartz grains will float up.)

Ductile materials are just deformed by a blow that would shatter a rigid, fragile one. On grinding a mixture of fragile and ductile materials, a multitude of coarse ductile particles in a fine pulp of the fragile phase is obtained; the two can be separated by screening or classifying. This procedure permits e.g. the concentration also of native copper or native gold.

The Bradford crusher exploits in concentration the different fragility (toughness) of coal and waste. It is a large-diameter, massively built trommel with a lifter ribbing made of angle steel that lifts the feed particles coarser than the screen apertures (40 to 50 mm) almost to the zenith of the cylinder. Dropping from that height, the more fragile part of the raw coal is broken up and passed by the screen, whereas the tougher lumps leave through the retained-fraction discharge. (In bituminous coals, it is the coal that tends to be the more fragile; in most brown coals and in lignites, on the other hand, it is the waste.)

A vibrating-type grizzly moving with a great amplitude (20 to 25 cm) may also be used to separate coal from a waste from which it differs as to toughness: the lumpy feed dumped onto the grizzly of 8 to 12 cm aperture is thrown forward and at the same time also against a rebound plate provided with spikes, placed at the proper height above the grizzly, by deck motion at $n = 130$ to 150 rpm.

R.o.m. material made up of mineral sufficiently different in fragility (hardness, cleavage, rigidity, friability and similar mechanical-structural properties) can as a rule be separated with some success into products more or less enriched in the individual mineral components by comminution in an impact mill run at the right speed and by screening subsequent to such selective crushing (Andreas 1969).

On the basis of their different fragility, the petrographic components of coal (fusain, durain and vitrain) can also be separated from one another, more or less. Fusain tends to be the most friable, durain the hardest.

By the impact comminution of a rock containing fibrous asbestos, the parent rock can be crushed to a powder while the asbestos fibres remain intact.

The resistance of minerals to natural weathering and induced decomposition is a function of their physical (mechanical-structural) and chemical properties.

In some r.o.m. ores, one mineral may constitute a coarser-grained dissemination in a fine-grained crystal aggregate of another mineral or minerals serving as the parent rock. Atmospheric weathering may decompose the parent rock into a fine dust while the disseminated mineral retains its original grain size. This is desirable whenever the disseminated mineral's value is a sensitive function of its grain size (as is the case with diamonds and other precious stones).

Clay sticking to harder lumps of the r.o.m. material may be disintegrated into fine slimes by soaking and wet attrition, thanks to the more or less great propensity of clay to fall apart in water. Washers such as drum scrubbers or kneading-arm devices (log washer, Excelsior washer, etc.) are used for the purpose: serving at the same time as classifiers as well, these devices will simultaneously also separate the harder lumps from the clay suspension washed and rubbed off them (Tarján 1954). A sufficiently friable clayey impurity may be washed off the mineral lumps using a jet of water of appropriate strength and sometimes even by simple spraying (e.g. on a screen provided with spray nozzles).

Drum scrubbers are cylindrical tanks rotating about a horizontal or near-horizontal shaft. In them, clayey impurities are rubbed under water off a feed introduced at one end and removed at the other. Water fills the bottom of the drum to a suitably adjusted height: wash-water flow may be concurrent or countercurrent to the progress of the solid charge. In the latter case, the emerging charge encounters clear water; the output of a concurrent scrubber must, on the other hand, be separated from the clay rubbed off in a separate device (e.g. a trommel installed downstream of the scrubber). The scrubbers are usually provided with a short lifter ribbing made of angle steel that will lift the lumps and drop them from some height. A radial or spiral ribbing may help to remove the washed material at the discharge end or to move the fill along in the drum near the feed end.

More recent types of drum scrubber are likely to incorporate cutting-kneadings arms mounted along spirals and a diaphragm with a central opening, separating the upstream two-thirds of the drum from its downstream third. Charge depth in the upstream compartment is determined by the geometry of the diaphragm aperture: it should be greater for feeds richer in slimes. Wash water runs counter to the feed. The drum may be supported e.g. by smooth-treaded truck tires at 7 bars gauge pressure. A 120-ton drum of 3.6 m dia. $\times$ 10 m length may e.g. be borne by 32 such tires: it will typically have a 165 kW drive motor and a throughput of 300 tph minus-200 mm washed stone at an input clay content of 17 percent. Clay content is related to throughput as follows:

clay content:	13	17	20	25	30	40	50%
throughput:	132	100	80	60	47	32	20%

of the throughput referred to above.

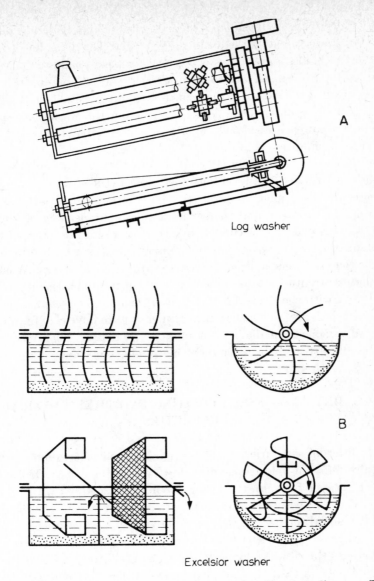

Log washer

Excelsior washer

Fig. 5.4. Diagrams of two washer designs. *A* — log washer, *B* — kneading-arm (Excelsior or Bavaria) scrubber

The log washer (Part A of Fig. 5.4) is essentially a mechanical classifier whose mechanism for tumbling and moving along the coarse fraction is strong enough to handle lumps of size up to 10 cm or so. Its single or dual "logs" (shafts provided with metal blades) are installed in a tank of sloping bottom: the blades, mounted on the shafts in a spiral, include a certain pitch angle with the shaft axes. With the shafts rotating, the blades pass the lumps of rock on towards the top end of the tank, kneading, rubbing and breaking them in the process. The clayey slimes rubbed off leave in the overflow. The diameter of the circle defined by the blades' outer edges is 50 to 100 cm; peripheral velocity is 0.7 to 1.3 m/s; shaft (log) length is 6 to 10 m. Throughput and power draft are sensitive functions of the nature of the feed. For example, a dual-shaft log washer 7.5 m long with an outer blade diameter of 90 cm will wash 30 to 50 tph of limestone at a power draft of 50 to 60 kW or 35 to 65 tph of gravel at 30 to 70 kW. Water consumption is in the 1 to 5 m³/t range.

In the Excelsior or Bavaria (Part B of Fig. 5.4), clayey ores and similar materials are scrubbed in a level-bottomed tank by means of kneading-scrubbing blades mounted along a spiral on a horizontal shaft rotating above the pulp level. The sand-size and coarser material's final cleaning of any clayey impurities takes place in a second, compartmented tank: the washed material is lifted out of the successive compartments by elevator wheels provided with screen-bottom launders and so moved towards the discharge. Wash water flows countercurrent to the ore from compartment to compartment, and thence into the tank with the kneading blades, carrying the clay suspension with it. Excelsior washers are used at Úrkút in Hungary to remove clay from lumps of manganese ore: one 2.1 m dia. × 4.6 m plus one 1.6 m dia. × 3.6 m size Excelsior washer handle 40 tph ore between them, consuming 4 m³ of wash water per ton.

5.6. DRY PROCESSES PROFITING BY OTHER PHYSICAL PROPERTIES

Lumps differing as to friction coefficient (e.g. coal 0.35 to 0.5; shale about 0.6) acquire different velocities sliding down an inclined sheet. If the bottom end of the sheet is bent up, the faster-moving lumps (those with the smaller friction coefficient) will be thrown further than the others. In another arrangement (a dry spiral separator), the faster-moving lumps (clean coal) of a sized feed will be driven by the centrifugal force from the spiral into an outer collector chute, whereas the slower-moving lumps (shale) will remain in the spiral and leave at its bottom end. It is usual to mount three spirals about a common vertical axis. The coal throughput of a separator 3.2 m high with an outer spiral diameter of 1.6 m will be in the 6 to 10 tph range depending on feed size (Halblich 1967).

Differences in the elasticity of minerals may also be exploited in concentration. Elastic particles such as lumps of coal or roundish pebbles thrown at an angle onto a thick sheet of glass or a sheet of steel will fly farther on rebound than the less elastic waste (such as shale, marl, lumps of clay). For an ideally elastic material, the velocity of impact, v_1, equals the velocity of rebound, v_2; for real bodies, $v_2 = \varepsilon v_1$, where $\varepsilon < 1$ is the coefficient of elasticity. If the rebound angle (the initial direction of the rebound trajectory) includes an angle α with the horizontal, the rebound parabola will return to the height of the point of first impact at a horizontal distance

$$l = \frac{v_2^2}{g} \sin 2\alpha$$

from that point. Given two lumps of elasticity coefficients ε_1 and ε_2, respectively, the horizontal distance between their rebound trajectories on their return to the height of first impact will be

$$\Delta l = (\varepsilon_1^2 - \varepsilon_2^2) \frac{v_1^2}{g} \sin 2\alpha$$

with Δl a maximum at $\alpha = 45°$ (Ocella 1965).

Differences in particle shape may serve as a basis for sorting on screens provided with suitably shaped apertures. For example, shale often breaks up into flat, oblong lumps whereas coal tends to fall into more cube-like ones. To separate them, grizzlies made up of specially shaped bars are used: the top ends of the bars constitute a closed zigzag surface whereas their tilted-up bottom ends have gaps of increasing width between them. The flat lumps of shale, which are turned vertical between the bars, can drop through in such a presentation. Rotating-roll rollers and chutes provided with appropriate gaps can also be used for separation by shape, the idea being in every case to make the flat lumps drop through the gaps.

Roundish particles will tend to roll down inclined planes where flat ones will slide. It is the former that gain the greater speed. In other words, in devices exploiting differences in friction coefficient such as a spiral concentrator, minerals may be separated by particle shape as well, provided the particles of the one mineral roll down where those of the other(s) slide (Waldie 1973).

5.7. LITERATURE ON OTHER PROCESSES OF CONCENTRATION

ANDREAS, A. E.: The preparation of low grade U_3O_8 and Pb ores by impact crushing. *Canad. Min. J.* 1969 Aug., 63—65.
BALINT, A.: Einführung in die Photometrische Sortierung von Erzen. *Bergbauwiss.* 1966, 204—210.
BIERBRAUER, E.: Das Pickverfahren — Eine neue Aufbereitungsmöglichkeit für grobkörnige Mineralgemische. *Metall und Erz*, 1937, No. 23.
BISCHOFF, E.: Über Flockung und Flotation. *Z. Phys. Chem.* 1960, 265—288.
BRAND, R.: Das optische Sortierung von Gesteinen nach der Farbe. *Die Industrie der Steine und Erden* 1969, H.1, 2—4.
BRISSE, A. H.—W. L. MORRIS, Jr.: Convertol process. *Min. Engng* 1958, 258—261.
CAVANAGH, R. L.—A. J. LAST: Potential for sonics and ultrasonics in mineral processing. *E/MJ* 1965 May, 98—102.

CHAPMAN, W. R.: The cleaning of coal by hand and by mechanical means. *Trans. IME* 1951/52, 323—341.

COLLIER, D. (et al.): Ore sorters for asbestos and scheelite. 10. *IMPC*, London 1973, R13.

FARNAND, J. R. (et al.): The beneficiation of gold ore by oil-phase agglomeration. *CIM Bull.* 1969, 1326—1329.

FRENCH, R. R.: Beneficiation of low-grade gypsum by electronic color sorting. *Trans. AIME* 1968, 331—334.

FRIEND, J. P.—J. ISKRA—J. A. KITCHENER: Cleaning a selectively flocculated mineral slurry. *Trans. IMM* 1973, C235—C236.

FUNKEMEYER, M.: Technische und wirtschaftliche Auswirkungen der Einführung eines Federblatt-Scheiders in die Steinkohlenwasche einer westdeutschen Zeche. *Aachener Bl.* 1968, 128—162.

GÖTTE, A.—M. SCHÄFER: Untersuchungen zu den Grundlagen des Convertol-Verfahrens. *Aachener Bl.* 1960, 49—95.

HALBLICH, W.: Sortierverfahren auf Grund von Kornform, Reubung und Elastizität. Bergakademie 1967, 43—49.

HINTIKKA, O. V. J.—A. BALINT: Optical separation of limestone in Southern Finland by Lohjan Kalkkitehdas Oy. *Trans. AIME* 1971, 203—207.

IOHN, P.: Zur Einzelsortierung von Mineralien. *AT* 1970, 87—95.

JENKINSON, P. (et al.): Coal sorting by X-ray transmission. 10. *IMPC*, London 1973.

KIRCHBERG, H.: Die Aufbereitung von Mineralien auf Grund ihrer Wärmeeigenschaften. *Metall und Erz* 1937, 301—318.

LEMKE, K.: Sortierung und Entwässerung von Schlamm nach dem Convertol-Verfahren. 2. *ICPC*, Essen 1954, AIV 2.

LINARI-LINHOLM, A. A.: An optical method of separating diamonds from opaque gravels. *IMPC*, London 1960, 789—799.

LOFTUS, W. K. B.—H. S. SIMPSON—M. J. KING: Recovery plant practice at De Beers Consolidated Mines, Kimberley, with particular reference to improvements made for the sorting of final concentrates. *J. S. Afr. Inst. Min. Met.* 1970, 317—328.

LORBACH, M.: Die Kosten der Klaubearbeit für Steinkohle in Abhängigkeit der verschiedenen Einflussgrössen. *Aachener Bl.* 1953, 142—150.

MEADUS, F. W.—I. E. PUDDINGTON: The beneficiation of baryte by agglomeration. *CIM Bull.* 1973 June, 123—126.

MEADUS, F. W.—G. PAILLARD—A. F. SIRIANI—I. E. PUDDINGTON: Fractionation of coking coals by spherical agglomeration methods. *Can. M. M. Bull.* 1968, 736—738.

MELLGREN, O.—H. L. SHERGOLD: Method for recovering ultrafine mineral particles by extraction with an organic phase. *Trans. IMM* 1966, C267—C268.

MULAR, A. L.—I. E. PULLINGTON: A technically feasible agglomeration-separation process. *Can. M. M. Bull.* 1968, 726—730.

MÜSCHENBORN, W.: Neue Versuche zur Feinstkornaufbereitung, insbesondere zur Aufbereitung von Steinkohlenschlämmen. *Glückauf* 1952, 340—342.

NEWMAN, P. C.—P. F. WHELAN: Photometric separation of ores in lump form. *RDMD*, London 1953, 359—383.

OCELLA, E.: Die Trennung von Mineralien und Gesteinen auf Grund ihrer elastischen Eigenschaften. *Freib. Fh. A350* 1965, 69—80.

OSTERLOW, W.: Trockensortierung der Rohstückkohle durch Lesebetrieb in Siebereien. Der deutsche Steinkohlenbergbau, Bd. 4: Aufbereitung der Steinkohle. *Glückauf*, Essen 1960, 125—161.

PIERSON, C. Y.: Electronic sorting of crushed rock by color. *Min. Congr. J.* 1964, No. 10, 111—115.

POLKIN, S. J.—V. V. PANIN—E. V. ADAMOV—G. J. KARAVAIKO—A. S. CHERNYAK: Theory and practice of utilizing microorganisms in processing difficult-to-dress ores and concentrates. 11. *IMPC*, Cagliari 1975, 901—923.

RAMDOHR, H.: Radioaktivität als Hilfsmittel bei Sortierverfahren in der Erzaufbereitung. *AT* 1963, 214—218.

RAO, S. R.—L. L. SIROIS: Study of surface chemical characteristics in gravity separation. *CIM Bull.* 1974 June, 78—83.

READ, A. D.: Selective flocculation separations involving hematite. *Trans. IMM* 1971, C24—C31.

READ, A. D.—A. WHITEHEAD: Selektive Flockung bei Verarbeitung von Schlämmen. *Erzmetall* 1972, 64—69.

READ, A. D.—A. WHITEHEAD: Treatment of mineral combinations by selective flocculation. 10. *IMPC*, London 1973, P. 1.

REVNITZEV, V. I.—Y. G. DMITRIEV: Ultrasonic cleaning of minerals. 7. *IMPC*, New York 1964, 43—49.

SHERGOLD, H. L.—O. MELLGREN: Concentration of minerals at the oil/water interface. *Trans. SME/AIME* 1970, 149—159. (Or *Trans. IMM* 1969, C121—C132.)

SIRIANI, A. F. (et al.): Separation studies of iron ore bodies containing apatite by spherical agglomeration methods. *Can. M. M. Bull.* 1968, 731—735.

SLOTEMAKER, J. R.: New photocell sorting device piloted at limestone quarry. *Min. Engng* 1964, 41—43.

ŠPALDON, F.: Ein Beitrag zur Frage der Verwendung makromolekularer Reagenzien als Flockungsmittel in der Erzaufbereitung. *Freib. Fh. A163* 1960, 85—100.

ŠPALDON, F.: Verwendung von Hochpolymeren bei der Aufbereitung feinstkörniger Mineralteilchen. *Glückauf-Forschungshefte* 1969, 241—247.

ŠPALDON, F.—K. TKÁCOVÁ: Der Einfluss des pH-Wertes auf die Aggregationswirkung anionischer Polyelektrolyte für Mineralsuspensionen unterschiedlichen Charakters. *Bergakademie* 1967, 344—353.

SPARKS, B. D.—R. H. T. WRONG: Selective spherical agglomeration of ilmenite concentrates. *CIM Bull.* 1973, 73—77.

SPARKS, B. D.—F. W. MEADUS—I. E. PUDDINGTON: The continuous separation of tar sands by oil-phase agglomeration. *CIM Bull.* 1971 June, 67—72.

STEWART, J.: Elektronisches Sortieren nach der Farbe von Kalkstein. *AT* 1967, 212—213.

STUMPF, K.: Die Reinigung von Kalk- und Dolomitgestein im Trocken- und Nassverfahren. 9. *IMPC*, Praha 1970, 141—147.

TARJÁN, G.: 40,0 mm-es petőfibányai lignittel végzett mosási kísérletek. (Washing tests in minus-40 mm lignite from Petőfibánya, NE Hungary.) *Bány. Lapok* 1954, 232—238.

TURALL, W. T.—D. PORTER: Photoelectric sorting of optical fluorspar. *Min. Engng* 1952, 803—806.

USONI, L.—G. RINELLI—A. M. MARABINI—G. GHIGI: Selective properties of flocculants and possibilities of their use in flotation of fine minerals. 8. *IMPC*, Leningrad 1968, D-13.

VAN LIERDE, A.: Flocculation and dispersion of dolomite by acrylate polymers. *Int. J. Min. Proc.* 1974, 81—100.

VOLŠICKÝ, Z.—G. ŠEBOR—V. BORTLIK: Selektive Flockung von Kohlenschlämmen. *Freib. Fh. A415* 1967, 181—191.

WALDIE, B.: Separation of particles according to shape. *Powder Technology* (7) 1973, 244—246.

WYMAN, R. A.: Photometric sorting. *Canad. Min. J.* 1969 May, 79—80.

WYMAN, R. A.—F. H. HARTMAN: Examples of mineral beneficiation by colour sorting. *Can. M. M. Bull.* 1965, 1194—1197.

YARAR, B.—J. A. KITCHENER: Selective flocculation of minerals. 1. Basic principles, 2. Experimental investigation of quartz, calcite and galena. *Trans. IMM* 1970, C23—C33.

YOUROVSKY, A. Z.—V. D. GOROSHKO—V. I. KORSHUNOV—J. D. REMESNIKOV: New, dry processes for coal preparation. Magnetic, aero-suspension, radiometric. 2. *ICPC* Harrogate 1962, G2, 403—410.

6. HYDROMETALLURGY OR CHEMICAL EXTRACTION

Instead of or in combination with the processes of physical beneficiation and/or pyrometallurgy, hydrometallurgical processes involving the dissolution of the pay metal(s) are gaining ground in the recovery of values from finely intergrown complex or low-grade r.o.m. ores and even from usual-grade concentrates. In hydrometallurgy, it is not necessary to comminute the r.o.m. ore to the fineness required in physical beneficiation: the metal content may be leached out of an intergrown grain also, provided the solvent can reach the mineral containing it. It is only the rates of dissolution that will be different according as the solvent has access to the entire surface of the finely ground (or coarser-grained but liberated) particles or to part only of the surface of an intergrown grain, or possibly to a small fraction only of the pay mineral surface through a fine fissure in the gangue enclosing it.

The ore is often roasted prior to leaching (dissolution): oxidizing, reducing, sulphatizing or chlorinating roasting may convert the mineral into a more soluble compound. Leaching will not as a rule selectively and exclusively dissolve the desirable metal component, but is liable to dissolve some other components of the r.o.m. ore as well: in fact, the concentration of these latter in the aqueous leach liquor may exceed that of the pay metal several times over. In such cases, the pay metal must be enriched in the leach liquor by one means or another, and must thereupon be separated from the undesirable components (the interferents). The methods that enter into consideration for the purpose include ion exchange by means of resins, solvent extraction, ion flotation, or precipitation of the undesirable components. The solvate (liquid) phase must, either before or after these operations, be separated by filtration or decantation from the solid (undissolved) fraction of the r.o.m. ore. Finally, the pay metal must be recovered from the clear liquor in solid form by chemical precipitation, crystallization, electrolysis, etc.

Dissolution may take place in an alkaline or acid liquor, using a Cl^-, NO^{2-}, SO_3^{2-}, SO_4^{2-}, KCN, caustic soda, soda ash, etc. solvent at atmospheric pressure or in a pressure vessel (autoclave or digester); it may employ electrolysis or bacterial leaching. The clear liquor can be separated from the solid residue by filtration, settling, thickening, flocculation, countercurrent decantation, etc.

The pay metal can be recovered from the clear liquor by chemical precipitation [using e.g. one of the reagents H_2S, Na_2CO_3, $Ca(OH)_2$, $CaCO_3$, $NaOH$, NH_4OH, etc.], crystallization, cementation, electrolysis, ion flotation, froth fractionation, reverse osmosis, ion exchange on a resin, solvent extraction, etc. (In the last two processes, the solvated pay metal is taken into a pure aqueous solution by elution or stripping [reextraction] prior to precipitation.) Some operations such as cementation, ion flotation, ion exchange and solvent extraction can be performed in a pulp also, eliminating the costly operation of separating the solid phase from the leach liquor and the concomitant losses of metal.

6.1. DISSOLUTION

Dissolution (leaching) is the result of interaction between the solid ore and a liquid solvent. Hydration, e.g. in the case of ionic chloride and sulphate lattices highly soluble in water, brings about simple or physical dissolution:

$$(MCl)_s + \text{water} \rightarrow (MCl)_a;$$
$$(MSO_4)_s + \text{water} \rightarrow (MSO_4)_a,$$

where M is some metal. Of the subscripts, s indicates the solid phase; a indicates the aqueous phase.

The dissolution of "water-insoluble minerals" requires the addition of some solvent (e.g. sulphuric acid, caustic soda, KCN, etc.) to the leach, in order to help transform the mineral into a soluble compound by a double-decomposition reaction such as

$$(MO)_s + H_2SO_4 \rightarrow (MSO_4)_a + H_2O,$$

or

$$(MCO_3)_s + H_2SO_4 \rightarrow (MSO_4)_a + H_2O + CO_2;$$

an oxidation reaction such as

$$M_s + H_2SO_4 + {}^1/_2O_2 \rightarrow (MSO_4)_a + H_2O,$$

or

$$(MS)_s + H_2SO_4 + {}^1/_2O_2 \rightarrow (MSO_4)_a + H_2O + S;$$

or a complex-forming reaction such as

$$2Au + 4KCN + {}^1/_2O_2 + H_2O \rightarrow 2KOH + 2[KAu(CN)_2]_a.$$

In double decomposition or metathesis, a metal oxide or metal salt reacts with an acid, a base or a dissolved salt to produce a soluble sulphate, chloride, nitrate or some other salt; a metal sulphide can be dissolved by means of dilute acids and/or certain salts; a tungstate can be dissolved using caustic soda or soda ash, etc. In oxidation, a new (soluble) compound is constituted by the anion or the cation of the mineral. In the leaching of uranium ores, for example,

434

it is the cation that is oxidized, forming uranyl sulphate or carbonate ions: when a metal sulphide is turned into a sulphate in an autoclave on the other hand, it is the anion that is oxidized. The constitution of complex compounds permits a highly selective leaching as a rule (as e.g. in the cyanidation of gold).

The solvents most important in practice are H_2SO_4, $Fe_2(SO_4)_3$, HCl, NaOH, NH_3, Na_2CO_3, NaCN (or KCN). The choice of solvent may be influenced by the nature of the gangue or of the host rock. In the presence of a carbonate gangue, e.g., no acid solvents should be used, as they would dissolve the gangue as well (more avidly, in fact, than the pay mineral proper).

Some minerals (sulphides in particular) are hard to dissolve by simple leaching. These may be transformed into sufficiently water-soluble (readily leachable) compounds by oxidizing, chlorinating or sulphatizing roasting. In other cases, leaching under pressure (in a digester vessel, at an elevated temperature and elevated partial pressures of the gaseous ingredients of the reaction), bacterial leaching or the activation of the feed (attacking the crystal lattice by protracted grinding, the creation of lattice defects, amorphization, etc.) may help.

Dissolution proper can be achieved in certain situations by letting the liquor containing the solvent seep (percolate) through an aggregate of the solid phase. The aggregate may be stationary if the particles making it up are comparatively coarse-grained. If they are fine-grained, on the other hand, they should be leached as a dispersed pulp in mechanically or pneumatically agitated cells.

Percolation through an aggregate at rest may be performed in a double-bottomed tank, in dumps stacked in the open (heap leaching) or in underground cavities (pit leaching).

When filling a tank or cavity, any spontaneous sorting of the aggregate should be avoided in order to maintain a homogeneous percolation flow. The percolating solvent is recirculated until it attains the desired metal concentration. If there is a bank of several leach tanks, the thin solution from the tank to be emptied next (which contains a leached-out fill) is led back to the tank filled most recently, possibly with some makeup solvent added. In another arrangement, the tanks are connected in series and flushed countercurrent with solvent from the last tank (the one to be emptied first) passed back to the first (the one filled most recently). After leaching has been completed, the aggregate is removed from the tank through a suitable bottom aperture and the tank is filled with fresh aggregate. Percolating tanks or bins may be round or square in plan; they may be made of sheet steel, wood or concrete and may have up to $\sim$1,000 m^3 volume for a height of $\sim$5 m.

The leaching of dumps or heaps stacked in the open has the cheap recovery of pay metal contents from low-grade ores (e.g. of Cu or U) or from concentrator tailings for its aim. It is best to stack up the material on flat gently sloping terrain coated with an impermeable layer (e.g. of clay) and provided with runnels that will collect the percolate.

If the ore contains pyrite and/or pyrrhotite also, the weathering of the ore will generate the solvent required for its own leaching: it is sufficient just to wet the dump time and again (acid mine water is to be preferred for the purpose) and to provide adequate aeration. The oxidation of pyrite gives rise to ferrous sulphate and sulphuric acid:

$$FeS_2 + 3.5O_2 + H_2O \rightarrow FeSO_4 + H_2SO_4.$$

Now the bacteria invariably present on pyritic ores (and in acid mine waters) will oxidize the ferrous sulphate into ferric sulphate, a high-grade solvent of copper sulphides and of pyrite proper:

$$2FeSO_4 + H_2SO_4 + {}^1/_2O_2 \rightarrow Fe_2(SO_4)_3 + H_2O.$$

In the presence of bacteria, some ferric sulphate will form direct on the oxidation of pyrite:

$$2FeS_2 + 7.5O_2 + H_2O \rightarrow Fe_2(SO_4)_3 + H_2SO_4,$$

$$CuFeS_2 + 2Fe_2(SO_4)_3 + 3O_2 + 2H_2O \rightarrow CuSO_4 + 5FeSO_4 + 2H_2SO_4,$$

$$FeS_2 + 7Fe_2(SO_4)_3 + 8H_2O \rightarrow 15FeSO_4 + 8H_2SO_4$$

The leaching of underground cavities (stopes) may, after the comminution of the ore by blasting, be organized in much the same way as in the case of open-air dumps. The main problem in such a setup is the collection of the percolate, which should be as complete as feasible.

Part A of Fig. 6.1 shows an old copper-concentrator tailings dump; Part B shows "chemical mining" at Miami Copper Co. in Arizona. Both drawings indicate the approximate parameters (pH, temperature in °C, g/l Cu and Fe concentration) of the solution in circuit. Copper is recovered from the pregnant solution ("pregs") by cementation on iron swarf. At Miami, where the higher-grade parts of a porphyry copper deposit had been worked by conventional underground mining, leaching was reserved for the ore left behind in the safety pillars, the copper oxide ore and the low-grade copper sulphide ore. The old galleries of the mine are used to collect and store the percolate. The recovery of one kg of copper consumes 1.3 kg of iron and 2.4 kg of acid. It takes 3 to 4 weeks for the solvent sprinkled onto the ground surface to percolate through the fissured and broken-up ore stock whose average thickness is 185 m and to collect in the deep-level galleries. The Cu, Fe^{2+} and Fe^{3+} contents stated in the figure (2, 1 and 1 g/l, respectively) and the solution pH of 2.4 are average values: the extremes were 0.75 and 2.16 g/l for the copper content, 0.1 to 3.6 g/l for the Fe^{2+} content, 0.2 to 3.0 g/l for the Fe^{3+} content and 1.9 to 3.0 for the pH (Fletcher 1971).

It is usual to leach fine aggregates (pulps) in an aerated suspension. The turbulence required to keep the solids in suspension and to break up air into fine

436

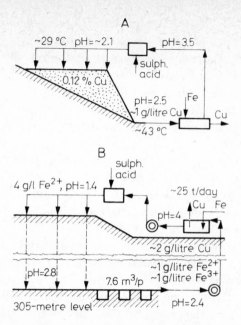

A

~29 °C pH=~2.1   pH=3.5

0.12 % Cu

sulph.
acid

pH=2.5   Fe
~1 g/litre Cu   Cu

~43 °C

B

sulph.
acid

4 g/l Fe²⁺, pH=1.4   ~25 t/day

Cu Fe

pH=4

~2 g/litre Cu

pH=2.8   ~1 g/litre Fe²⁺
7.6 m³/p   ~1 g/litre Fe³⁺

305-metre level   pH=2.4

Fig. 6.1. Diagram of chemical mining, *A* — of an old copper-bearing tailings dump,
B — at Miami Copper Co., Arizona, USA

bubbles is provided by mechanical or pneumatic agitation. If a vertical tube
open at both ends is installed in the pulp and the pulp in it is driven upward
(by an airlift) or downward (by an impeller) at a great enough speed, then a
reverse current will form in the tank outside the tube. The H/D (height-to-
diameter) ratio of the tank should be about unity for mechanically agitated
devices and about 3 to 5 for pneumatically agitated ones (such as the so-called
Pachuca tanks with their central airlift and coned bottom). Some leaching tanks
feature combined pneumatic-mechanical agitation; the solids settled out at the
bottom of such a large-diameter tank are swept by a rake either inward to a
centrally installed airlift or outward to a peripherally installed one.

It is usual to arrange several (two to eight) leaching tanks of identical design
in cascade, in countercurrent or concurrent hookup. (The concurrent hookup is
used when it is permissible for the concentration of solvent to drop comparatively low in the last tank.)

The emerging pregnant solution ("pregs") must be clarified to remove all
solids; the solution adhering to the solids going to the tailings dump must also
be recovered in its turn (by flushing with water). (The solutions percolating
through aggregates at rest contain no slimes as a rule.)

Leaching times may of course be much shorter in agitated tanks leaching a
fine pulp or fine-grained sand than in percolation tanks handling coarser-
grained aggregates at rest or in open-air or underground stacks (a few hours in

437

an agitated tank as against a few days or weeks in a percolation tank and a few months or years in open-air or underground dumps).

In an autoclave, dissolution takes place at pressure (high partial gas pressures in particular) and at temperatures above 100 °C; this intensifies the process greatly. Oxidation under pressure will dissolve many metal sulphides (e.g. sphalerite, galena, chalcocite, pentlandite, etc.) direct, at a fair metal recovery. Digestion in an autoclave enters into consideration for the leaching of concentrates above all.

Bacteria may accelerate dissolution considerably: in fact, their presence may be indispensable for generating or regenerating the solvent. They play an important role especially in the handling of sulphide ores containing pyrite. However, non-sulphides and metals (e.g. gold) may also be got into solution using bacteria (by the "biometallurgical route").

In weakly acid mine waters (which contain a variety of dissolved salts in a low concentration), autotrophic aerobic bacteria that oxidize metal sulphides to sulphates and ferrous iron, Fe^{2+}, to ferric iron, Fe^{3+}, are invariably present. (The life processes of autotrophic microorganisms are fuelled by the oxidation of inorganic substances; they build up the C and N compounds of their cell out of water and air [CO_2, N_2 and O_2]; a microorganism is called aerobic if it uses the molecular oxygen of the atmosphere for breathing.) One such bacterium is *Thiobacillus ferrooxidans*, an organism of about one μm length and 0.4 μm diameter.

True, oxidizing bacteria are sensitive to sudden, wide-ranging fluctuations of ion concentration in the solution, but they can be bred to tolerate quite high values by letting the concentration increase gradually, in small doses. Strains of bacteria can e.g. be bred to remain active in a strong acid solution (e.g. pH = 0.5) with a high ion concentration (e.g. 15 g/l Cu or 50 g/l Fe^{2+}): such a strain will effect oxidation much more rapidly than any found in nature. Reaction rates per day e.g. of 20 g/l Fe^{2+} transformed in to ferric iron and 160 g/l $Fe_2(SO_4)_3$ recovered on the regeneration of leach liquors can be attained. The bacterial cultures are inactivated but not killed by direct sunlight, whereas ultraviolet radiation will sterilize them (kill them off). Bacterial activity in terms of conversion of ferrous to ferric iron is liveliest in the pH range from 2.0 to 3.5 and at a temperature of about 35 °C. A temperature higher than 50 °C kills *Th. ferrooxidans* and sterilizes the solution. At a pH below 2.0 or above 3.5, the rate of bacterial leaching decreases gradually, to cease practically above pH = 6; *Th. ferrooxidans* does not survive in an alkaline medium (pH $\gtrsim$ 9).

The metabolism of aerobic bacteria requires a supply of molecular oxygen. Aerating the solution or interrupting at intervals the sprinkling with the leach liquor of aggregates at rest (dumps) for some weeks or months may significantly accelerate bacterial leaching. For example, uranium recovery from a low-grade ore (0.1% U_3O_8) containing 2% pyrite was increased from 43% to 54 and 75%, respectively, when leaching for a total duration of 20 weeks with water of pH = = 1.9 containing *Th. ferrooxidans* was interrupted once and twice, respectively. (The wetting of an ore containing no pyrite at all gave an U recovery no higher than 1.5%, the reason being that no ferric sulphate — a very effective solvent of uranium minerals, resulting from the oxidation of pyrite — was present in the system.) (Fletcher 1970.)

In an abandoned Canadian mine of pyritic uranium ore, some 1,200 cavities were left behind, each of a surface of $\sim$500 m^2 or so. Here, the walls of 12 cavities are daily sprinkled or washed off with mine water whose pH is about 2.3 to 2.8; the leach liquor collecting in underground sumps is pumped to the surface, its U content is stripped using ion-exchange resins and precipitated with ammonia. Each cavity has its turn about once every three months (four times a year). After ten cycles, no decline in uranium recovery was recorded.

Another group of autotrophic aerobic bacteria utilizes sulphur as a source of energy, converting sulphide sulphur into elementary sulphur and elementary sulphur into sulphuric acid. Even in solutions containing metal ions (Cu, Fe, Al, Mg, Zn, U, etc.), these organisms can be bred in great abundance in a few days. The oxidation of sulphur compounds gradually increases the concentration of sulphuric acid in the solution. The breeding of the microorganisms in question is first slowed and then completely arrested by the buildup of sulphuric acid (at rates that are different for different species). For example, *Thiobacillus thioparus*, an autotrophic-aerobic bacterium, is most vigorous in oxidizing the sulphur of metal sulphides in an alkaline medium (pH = 7.1 to 9.0). Oxidation producing sulphuric acid and water-soluble metal sulphates gradually decreases the pH. Below a pH about 4, the life functions of *Th. thioparus* are suspended: the task of further oxidizing the sulphides is taken over by *Th. thiooxidans* and *ferrooxidans* (which oxidize ferrous to ferric iron in the pH range from 1.5 to 4.0).

The optimal pH is about 1.8 for the bacterial oxidation of pyrite but about 3.5 for the multiplication of the bacteria. The discrepancy is due to the fact that, above a pH = 2, ferric salts have a propensity to hydrolyse and precipitate, and the ferric compounds forming on the pyrite surfaces isolate those from the bacteria. This is why the optimum of pyrite oxidation is where the hydrolysis of iron is a minimum. (Ferric iron can precipitate out of the liquor, removing hydroxyl ions; the hydrogen ions left behind increase the acidity of the liquor.)

Metallurgy of any kind is essentially based on processes of oxidation and reduction. There are microorganisms capable of bringing about and/or accelerating both types of reaction. Some authors attribute the formation of all sulphide ores in general to the action of sulphate-reducing anaerobic miroorganisms such as *Desulfovibrio desulfuricans* or *Clostridium desulfuricans*, which extract oxygen from sulphates or nitrates. By the hypothesis, the process comprises two reactions in succession: in the first, saprophytic bacteria produce organic acids or alcohols; these are converted in the second to carbon dioxide and methane by methane bacteria. The sulphur compounds then produce hydrogen sulphide, which constitutes insoluble metal sulphides with the metal ions in the liquor (Malouf 1971).

Anaerobic bacteria reducing sulphates to sulphides are fairly widespread in the bottom mud of some lakes. Their presence is betrayed by the formation of hydrogen sulphide. These bacteria, which can transform the surfaces of metal

Table 6.1. Schematic reaction equations and optimum pH ranges of the bacterial oxidation of sulphide minerals by six species of *Thiobacillus*

Thiobacillus ferrooxidans pH 1.0—3.5 MS → MSO_4, Fe^{2+} → Fe^{3+}, S^0 → SO_4^{2-}

Th. thiooxidans pH 0.5—5.0 MS → $S^0 + M^{2+}$, S^0 → SO_4^{2-}

Th. thiocyanoxidans pH 4.5—7.5 MS → $S^0 + M^{2+}$, S^0 → SO_4^{2-}

Th. neapolitanus pH 3.5—7.2 MS → $S^0 + M^{2+}$, S^0 → SO_4^{2-}, Sb_2S_5 → SO_4^{2-}

Th. thioparus pH 3.5—9.5 Sb_2S_3 → Sb_2O_3, Sb_2O_4, $Sb_2O_4 \cdot nH_2O$, Bi_2S_3 → $Bi(OH^-)$

Thiobacillus "y": S^0 → SO_4^{2-}, PbS → $PbSO_4$

---

oxides and carbonates into sulphides, can be put to good use in the pre-flotation sulphidizing of oxidic copper, lead and zinc minerals, to replace the usual chemical treatment with sodium sulphide. Malachite grains kept for the same length of time (five days) in a sterile and in a *Desulfovibrio desulfuricans* containing Na_2S solution, respectively, both of the same S^{2-} concentration, grew a covellite coating only 5 to 10 μm thick in the first liquor but 30 to 50 μm thick in the second (Fletcher 1970, 1971).

In the oxidation of sulphide minerals in ore and coal mines, thiobacteria play the prime role. The schematic reactions involved and the optimum pH ranges of their operation are presented in Table 6.1.

Some heterotrophic bacteria also utilize organic compounds (e.g. organic acids) in their metabolism, the reaction involved being

$$MS \rightarrow \text{organic metal salt} + S^{2-},$$

where M is a metal, e.g. Cu, Ni, Fe, etc. (Polkin et al. 1975).

At present, the most important field of application of chemical mining is the leaching of copper out of low-grade copper ores or copper-bearing tailings. In the US, for example, some 300,000 t of copper is won a year by this very cheap method. As referred to in connection with Fig. 6.1A, B, copper is precipitated out of the liquor as a cement on iron swarf, according to the reaction

$$Fe + CuSO_4 \rightarrow Cu + FeSO_4.$$

The spent liquor is then regenerated and recycled.

440

6.2. METAL RECOVERY

In the metal-laden (pregnant) liquor obtained by leaching, the concentration of pay metal is too low and that of interfering constituents too high to permit the economically viable direct winning of a metal product of shipping (market-able) purity. This means that the values in the liquor must first be concentrated and the interferents (impurities) removed. This can be achieved using ion-exchange resins, solvent extraction or ion flotation. Ion-exchange resins sorb the pay metal(s) on their surfaces: the organic solvents immiscible with water used in solvent extraction collect them in the organic liquid phase; in ion flota-tion, the pay metal ions in the aqueous liquor are selectively attached to air bubbles.

6.2.1. Ion exchange or IX. On the porous spherules (beads) of large internal surface of the ion-exchange resins, exchangeable active cations (K_1) or anions (A_1) or radicals are attached by chemical bonds. Up until an equilibrium is reached, these ions can be exchanged (displaced) by the ions in the pregnant liquor (K_2 or A_2) without affecting the resin structure to any significant degree:

$$R^- K_1^+ + K_2^+ \rightleftarrows R^- K_2^+ + K_1^+$$

or

$$R^+ A_1^- + A_2^- \rightleftarrows R^+ A_2^- + A_1^-.$$

In cation-exchange resins, the active (exchangeable) radical is an organic-acid radical (e.g. the radical of a sulphonic acid, a phosphonic or phosphinic acid, an arsonic acid, or the carboxyl or phenolic hydroxyl radical); in anion-exchange resins, it is a primary, secondary, tertiary or quaternary amine, a quaternary phosphonium or tertiary sulphonium radical. There exist also amphoteric and chelating ion exchangers (polyelectrolytes) capable of exchanging both cations and anions.

Resins are produced by condensation or polymerization. Of the polymers, styrenes seem to be the most popular. There are weak, medium-strong and strong acid and basic resins. Let us cite as examples the $-SO_3H$ radical (pK $= 1$) as a strong-acid, $-COOH$ (pK $= 4$ to 6) as a weak-acid, $-N(CH_3)_3$ OH as a strong-base, $-NH_3OH$ or $=NH_2OH$ (pK $= 6$ to 9) as a weak-base radical. Useful adsorptive capacity (the loading factor) is a function, among other things, also of liquor pH (which affects the dissociation or hydrolysis of the polar radicals). High selectivity is an important precondition in the use of a resin: the ion to be extracted should be selectively sorbed even in the abundant presence of interferent ions.

Ion exchange observes the law of mass action as a rule: if the resin has the same affinity to two metals in the same liquor, it will sorb the more abundant one. The affinities of different ions to a resin tend to be widely different, how-ever. It is usually the ions that have a greater valence, a smaller hydrated radius, greater polarizability, a greater propensity to associate with the displaced radical and a lesser one to associate with their own kind in the liquor which have the stronger affinity. In the cation-exchange group, for example, affinity decreases from tetravalent to trivalent, thence to divalent and monovalent metal ions: the order of decrease within each of these groups is as follows:

tetravalent: $Th > Hf > Zr$;
trivalent: $Ac > La > Y > Sc > Al$;
divalent: $Ba > Sr > Ca > Mg > Be$;
monovalent: $Ag > Tl > Cs > Rb > NH_4 \simeq K > Na > H > Li$.

The order of decreasing affinities in anion-exchange resins is

$$OH^- > SO_4^{2-} > CrO_3^{2-} > \text{citrate}^{2-} > \text{tartrate}^{2-} > NO_3^- > AsO_3^{3-} >$$
$$> PO_3^{3-} > MoO_4^{2-} > \text{acetate}^- > I^- > Br^- > Cl^-.$$

Selectivity will decrease as a rule as the liquor's concentration and temperature rise, but there are some exceptions to this rule.

Ion exchange may be performed using a stationary (fixed) or moving resin bed or resin beads in suspension; the liquor may be a pulp containing fine-grained solids or it may be entirely clear.

Columns with fixed resin beds are operated in series connection. The first column, in which the resin has become nearly saturated, is taken off line, flushed out with water and eluted (regenerated) by means of a solution (eluant) that achieves the desorption of the pay metal load from the resin. The next column then takes over as first column: at the same time, a fresh (regenerated) column is connected up to the end of the series. Desorption (stripping) is achieved by means of an eluant with a high enough concentration of some counter-ion (e.g. Cl^- in anion exchange), which displaces the sorbed ions from the resin by the law of mass action. The spherules (beads) of resin in the columns are of 0.1 to 0.5 mm diameter. Fixed-bed columns are fed clear liquor. In order, however, to avoid the cost and bother of filtering out the fine slimes, often only the coarser solids (sands) are removed after leaching, and the liquor is fed to the columns with the slimes still in it (this is called the RIP — resin-in-pulp — process). In this type of setup, baskets made of screen shetting filled with coarser-grained resin beads (>0.8 mm) are jigged up and down in the pulp flowing in series-connected banks (the term used for rubber-lined tanks). The resin is not removed from the baskets even for regeneration.

Also in processes using fluid-bed columns, the liquor may contain some pulp. Coarser-grained (0.8 to 2 mm) resin suspended in the pulp is also used to perform ion exchange: in this case, pulp and resin move in uninterrupted counter-current. The pulp-and-resin mixture is removed from the tanks connected in series e.g. by airlift and separated by screening: the resin is then led to the next tank up the line, and the pulp to the next tank down the line.

The necessary number of stages of sorption can be determined by recording an exchange isotherm for the operating conditions envisaged. The isotherm represents the relationship

$$K = f(c)$$

between concentration c in the liquor and the saturation (loading) K of the resin (Fig. 6.2). The working line passing through the points determined by con-

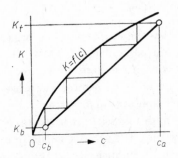

Fig. 6.2. Graphic construction for finding the number of stages of adsorption, using the saturation curve $K = f(c)$ and the working line

centration c_b in the spent pulp and residual load K_b in the resin on the one hand and concentration c_a of the pregnant pulp and the desired terminal loading K_t on the resin on the other is also traced in. The number of stages required can be determined by drawing between line and curve the ladder shown in the figure. The retention time of pulp in the stages should be determined by experiment. (In the case of uranium leaching, most resins attain 80% of their equilibrium load in about ten minutes.)

Using strong-base anion-exchange resins, uranium can be selectively extracted even from very poor liquors, both acid and alkaline, in the form of

$$[UO_2(SO_4)_3]^{4-} \quad \text{or} \quad [UO_2(CO_3)_3]^{4-}.$$

Chelating-type ion-exchange resins seem to hold the greatest promise for the selective recovery of the most diverse metals out of liquors containing interferents also.

6.2.2. In solvent (liquid-into-liquid) **extraction** (SX), an organic phase insoluble in or immiscible with water (O) selectively extracts the pay component from an aqueous liquor (A). The distribution ratio E_A^O of equilibrium concentrations in the two phases must be high for the pay metal and low for the interferents. That ratio is in the ideal case a function of temperature only, and is independent of concentration (i.e., the equilibrium isotherm is a straight line). In practice, however, the E_A^O function is a concentration-dependent curve [just as the $K = f(c)$ curve in Fig. 6.2]. At the end of the extraction (selective-trans-

443

fer) pass, the two phases can be disengaged (separated) by settling, thanks to their different densities: the pay metal is subsequently reextracted (stripped; that is, transferred into a clean aqueous phase called the stripping solution).

One of several available extraction mechanisms can be chosen.

Neutral and, most often, unhydrated molecules can be extracted by purely physical means relying on the distribution ratio E_A^O: for example,

$$(GeCl_4)_a \rightleftarrows (GeCl_4)_o.$$

Of the subscripts, a indicates the aqueous, o the organic phase.

Polar solvents extract ion pairs which dissolve in the organic liquid after more or less solvation or constitute complex compounds therewith (as in the case of uranyl nitrate). The most widespread representative of this group of solvents is a neutral phosphoric acid ester, tributyl phosphate (TBP), $(C_4H_9O)_3PO$. Owing to its high viscosity, it is dissolved before dosage in a carrier solvent (usually an alkane); the solvent actually added may e.g. be a 10% solution of TBP in kerosene. Phosphoric acid esterized with some higher alcohol is another effective solvent of uranium. The distribution ratio E_A^O increases up to a chain length of 9C but declines beyond that. The polarity of the P=O bond and hence the complex-forming propensity of the compound is enhanced by the direct bond between the alkyl radicals and the P atom:

$$(RO)_3{\equiv}P{=}O < (RO)_2{=}P{=} \underset{\underset{R}{|}}{\overset{\overset{R}{|}}{<}} RO{-}P{=}O \underset{\underset{R}{|}}{\overset{\overset{R}{|}}{<}} R{-}P{=}O.$$

Mixtures of phosphates, phosphinates and phosphine oxides exhibit synergism; that is, they mutually enhance one another's extractive properties.

The reaction between TBP and uranyl nitrate is described by

$$(UO_2^{2+})_a + 2(NO_3^-)_a + 2[(RO)_3PO]_o \rightleftarrows UO_2(NO_3)_2 \cdot 2[(RO_3)PO]_o.$$

Ethers, alcohols and ketones constitute oxonium salts by means of hydrogen bonds: e.g.,

$$[H(FeCl_4)]_a + (R_2 = O)_o \rightleftarrows [R_2 = O \ldots H(FeCl_4)]_o.$$

Acid phosphoric-acid esters serve as liquid cation exchangers; aliphatic (primary, secondary, tertiary) amines or quaternary ammonium compounds serve as liquid anion exchangers. Their reaction mechanism is the same as that of the solid ion exchangers: they constitute salt-type compounds by means of ion-to-ion interactions. The reactions e.g. of uranium extraction are

$$(UO_2^{2+})_a + 2(ROPO_3H_2)_o \rightleftarrows (UO_2[ROPO_3H]_2)_o + 2(H^+)_a$$

or

$$[UO_2(SO_4)_2]_a^{2-} + 2[(R_2NH_2)Cl]_o \rightleftarrows [(R_2NH_2)_2 \cdot UO_2(SO_4)_2]_o + 2(Cl^-)_a.$$

The solubility of the salts thus formed in the organic solvents used is low: this is why liquid ion exchangers are likewise dosed in carrier solvents (e.g. a liquid alkane). The esters of higher molecular weight are water-insoluble. The most widely used ones include the dialkyl esters of phosphoric acid, the most prominent of which are DEHPA (di-2-ethyl-hexyl-phosphoric acid ester) and the dithiophosphoric acid esters

$$(RO_2)POOH \text{ and } (RO_2)PSSH,$$

where

$$R: CH_3-CH-CH_2-CH_2-CH_2-CH_2.$$
$$| $$
$$CH_2-CH_3$$

These diesters extract uranium with a high selectivity from hydrochloric, sulphuric and phosphoric acid liquors. As the acid concentration in the aqueous liquor increases, the equilibrium distribution ratio E_A^O decreases.

One may write up e.g. for the extraction with DEHPA of a divalent cation, M^{2+},

$$2(RO)_2POOH_o + M^{2+} \rightleftarrows \{(RO)_2POO\}_2M_o + 2H_a^+;$$

for this reversible process,

$$K = \frac{[\{(RO_2)POO\}_2M][H^+]^2}{[M^{2+}][(RO)_2POOH]^2}.$$

Now if the metal is fully ionic in the aqueous liquor and fully complex in the organic phase, then

$$E_A^O = \frac{[\{(RO)_2POO\}_2M]}{[M^{2+}]} = \frac{K[(RO)_2POOH]^2}{[H^+]^2}$$

is obtained as the extraction constant (distribution ratio of equilibrium concentrations). It follows that, in the case of a divalent metal, the degree of extraction will vary as the square of organic solvent concentration and inversely as the square of hydrogen ion concentration. In other words, extraction can be promoted by increasing organic solvent concentration and/or the pH of the liquor.

Figure 6.3 is a flowsheet of uranium extraction with DEHPA and stripping with Na_2CO_3, where the reaction equations entering into play are

$$2(RO)_2PO_2H + UO_2^{2+} \rightarrow UO_2[(RO)_2PO_2]_2 + 2H^+$$

for extraction,

$$UO_2[(RO)_2PO_2]_2 + 3Na_2CO_3 \rightarrow 2Na(RO)_2PO_2 + Na_4UO_2(CO_3)_3$$

445

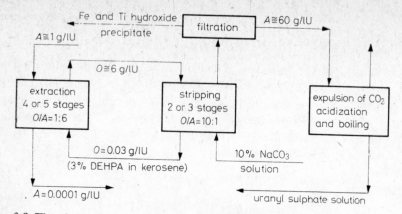

Fig. 6.3. Flowsheet of uranium extraction using DEHPA, a liquid ion exchanger, and stripping with Na_2CO_3

for stripping and

$$2Na(RO)_2PO_2 + H_2SO_4 \rightarrow 2(RO)_2PO_2H + Na_2SO_4$$

for regeneration in an acid solution.

Liquid anion exchangers are also dosed in a kerosene carrier or in a mixture of kerosene and some higher alcohol. Selectivity depends rather greatly on amine structure; it tends to be highest for tertiary amines. The equilibrium distribution ratio E_A^O of primary amines is comparatively low.

Chelating agents have a very high selectivity with respect to the metals with which they constitute chelates. Selective chelators of copper include dimethyl glyoxime,

$$\begin{array}{l} CH_3-C=NOH \\ \quad\quad | \\ CH_3-C=NOH, \end{array}$$

beta diketones,

$$\begin{array}{l} HO \quad NOH \\ | \quad\quad || \\ R_2=C-C-R, \end{array}$$

hydroxy oximes such as the LIX reagents of General Mills Chemicals, such as LIX-63 (alpha hydroxy oxime);

$$\begin{array}{l} H \\ | \\ R-C-C-R \\ | \quad\quad || \\ HO \quad NOH \end{array}$$

446

(also suitable for extraction out of an ammoniated [alkaline] liquor), or LIX-64 (alkyl-hydroxy benzophenonoxime),

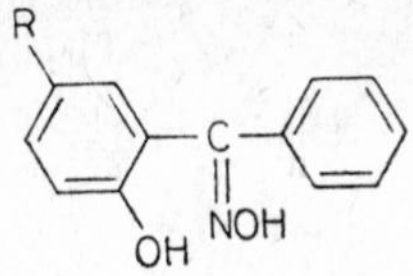

R—(benzene ring, OH, C=NOH, phenyl)

to be used in acid solutions; **LIX-64N**; **LIX-70** (a chlorinated LIX-64N plus **LIX-63**):

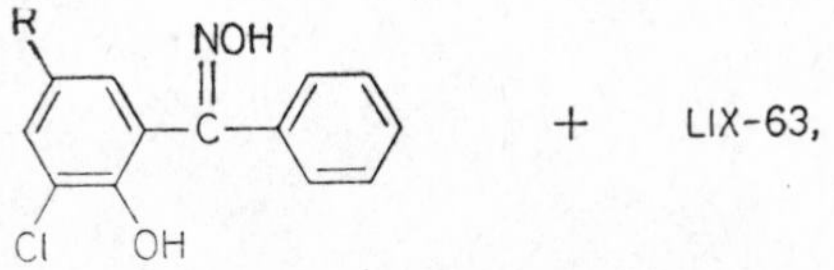

R—(benzene ring, Cl, OH, NOH, C, phenyl)   +   LIX-63,

where R: C_9H_{17}, etc.; or Shell's SME 529 or Acorga's P-17 (orthohydroxy aryl oxime); or the Kelex reagents of Ashland Chemicals (beta-alkenyl 8-hydroxy quinoline):

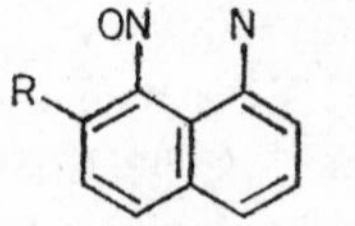

R—(naphthalene, ON, N)

where R is a 10C alkane radical, etc. For example, the chelate structures of Cu^{2+} have the form

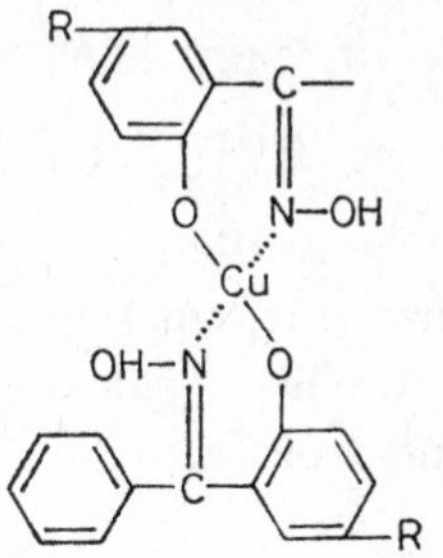

(Cu chelate structure)

for LIX-64,

(Cu chelate structure)

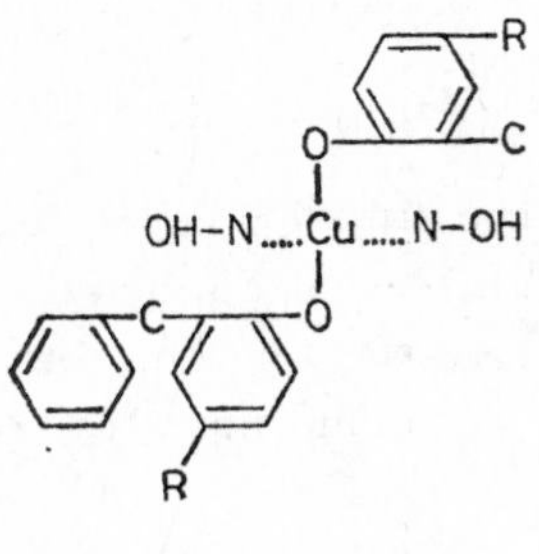

for LIX-64N,

$$HO-N\overset{O}{\underset{||}{\underset{N}{\cdots}}}\,\,Cu\,\,\overset{||}{\underset{O}{\underset{|}{\cdots}}}\,N-OH$$

for beta diketone and

$$\begin{array}{cc} \overset{O}{\underset{||}{CH_3-C=N}} & \overset{OH}{\underset{|}{N=C-CH_3}} \\ & Cu \\ \underset{OH}{CH_3-C=N} & \overset{||}{\underset{O}{N=C-CH_3}} \end{array}$$

for dimethyl glyoxime.

The chelating reagents of solvent extraction are also dosed in 5 to 10% concentration in an organic carrier solvent immiscible with water (e.g. in kerosene). Their principal advantage is their strong selective affinity to copper, stronger than to any other metal. For example, LIX-64 at a pH about 2 will extract Fe^{3+}, harmful in copper electrolysis, very weakly from the aqueous liquor; it will extract the ions M^{6+} and V^{4+} even more slightly, and the ions Zn^{2+}, Sn^{3+}, Ca^{2+}, Mg^{2+}, As^{3+}, Al^{3+}, Fe^{2+}, Si^{4+}, Co^{2+} and Ni^{3+} practically not at all. For another example, a 0.5 mole/l solution of Kelex in the organic carrier solvent Solvesso 150 (which contains 10% isodecanol) at the phase ratios

$$O/A = 1/2 \quad 1/1 \quad 3/1$$

gives the Cu/Fe ratios

$$540 \quad 300 \quad 180 \text{ at pH} = 1 \text{ and}$$
$$810 \quad 810 \quad 120 \text{ at pH} = 2.$$

In the pH range from 1 to 9, the solubility of Kelex in water is less than one part per million. At an O/A phase ratio of $1/1$, and at a pH of say, 1.5, the concentration of Cu is about 5.1 g/l in a 7% solution of Kelex-100, about 1.7 g/l in a 7% solution of LIX-64N and a pro rata of the two in mixtures of the two solvents.

The extraction-reextraction (extraction-and-stripping) reaction is described by the equation

$$2(RH)_o + (CU^{2+} + SO_4^{2-})_a \rightleftarrows (R_2Cu)_o + (2H^+ + SO_4^{2-})_a$$

where extraction proceeds in the direction of the upper arrow and reextraction (stripping) the other way round. The clear aqueous liquor obtained on stripping can be taken direct to electrolysis while the organic phase is recycled into extraction. The progress of the reaction from left to right or right to left depends on the pH also.

For example, on adding kerosene containing 10 volume% LIX-64 to 1.95 times as much aqueous liquor of pH = 2.2 containing 1.11 g/l Cu and 2.78 g/l Fe^{3+}, extraction in four countercurrent stages gave an aqueous phase containing 0.03 g/l Cu and an organic phase containing 2.42 g/l Cu and 0.016 g/l Fe^{3+} at a Cu recovery of 97.5% (Fig. 6.4). On stripping the organic phase in three

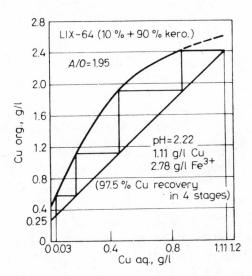

Fig. 6.4. Extraction isotherm of ten percent LIX-64 at $A/O = 1.95$ and pH = 2.22

stages with a spent aqueous solution containing 200 g/l H_2SO_4 and 8.0 g/l Cu discharged from electrolysis in a volume ratio 1/47, a pure aqueous liquor containing 96.8 g/l Cu and 0.78 g/l Fe^{3+} was obtained that could be taken back direct to the electrolysis; the organic phase recycled to solvent extraction had a Cu content of 0.25 g/l. (A clear liquor containing no more than about 30 g/l Cu is sufficient for electrolysis; such a liquor can be obtained by single-stage flushing with a stripping solution containing 8 to 10 g/l Cu and about 200 g/l H_2SO_4.) (Agers et al. 1965.)

The extraction isotherm of 10% LIX-64 in kerosene is also shown in Fig. 6.4. The number of stages required for extraction is found using the ladder construction introduced in Fig. 6.2 in connection with ion-exchange resins.

General Mills Chemicals manufactures some solvent-extraction agents more powerful than LIX 64: trademarked LIX-64N, LIX-65N, LIX-70, LIX-71 and LIX-73; these are mixtures of hydroxy oximes, performing well even in liquors that are richer in copper and/or are more strongly acid. (For example, LIX-70 will serve in solutions containing 60 g/l Cu and 100 g/l H_2SO_4.) Stripping them of course requires an even stronger acid. For example, at a H_2SO_4 concentration of 300 g/l, a transfer capacity of 40% was recorded. Transfer capacity K_A is the

449

ratio of the difference in Cu content before and after stripping to the maximum possible saturation of the solvent: for example, if the Cu content of 1.5 g/l in an 8% pregnant solution of the solvent LIX-64N is reduced to 0.1 g/l by stripping, and the maximum possible saturation of the solvent is 2.0 g/l Cu, then

$$K_A = \frac{1.5 - 0.1}{2.0} = 70\%.$$

The cost of solvent loss per kilogram of Cu metal varies approximately inversely as the Cu content in the leach liquor to be exposed to extraction: hence, if the liquor is richer, a lower transfer capacity may be admissible. The Cu content in the stripped solvent is the greater, the higher the

$$R = Cu\ (g/l) + free\ H_2SO_4\ (g/l)$$

parameter of the liquor exposed to extraction. Table 6.2 presents residual Cu concentrations at different values of R for the strong LIX reagents, at 75% saturation (Agers and DeMent 1974).

Figure 6.5 is a plot vs. the equilibrium pH of the ratio of concentrations E_A^O in the organic phase O (Solvesso 150 containing 10 volume % isodencanol) and of the residual concentration in the aqueous liquor A achieved using a 0.5-mole solution of the extractant Kelex-100 at a phase ratio $O/A = 1/3$ from clear aqueous liquors containing 5 g/l metal each. In the alkaline range (pH > 7), full curves refer to $(NH_4)_2CO_3$, dotted ones to $(NH_4)_2SO_4$. In an alkaline solution (in the case of either Kelex or LIX), iron, hydrolysing together with the other interferents, constitutes no amine complexes with ammonia: it precipitates as iron oxide. In the absence of iron and other interferents, the successive separa-

Table 6.2. Residual (after-stripping) Cu content in grams per litre in solutions of various LIX reagents saturated to 75%, as a function of the parameter R (Cu, g/l, plus free sulphuric acid, g/l)

LIX °C	—64N 20	—65N 40	—65N 50	—73 20 —71 40	—71 50	—70 20
R = 6	0.11	0.08	0.04	0.04	0.02	0.01
8	0.32	0.17	0.06	0.05	0.02	0.01
10	0.90	0.30	0.14	0.07	0.03	0.02
15	—	0.82	0.50	0.12	0.04	0.02
20	—	1.94	1.24	0.18	0.06	0.03
30	—	—	—	0.37	0.15	0.06
40	—	—	—	0.77	0.42	0.16
50	—	—	—	1.36	0.80	0.29
60	—	—	—	2.20	1.25	0.48
70	—	—	—	2.86	1.70	0.70
80	—	—	—	—	2.17	1.00

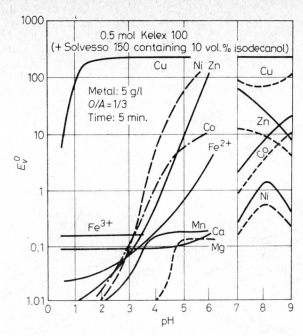

Fig. 6.5. Extraction with Kelex-100 vs. the pH

tion of the dissolved metals taken into solution (such as Cu, Ni, Zn, Co, etc.) is greatly simplified (Ritcey and Lucas 1974, 1975).

Parts A to H of Fig. 6.6 illustrate extraction operations using different solvents. The abscissa axis is calibrated in the hydrochloric-acid concentration of the aqueous liquor in Parts D and E and in the pH in all the other diagrams: the ordinate axis is calibrated in the recovery of extracted metals in the organic phase ($m\%$) in Parts A to D, in the distribution ratio E_A^O (the ratio of metal concentrations in the organic phase and in the aqueous liquor, respectively) in Parts E and F and in metal concentration g/l in the extract (in the organic phase) in Parts G and H. DOMSC is di-n-octyl-methyl-sulphonium chloride dissolved in dichloroethane; versatilic acid is a tertiary monocarboxylic acid that is insoluble in water but readily soluble in kerosene. The aqueous liquor is acidified with hydrochloric acid in A, D and E and with sulphuric acid in B; the acid may be sulphuric or hydrochloric in C, sulphuric or nitric in F, nitric or sulphuric in G and H. Focussing now e.g. on Part A, one recognizes how easy it is, in an extraction operation using naphthenic acid, to separate copper from nickel, whereas Co cannot be separated from Ni, or Cd from Zn.

Table 6.3 lists some of the more widely used reagents of extraction, together with their principal fields of application. The selective separation of metals is influenced crucially by anion concentration for Group I (solvating) reagents, by pH regulation for Group II (acid non-chelating) and Group IV (chelating)

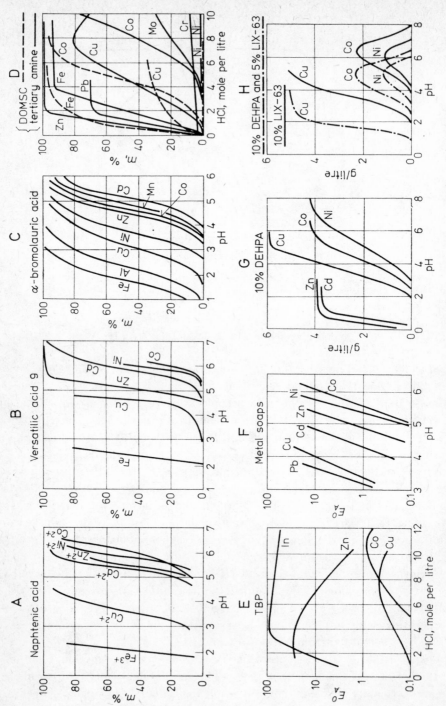

Fig. 6.6. Extraction of different metal ions using different solvents. For the details see text

Table 6.3. Principal uses of some organic agents of solvent extraction

Reagent	Principal uses
I. Organic solvents	
Tributyl phosphate (TBP)	Cleaning of U concentrates. Separation of U from Pu, Zr from Hf; separation of rare earths; Th extraction
Methyl isobutyl ketone (MIBK)	Separation of Nb from Ta, Zr from Hf
Butyl or amyl alcohol	Extraction of H_3PO_4 out of acid chloride leaches
II. Acid (non-chelating) reagents	
Naphthenic acids	Extraction of various metal ions
Diethyl-hexyl-phosphoric acid (DEHPA)	Separation of rare earths; extraction of U, Be
III. Liquid anion exchangers (amines)	
Primene JMT (RNH_2)	Removal of Fe from an Al or NH_3 sulphate leach
LA-1 and LA-2 (R_2NH)	Extraction of U
Alamine 336 (R_3N)	Extraction of U, V, W; separation of Ni, Co out of chloride leaches
Aliquat 336 ($R_3N^+CH_3 \cdot Cl^-$)	Extraction of V, Cr
IV. Chelating agents	
LIX-63 (General Mills)	Cu extraction out of an ammonia leach, with separation of Ni and Co
LIX-64	Fe^+-free extraction of Cu out of acid leaches
Kelex (Ashland)	
Polyol (Dow)	Extraction of B out of salt leaches

MIBK:

$$\begin{array}{c} CH_3 \\ \\ C_4H_9 \end{array}\!\!\!\!\!\!>\!\!C=O$$

Polyol:

Naphthenic acid:

Primene and LA: mixtures of the homologues $R = C_{18}$ to C_{24}

Alamine and Aliquat: mixtures of the homologues $R = C_8$ to C_{18}

reagents, by the regulation of anion concentration and/or of the pH in the case of Group III (amine) reagents. (For example, in the winning of complex metal anions such as $FeCl_4^-$, $CoCl_4^-$, etc., it is the anion concentration that is crucial; in the extraction of Mo, V, W, etc., it is the pH.)

If TBP, DEHPA or amines are to be used, ferric iron must be removed from the solution beforehand or converted into ferrous iron. Some carboxylic acids, the ketones and the alcohols are rather readily soluble in water; this fact entails comparatively great losses of reagent.

By means of fatty acids in the 7C to 13C range dissolved in kerosene, metals carried in the aqueous liquor can be extracted in the succession

Sn—Bi—Fe—Pb—Al—Cu—Cd—Zn—Ni—Co—Mn—Ca—Mg—Na.

Sn^{4+} is the metal of the most acidic nature; Na^+ is the most alkaline one. In fatty-acid extraction, the ratios of the factors of extraction for some pairs of metals are

$$\begin{array}{ll} \text{Ni—Co} & 1.8; \\ \text{Zn—Co} & 5; \\ \text{Cd—Co} & 35; \\ \text{Cu—Co} & 100—500; \\ \text{Fe—Co} & >1000; \\ \text{Co—Mn} & 1.4; \\ \text{Co—Na} & 100—200. \end{array}$$

On the extraction of different metals using MIBK, $[CH_3COCH_2CH(CH_2)_2$, whose solubility in water is 1.9% at 20 °C], the following distribution ratios E_A^O are obtained:

— in a one-mole solution of HCl:

$10^3 >$ Au $> 10^2$, 10 $>$ Re, Cr, Pt $> 1 >$ Tc, Fe, Ir, In, Ga $> 10^{-1} >$ Os, Se, Ru, Hf, Sr, Zn, Rb, Nb $> 10^{-2} >$ Cd, Mo, Eu, Ba, Na, Pd, K, Th, $Np^{5+} > 10^{-3} >$ Pa, Tb, Zr, Co, Sc, Y, U $> 10^{-4} >$ Pm, Lu, Ni, Cu, Ce^{3+}, Cs, La, Mn, Ta;

— in a six-mole solution of HCl:

$10^3 >$ Ga $> 10^2$ Au, In, Pa, Mo $> 10 >$ Re, Fe, Se, Pt, Cr $> 1 >$ Tc, Cd, U^{6+}, Ir, Os $> 10^{-1}$ Np, Zn, Ru, Nb, Zn, Hf, Zr $> 10^{-2} >$ Rb, Sr, Pd, Mn, K, Ni, Ba, Eu, Co, Lu, Tb, $Ce^{3+} > 10^{-3}$ Sc, Th, Ni, Pm, Na, Y $> 10^{-4} >$ Ca, Ta, Cs, La $> 10^{-5}$;

— in a two-mole solution of HNO_3:

10 $> Hg^{2+} > 1 >$ Tc, Re, Pt, U^{6+}, Pd $> 10^{-1} >$ W, Ir, Cr, Nb, Pa $> 10^{-2} >$ Mo, Pb, Ce^{4+}, Lu, Zr, Ru, Mn, Ag, Eu, Cs, Ba, Th, K $>$ $> 10^{-3} >$ Sc, Na, Zn, Sr, Np^{5+}, Ca, Ni, La, Ta, Cd, Ga, $Ce^{3+} > 10^{-4} >$ $>$ Rb, Pm, In, Y, Tl^+, Cu, Tb, Hf, Fe;

— in a ten-mole solution of HNO:

10 $> U^{6+} > 1 >$ Pa, Hg^{2+}, Tc, Pd, Pt, Ce^{4+}, Cr, Re, Zr, Hf,

454

W $> 10^{-1} >$ Np, Ir, Rb, Nb, K, Cs, Mo, Ru $> 10^{-2} >$ Lu, Sc, Eu, Na, Co, Ca, Fe, Tl$^+$, Mn, Zn, Cu, Ce^{3+}, Ag, Os, Y, Ni, La, Ca, Sr $> 10^{-3} >$ $>$ Ba, Ga, In, Ta $> 10^{-4}$.

(Union Carbide Bulletin F-44613).

In extraction and stripping, the transfer of dissolved components from one liquid phase into the other can be accelerated by increased turbulence and the dispersion of the organic phase into finer droplets.

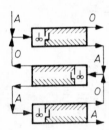

Fig. 6.7. Mixer-settlers in series countercurrent hookup

It is usual to perform extraction and stripping in several mixer-settlers connected in series, with the phases moving countercurrent (cf. Fig. 6.7). In the mixing compartment, the phases are stirred to a fine dispersion: in the settling compartment, they separate by density. (Agitation and dispersion may be performed in another setup by pumps installed before the settling tanks.) Extracting columns and centrifugal extractors may also be used with intense (countercurrent) mixing and separation by settling. These devices in fact require less space.

Liquid-liquid extraction is usually performed on clear (slimeless) solutions, but SIP (solvent-in-pulp) processes have also been employed industrially.

Solvent loss is less in clear solutions than in pulps; however, the separation of the solids from the solution can be avoided in the latter. Solvent loss increases as the intensity and duration of mixing. The phase volume ratio O/A should not be too small, in order to avoid the formation of an emulsion impossible to break up by settling. (In view of this contingency, the dosage of suitable surfactants may be indicated.)

Solvent extraction has both advantages and drawbacks as compared with processes using ion-exchange resins. Its advantages are a greater simplicity and flexibility, a broader range of applications, greater ease of regulation, greater tolerance to certain interferents, the easy recovery of by-products such as V, Mo or Th, etc. It also permits the direct production of reactor-grade U. Its main drawback is that the organic phase is invariably soluble in water to some extent (and will also get emulsified in it more or less): all this results in solvent losses. (The losses are considerably greater if the process is applied to a pulp rather than to a clear solution.) There is for the time being no commer-

Table 6.4. Approximate solvent prices, solvent losses, solvent makeup and overall costs in solvent extraction at an aqueous liquor throughput rate of 100 US gals. per minute

Reagent	£/kg	pH	~g/m³	~d⁺/m³	c%	Extracted metal
TBP	0.50	2.0	25—40	0.3—0.5	7.0	U
MIBK	0 15	1—5 M HCl	20,000	36.0	11.3	Hf
Naphthenic acids	0.12	{ 4.0 / 6.5 }	{ 90 / 900 }	{ 2.6 / 26.0 }	23.6	Ni
DEHPA	1.20	{ 2.0 / 6.0 }	{ 5 / 30 }	{ 1.4 / 8.4 }	8.7	rare earths / Co
Tertiary amines	0.75	1.5—2.0	10—40	1.8—7.2	31.0	U
LIX-64	2.40	1.5—2.0	4—15	2.3—8.6	2.0	Cu
Kelex-100	5.90	1.5	8	11.3	6.9	Cu
Versatilic acid 911	?	{ 7.0 / 7.7 }	300—900 / 100	?		Ni / Co

Metal	Metal conc. g/l	Aqueous phase	Organic solvent	A/O	US cents/kg of metal	Cost¹			Extr.² device
						a%	b%	c%	
Co—Ni	10 Co, 10 Ni	5—6 pH, H_2SO_4	20% DEHPA	1/1	18.9	16.3	15.1	7.0	co
Cu	{ 2 Cu	2 pH, H_2SO_4	10 LIX-64N	2/1	29.3	24.8	52.6	11.3	m-s
	15 Cu	2 pH, H_2SO_4	20% Kelex100	1/1	8.4	7.9	29.0	23.6	m-s
Rare earths	Y 0.10 Y	1.7 pH, H_2SO_4	3.3% DEHPA	20/1	178.5	0.7	30.9	8.7	ce & co
U	2.0 U	1.7 pH, H_2SO_4	5% adogene 364 or alamine 336	25/1	21.4	25.8	25.8	31.0	m-s
Zr—Hf	{ 95 Zr, 1.5 Hf	7.5 N HNO_3	50% TBP	1/3	90.4	0.5	0.1	2.0	co
	100 Zr, 2 Hf 1 M	HCl-3M MCNS	MIBK	1/2	124.2	8.2	53.2	6.9	co

¹ a%: depreciation of investment over ten years; b%: wage bill; c%: solvent make-up cost.
² co: column; ce: centrifuge; m-s: mixer-settler.
d⁺ denotes old pence (one 240th of a pound sterling).

cially available economical solvent for carbonate ores. The formation of emulsions (or possibly of solid precipitates) may be another worry. For a comparison referring to uranium extraction, one m³ of resin can adsorb 50 to 75 kg of U_3O_8, which permits the daily recovery of 30 to 50 kg of U_3O_8 whereas one m³ of organic liquid of 0.1-mole concentration, which cannot extract more than 5 to 10 kg of U_3O_8, permits the daily recovery of 60 to 130 kg of U_3O_8.

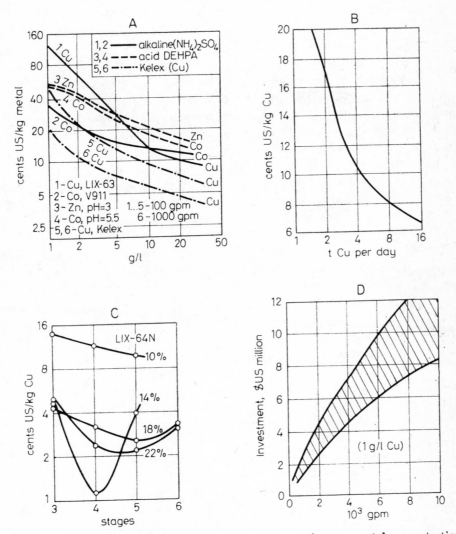

Fig. 6.8. A — operating costs of solvent-extraction operations vs. metal concentration, g/l, in the liquor. The parameter is liquor throughput in US gallons per minute. *B, C* — operating costs of Cu production vs. daily Cu output (*B*) and the number of stages of extraction, with LIX concentration in the organic phase as the parameter (*C*). *D* — investment cost vs. aqueous-liquor throughput in thousand US gallons per minute

Some of the organic solvents are quite cheap; others are very expensive; most are somewhere in between. The economics of the process, however, hinges first and foremost on the losses in the circuit per unit of metal recovered, rather than on the cost of a first filling-up of the circuit. The other reagents required for running the process (for pH regulation, stripping, electrolyte purification, etc.) are also important cost items. The upper part of Table 6.4 shows the 1970 prices of some extractants, approximate solvent losses per cubic metre of aqueous liquor recirculated (regenerated) at a given pH, and the costs incurred on this account. The bottom part of the table shows extraction costs for individual metals at an aqueous-liquor circulation rate of 100 US gallons per minute (1 G = 378.5 litres per minute = 22.7 m³/h) (Ritcey 1975).

Part A of Fig. 6.8 shows the cost of metal produced by different solvent-extraction processes vs. the concentration of the metal in the leach liquor, for given leach circulation rates (100 gallons per minute for Curves 1 to 5 and 1,000 gpm for Curve 6). Part B of Fig. 6.8 presents the direct operating costs of copper extraction vs. daily metal output. Part C of the figure presents the influence of LIX-64N concentration (from 10 to 22%) upon the operating costs, vs. the number of extraction stages. (The optimum in the case under scrutiny is seen to be provided by four-stage extraction at a LIX concentration of 14%.) Part D of the figure shows investment cost vs. aqueous-liquor throughput at a concentration of one g/l Cu in the leach solution.

The viewpoints to be considered when choosing the organic solvent is selectivity first and foremost, followed by as complete a solvent recovery as possible on stripping (regeneration), miscibility with suitable organic carrier diluents, solubility or otherwise in the aqueous phase, a rapid and complete disengagement from the aqueous liquor after extraction, and the uptake (load) capacity in respect of the element to be recovered. A high price is none too relevant if losses of expensive extractant in the circuit can be kept low.

Solvent extraction is widely used for the extraction of uranium but mainly for the extraction of copper from both low-grade ores and concentrates and also of rare earths. Table 6.5 presents solvent extraction routes used in practice to recover certain chemical elements (Rosenbaum et al. 1971: Ritcey 1969).

6.2.3. In ion flotation, the ions of an element in low concentration are attached one by one to heteropolar ions (tensids or surfactants) of opposite polarity lining finely dispersed air bubbles in the solution. Rising to the surface of the solution, the bubbles aggregate to form an unstable froth. When the froth collapses, its ion load is retained on the surface in a thin film that can be skimmed off. A suitable tensid can be chosen from among the conventional collectors of flotation (from those that have a selective affinity to the ion to be flotated out). Of the anionic collectors, alkyl or aryl thiophosphates, thiocarbonates, thiocarbamates, carboxyls, etc. enter into consideration; the cationic collector

Table 6.5. Principal features of solvent extraction operations used to recover various chemical elements

Element	Extracted as*	Leach	Organic solvent	Stripping agent
Au		acid chloride	dibutyl carbinol	$HCl-HNO_3$
Be	c	acid sulphate	DEHPA	$(NH_4)_2CO_3$
B	n	alkaline salt leach	phenylglycol	H_2SO_4
Br	n	salt leach	tetrabrome-thane	C_2H_2
Cb—Ta	n Cb H_2SO_4—HE n Ta		MIBK	Cb: H_2SO_4 Ta: KF
Co—Ni		acid chloride	tertiary amine	HCl
		acid sulphate	DEHPA, versatilic acid 911	H_2SO_4
Cu	c	acid sulphate or $NH_4OH-(NH_4)_2CO_3$	LIX-64N	H_2SO_4
Cu–Co–Fe		acid chloride	TBP, tertiary amine	HCl (Fe extr. with TBP, Cu + Co with amine)
Cu—Ni		acid sulphate	LIX-64N	H_2SO_4 (extr. Cu at a low, Ni at a high pH)
Hf—Zr	n Hf HCl—HCNS		MIBK	H_2SO_4 (Zr left behind)
	n Zr HNO_3		TBP	H_2O (Hf left behind)
No	a	acid sulphate	tertiary amine	NH_4OH
Nb		acid sulphate	MIBK	H_2SO_4-HF
P	n	$H_3PO_4-CaCl_2$	C_4-C_5 alcohol	H_2O
Rh	a	alcaline sulphate	quaternary amine	$HClO_4$ or NH_4SCN
Rare earths	c	acid sulphate or chloride acid nitrate	DEHPA, versatilic acid 911	H_2SO_4 or HCl
Th	c	acid sulphate	heptadecyl phosphoric acid	H_2SO_4
U	a	acid sulphate	tertiary amine	$NH_3-(NH_4)_2SO_4$
	c	acid sulphate or chloride	DEHPA	Na_2CO_3
	n	acid nitrate	TBP	H_2O
V	a	acid chloride	tertiary amine	NH_3-NH_4Cl
	c	acid sulphate or chloride	DEHPA	H_2SO_4
W	a	acid sulphate	secondary	NH_4OH

* a: anion, c: cation, n: neutral.

chosen is likely to be an "onium" compound (ammonium, sulphonium, phosphonium, etc.). The tensids should not form micellae: the number of molecules in the solution or on the bubble surfaces should not exceed significantly the number of ions to be flotated out. The regeneration and recycling of these molecules are also feasible. Ion flotation enters into consideration for the winning of rare earths or other valuable metals present in low concentration in a leach or for the removal of interferents. (The idea of recovering gold, uranium or boron contained in sea water by means of ion flotation has been put forward.)

6.2.4. Metal recovery. The winning of metal in solid form from an aqueous liquor of adequate purity and concentration may be achieved by electrolysis, chemical precipitation (cf. the cementation of copper) or the evaporation of the solution (crystallization). The solubility of a solid (expressed e.g. in kilograms of dissolved solid per kilogram of solvent) is a function of temperature. The $X = f(T)$ function is different for any combination of solvent and solid to be dissolved. For example, the solubility of potassium nitrate increases rapidly as the temperature rises, whereas that of rock salt increases much more slowly; that of zinc sulphate increases up to 55.5 °C but decreases beyond that temperature. Most solutions can be supersaturated: crystallization (the formation of nuclei and their growth to macroscopic crystals) then takes place out of a more or less supersaturated (metastable) solution.

6.3. HYDROMETALLURGY OF SPECIFIC ORES, CONCENTRATES OR TAILINGS

If the process involves solvent extraction, then dissolution, extraction, stripping and electrolysis (or chemical precipitation) are connected up into a flowsheet as shown in Fig. 6.9. The flowsheet permits the recycling of both the organic phase and the aqueous liquor (and their regeneration if and when the need arises).

In the treatment of copper ores, the chelating reagents Kelex (hydroquinoline) and LIX (benzophenoxime) are the most popular, thanks to their excellent selectivity. From both, copper can be transferred to a pure (Fe^{3+}-less) acid copper sulphate stripping solution whose concentration is ideal for electrolysis.

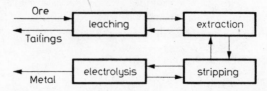

Fig. 6.9. Flowsheet of leaching, extraction, stripping and electrolysis

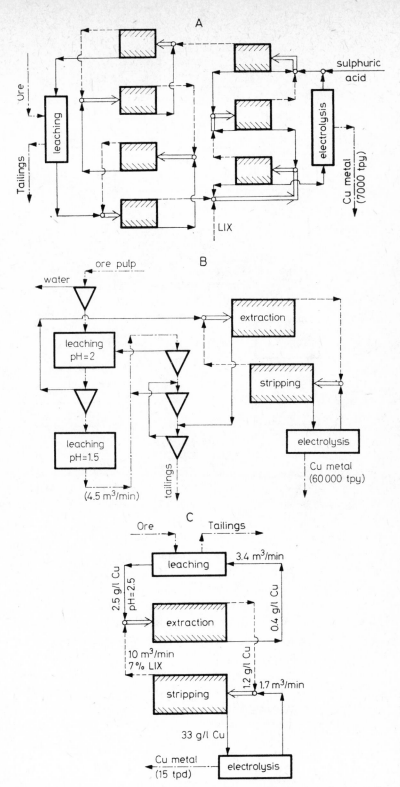

Fig. 6.10. Solvent extraction operations: flowsheets used at *A* — Bagdad Copper Co., *B* — Nchanga Consolidated, *C* — Ranchers Bluebird mines

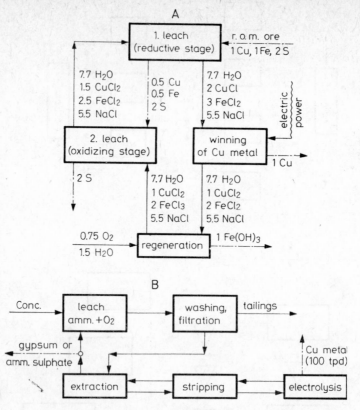

6.11. Flowsheet of A — the CLEAR process, B — the Arbiter process

The Bagdad Copper Co. of Arizona produces 7,000 tons of copper metal per year out of an aqueous liquor circulated at a rate of 1.25 m³/min, using the LIX-64 extractant dissolved in kerosene. The investment cost of the facility was $5 million. The analogous parameters were 5,400 tons, 3.4 m³/min and $3 million for the Ranchers Bluebird mine of Miami Copper Co. and 60,000 tons, 4.5 m³/min and $43.4 million for the Nchanga Consolidated copper facility in Zambia. Investment cost breaks down as follows: 20% for the first fill-up with solvent, 20% for the extraction plant and 60% for the electrolysis plant. Simplified flowsheets of the three operations are shown in Fig. 6.10. Part A refers to Bagdad Copper, Part B to Nchanga and Part C to Ranchers Bluebird. The Bluebird ore is oxidic. Extraction is four- or three-stage: stripping takes place in three- or two-stage countercurrent mixer-settlers. In the diagrams, the progress of the two-phase mixture is shown in double line, that of the aqueous phase in single full line and that of the organic phase in dotted line. The progress of the solids is shown in dot-dash line. The triangles in Part B of the figure denote thickeners.

462

Copper oxide ores (such as those handled by the flowsheets in Fig. 6.10) are dissolved with sulphuric acid; sulphide ores are dissolved either simply with ferric sulphate (formed by the bacterial oxidation of ferrous ions produced by the reaction in the circuit) or in a digester at a high temperature and pressure, or with ammonia at atmospheric pressure. The Cymet process of Cyprus Metallurgical Corp. and the CLEAR process of Duval Corp. use ferric chloride to dissolve copper sulphide ores on a large scale. A chalcopyrite concentrate is taken into solution with ammonia plus ammonium sulphate (plus oxygen) in Anaconda's Arbiter-process. Outokumpu Oy's conversion process dissolves a zinc ore with sulphuric acid. The fluid-bed hydrolysis process of Falconbridge Nickel Mines Ltd. uses hydrochloric acid to get a nickel ore into a Ni-Fe chloride solution. Sherritt–Gordon Mines Ltd. dissolves a Ni-Co ore with ammonia in a high-pressure digester (Dresher 1975).

Part A of Fig. 6.11 shows the flowsheet of the CLEAR process, complete with materials balances (the figures written in the figure state them in moles). Part B of the figure is the flowsheet of the Arbiter process for the hydrometallurgical treatment of concentrates of chalcopyrite or other copper sulphide ores. In the Arbiter process, the ore is dissolved in an aqueous ammonia leach in the presence of oxygen, at ambient temperature and pressure (no autoclave required). Iron is precipitated out. Countercurrent washing and filtration produce a clear aqueous liquor from which copper is recovered by extraction with LIX, stripping and electrolysis, whereas sulphur is removed from the circuit in the form of ammonium sulphate, which is sold as a fertilizer or, after recovery of the ammonia also, in the form of gypsum. Copper recovery is between 97 and 99% (Dasher 1973; Kuhn et al. 1974; Kuxmann 1974). Pyrite

Table 6.6. Reaction equations of the leaching with ammonia of copper, zinc and cadmium sulphides

Chalcocite	$Cu_2S + 2^1/_2O_2 + 8NH_3 + H_2O \rightarrow 2Cu(NH_3)_4^{2+} + SO_4^{2-} + 2OH^-$
Covellite	$CuS + 2O_2 + 4NH_3 + H_2O \rightarrow Cu(NH_3)_4^{2+} + SO_4^{2-} + H_2O$
Bornite	$Cu_5FeS_4 + 9^1/_4O_2 + 20NH_3 + H_2O \rightarrow 5Cu(NH_3)_4^{2+} + 4SO^{2-} + \\ + {}^1/_2Fe_2O_3 + 2OH^-$
Chalcopyrite	$CuFeS_2 + 4^1/_2O_2 + 4NH_3 + H_2O \rightarrow Cu(NH_3)_4^{2+} + 2SO_4^{2-} + \\ + {}^1/_2Fe_2O_3 + 2H^+$
Enargite	$Cu_3AsS_4 + 8^3/_4O_2 + 13NH_3 + 2^1/_2H_2O \rightarrow 3Cu(NH_3)_4^{2+} + 4SO_4^{2-} + \\ + NH_4H_2AsO_4 + 2H^+$
Sphalerite	$ZnS + 2O_2 + 4NH_3 \rightarrow Zn(NH_3)_4^{2+} + SO_4^{2-}$
Greenockrite	$CdS + 2O_2 + 4NH_3 \rightarrow Cd(NH_3)_4^{2+} + SO_4^{2-}$

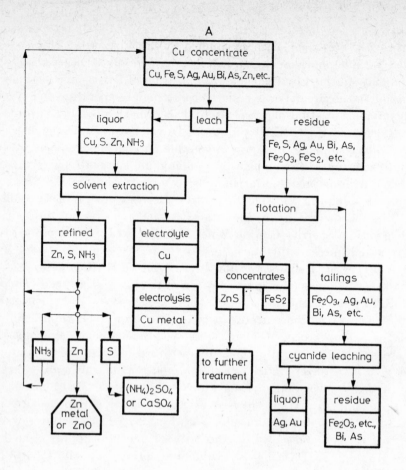

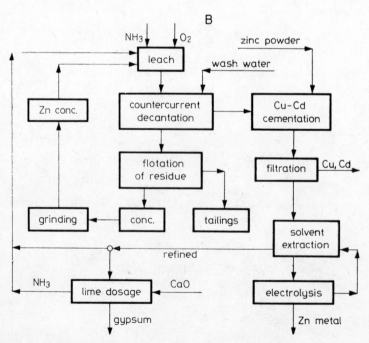

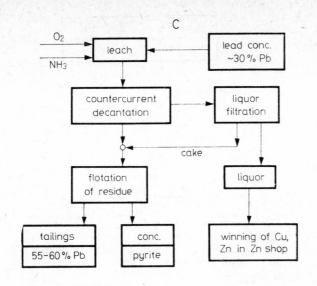

C

- O₂ → leach ← lead conc. ~30% Pb
- NH₃ → leach
- leach → countercurrent decantation → liquor filtration
- countercurrent decantation → (cake) → flotation of residue
- liquor filtration → cake → countercurrent decantation
- liquor filtration → liquor
- flotation of residue → tailings 55–60% Pb
- flotation of residue → conc. pyrite
- liquor → winning of Cu, Zn in Zn shop

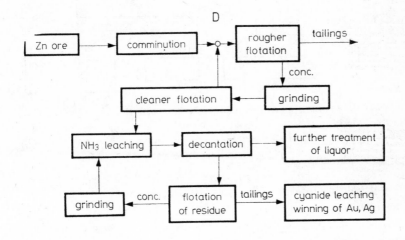

D

- Zn ore → comminution → rougher flotation → tailings
- rougher flotation → conc. → grinding → cleaner flotation
- cleaner flotation → NH₃ leaching → decantation → further treatment of liquor
- decantation → flotation of residue
- flotation of residue → tailings → cyanide leaching winning of Au, Ag
- flotation of residue → conc. → grinding → NH₃ leaching

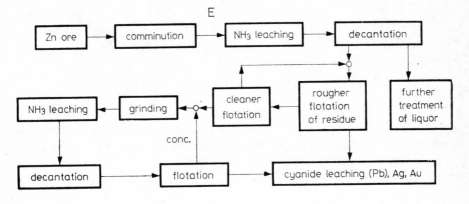

E

- Zn ore → comminution → NH₃ leaching → decantation
- decantation → rougher flotation of residue
- decantation → further treatment of liquor
- rougher flotation of residue → cleaner flotation → grinding → NH₃ leaching → decantation → flotation
- flotation → conc. → grinding
- rougher flotation of residue → cyanide leaching (Pb), Ag, Au

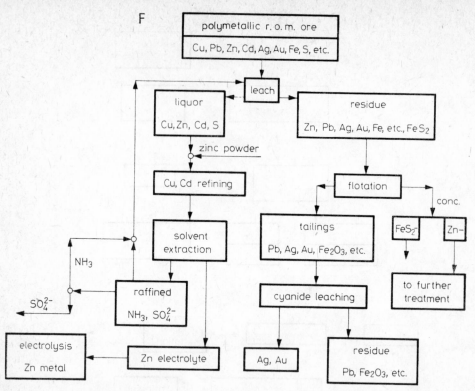

Fig. 6.12. Possible combinations of leaching, solvent extraction and flotation into a single flowsheet, for handling A — a copper concentrate, B — a zinc concentrate, C — a low-grade lead concentrate, D and E — a r.o.m. zinc ore, F — a polymetallic Cu−Pb−Zn ore

which is not soluble in ammonia, finds its way into the leach residue whence it can be recovered by flotation.

The reaction equations of the ammonia leaching of various copper, zinc and cadmium sulphides are presented in Table 6.6.

In certain circumstances, galena (PbS) will also dissolve in a solution of ammonia and ammonium sulphate, but under differently adjusted conditions the process produces a solid lead oxide or lanarkite (PbO · PbSO$_4$) or anglesite (PbSO$_4$), e.g. by the reaction

$$2PbS + 4O_2 + H_2O \rightarrow PbO \cdot PbSO_4 + SO_4^{2-} + 2H^+.$$

The rates of dissolution of copper sulphides decrease in the order of their listing in Table 6.6 (that of chalcocite is fastest; that of enargite is slowest). Examples of flowsheets suitable for coping with sulphide ores are shown in Fig. 6.12. Parts A and B of the figure refer to the usual run of copper and zinc concentrates, Part C to a low-grade Pb concentrate rich in interferents, Parts D and E to r.o.m. zinc ores, Part F to a polymetallic r.o.m. Cu—Pb—Zn ore. These flowsheets combine leaching, solvent extraction and flotation. This combination possesses a great deal of flexibility which permits to overcome the problems of many a hard-to-concentrate r.o.m. ore, to enrich low-grade concentrates of poorly flotatable ores and to remove interferents from the usual run of concentrates, all this at very fair metal recoveries (Kuhn and Arbiter 1975).

Chalcopyrite concentrates dissolve relatively fast in a sulphuric-acid leach liquor in a digester at 110 °C and 20 bars partial pressure for oxygen, provided the crystal lattice of the chalcopyrite is shattered first by activating grinding, e.g. in a vibromill (Kuxmann 1974).

The investment required for the Power Plate process serving for the recovery causing no environmental pollution of copper metal from copper sulphide concentrates (or cementation copper, copper wastes or oxidic copper pulps) is one-third only of an equivalent blister copper facility. The leach contains ferric sulphate, sulphuric acid and oxygen (part of the latter is dissolved in the solution; the rest forms as nascent O_2 on the anode). The reaction equations of dissolution (e.g. in the case of a chalcocite concentrate) are:

$$Cu_2S + 2Fe_2(SO_4)_3 + H_2O + 1.5O_2 \rightarrow 2CuSO_4 + 4FeSO_4 + H_2SO_4$$
$$Cu_2S + Fe_2(SO_4)_3 \rightarrow CuSO_4 + 2FeSO_4 + CuS^0$$
$$CuS + Fe_2(SO_4)_3 \rightarrow CuSO_4 + 2FeSO_4 + S^0$$
$$CuS + {}^1/_2O_2 + H_2SO_4 \rightarrow CuSO_4 + H_2O + S$$
$$S^0 + 1.5O_2 + H_2O \rightarrow H_2SO_4.$$

The last reaction proceeds very slowly under the conditions prevailing in the vessel: hence, in the final reckoning, $CuSO_4$ and $FeSO_4$ go into solution, whereas the waste pulp leaving the vessel takes the sulphur out in indissoluble elementary form. The reactions on the anode surfaces are

$$H_2O \rightarrow 2H^+ + {}^1/_2O_2 + 2e^-$$

and

$$Fe^{2+} \rightarrow Fe^{3+} + e^-;$$

those on the cathode surfaces are

$$Cu^{2+} + 2e^- \rightarrow Cu^0$$

and

$$Fe^{3+} + e^- \rightarrow Fe^{2+}$$

The electrolyte of ferric sulphate and sulphuric acid is added to the flotated copper sulphide concentrate in a conditioning tank. After adjustment of the desired density and temperature, the pulp is led to the electrolysis cells, whence, after a sufficient retention time, a spent pulp containing elementary sulphur and possibly precious metals emerges. The electrolyte, separated on filters or in thickeners, can be returned to the conditioning tank. Harmful buildups of salts are prevented by splitting off part of the stream into a parallel de-salting circuit. When handling a chalcocite concentrate, a high current density is used (1,300 to 2,200 amperes per m² of cathode surface); output varies between 1.3 and 2.1 kg Cu/m² · h. Current density used is about 2,200 A/m² for cementation copper and about 1,100 A/m² for copper oxide pulps; output in the latter case is on the order of one kg Cu/m² · h. (In conventional electrolysis, current densities tend to remain below 330 A/m².)

In August 1974, the investment cost for an output of 62,000 t/year of copper metal would have been $70 million for a blister facility and only $23 million for a Power Plate facility. For other types of hydrometallurgical plant, the investment costs for an output of 80,000 t/year were estimated at $15 million for conventional leaching and electrolysis at 330 A/m² or less, at 30 million for roasting, leaching and electrolysis, at $35 million for ammonia leaching (Sherrit–Gordon process), and at $30 million for Power Plate leaching and electrolysis at 1,100 A/m² (Pearson 1974).

A cost comparison of solvent extraction and the other processes that could have been chosen instead at Nchanga (producing 60,000 t of Cu metal per year) are presented in Table 6.7. For example the smelting-included cost of process 3 (cementation), would have been 50 cents per kg of Cu as compared with just 27.1 cents for solvent extraction plus electrolysis (Ritcey 1975). Operating costs split about halfway between extraction and electrolysis.

Every hydrometallurgical process has the not inconsiderable advantage over every process of igneous metallurgy that the former produces no polluting SO_2 gas. True, the more modern blister smelters produce SO_2 at a higher concentration, suitable as a sulphuric-acid plant feed, but the resulting large quantities of by-product sulphuric acid are often hard if not impossible to sell, in which case storage or disposal is a considerable problem. The hydrometallurgical

Table 6.7. Cost comparison of different processes envisaged for Nchanga Consolidated's 60,000 tpy copper facility, Zambia

Process	Product %Cu	Investment cost US million $	Operating cost ¢/kg Cu	Further processing
1 Precipitation with H₂S out of a pulp	25	22.2	20.0	flotation
2 Cementation with iron powder in a pulp	85	15.4	33.1	and smelting
3 Cementation with iron swarf in a liquor	85	17.7	27.4	smelting
4 Precipitation with lime out of a liquor	17	17.3	13.3	
5 [Cu(OH)₂; pH = 7.5 to 8]				
Solvent extraction out of a liquor	99.9	43.4	27.1	no further processing required

processes, on the other hand, produce sulphur in the readily marketable or storable form of elementary sulphur or solid sulphate (e.g. ammonium sulphate or gypsum in the case of the Arbiter process). Bulk concentrates containing several pay metals can also be processed to advantage using hydrometallurgical means: the presence of gangue minerals is not as much of a problem, either, as it is in igneous metallurgy which requires one-metal concentrates that are as pure as possible. The principal criterion of economic viability is whether it is possible to regenerate and recycle the expensive leach liquor and/or extractant without excessive losses (Agers et al. 1965; Bridges and Rosenbaum 1962; Flett 1974; Kindig and Hazen 1971; McGarr 1970; Rintoul 1971; Schubert 1972; Smith 1971; Zakarias and Calahan 1966).

The LPF (leach-precipitate-float) process is a combination of **hydrometallurgy** and flotation. It can be used to advantage where low-solubility (sulphide) and high-solubility (oxide, sulphate, carbonate) minerals of a metal (say, copper) occur together. The metallic copper won by cementation on iron powder after acid leaching can be flotated out together with the copper sulphides.

Conventional hydrometallurgy as applied to *uranium ores* comprises the following steps: (1) uranium is taken into an acid or alkaline aqueous solution, (2) a $\approx 75\%$ U_3O_8 concentrate is produced out of the solution, (3) the raw concentrate is refined to reactor purity. Low-grade ores may be pre-concentrated by some physical method, froth flotation being the most obvious choice. (For example, an r.o.m. ore containing 0.1% U_3O_8 was enriched to a concentration of 0.2 to 0.6% U_3O_8 by flotation with fatty acids or kerosene sulphonate, at a U recovery of 85 to 98%.)

(1) Uranium is most often leached with dilute sulphuric acid (8 to 10%) at a pH = 0.5 to 1.5:

$$UO_3 + H_2SO_4 \rightarrow UO_2SO_4 + H_2O,$$

or

$$U_3O_8 + 2H_2SO_4 \rightarrow 3UO_2^{2+} + 2SO_4^{2-} + 2H_2O;$$

$$UO_2^{2+} + 3SO_4^{2-} \rightleftarrows UO_2(SO_4)_3^{4-}$$

and/or

$$UO_2^{2+} + 2SO_4^{2-} \rightarrow UO_2(SO_4)_2^{2-}.$$

The compounds of six-valent uranium are readily soluble; those of four-valent uranium are less so. When handling the latter sort of mineral, an oxidizing agent (manganese dioxide, sodium chlorate, etc.) is added to the pulp. Leaching is performed with cold or hot acid in a dense pulp of minus-0.5 mm particle size at a retention time of 16 to 24 hours in tanks agitated by an airlift or by mechanical stirring. In places, cheaper batch leaching is chosen instead of the continuous countercurrent arrangement. The leach liquor enriched in uranium is separated from the solid waste by filtration or countercurrent decantation. If the r.o.m. ore contains much carbonate (e.g. limestone), which would consume too much acid, the uranium is leached with an aqueous solution of a mixture of sodium carbonate and sodium bicarbonate.

(2) The most widespread method of recovering the uranium out of the solution uses strong-base anion exchange resins which will selectively sorb uranyl trisulphate and disulphate anions out of a sulphuric-acid leach:

$$4RCl + UO_2(SO_4)_3^{4-} \rightleftarrows R_4UO_2(SO_4)_3 + 4Cl^-$$

or

$$2RCl + UO_2(SO_4)_2^{2-} \rightleftarrows R_2UO_2(SO_4)_2 + 2Cl^-.$$

where Cl^- may be replaced by NO_3^-. The quantity of uranium that can be adsorbed by the resin increases as the pH increases. After flushing the resin with water, sorbed uranium is eluted with an acid nitrate or chloride solution (e.g. one-mole ammonium nitrate or ammonium chloride acidified with sulphuric acid to a pH = 1 to 2). The nitrate or chloride anions displace the uranyl anions sorbed on the resin and regenerate the resin at the same time, enabling it to sorb uranium once more. Uranium eluted off the resin is neutralized with ammonia to a pH in the vicinity of 7 and precipitated in the form of ammonium diuranate. The spent liquor may, after acidification, be returned to the elution circuit. Solid anion-exchange resins may be replaced by a liquid exchanger such as an alkyl phosphate, an alkyl phosphoric acid or the ester of such an acid, a secondary or tertiary alkyl amine, etc., dissolved in kerosene. (Cf. Part A of Fig. 6.8 and Tables 6.3 and 6.4.)

Uranium can be recovered from the solution also without benefit of an ion-exchange resin or organic extractant, by simple chemical precipitation. In such a setup, the six-valent uranium of the clear acid leach liquor is reduced to four-valent by the addition of iron or aluminium powder or swarf and precipitated by the addition of phosphate ions in the form of $U_3(PO_4)_4$ at a pH = 1.0 to 2.5. The precipitate is filtered and then repulped in a hot solution of caustic soda (NaOH). This transforms the precipitate into urano-hydrate which separates it from the bulk of the aluminium and of the other interferents.

(3) Solvent extraction can produce reactor-grade U_3O_8 also. The uranium concentrate is leached out e.g. with nitric acid in the form of uranyl nitrate, and extracted from the aqueous leach liquor by means of tributyl phosphate (TBP) dissolved in kerosene. From the organic phase, high-purity uranyl nitrate can be transferred into a dilute nitric acid stripping solution. On evaporation, uranyl nitrate undergoes thermal decomposition and U_3O_8 is left behind (Kunin 1969; Smith and White 1969).

In the conventional hydrometallurgy of *gold ores*, gold in the presence of oxygen is transformed with cyanide into a complex compound soluble readily enough in water:

$$4Au + 8NaCN + O_2 + 2H_2O \rightarrow 4NaAu(CN)_2 + 4NaOH.$$

After separation from the solid waste, gold can be precipitated from the liquor e.g. using metallic zinc:

$$Zn + 2NaAu(CN)_2 \rightarrow 2Au + Na_2Zn(CN)_4$$

or

$$Zn + 2H_2O \rightarrow Zn(OH)_2 + 2H;$$

$$Zn + 2NaOH \rightarrow Na_2ZnO_2 + 2H;$$

$$Zn + 4NaCN + 2H_2O \rightarrow Na_2Zn(CN)_4 + 2NaOH + 2H$$

and

$$2NaAu(CN)_2 + 2H \rightarrow 2Au + 2HCN + 2NaCN.$$

Instead of zinc metal, an anion-exchange resin can also be used to extract the gold from the cyanide leach.

The presence of oxygen in the precipitation phase is a drawback (forming as it does zinc oxide with the metallic zinc). The gold-containing filtrate is therefore subjected to vacuum degassing prior to precipitation. Substances interfering with the cyanidation process include acids (which produce hydrogen cyanide — the solution must be kept weakly alkaline throughout!), soluble compounds of other metals with an affinity to cyanide (copper carbonates and oxides, ferrous compounds, zinc carbonates, tellurium and selenium minerals, etc.), sulphides of arsenic and antimony (these form an alkali sulphide with NaOH, which in turn is oxidized to thiosulphate, consuming the oxygen in the pulp), MnO_2 (which oxidizes the cyanide ions into cyanate ions, CNO^-), carbon compounds (organic matter, whose reductive effect precipitates gold prematurely), etc. (Hull and Stent 1956).

Aluminium metal is made out of alumina (Al_2O_3) by igneous electrolysis: alumina is leached out of *bauxite* by the Bayer process.

The aluminium minerals making up bauxite include diaspore and boehmite ($Al_2O_3 \cdot H_2O$ or $AlOOH$) and gibbsite [hydrargyllite, $Al_2O_3 \cdot 3H_2O$ or $Al(OH)_3$]. The Al content is leached out of these with caustic soda at a temperature above 100 °C and precipitated as alumina hydrate out of the filtered clear pregnant liquor by cooling it to below 100 °C. The alumina hydrate is then transformed into calcined alumina. The bulk of the caustic soda remains in the circuit. The direction in which the reactions

$$NaOH + Al(OH)_3 \rightleftarrows NaAl(OH)_4$$

or

$$NaOH + AlOOH + H_2O \rightleftarrows NaAl(OH)_4$$

proceed is a function of temperature. The trihydrate is soluble readily enough, the monohydrates less so (it takes a pressure of 7 to 8 atm and a temperature of 105 to 250 °C in a digester vessel to dissolve them). Most of the bauxite refined into alumina in Europe is monohydrate-type or mixed monohydrate-trihydrate-type, whereas on the other continents the bulk of the bauxite being

471

treated is trihydratic. In bauxite, the aluminium minerals are accompanied by larger or smaller quantities of silicate and iron minerals. The iron minerals are not dissolved: they can be settled out of the sodium aluminate liquor to form a waste known as red mud. Silica on the other hand is soluble in caustic soda; in the liquor, it constitutes insoluble silico-aluminates:

sodalite: $3Na_2O \cdot 3Al_2O_3 \cdot 6SiO_2 \cdot 2NaOH$,

natrolite: $Na_2O \cdot Al_2O_3 \cdot SiO_2 \cdot nH_2O$,

both of which cause losses of alumina and caustic soda. This is why the Bayer process is economically non-viable for high-silica bauxite. Other accessory elements (Ti, Ca, Mn, Cr, V, Ni, Ga, P, S, C, etc.) whose concentration varies from one bauxite to the next may also greatly influence the process and its outcome if they get dissolved and then precipitated in the circuit.

Depending on ore composition, the making of one kg of alumina takes 2.2 to 3.5 kg of bauxite, 3 to 5 kg of steam, 0.05 to 0.20 kg of caustic soda, 0.12 to 0.15 kg of fuel oil and 0.35 to 0.40 kW h of electric power.

Electrolysis is performed in pots (cells) made of mild steel sheet. The cell bottom is stamped out with coke. The coke is the direct cathode. Carbon anodes reach into the electrolysis cells from above. The electrolyte is alumina dissolved (actually molten) in cryolite: its melting point is below 1,000 °C (the melting point of pure Al_2O_3 would be above 2,000 °C). Molten aluminium metal collects in the cathode bottom, whence it is tapped at intervals. The terminal voltage across a cell is 4 to 4.5 V, of which about 1.7 V is the decomposition voltage. (that is, the voltage corresponding to the actual electrochemical process). One thousand ampere-hours will produce 0.335 kg of Al in theory. The actual requisites of producing one kg of aluminium metal include 1.9 kg of alumina, 0.50 to 0.55 kg of anode mass, 0.05 to 0.06 kg of cryolite and/or aluminium fluoride and 13.7 to 16 kW h of electricity. (The d.c. power consumption of aluminium electrolysis per kg of metal declined from 30 kW h in 1914 to 25 kW h in 1920, 19 kW h in 1930 and 18 kW h in 1940, to ~13 kW h in the best smelters of today.)

6.4. LITERATURE ON HYDROMETALLURGY OR CHEMICAL EXTRACTION

AGERS, D. W. (et al.): A new reagent for liquid ion exchange recovery of copper. *Min. Eng.* 1965 Dec., 76—80.

AGERS, D. W.—E. R. DeMENT: The evolution of new LIX reagents for the extraction of copper. *TMS AIME* 1974, Paper No. A72—87.

ANONYMUS: In clean-air copper production, Arbiter Process is first off the mark. *E/MJ* 1973 Feb., 74—75.

APLAN, F. F.: Hydrometallurgy. *Min. Eng.* 1974 Feb., 70—72.

ATWOOD, R. L.—J. D. MILLER: Structure and composition of commercial copper chelate extractans. *Trans. AIME* 1973, 319—323.

BEETNER, G. A. (et al.): Simulation study of a multistage mixer-settler extractor. *Trans. AIME* 1973, 349—353.

BIELFELDT, K.: Das Aluminiumoxid-Erzeugung als verfahrenstechnische Aufgabe. *Erzmetall* 1972, 539—547.

BITZER, E. C.: Cementation-in-pulp of copper leach liquors — an attractive route to copper extraction. *E/MJ* 1974 Oct., 72—78.

BRIDGES, D. W.—J. B. ROSENBAUM: Metallurgical application of solvent extraction. Part I: Fundamentals of the process. *Bu Mines IC 8193* 1962.

BRITTINGHAM, G. J.: Recently developed system for copper production. *Austr. Min.* 1973 Nov., 86—96.

CHASE, C. K.: Continuous countercurrent ion exchange in hydrometallurgical separators. *Min. Eng.* 1957, 1001—1003.

CRAIGEN, W. J. S.—G. M. RITCEY—B. H. LUCAS: By-product ion discard or recover. *CIM Bull.* 1975 Apr., 70—83.

CZEGLÉDI, B.: Oldószeres extrakció a ritkafémek kohászatában. (Solvent extraction in rare-metal metallurgy.) *BKL-Kohászat* 1971, 573—583.

DASHER, J.: Chemical processing — A wave of the future. *Min. Eng.* 1971 Apr., 48—51.

DASHER, J.: Hydrometallurgy for copper concentrates. *CIM Bull.* 1973 May, 48—56.

DRESHER, W. H.: Chemical processing. *Min. Eng.* 1975 Feb., 58—60.

DUNCAN, D. W.—A. BRUYNESTEYN: Enhancing bacterial activity in a uranium mine. *CIM Bull.* 1971 May, 32—36.

EBNER, H. G.—W. SCHWARTZ: Untersuchungen über die Laugung von Uranerzen mit Hilfe von Bakterien. *Erzmetall* 1973, 484—490.

FLETCHER, A. W.: Metal winning from low-grade ore by bacterial leaching. *Trans. IMM* 1970, C247—C252; 1971 C114—C116.

FLETCHER, J. B.: In-place leaching at Miami mine, Miami, Arizona. *Trans. AIME* 1971, 310—314. (Disc. 1972, 186—187.)

FLETT, D. S.: Solvent extraction in copper hydrometallurgy: a review. *Tans. IMM* 1974. C30—C38.

FLETT, D. S.—D. W. WEST: Comparative study of copper extraction by LIX 63 (bromolauric acid and LIX 63-di/2-ethyl hexyl) phosphoric acid. *Trans. IMM* 1973, C107—C110.

FONSECA, A. G.: Ammonia-oxidative leach of chalcopyrite. *CIM Bull.* 1974 July, 105—110.

FOOS, R. A.: Hydrometallurgy of uranium. *Min. Eng.* 1956, 893—900.

GILMORE, A. J.: A proposed use for ion exchange in gold cyanidation. *Can. Min. J.* 1967 May, 63—65.

HABASHI, F.: Pressure hydrometallurgy: key to better and nonpolluting process. *E/MJ* 1971 May, 88—94.

HARRISON, V. F.—W. A. GOW—K. C. IVARSON: Leaching of uranium from Elliot Lake ore in the presence of bacteria. *Can. Min. J.* 1966 May, 64—67.

HARTLAGE, J. A.—A. D. CRONBERG: Chemical and physical factors to be evaluated on dressing a Kelex extraction system. *CIM Bull.* 1975 Feb., 99—104.

HOLLIS, S. F.—C. K. McARTHUR: The resin-in-pulp method for recovery of uranium. *Min. Eng.* 1957, 1326—1335.

HULL, W. Q.—C. STENT: Gold processing. *Ind. & Eng. Chem.* 1956, 2095—2106.

KINDIG, J. K.—W. C. HAZEN: Cyclone separators for solvent extraction metallurgy. *Trans. AIME* 1971, 68—71.

Koch, W. E.—H. B. Pietsch: Treatment of oxide copper ores by reduction and ammoniacal leaching. *Trans. IMM* 1974, C14—C17.

Kruesi, P. R. (et al.): Cymet-process — Hydrometallurgical conversion of base-metal sulphides to pure metals. *CIM Bull.* 1973 June, 81—87.

Kuhn, M. C.—N. Arbiter: Physical and chemical separations via the Arbiter process. 11. *IMPC*, Cagliari 1975, Paper 30.

Kuhn, M. C.—N. Arbiter—H. Kling: Anaconda's Arbiter process for copper. *CIM Bull.* 1974 Feb., 82—86.

Kunin, R. (et al.): Ion exchange resins for uranium hydrometallurgy. *E/MJ* 1969 July, 73—79.

Kuxmann, U.: Entwicklungstendenzen der Verfahren zur Gewinnung von Kupfer. *Erzmetall* 1974, 55—64.

Lendrum, F. C.: Developments in uranium ore processing. *CIM Bull.* 1974 Sep., 51—54.

LeRoux, N. W. (et al.): Bacterial oxidation of pyrite. *IMPC*, London 1973, Paper 45.

MacGregor, R. A.: Uranium dividends from bacterial leaching. *Min. Eng.* 1969 March, 54—55.

Malouf, E. E.: The role of microorganisms in chemical mining. *Min. Eng.* 1971 Nov., 43—46.

Malouf, E. E.: Current copper leaching practices. *Min. Eng.* 1972 Aug., 58—60.

Marrs, L. F.: Underground leaching of uranium at the Pitch Mine. *Min. Congr. J.* 1970. Nov., 35—43.

McAndrew, R. T. (et al.): Precipitation of iron compounds from sulphuric acid leach solutions. *CIM Bull.* 1975 Jan., 101—110.

McCreedy, H. H. (et al.): A proposed method, using bacteria for the continuous leaching of a uranium ore. *CIM Bull.* 1969, 135—140.

McGarr, H. J.: Liquid ion-exchange recovers copper from wastes and low-grade ores *E/MJ* 1970 Oct., 58—81.

Meddings, B.—D. J. I. Evans: The changing role of hydrometallurgy. *CIM Bull.* 1971 Feb., 48—57.

Pearson, E. W.: A new pollution-free copper process via simultaneous leaching and electrowinning. *Min. Eng.* 1974 Dec., 40—41.

Polkin, S. I. (et al.): Theory and practice of utilizing microorganisms in processing difficult-to-dress ores and concentrates. 11. *IMPC*, Cagliari 1975, Paper 33.

Rabb, D. D.: Solution mining. *Min. Eng.* 1972 Feb., 62—64.

Rickard, R. S.: Mill men see growing applications for chemical processing. *Min. Eng.* 1970 Feb., 106—107.

Rintoul, A. H.: Solvent extraction — A hydrometallurgical route to copper metal. *Australian Mining* 1971 May, 43—45.

Ritcey, G. M.: Application of solvent extraction to common base metals (a review). *Can. Min. J.* 1969 June, 73—78.

Ritcey, G. M.: Recovery of copper from concentrated solution by solvent extraction using Kelex 100. *CIM Bull.* 1973 Apr., 75—83.

Ritcey, G. M.: Some economic considerations in the recovery of metals by solvent extraction processing. *CIM Bull.* 1975 June, 85—94.

Ritcey, G. M.—B. H. Lucas: Some aspects of the extraction of metal from acidic solutions by Kelex 100. *CIM Bull.* 1974 Feb., 93—98.

Ritcey, G. M.—B. H. Lucas: Extraction and separation of copper, nickel, zinc and cobalt from ammoniacal solution using Kelex 100. *CIM Bull.* 1975 Feb., 105—113.

Rosenbaum, J. B. (et al.): Innovations in processing uranium ores. *Min. Eng.* 1957, 976—981.

474

Rosenbaum, J. B.—D. R. George—J. T. May: Metallurgical application of solvent extraction. Part II: Practice and trends. *Bu Mines 10 8502* 1971.

Ross, J. R.—D. R. George: Recovery of uranium from natural mine waters by countercurrent ion exchange. *Bu Mines RI 7471* 1971.

Schubert, H.: *Aufbereitung fester mineralischer Rohstoffe.* Bd. III. VEB Deutscher Verlag für Grundstoffindustrie, Leipzig 1972.

Scuffam, J. B.—G. A. Rowden: Solvent extraction of metals from ammoniacal solutions. *Min. Eng.* 1973 Dec., 33—34.

Slater, M. J.: Continuous countercurrent ion exchange in the mining industry. *CIM Bull.* 1974 Feb., 93—98.

Smith, C. D. B.: Process & engineering techniques in new base metal extraction project. *Australian Mining* 1971 Feb., 52—55.

Smith, S. E.—P. A. White: Review of uranium ore processing research. *Can. Min. J.* 1969 May, 71—74.

Submaranian, K. N.—H. Kanduth: Activation and leaching of chalcopyrite concentrate. *CIM Bull.* 1973 June, 88—91.

Tarján, G.: Kémiai bányászat. (Chemical mining.) *BKL-Bányászat* 1972, 713—720.

Tataru, S. A.: Recovery of gold from cyanide solutions by ion exchange. *IMPC*, London 1973, Paper 39.

Thunaes, A.—G. F. Colborne: Pulsed columns for solvent extraction from aqueous solutions and slurries. *Min. Proc. & Extr. Met. 9. CMMC*, London 1969, 81—93.

Torma, A. E.—K. N. Submaranian: Selective bacterial leaching of a lead sulphide concentrate. *Int. J. Min. Proc.* 1974, 125—134.

Trussel, P. C.—D. W. Duncan—C. C. Walden: Biological mining. *Canad. Min. J.* 1964, 46—49.

Warshawsky, A.: Solvent-impregnated resins in hydrometallurgical applications. *Trans. IMM* 1974, C101—C104.

Wenberg, G. M. (et al.): Leaching of copper by fungi. *Trans. AIME* 1971, 207—212.

Wilmhurst, R. E.: Development of an ammonia leach process for a dolomite copper ore. *IMPC*, London 1973, Paper 26.

Zakarias, J. J.—M. J. Calahan: Solvent extraction for metal recovery. *Trans. IMM* 1966, C245—C259.

7. SEPARATION OF SOLIDS FROM LIQUIDS (DEWATERING)

7.1. FUNDAMENTALS

Particulate aggregates can, up to a point, be dewatered by mechanical means: the remaining moisture can be removed by drying. The ultimate moisture content that can be attained mechanically is a sensitive function of the aggregate's granulometry, specially of the abundance of particles finer than 0.5 mm or so, the reason being that the external (physical) water (moisture) content of the aggregate is made up of water bound by adhesive and capillary forces. Adhesive moisture is a function of specific surface, which varies inversely as the particle size. In an aggregate of particles finer than about 0.5 mm, under the unassisted action of gravity, capillary action keeps the entire pore volume above the water table filled with water up to the height of capillary rise.

The ultimate (terminal) moisture content of an aggregate of given granulometry can be further reduced after simple gravity draining by tapping and shaking as on a dewatering screen, and even further by exploiting the centrifugal force of a centrifuge which greatly exceeds the force of gravity.

Ultimate moisture contents $n\%$ of coal samples different as to particle size x are plotted in Fig. 7.1. Full curves refer to an aggregate passed by a screen of aperture size x; dashed curves refer to monodisperse aggregates of particle size x. g refers to draining by gravity in a laboratory filter funnel; $10\,g$ refers to forced dewatering (tapping the filter funnel to the lab bench); $80\,g$ refers to dewatering in a centrifuge providing an acceleration 80 times that of gravity. In the domain of fine grain sizes, the dashed $10\,g$ curve (grain size: x) is above the full $10\,g$ curve (grain size: minus-x) because unsized or loosely sized aggregates tend to compact better when tapped (their pore volume becomes smaller and their volumetric solids content greater: hence, their moisture content is also reduced).

To every curved liquid surface there belongs a capillary pressure

$$p = a \left(\frac{1}{R_1} + \frac{1}{R_2} \right),$$

where R_1 and R_2 are the two principal radii of curvature of the surface, and a is the surface tension of the liquid. p is positive (meaning an overpressure)

476

if the surface is convex as seen from outside the liquid; p is negative (meaning an underpressure) if the surface, so seen, is concave. In a capillary of radius r and contact angle ϑ immersed in a liquid of s.g. γ [density $\varrho = \gamma/g$] and surface tension a, capillary action will lift the liquid to a height h. The relationship

$$2r\pi a \cos\vartheta = r^2\pi h\gamma g$$

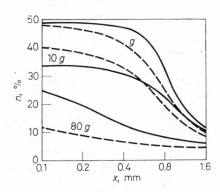

Fig. 7.1. Ultimate moisture (surface water) content of a minus-x mm coal slurry (full curves) and of a monodisperse coal-particle aggregate of particle size x (dashed curves) at $z/g = 1$, 10 and 80

or

$$p = 2a\frac{\cos\vartheta}{r} = h\gamma g$$

holds.

$$R_1 = R_2 = R = \frac{r}{\cos\vartheta}\,,$$

and the force

$$a \cos\vartheta \quad \text{dynes per centimetre}$$

acting on a circumference of $2r\pi$ cm balances the weight

$$V\gamma \text{ ponds} = V\gamma g \text{ dynes}$$

of the liquid column of volume

$$V = r^2\pi h \text{ cm}^3.$$

In other terms, one may say that the capillary pressure p balancing the hydrostatic pressure of the capillary column is directed from the side where the radii of curvature on the curved liquid surface (on the meniscus) diverge to the side where they converge. A third way of putting it is that, e.g., a column of water between two meniscuses in a capillary is underpressured, whereas the pressure in a bubble in water is greater than the pressure in the surrounding liquid.

477

Where two roundish particles touch, the capillary force retains a ring (toroid) of water looks rather like a sheave wheel, in the interior of which capillary suction is

$$p = a \left(\frac{1}{R_1} - \frac{1}{R_2} \right).$$

The principal radii of curvature R_1 and R_2 of the outer sheave-wheel surface of the toroid are of opposite sign: R_1 is the radius of the concave meniscus, and R_2 is that of the ring proper. If an external force also acts on the liquid, it distorts the toroid: the principal radii of curvature also get distorted in function of their orientation relative to the external force. Positing $R_1' < R_1''$, the relationship

$$p = a \left(\frac{1}{R_1'} - \frac{1}{R_1''} \right) = z h \gamma g$$

will hold, where $h = 2R_2$ is the diameter of the water ring, and z is the factor by which acceleration due to the external force exceeds g, the acceleration of gravity. An acceleration greater than zg is thus required to detach a water ring of diameter (= height) h from the particles. In the interior of the ring, capillary suction (i.e. underpressure) is greater at the radius R_1' than at R_1'': it is the difference between the two that holds the distorted water ring of height h in place. Underpressure sucks water from the adhesive water films of the adjoining particles into the toroid in the vicinity of the point R_1'; excess water which the capillary force is too weak to hold leaves the toroid in the form of R_1''.

In particulate aggregates, the situation is more complex because only a fraction of the water rings is coplanar with the external force: the majority includes various angles with it. Water can seep to the toroids of favourable orientation in the adhesive water films on the particles, which join the toroids together.

The pores of the aggregate constitute a branching system of capillaries of varying cross section, in which capillary action can retain more or less liquid. Consider a capillary of varying internal radius, r_1 at its upper and r_2 at its lower end. The two ends of a liquid column of height h in the capillary form meniscuses of opposite curvature, of radii

$$R' = \frac{r_1}{\cos \vartheta} \quad \text{and} \quad R'' = \frac{r_2}{\cos \vartheta}$$

respectively. The liquid column will move in the direction of the smaller radius: equilibrium sets in when

$$p = z h \gamma g = 2 a \gamma \cos \vartheta \left(\frac{1}{r_1} - \frac{1}{r_2} \right).$$

The radii of the passages in a particulate aggregate are determined by granulometry combined with compaction. At the bottom of the aggregate, R'' is very great and $1/r_2$ is negligible, regardless of whether the aggregate rests on a perforated or an impermeable sheet.

If the bottom of the aggregate is immersed in a liquid, the capillary rise h furnishes $r_1 = r_{min}$; a measure of passage radius, on the assumption that $R'' \to \infty$ $[1/r_2 = 0]$. If the pores of the aggregate are filled with water to a height exceeding h to start with, water will drain off in the direction of the external force until the equilibrium

$$p = zh\gamma g = 2a\frac{\cos\vartheta}{r_1}$$

sets in. At that point, the pores of the aggregate remain completely filled with water to a height h, whereas, above that height, only the water rings at the points of contact of the particles and the water films adhering to them are left behind.

The estimated least radius of the capillary passages in a monodisperse aggregate of roundish particles of size $x \gtrsim 0.1$ mm is $r_1 \simeq x/5$. In that case, assuming $a = 72$ dynes per cm, $\gamma = 1$, $z = 1$ and $\vartheta = 0°$, one has

a capillary rise	$h = 7$	15	73	cm
for particle sizes	$x = 1$	0.5	0.1	mm.

In the filtration of pulps, capillary rise h tends to exceed cake thickness by a broad margin. The pressure differential between the two sides of the cake, required to expel capillary water, must obey the condition

$$p \geq zh\gamma g.$$

Water is expelled first from the comparatively wider passages. Once air has "broken through" the cake, it can entrain more or less capillary water also from the capillaries branching off those, but most of the air will pass uselessly through capillaries already dewatered, the residual pressure drop across the cake being insufficient as a rule to dewater (to blow out) the finer water-filled capillaries. (Residual moisture in the cake is determined by the rate of air passage and the useful pressure drop.)

The hydraulic radius r_h of a capillary of geometric radius r_1 is defined as

$$r_h = \frac{r_1^2\pi}{2r_1\pi} = \frac{r_1}{2},$$

the ratio of liquid cross section area to wetted circumference. r_h remains unchanged if both the numerator and the denominator are multiplied by h, the height of capillary rise, to give

$$r_h = \frac{r_1^2 \pi h}{2 r_1 \pi h} = \frac{V}{A} \,,$$

where V is the volume of water raised in the capillary and A is the surface wetted by it. In an aggregate of volumetric solids content σ, made up of particles of size x, the volume of water contained in a unit of aggregate volume is $V = 1 - \sigma$, and the wetted solid surface is

$$A = \sigma F = \frac{k\sigma}{x} \,;$$

hence,

$$r_h = \frac{1-\sigma}{k\sigma}\, x \,.$$

$F = k/x$ is specific surface; k is 6 for spheres and >6 for particles of irregular shape (e.g. 8 for worn grains of sand). In other terms,

$$p = zh\gamma g = 2a\, \frac{\cos\vartheta}{r_1} = a\, \frac{\cos\vartheta}{r_h} = k\sigma a\, \frac{\cos\vartheta}{(1-\sigma)\,x} \,.$$

In polydisperse aggregates (aggregates of particles of different size), x is to be interpreted as the surface-average particle size (the average size which would give a monodisperse aggregate, the surface which the polydisperse aggregate actually has — cf. Vol. 1, p. 78).

In the above argument, capillary radius r_1 ($= r_{min}$) was assumed to be a constant. A result fitting experimental findings better can be obtained by replacing it with the average radius r_{avg} of the irregularly branching and crossing capillaries and assuming the average length of those to be about $2r_{avg}$. (x_{avg} is the arithmetic average particle size.) The number of particles or capillary pores per unit of aggregate volume is

$$n \cong \frac{F}{x_{avg}^2} = \frac{k}{x_{avg}^3} \,.$$

The average volume of a pore is

$$2\pi r_{avg}^3 = \frac{V}{n} = \frac{1-\sigma}{n} = \frac{1-\sigma}{\sigma k}\, x_{avg}^3 \,,$$

that is,

$$r_{avg} = x_{avg} \sqrt[3]{\frac{1-\sigma}{2\pi k \sigma}} = C x_{avg} \sqrt[3]{\frac{1-\sigma}{\sigma}} \,,$$

and

$$p = zh\gamma g = \frac{Ka\cos\vartheta}{x_{avg}} \sqrt[3]{\frac{\sigma}{1-\sigma}} \,.$$

or

$$h = \frac{Ka \cos \vartheta}{x_{avg} z \gamma g} \sqrt[3]{\frac{\sigma}{1 - \sigma}}.$$

Here,

$$K = \frac{2}{\sqrt[3]{2\pi k}};$$

for example, K approximately equals 0.55 at $k = 8$.

If $\qquad \sigma = 0.5 \qquad\quad 0.6 \qquad\quad 0.7 \qquad\quad 0.8,$

then $\sqrt[3]{\dfrac{\sigma}{1 - \sigma}} = 1 \qquad\quad 1.15 \qquad\quad 1.33 \qquad\quad 1.59.$

In a capillary of radius r (assuming $z = 1$), capillary rise is

$$h = 2a \frac{\cos \vartheta}{\gamma r},$$

and the flow rate of liquid in the capillary is

$$q = \frac{\pi r^4}{8\mu} \frac{dp}{dl},$$

where μ is the viscosity of the liquid, and dp/dl is pressure drop. Assuming $r = r_{avg}$ for the pores of the aggregate, seepage rate is found to be proportional to r_{avg}^2 because the number of capillaries varies as $1/r_{avg}^2$.

The drag coefficient

$$K = \frac{x_{avg}}{2g\gamma u^2} \frac{dp}{dl}$$

of the bed and the Reynolds number

$$\mathrm{Re} = x_{avg} \frac{u}{\nu}$$

are related by

$$K \, \mathrm{Re} \simeq 2{,}000$$

as long as the flow is viscous ($\mathrm{Re} < 10$). Here,

$$\nu = \frac{\mu}{\gamma} g$$

is the kinematic viscosity of the liquid; u is the velocity of flow. u is a linear function of x_{avg} (and so is, in consequence, x_{avg}/u^2 of $1/x_{avg}u$).

The capillary rise h m in an aggregate of uniform granulometry and the liquid volume q l/h · m² drained from that aggregate if it is just saturated but not covered with water are related at a pressure gradient $\mathrm{d}p/\mathrm{d}l = 1{,}000$ kp/m² · m by the approximate formula

$$q \cong \frac{22}{h^2}.$$

In other terms,

if	$h =$	0.25	0.5	1	2	m,
then	$q =$	350	88	22	5.5	l/h · m²

will be the volume of water draining off. A bed of inhomogeneous granulometry will drain more water as a rule, owing to the easier passage of liquid through its larger pores (Gillmore and Wright 1952; Harris and Smith 1957).

Part A of Fig. 7.2 is a plot of the pores' saturation S with a liquid vs. the capillary pressure differential $p\Delta$. $S = 100\%$ up to the point a (the corresponding differential is denoted Δp_0). Point r represents the state when the adhesive films of liquid on the particles cease to be continuous (when even a boost to suction will fail to dislodge more liquid from the aggregate). In the possession of such a plot, liquid distribution in the bed can be determined. If, at the top of the bed, saturation is S_c (point c) and the corresponding suction (pressure differential) is Δp_c, then at a depth L below the top of the bed (at the point b) the pressure differential is less by $L\gamma$:

$$\Delta p_b = \Delta p_c - L\gamma.$$

The saturation corresponding to Δp_b is S_b. Using the diagram, saturation at any depth can be determined as a function of depth (or height) L (cf. Part B of Fig. 7.2). By an equal-area transformation of the liquid distribution curve $S = f(L)$, the average saturation $\bar{S}$ can be derived as shown in the figure.

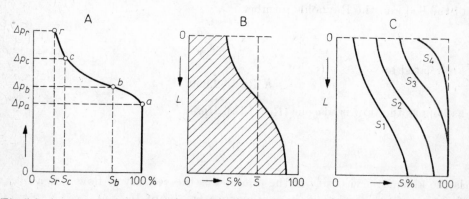

Fig. 7.2. A — pressure differential Δp vs. the pores' saturation with liquid, S; B — local saturation S vs. depth L in the aggregate; C — distributions of S corresponding to different surface saturations

Starting from other values of surface saturation, different distribution curves for the liquid in the bed will be obtained: average saturation will also be different in each case (cf. Part C of Fig. 7.2).

Given a capillary of radius r (or an equivalent aggregate) immersed in a liquid to a depth b, it takes a time t for the liquid to rise from the bottom of the capillary to a height s. (The equivalent capillary radius in an aggregate of, say, spheres of equal diameter x is

$$r = 2r_h = (1 - \sigma)\, x/3\sigma).$$

The dimensionless parameters

$$S = \frac{s}{2r}; \qquad B = \frac{b}{2r}$$

and

$$T = \frac{a \cos \vartheta}{2r\mu}\, t$$

are related by

$$S = \frac{1}{2}\sqrt{1 + \frac{B}{C}}\,\sqrt{T + \frac{e^{-KT} - 1}{K}}\,,$$

where

$$C = \frac{a \cos \vartheta}{r^2 \gamma}$$

and

$$K = \frac{16\mu^2 g}{r\gamma a \cos \vartheta}\,.$$

If $\vartheta > 90°$, the liquid will enter the capillary only if $B \geq -C$ or

$$b \geq \frac{-2a \cos \vartheta}{r\gamma}\; (= -h)\,.$$

In the case that $T \to 0$, the initial rise velocity is obtained as

$$\left(\frac{dS}{dT}\right)_0 = \sqrt{\left(1 + \frac{B}{C}\right) K}$$

or

$$\left(\frac{ds}{dt}\right)_0 = \sqrt{\frac{2a \cos \vartheta}{r\gamma}\, g} = \sqrt{hg}\,.$$

If, on the other hand, $T \to \infty$, then $S_\infty \to B + C$ or

$$s_\infty = b + \frac{2a \cos \vartheta}{r\gamma} = b + h\,.$$

31*

When the liquid is drained off, the liquid-filled fraction S of the pores (the saturation) decreases to a residue S_r proportionally to the relative drainage velocity of the liquid. S_r is residual saturation at zero drainage velocity. At $S = 1$ — where the pores are all filled with liquid — drainage velocity is a maximum. As the liquid runs out, some of the pores (capillaries) remain filled with immobile liquid: that fraction of pore volume which is so filled gives fixed saturation S_F. As drainage velocity decreases, S_F tends to S_r. Effective saturation is

$$S_e = \frac{S - S_F}{1 - S_F},$$

where the numerator is that part of pore volume which is occupied by liquid in motion whereas the denominator is the total pore volume occupied by liquid in motion plus the gas phase. S, S_F and S_r are related by

$$S_F = S_r \frac{1 - S}{1 - S_r}.$$

The apparent velocity of drainage is furnished by the formula

$$u = K S_e^n \frac{\Delta p + \gamma l}{\mu l},$$

where

$$K = \frac{(1 - \sigma)^3}{5 F'^2 \sigma^2}$$

is the permeability of the dry aggregate and F is its specific surface; Δp is the gas pressure differential between the top and the bottom of a layer of l thickness; γ and μ are the density and viscosity, respectively, of the liquid; and the exponent n is a function of the effective average particle size $x = 6k/F$ of the aggregate (where k is the form factor):

$n \simeq$	3.5	3.0	2.6	2.2	1.9	1.7	1.5	1.4	
if $x =$	30	100	300	1,000	3,000	10,000	40,000	100,000	μm.

An empirical formula for residual saturation states

$$S_r \simeq 0.0116 K \left(\frac{\Delta p + \gamma l}{la \cos \vartheta} \right)^{-0.264}.$$

where a is the surface tension of the liquid and ϑ is the contact angle of the particles.

Residual moisture n is obtained as the sum of six components n_i ($i = 1, \ldots, 6$) where n_1 is adsorbed and n_2 is adhesive water; n_3 is made up of the capillary rings about the points of contact of the particles; n_4 is capillary water in the interstitial pores; n_5 is capillary water in the fissures of the particles, if any; and n_6 is the internal water of the material. Of these, n_1 and n_6 are not accessible to physical methods of dewatering. n_5 also is irrelevant if the aggregate is made up of smooth unfissured particles. For the fraction $n_2 + n_3 + n_4$ of residual water one may write

$$n_{2+3+4} = \frac{hn_4 + (l - h)(n_2 + n_3)}{l} ,$$

where h is capillary rise and $l\,(> h)$ is the thickness of the bed. n_4 can be derived from the bulk density and the compact s.g. for aggregates of nonporous particles;

$$n_2 + n_3 = \frac{\gamma}{\delta} C \sqrt[4]{\frac{Fa \cos \vartheta}{z \gamma g x}}$$

and

$$h = K \frac{a \cos \vartheta}{z \gamma g} \sqrt[3]{\frac{\sigma F}{(1 - \sigma) x^2}} ,$$

where C and K are constants; γ is the density of the liquid and δ is the s.g. of the solid phase (in g/cm³); a is surface tension in dynes per cm; ϑ is contact angle; z is the factor by which the acceleration acting on the liquid exceeds the acceleration of gravity; F is the specific surface of the material; σ is volumetric solids content, and $x = 6k/F$ is the surface average particle size.

In sationary dewatering (drainage in tanks), an optimum retention time can be assigned to every particle size.

The six diagrams in Fig. 7.3 show residual moisture $n\%$ in sand fractions of different granulometry at a given bed thickness, respectively as a function of time, the percentage abundance of the minus-0.2 mm fraction, aggregate bed thickness l and height H measured from the bottom of the bed. The dosage of a surfactant (sodium oleate) lowers the residual moisture that can be attained, but shaking will cause further dripping even then (Batel 1955, 1961).

Coarse (plus-10 mm) aggregates can be dewatered easily and rapidly in a perforated-bucket conveyor, on stationary or shaken dewatering screens, in bins from which the water can run out, or simply by dumping in the open.

Finer-grained aggregates (about plus-0.5 to minus-10 mm) can also be dewatered in a tank (a draining tower), in the course of transportation to the tank (on a dewatering screen, dewatering conveyor or elevator) or by means of a centrifuge. On dewatering screens, the aggregate is often flushed with a spray of clear water in order to remove any slimes adhering to it.

The mechanical dewatering of pulps (minus-0.5 mm) is usually effected in two stages. The dilute pulp is first separated into a clear liquor and a thick pulp (by thickening or clarification), and the thickened pulp is then further dewatered on filters (Fejes and Tarján 1973).

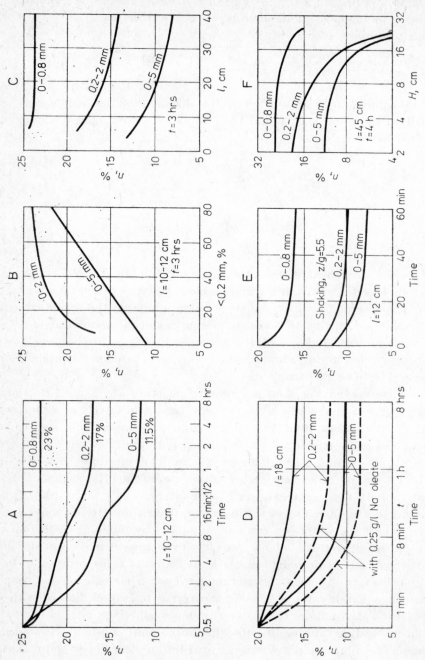

Fig. 7.3. Residual moisture $n\%$ in sand fractions different as to granulometry, vs. time, the abundance of the minus-0.2 mm fraction, aggregate thickness l and height H from the bottom of the tank

7.2. DEWATERING OF PARTICULATE AGGREGATES

Particulate aggregates that contain little fines of minus-0.5 mm or none at all may be dewatered in tanks or on their way to those, on screens or in centrifuges.

7.2.1. Draining tanks. In a draining tower, water is drained from the aggregate by gravity, in a trickle or in drops. In order to facilitate drainage, the tank may be provided with an outer filter (Part A of Fig. 7.4) or several inner filters (Part B of Fig. 7.4). (The perforated pipes made of galvanized sheet reaching into the tank may e.g. be filled with lumps of coke.) The tanks should be filled in a way that permits to avoid segregation by particle size, because a uniform fill will be dewatered more thoroughly by gravity. Segregation does take place if the fill poured into the tank has the consistency of a fluid (a pulp), but also if the aggregate has been overdried in a pre-drying operation, so that it will run (its particles will roll on one another). More recently, drying towers have been designed so that air can enter (or is blown in by a fan) at the bottom end of the tall, stack-like towers, drying the aggregate as it passes through its pores. Ultimate moisture can be efficaciously reduced thereby.

Slant-zone dewatering tanks are provided with numerous pairs of parallel sheets inclined at 65° or thereabouts (the upper sheet is a screen; the lower one is unperforated). Between the two, the water draining off has a free passage: it must accordingly traverse a thickness of aggregate of 2 to 4 m only, as against the full bin height of 10 to 14 m in upright bins (Graf 1955).

If the material filled in is a fluid (a pulp), the bottom outlet of the dewatering bin should be kept closed so as to avoid too much slimes being drained to the filter. In the course of filling, water with slime overflows the tank top;

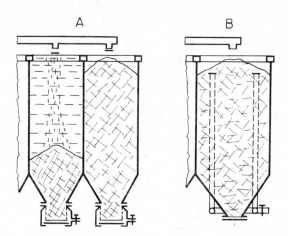

Fig. 7.4. Draining towers with *A* — outer filters and *B* — inner filters

487

it is led to a settling tank. When the bin has been filled with solids, the bottom outlet is opened: this is when drainage proper begins. The retention time of the aggregate in the bin is several hours at least and may attain one or two days. The ultimate moisture content that can be attained depends on the granulometry of the fill, and especially on the abundance of minus-0.5 mm fines (Sommer 1965; Stern 1952; Wersch 1954).

7.2.2. Dewatering conveyors; elevators. Apron conveyors or elevators are designed to suit the task of dewatering in hand. The waste-discharge elevators of Baum jigs or coarse rheolaveurs, e.g., have buckets made of perforated sheet mounted on their links. Figure 7.5 shows a dewatering pan conveyor. Sands settling in the spitzkastens S are taken out and spread on top of the bed on the pan elements made of perforated sheet where they emerge from under water. Fine slimes leaving in the overflow are led to clarification tanks. A diagram of the pans is also shown: the bed to be dewatered, contained in the pan compartments, is alternately compressed and distended, which makes for better dewatering. The speed of these dewatering pan conveyors tends to be fairly low (0.5 to 3.5 m/min), in order to give the water ample time to drain off. For example, when handling minus-10 mm coal fines, surface moisture may be reduced to between 10 and 12%, provided slimes content is low. Dewatering elevators may be used for a first-phase dewatering or de-sliming not only of coarse (plus-10 mm) aggregates but of fine ones (minus-5 mm) as well.

7.2.3. Dewatering screens. For the dewatering of granular (non colloidal) aggregates, and possibly for a first dewatering of feeds to centrifuges or drying towers too, perforated-sheet screens of an aperture size of about 0.5 mm or less or slot (elongate-mesh) screens made of profile wire are often used. The most usual dewatering screens are vigorously shaken impact screens run at a considerable screening power or vibrating screens. Using them, the forced dewatering referred to by the curves marked 10 g in Fig. 7.1 can be achieved.

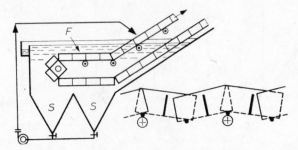

Fig. 7.5. A dewatering pan conveyor

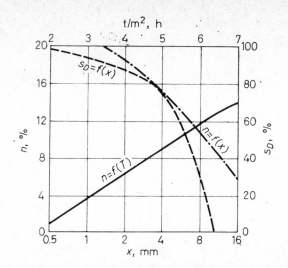

Fig. 7.6. Moisture $n = f(x)$ vs. average particle size x in screen fractions dewatered on a shaking screen; ultimate moisture $n = f(T)$ of coal of granulometry $s_D = f(x)$ vs. screen load T t/m² · h

Figure 7.6 shows ᴜe curve $n = f(x)$ of surface moisture vs. average particle size x for screen fractions dewatered on shaking screens of aperture size 0.6 mm, run at a speed of 300 to 400 rpm and a stroke of 2 to 3 cm; for coal whose granulometry is as stated by the dashed curve, $s_D = f(x)$, the moisture content attainable at varying screen loads T t/m² · h is given by the line $n = f(T)$. For the $n = f(x)$ curve,

$$n \simeq \frac{20}{\sqrt[3]{x}} \, ,$$

provided $x \lessapprox 16$ mm and, for the $n = f(T)$ curve,

$$n \simeq 2.6T - 3.9.$$

Using the maximum rather than the average particle size of the screen fractions, n for dewatering on shaking screens is given by

$$n \simeq \frac{23}{(x_{max})^{1/6}}$$

provided $x_{max} < 8$ mm, and

$$n \simeq \frac{107}{(x_{max})^{0.9}}$$

provided $x_{max} > 8$ mm.

The dewatering performance of vibrating screens is less sensitive to the load on the screen. The least surface moisture content that can be attained

489

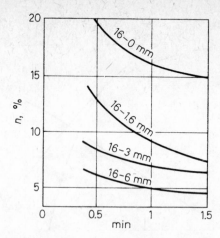

Fig. 7.7. Moisture content of minus-16 mm coal dewatered for p minutes on a vibrating screen, with lower limiting particle size as the parameter

depends primarily on the granulometry of the feed and on the average particle size of the dewatered product. A rule-of-thumb formula for coal of average particle size $x < 8$ mm is

$$n \cong \frac{45}{x} \, .$$

Figure 7.7 shows the surface moisture content of minus-16 mm coal dewatered on a vibrating screen for 0.5 to 1.5 min, with lower limiting particle size as the parameter.

On most dewatering screens, a fresh-water spray is applied to help remove adhering slimes. Moisture content can thus be lowered more than if a major percentage of the particles finer than the screen aperture is retained in the dewatered product (Pečinka 1968; Scharmer 1967; Ternes 1956).

7.2.4. Dewatering centrifuges are conical or cylindrical drums rotating at speed about a horizontal or vertical shaft. Their walls may be perforated or whole. Perforated-wall (screen) centrifuges are usually employed in the dewatering of granular aggregates containing no fine slimes, whereas whole-wall (settling) centrifuges serve primarily for the dewatering of muds.

The acceleration acting upon a body rotating at angular velocity $\omega = v/R$ on a radius R at peripheral velocity v is

$$c = \frac{v^2}{R} = R\omega^2 \, .$$

The substitution

$$v = \frac{R\pi n}{30}$$

gives rise to the formula

$$c = \pi^2 \frac{Rn^2}{900} = \frac{Rn^2}{91.3} \; ,$$

where n is speed in rpm and R is in metres. Centrifugal acceleration is related to the acceleration of gravity by

$$z = \frac{c}{g} = \frac{v^2}{gR} = \frac{R\pi^2 n^2}{900g} \; ;$$

z is a centrifuge performance indicator. With R in metres,

$$z \cong \frac{Rn^2}{900} \; .$$

In mineral processing, z tends to be less than about 1,500.

Diagrams of some centrifuge types are shown in Fig. 7.8. Screen centrifuges are fast-spinning cylindrical or conical trommel screens rotating about a vertical or horizontal shaft. Part A of the figure shows a spiral centrifuge, in which a spiral spinning in the same sense as the screen but at a slightly different speed removes the dewatered (retained) fraction from the drum. Its output is 120 tph at a radius of about 0.5 m. Some spiral centrifuges have horizontal-shaft cylindrical trommels. In the reciprocating centrifuge of Part B, a conical trommel spinning about a horizontal (or vertical) shaft is in recipro-

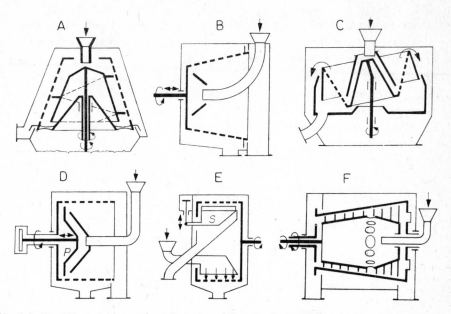

Fig. 7.8. Centrifuge designs. A — Carpenter, B — Reineveld, C — Habermann–Haubold, D — Bird settling, E — Humboldt, F — push

cating axial motion: it is this motion which transports the dewatered material down the slope. The cone angle of the trommel should be only slightly less than the angle $\varrho = \arctan f$ of sliding friction, the acceleration of the reciprocating motion should be greater than about one-tenth of centrifugal acceleration $R\omega^2$. Output is about 250 thp at a radius of $R = 0.65$ m. Part C is the diagram of a gyratory centrifuge, a variation on the reciprocating centrifuge: transport of the material on the screen is achieved by the gyration of the conical trommel (the evolution of its axis about a conical surface). In the push centrifuge of Part D, the retained material is pushed towards the open end of the cylindrical trommel by an axially reciprocating push disk P; fresh feed is injected into the annular space freed by the return stroke of the disk. Multistage push centrifuges have also been designed: their screen diameters increase stage by stage (and so, in consequence, does the indicator $z = c/g$); material taken out of one stage is loosened up and rearranged on the next; this increases its permeability and hence the degree of dewatering that can be attained. Part E is a batch-process peeler centrifuge with a cylindrical trommel: after centrifuging for a certain time, the retained fraction is peeled off and dropped into a chute by a scraper blade S slowly approaching the screen. Loading and emptying are often performed at a slower speed than centrifuging proper (e.g. at half-speed). The control of the successive phases is automated by hydraulic means. There are whole-wall peeler centrifuges also, where the removal of the solids compacted onto the cylinder is preceded by the removal of the clear liquor by a peeling tube.

Approximate values of the indicator z, radius R cm and peripheral velocity v m/s of screen centrifuges and approximate grain size spectra in mm of their range of utilization are presented in Table 7.1.

Part F of Fig. 7.8 is the diagram of a settling centrifuge. It can be regarded as an Akins classifier rotating about a horizontal shaft. The centrifuged-out solids are removed by a spiral band rotating at a slightly different speed, as in the spiral centrifuge. The indicator z is in the 300 to 1,500 range.

For settling centrifuge,

$$Q = Av_0$$

Table 7.1. Parameters and granulometry ranges of application of screen centrifuge types

Type	$z = c/g$	R cm	v m/s	mm
Spiral	200—2,000	8—50	30—60	0.1—10
Reciprocating	50—150	15—65	10—25	0.5—10
Gyratory	150—400	15—50	15—40	0.5—10
Push-disk	220—700	8—70	20—50	0.5—5
Peeler	300—1,800	23—120	50—95	0.02—0.5

and

$$A = zA' = \frac{Vz}{H} \, ,$$

where Q is the liquid throughput rate of the centrifuge, v_0 is the terminal settling velocity in the gravity field of the particles still to be settled, A is the plan area of a gravity settling tank whose settling performance would be equivalent to that of the centrifuge, V is the volume of liquid in the centrifuge, $H = R - r$ is its depth (the effective depth of settling), and

$$A' = \frac{V}{H} = 2\pi r L$$

(which turns into

$$A' \cong 2\pi R L$$

if the H/R ratio is small) is the surface area of the liquid in the cylindrical centrifuge. R is the radius of the cylinder, r is that of the overflow (of the liquid surface), and L is trommel length. In other terms, here,

$$A = zA' = \frac{2\pi^3 R^2 n^2 L}{900g} = \frac{R^2 n^2 L}{14.5g} \, ,$$

with n in rpm. If R and L are in metres, then

$$A = \frac{R^2 n^2 L}{142} \, .$$

In a conical trommel, whose greatest radius is R,

$$H = \frac{R - r}{2} \, ,$$

and

$$A = \frac{\pi^3 n^2 L'}{1,800g} \, (R^2 + 3Rr + 4r^2)$$

(here, L' is the distance between the feed and the overflow end).

In a cylindrical centrifuge of radius R and height H, the liquid surface is a cylinder of radius r_L; the surface of the compacted solids is one of radius r_S. The centrifugal force acting upon an elementary liquid shell of density $\varrho = \gamma/g$, thickness dr, surface area

$$A = 2\pi r H,$$

volume

$$dV = 2\pi r H \, dr$$

and mass

$$dm = A\varrho \, dr$$

is

$$dC = r\omega^2 \, dm = 2\pi \varrho H \omega^2 r^2 \, dr,$$

493

and the incremental pressure generated in the liquid is

$$dp = \frac{dC}{A} = \varrho \omega^2 r\, dr .$$

Integrating this differential equation between the limits r_L and R, one obtains the pressure differential available for filtration as

$$\Delta p = \varrho \omega^2 \frac{R^2 - r_L^2}{2} .$$

During filtration, the filtrate seeps radially outward at an apparent linear velocity

$$u = \frac{dQ}{A\, dt} = \frac{dp/dr}{k\mu}$$

through the solids contained in the elementary cylinder shell of thickness dr. The substitutions

$$q = \frac{dQ}{dt}$$

and $A = 2\pi r H$ result in

$$dp = \frac{qk\mu}{2\pi H} \frac{dr}{r} ;$$

integrating between the limits r_S and R provides the pressure differential overcoming the filter resistance:

$$\Delta p = \frac{qk\mu}{2\pi H} \ln\left(\frac{R}{r_S}\right) .$$

The equation holds as long as $r_L < r_S$ (that is, as long as the settled-out solids are covered with liquid). If $r_L > r_S$, then r_S in the formula is to be replaced by r_L because only the layer of deposit saturated with liquid will participate in the process. Further to be kept in mind is that velocity of filtration does not vary rigorously as ω^2 because the deposit is compressible to a certain extent, whence the unit resistance k of the bed is a function of drum speed.

The radial settling velocity of a particle at a distance r from the axis of rotation in a settling (whole-walled) centrifuge is

$$v_0 = \frac{dr}{dt} = \frac{x^2(\delta - \gamma)}{18\mu g} r\omega^2 ,$$

provided flow is viscous. Integrating the expression between the limits r_L and R, one obtains the time required for the particle to settle out as

$$t = \left[\frac{18\mu g}{x^2(\delta - \gamma)\, \omega^2}\right] \ln \frac{R}{r_L} .$$

494

This span of time is sufficient to settle out all particles of size x or greater and/or s.g. δ, but the particles smaller than that will not all settle on the trommel wall.

Settling centrifuges can be used to dewater coarser feeds (plus-0.5 mm) also, but their prime use is in the dewatering of slimes, in competition with filters. They can be used also for classification and de-sliming (e.g. for separation at

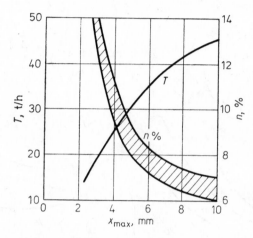

Fig. 7.9. Tests on a Carpenter centrifuge. Throughput T and moisture $n\%$ in the discharged coal vs. maximum feed particle size, x_{max}, in a machine of 1.5 m dia.

10 or 15 μm). Run with a dense liquid (e.g. a solution of $CaCl_2$) instead of water, settling centrifuges are used also in the gravity concentration of coal slurries. The size of the machines is in the 45 cm dia. $\times$ 70 cm to 140 cm. dia. $\times$ 180 cm range. Their power draft is 7 to 75 kW; their solids throughput is 10 to 70 tph in average situations (depending on the particle size of separation, the pulp density of the feed, the s.g. and granulometry of the solids, etc.).

Figure 7.9 presents for an example the coal throughput T tph of a Carpenter centrifuge of diameter 1.5 m driven by a 30 kW motor and the moisture content $n\%$ of the dewatered coal vs. the upper limiting grain size x_{max} of the feed. The Carpenter centrifuge, widespread in coal washeries, is a vertical-shaft conical step screen of large aperture angle. Feed is strewn onto the screen by a scatter disk at the top of the centrifuge. In the interior of the cone, there are rings with serrated edges: these rings retain on the filter a layer of the material sliding down the inner surface of the screen. The layer so held back is essentially the filter: the screen proper practically serves only as a support for it. The material scattered by the lower, serrated edges of the rings onto the next screen below can get rearranged in the process; this reduces the volume of capillary water in the particles' interstices. The inclination of the cone is such that the material slides down it under its own weight and inertia. Rule-of-thumb formulae are

$$T \simeq 4.5D^2x^{2/3}$$

and

$$n \simeq \frac{12}{x^{1/4}} \%$$

for $x > 6$ mm and

$$n \simeq \frac{30}{x^{3/4}} \%$$

for $x < 6$ mm. D m is the lower (greater) diameter of the centrifuge; x mm is the upper limiting particle size of the feed; $n\%$ is moisture in the retained

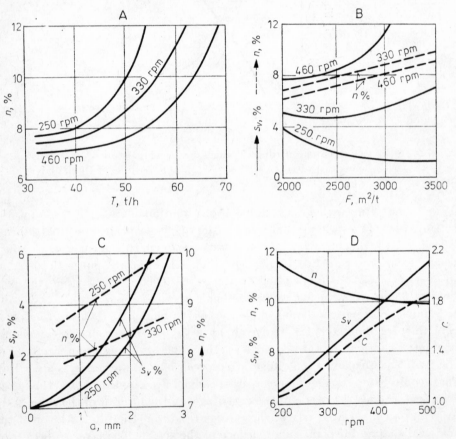

Fig. 7.10. Tests on a Carpenter centrifuge. A — moisture content $n\%$ in the discharge vs. throughput T, with speed as the parameter; B — discharge moisture $n\%$ and coal loss s_v vs. specific surface F, with speed as the parameter; C — $n\%$ and $s_v\%$ vs. screen aperture a, with speed as the parameter, D — $n\%$, $s_v\%$ and comminution coefficient C vs. speed

fraction, and T tph is throughput for coal. (For other feeds, throughput varies directly as the s.g. and moisture inversely as the s.g.)

Parts A to D of Fig. 7.10 present the results of industrial-scale tests on coal fines using a Carpenter centrifuge of $D = 2.2$ m bottom and 1.0 m top diameter, with a screen surface of 3.2 m². Part A shows the influence of feed rate T tph and centrifuge speed on the ultimate moisture content $n\%$ attained. For example, at a feed rate $T = 50$ tph and a speed of 250 rpm, moisture could be reduced to 10% at

$$z_{avg} = \frac{Rn^2}{900} \cong \frac{0.8n^2}{900} = 55$$

or

$$z_{max} = \frac{1.1n^2}{900} = 76,$$

to 8.5% at 330 rpm (at $z_{avg} = 98$) and to 7.5% at 460 rpm (at $z_{avg} = 188$). Part B of Fig. 7.10 shows the moisture $n\%$ attained with dashed lines and the percentage of coal lost, $s_v\%$ (comminuted on the screen and escaping in the slimy fluid passing through) with full curves for different centrifuge speeds, both vs. the particle size of the coal as expressed in terms of specific surface F m²/t. Coal loss s_v can be reduced efficaciously by reducing the aperture size a mm of the screen, as shown in Part C of the figure. (The centrifuge was run at a feed rate $T = 50$ tph in those tests.) Another implication of this diagram is that aperture size affects the extent of dewatering rather little. For example, at a speed of 330 rpm, ultimate moisture content was 8.5% using a screen of 2.2 mm aperture size and 8.2% using one of 1.5 mm aperture size. Part D of Fig. 7.10 shows ultimate moisture content $n\%$ and coal loss $v\%$ vs. centrifuge speed. The comminution coefficient C is also shown (by the dashed curve). Coal is broken up rather when dewatered in a centrifuge. The comminution coefficient,

$$C = \frac{f_1 + f_2}{f},$$

is the sum of the surface areas of the coal constituting the dewatered product (f_1) and of the coal leaving in the liquid (f_2), referred to the surface area f of the feed. True, ultimate moisture $n\%$ decreases as speed is increased, but coal loss $s_v\%$ and the comminution coefficient C are increased in the process.

It is to be pointed out that the coal loss $s_v\%$ plotted in the figure refers to dewatered coal rather than to total feed. (If the coal were not comminuted in the centrifuge, this type of loss would not occur.) A fairly substantial share of the feed will pass into the centrifuged-out slimes in any case. For larger-apertured screens, both the quantity and the percentage of slimes will be greater. For example, 45% on average of the solids finer than the apertures

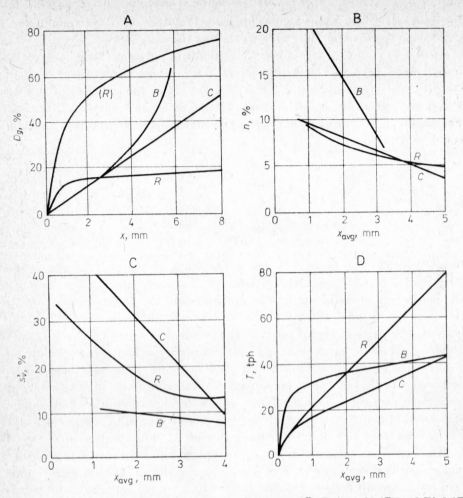

Fig. 7.11. Graphs of variables characterizing Carpenter (*C*), Reineveld (*R*) and Bird (*B*) centrifuges vs. particle size

will find its way into the slimy fluid in the 1.5 to 2.3 mm screen but only about 30 to 35% will if the screen apertures are in the 0.6 to 1.5 mm range.

Figure 7.11 presents data referring to Carpenter centrifuges (*C*), spiral Reinevelds (*R*) and Bird settling centrifuges (*B*). In Part A, the abscissa axis is calibrated in the particle size x of the coal fed to the centrifuge; in all other diagrams, it is calibrated in the average particle size x_{avg} of the dewatered product (the "cake"). Part A presents the percentage degradation

$$D_g = \frac{100(a-b)}{a} \%$$

498

of the different grain size fraction x (where a is the weight of the fraction of size x in the feed and b is its weight in the cake plus in the passed fraction). For example, if $a = 20\%$, $b = 15\%$ for the plus-4, minus-6 mm fraction, then, taking particle size to be

$$x = \frac{4 + 6}{2} = 5,$$

degradation for that fraction is

$$D_g = \frac{100(20 - 15)}{20} = 25\%.$$

In Diagram A, the curve (R) refers to friable (European) coal: all others refer to hard (American) coal. Diagram B presents cake moisture $n\%$; Diagram C shows coal loss $s_v'\%$ in the passed fraction, referred to the feed. Diagram D shows the variation of throughput T tph, vs. average particle size x_{avg} in the cake (Lyons 1951; Ferney 1966; Hoffmann 1953).

Figure 7.12 shows the granulometries of the feed to, and of two products of, a Bird settling centrifuge with slurry feed rate Q m³/h as the parameter. Increasing Q shifts the $s_F = f(x)$ lines of the products downward.

In mineral processing, no suspended and pendulum centrifuges operated in the batch mode in the $z = 600$ to $1,200$ range are used; nor are multi-disk and tube centrifuges (up to $z = 12,000$ and $z = 50,000$, respectively), of the kind employed by the chemical industry for the separation of emulsions or the clarification of dilute liquids containing fine slimes.

Screen centrifuges must be fed a drained feed, whereas settling centrifuges may be fed a pulp or mud as it is. The throughput of the centrifuge decreases

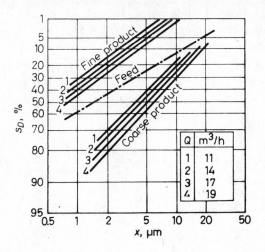

Fig. 7.12. Granulometry of the feed to and of two products of a Bird centrifuge with throughput as the parameter

and the ultimate moisture content increases as feed particle size gets finer (Fejes 1967; Köhling et al. 1972; Lemke 1954; Reuter et al. 1972; Schneider 1967; Smidth 1965; Špetl and Šebor 1966; Strehl 1970; v. Szantho and Mathiak 1966; Trawinski 1954, 1959; Wuhrmann 1969).

7.3. DEWATERING AND CLARIFICATION OF FINE PULPS

7.3.1. Thickeners; clarifying tanks. Thickening has for its purpose the reduction of the water content of dilute fine pulps by the removal of the clear liquor (or liquor containing very little suspended solids) collecting above the solids as they settle. The process is called clarification if the principal aim is the winning of a clear liquor and the solids in the feed constitute an indifferent (waste) product. A slimeless overflow can often be ensured only by coagulating the feed beforehand. In the thickeners or clarifiers, separation takes place according to the same principles as in classifiers (by terminal settling velocity), whereas filters operate on the principles of screening, more or less.

Thickening or clarification takes place either in a simple gravity field, in clarifying ponds or in pyramidal (spitzkasten-like), conical (funnel-shaped) or cylindrical thickeners (single- or multi-compartment Dorrs). Settling centrifuges and hydrocyclones employ a centrifugal force field (Davies 1965; Meerman 1954; Richardson and Zaki 1954).

A settling pond is an open-air settling device dug into the soil or bounded by levees. It may be operated in the continuous or in the batch mode. In a batch pond, after taking the basin off line and letting the fill drain, the settled-out fines are removed either manually or using a cable scraper or a pump designed for the handling of thick pulps. In such a setup, at least three settling ponds in parallel are required: one is being filled while the other is being drained and the third is being emptied. The bottom of a continuous-process settling pond may be e.g. a string of cones from which the thickened pulp is removed by means of a vacuum pump, without interrupting the settling process, into a container from which it can be expelled with compressed air towards its

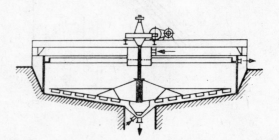

Fig. 7.13. The conventional Dorr thickener

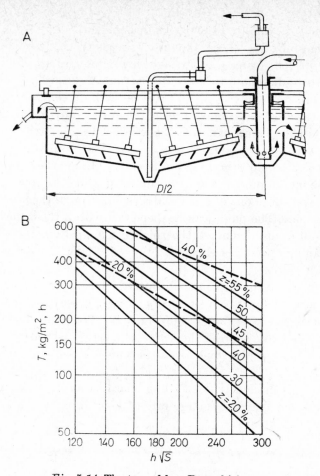

Fig. 7.14. The tunnel-less Dorr thickener

final storage. In mineral processing, it is usual not to remove the solids from the ponds to which the valueless tailing pulp is led; instead, the levees confining the pond are raised by degrees.

Of the continuously operated devices, the Dorr thickener is the most widespread. In it, the sediment settled out at the bottom is driven to a central outlet by ploughs or rakes fixed on slowly rotating radial arms. The outlet is connected by piping to a diaphragm pump. Clear liquor overflows the rim of the tank (Fig. 7.13). Whenever a stoppage occurs, the rake must be lifted above the sediment in order to prevent its getting trapped. Mechanisms for automatically lifting the rake whenever excessive torque (drag) occurs have been devised and installed. (Dorr thickeners with high-lift rakes are used in places for the storage e.g. of concentrate pulps.) The rotating radial arms may be installed above pulp level, with light trusses towing the rakes attached to them by chains or cables (cf. the design in Fig. 7.14).

In the biggest Dorrs, whose diameter exceeds 60 m, it is not the central shaft that is driven: instead, a carriage slowly moving around the tank rim drags along the radial main rake arm ("traction thickener").

Sediment can be removed peripherally as well as centrally, provided the rakes are installed so as to move the sediment outward. It has become usual lately to install the pump handling the thickened pulp in the central column of the tank; such a setup permits to save the costly piping tunnel under the thickeners which would otherwise be necessary. In another design, shown as Fig. 7.14, the intake pipe of a slurry pump installed on a rotating radial arm above pulp level sucks out of a concentric sump trough the sediment scraped in from either side. The pump can be dispensed with if the difference in water pressure is sufficient to remove the thickened pulp from the sump through pipes discharging into a vessel centrally placed under the water level (Böhm 1972; Schmidt 1967).

There are also multi-compartment Dorr thickeners (tray thickeners: six is the maximum number of compartments so far). These are operated either in parallel or in series (Parts A and B of Fig. 7.15). The parallel connection gives a greater throughput, whereas the series connection permits of a continuous decantation with countercurrent washing occupying comparatively little space.

7.3.2. Thickener design. If the settling (clarification) velocity of the pulp is v m³/h, then a clear-liquor discharge rate of V m³/h requires a clarifying tank (or thickener) of plan area

$$F = \frac{V}{v} \, \text{m}^2 \, .$$

Settling velocity, however — for granular (non-colloidal) pulps — is a function of dilution ($h = 1/c$ kg of water per kg of solids, or $D = 1/\delta$ m³ of pulp per m³ of solids). The relationship linking together h and D is

$$h = \frac{D - 1}{\delta}$$

or

$$D = 1 + \delta h \, ,$$

where δ is the s.g. of the solid particles. Dilution varies with depth in the thickener, decreasing from $h \to \infty$ in the overflow to h_a in the sediment of the underflow. Thickener surface F must therefore be calculated using the v and h values giving the largest area. If the settling velocity of a pulp of dilution h is v m/h, a thickener surface of F m² produces clear liquor at a discharge rate of

$$V = Fv = T(h - h_a) \, \text{m}^3/\text{h}$$

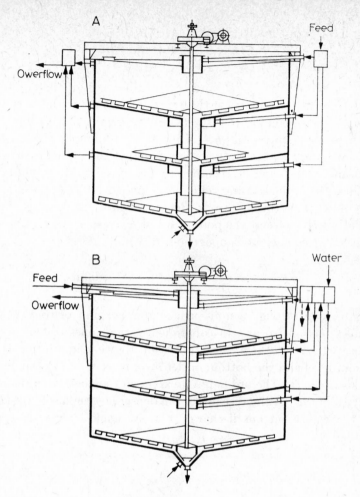

Fig. 7.15. Multi-compartment Dorr thickeners. *A* — parallel connection; *B* — series connection

for a solids feed rate of T tph. In other words, specific throughput (through-put per unit plan area per unit time) is

$$\frac{T}{F} = \frac{v}{h - h_a} \; \text{t/h} \cdot \text{m}^2,$$

and the thickener surface required is

$$F = T \frac{h - h_a}{v} \; \text{m}^2.$$

The substitution $T = Q\delta$ leads to the form

$$F = Q\frac{D - D_a}{v} \quad (Q \text{ in } m^3/h).$$

The critical values of h (or D) and of v can be read off the curve $v = f(h)$ [or $v = f(D)$] as the coordinates of the point of tangency of the tangent drawn to the curve from the point h_a (or D_a) of the abscissa axis in Part A of Fig. 7.16. This is where the expression $(h - h_a)/v$ is a maximum. The $v = f(h)$ [or $v = f(D)$] curves are obtained by joining together the plots of corresponding values of h and v (or D and v), recorded by observing in calibrated laboratory glass cylinders the initial settling velocities of pulps of different dilution. In the figure, the lines drawn through two different points D_a of the axis of abscissae touch the $v = f(D)$ curve at the points K and K', respectively.

In a thickener in continuous operation, flux

$$q = \frac{Q}{F} = \frac{v}{D - D_a} \quad [m^3/h \cdot m^2 = m/h]$$

(the solids passing through a unit surface area per unit of time) is the same for any cross section (so are, in consequence, the slopes of the lines drawn through the point D_a of the axis of abscissae). Hence, any dilution D between the feed inlet level and the bottom outlet level must fall onto the line passing through this point D_a. The ordinate intercept (in the negative direction) gives the velocity u of the bottom discharge. If a denser bottom discharge ($D_a' < D_a$) is required, then the bottom discharge velocity should be less, $u' < u$, and so

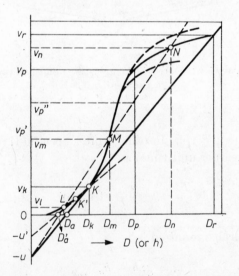

Fig. 7.16. $v = f(D)$ curve of a lab cylinder settling test

should the flux; this means that, if the feed rate Q is to be kept constant, a thickener of larger plan area F is required. When operating at a dilution D_a' and a velocity u, the dashed line in the diagram holds. In that case, the only possible dilutions in the settler are D_l, D_m and D_n, specified by the points of intersection L, M and N of the line with the curve $v=f(D)$. That is, the thickener will contain several sharply distinct zones, and the finished bottom pulp of dilution D_a', ready for discharge, will be overlain by a layer of dilution D_l, and that one in its turn by a layer of dilution D_m, with sharp boundaries separating any two adjacent layers. Between the dilutions D_l and D_m, on the other hand, the curve $v = f(D)$ passes below the dashed line: settling velocity is less than it should be; the throughput of the thickener is insufficient to produce the flux required. [The action of the rake in an actual Dorr thickener may modify the curve $v = f(D)$ established in a lab cylinder, though, so that it comes to coincide with the dashed line also over this interval.] Higher up in the thickener, between the feed inlet and the zone of dilution D_m, a zone develops whose dilution and settling velocity correspond to the point N. As pointed out by the dashed curve sections in the figure, particles different as to size, shape and s.g. may settle at different velocities in this zone. Dilution, however, is a unique value for the entire aggregate of particles; flux is also constant all over, from feed to discharge; hence, the relative abundances of the particles of different settling velocities will deviate from those prevailing in the feed. (The abundance of the slower-settling particles will increase as a rule.)

As the particles settle at a velocity v in a pulp of dilution D, water (liquor) rises at a velocity v_w in the thickener. The relevant relationship is

$$Fv_w = Q(D - D_a)$$

whence

$$v_w = \frac{Q(D - D_a)}{F} = v \ .$$

That is, the rise velocity of liquor in the thickener is the same as the velocity of clarification established at the same dilution D in the lab cylinder test.

If dilution right under the feed inlet is D_n, water rises from this zone at the corresponding velocity v_n. Between the end of the feed pipe and the overflow edge, however, the rise velocity of the liquor is not v_p but

$$v_w = Q\frac{D_0 - D_a}{F} = v_p'' \quad \text{or} \quad v_p',$$

according as the dashed or the full line in the figure is to be taken. However, v_n (and v_r) is greater than either v_p'' or v_p': that is, not all of the water rising from the zone below the feed inlet will reach the overflow; some of it will return to the feed inlet, diluting the feed from D_p to D_n or D_r, and concentrating at the same time the slower-settling finer feed particles (those which have a settling velocity greater than v_p'' but less than v_n: these particles can be made to settle by the dosage of a flocculant). The distribution of dilutions in the different zones of the thickener is illustrated by Fig. 7.17.

As time passes, a compacted sediment of increasing thickness will form at the bottom of the suspension in the lab cylinder. It is separated by a zone of transition, also called the zone of compression, from the overlying suspension whose solids concentration is uniform everywhere (provided the pulp has been flocculated), and in which the relative positions of the particles do not change in the course of settling (cf. Fig. 7.18). (In non-flocculated suspensions, the individual particles undergo hindered settling: the larger, heavier particles settle more rapidly than the smaller, lighter ones.) Above the flocculated settling suspension, a layer of clear liquor of increasing depth forms. (If the pulp is unflocculated, this zone will also remain more or less cloudy, owing to the fine colloidal particles left behind in it.) Since the suspension is not transparent, the upper and lower boundary of the zone of compression against the zones bracketing it cannot be distinguished any too sharply. As time passes, the thickness of this zone remains practically the same, but the zone as a whole moves upward while the thickness of the compacted sediment and the depth of the clear liquor increase, that is, the bottom and the top zone both swell. At the critical point, the zone of suspension disappears; all the solids have concentrated in the two bottom zones, the zone of compression and the com-

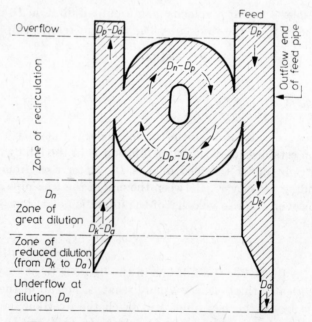

Fig. 7.17. Dilution D in the zones of the thickener

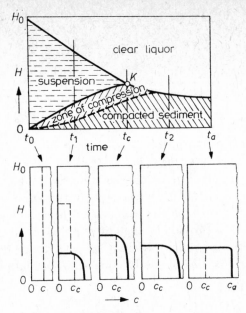

Fig. 7.18. Evolution in time of the suspension zones in a laboratory glass cylinder

pacted zone. Up to that point, the movement of the solid–liquid interface is a quasi-linear function of time: the rate of clarification remains a constant. Beyond the critical point, on the other hand, the velocity of clarification (the motion of the phase of compression) gradually slows down until all the solids concentrate in the bottom (compacted) phase. Here, part of the liquid is pressed out of the flocculated clusters by the weight of the overlying sediment, until finally that weight is balanced by the strength of the clusters.

The critical time t_c at which the suspension disappears and sediment only is left behind is a function of concentration in the suspension and of initial column height H_0. If the suspension, of the same initial height H_0 is more dilute, the critical time sets in earlier. At first, the layer of sediment grows and compacts simultaneously. Hence, pulp density at the critical time t_c is greater at the bottom of the cylinder than at the top of the sediment, where a critical concentration c_c (and a triplet of other critical values, mutually determining one another, $h_c = 1/c_c$, σ_c and D_c) prevail. The distribution of concentrations also changes in the sediment as time passes, as suggested by the bottom half of Fig. 7.18. After the critical time t_c, the quantity of sediment does not change any more, but concentration starts increasing in its top parts also.

In thickeners in continuous operation, too, a critical concentration c_c corresponding to the critical settling velocity v_c develops next to the top of the sediment. In steady-state settling, the top of the sediment remains at the same height; that is, the rise velocity of water above the sediment is also v_c. The relationship

$$v_c = T \frac{h_c - h_a}{F}$$

is obtained by direct inference. [In a thickener of plan area F, a quantity of liquor $T(h_c - h_a)$ will rise at velocity v_c while a quantity of liquor Th_a leaves by the bottom outlet.]

Instead of observing the initial rates of clarification of suspensions of different dilution (Coe and Clevenger method), thickeners can be designed using the $H = f(t)$ curve recorded in a single settling test (Fitch 1962, 1966; Kynch 1952; Talmage and Fitch 1955). The tangents to this curve at different instants t provide the clarification velocity $v = dH/dt$ direct, whereas their ordinate intercepts $H' = H + vt$ provide the height of pulp column at which the initial clarification velocities of pulps different as to average dilution h or D (or density $\sigma = 1/D$ or $c = 1/h$) precisely equal v. The relationship

$$\left(H\sigma = \frac{H}{D}\right) = \left(H'\sigma' = \frac{H'}{D'}\right) = \left(H_0\sigma_0 = \frac{H_0}{D_0}\right) = \text{const.}$$

holds for any instant of time or any depth of pulp. In other terms,

$$\sigma' = \sigma_0 \frac{H_0}{H'}$$

or

$$D' = D_0 \frac{H'}{H_0},$$

where H_0 and σ_0 (or D_0) are pulp column height and density (or dilution) at the instant $t = 0$.

Table 7.2. Results of a settling test in a calibrated laboratory glass cylinder

t h	H cm	H' cm	v cm/h	$\sigma'\%$	h'
0	36.0	36.0	24.0	8.0	5.76
0.25	30.5	36.0	24.0	8.0	5.76
0.5	24.5	34.0	20.0	8.46	5.41
1	17.5	28.6	11.0	10.06	4.47
1.5	13.7	21.5	5.37	13.40	3.24
2	11.4	18.2	3.52	15.83	2.67
3	8.8	13.7	1.70	21.02	1.88
4	7.7	9.8	0.55	29.40	1.20
5	6.9	8.2	0.26	35.10	0.92
∞	6.4	6.4	0	45.00	0.61

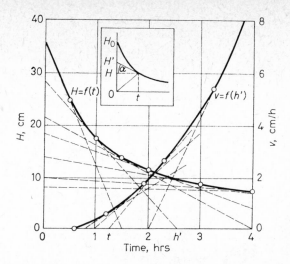

Fig. 7.19. $H = f(t)$ and $v = f(h)$ curves of the lab cylinder settling tests presented in Table 7.2

Example. To be settled is a pulp of solids s.g. $\delta = 2.0$ and initial density $\sigma_0 = 0.08$, at a rate $T = 20$ tph. The outcome of the cylinder settling test is stated in the first two columns of Table 7.2; the clarification curve $H = f(t)$ is shown in Fig. 7.19. The $v = dH/dt$ and $H' = H + vt$ values read off the curve as well as the σ' and

$$h' = \frac{1 - \sigma'}{\delta \sigma'}$$

values are listed in the subsequent columns of the table. The figure presents the $v = f(h')$ curve also, with tangents corresponding to different final dilutions h'_a (0.75, 1.0, 1.25, 2.0). The densities σ'_a corresponding to the dilutions h'_a, the h' and v data corresponding to the points of tangency, the values

$$f = \frac{h' - h'_a}{v} \text{ m}^2/\text{t} \cdot \text{h,}$$

$F = Tf$ m² and D m dia. and the approximate times of clarification required are summarized in Table 7.3.

Table 7.3. Parameters read off and derived from the diagrams in Fig. 7.19

h'_a	$\sigma'_a\%$	h'	v cm/h	f m²/t·h'	F m²	D m ∅	t h
0.75	40	1.20	0.55	81.7	1,634	48.6	4
1.00	33.3	1.80	1.50	53.4	1,068	39.4	3.1
1.25	28.6	2.35	2.60	46.2	924	36.6	2.5
2.00	20	3.50	6.20	24.2	484	26.5	1.3

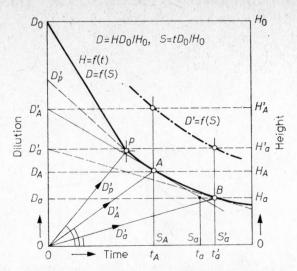

Fig. 7.20. Diagram presenting the principal relationships of pulp thickening. Variation of *H* vs. *t* and of *D* vs. *S* in the lab cylinder settling test

Settling velocity in a cylinder (the subsidence of the interface between the turbulent pulp and the clear liquor forming above it) is shown by the $H = f(t)$ curve of Fig. 7.20 to be constant at first and then to break at the point P. In the constant-velocity section, the hindered settling of the particles immediately beneath the interface continues at unchanged dilution D_0 (or h_0, or concentration $c_0 = 1/h_0$ or volumetric solids content $\sigma_0 = 1/D_0$). In the section of slowing velocity, on the other hand, D decreases because some compaction also takes place there.

By the relationship

$$D = D_0 \frac{H}{H_0}$$

(where D is the average dilution of the pulp column of height H), the $H = f(t)$ curve represents also the variation of D in time, $D = f(t)$ or, if the calibration of the axis of abscissae is suitably changed, also $D = f(S)$, the variation of D as a function of a parameter S, defined as

$$S = t \frac{D_0}{H_0}.$$

Dilution just below the interface at height H is represented by the dot-dash curve D'. For the tangent to the $D = f(S)$ curve at its point A, the relationship

$$v_A = \frac{D'_A - D_a}{S_a}$$

510

holds: in other terms,

$$S_a = \frac{D'_A - D_a}{v_A} = \frac{F}{Q} = \frac{1}{q} \text{ m}^2/\text{m}^3 \cdot \text{h}.$$

S_a, the thickener area required to handle solids at the specified rate, is defined by the point of intersection of the tangent to the point A and the horizontal line through the point D_a corresponding to the average dilution of the pulp to be discharged from the thickener. By shifting the point of tangency A, the value of S_a belonging to a given value of D_a can be changed, but it is not possible to find the critical point [where the tangent to the curve $v = f(D')$ passes precisely through the point D'_a of the axis of abscissae] direct on the $D = f(S)$ curve. However, the S_a which specifies the maximum plan area required cannot in any case be greater than the S'_a corresponding to the point D_a of the curve.

At the point P, where the curve $H = f(t)$ breaks away from its linear section, the interface which, up till then, has been settling at a constant rate and dilution D_0, makes contact with the gradually rising interface of the sediment of dilution D'_P collecting at the bottom; from then on, the pulp at the coalesced interfaces will have the dilution D'_P. The point P is where this abrupt change from D_0 to D'_P takes place; the graph proper indicates the change of velocity. D_0 and D'_P are corresponding, "conjugate" dilutions. The line OP represents the rise of the interface of dilution D'_P from the bottom; its slope provides the rise velocity. Other lines, joining the origin to points A, B, etc. on the curve, represent the rise velocities $u = H(t)$ of the interfaces of dilutions D'_P, D'_a, etc. in the rising sediment. The pulp discharged by a thickener in continuous operation has average dilution D_a; its rate of discharge is

$$u_a = \frac{H_a}{t'_a} = \frac{D_a Q}{F} = \frac{q}{\sigma_a}.$$

The flux (the volume of solids passing per unit of time through a unit of horizontal surface anywhere in the lab cylinder) is obtained as

$$q = \frac{Q}{F} = \frac{v}{D} = \sigma v.$$

In thickeners in continuous operation at a bottom discharge velocity u_a, the velocity v established in the cylinder is to be increased by u_a, giving

$$q' = \sigma_a u_a = \sigma v + \sigma u_a = \sigma(v + u_a) = q + \sigma u_a = \frac{v + u_a}{D}.$$

511

In part A of Fig. 7.21, the curve $q = \sigma v$ shows the variation of the flux in a lab cylinder test as a function of σ. The tangent to any point of the q curve provides

$$u = \frac{dq}{d\sigma} = v + \frac{\sigma \, dv}{d\sigma} \ .$$

For example, the point of tangency of the line of slope u_a passing through the point σ_a of the axis of abscissae is at B; the curve is intersected by the line

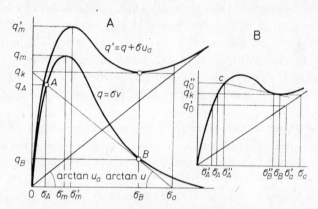

Fig. 7.21. A — Variation of flux q vs. volumetric solids content, B — shifts of σ vs. shifts in q_0 relative to q_k

farther to the left, at A, where

$$u_a = \frac{q_A - q_B}{\sigma_B - \sigma_A} \ .$$

σ_A and σ_B are conjugate densities. The figure further reveals that

$$\sigma_a = \sigma_A + \frac{q_A}{u_a} = \frac{q_k}{u_a} \ ,$$

and that

$$q_k = q_A + u_a \sigma_A = q_B + u_a \sigma_B \ .$$

If there is a bottom outlet, then the ordinates of the line of slope u_a representing the discharge velocity are to be added to the curve obtained in the lab cylinder test:

$$q' = q + u_a \sigma .$$

This q' curve has a maximum and a minimum. The maximum, at which density is somewhat greater than at the maximum of the cylinder-test curve, is situated where the slope of the descending branch of the latter curve attains $-u_a$. The density σ_B limiting the throughput of the thickener corresponds to the mini-

512

mum (critical) flux q_k of the q' curve. If flux in the feed equals this minimum, then discharge density will be

$$\sigma_a = \frac{q_k}{u_a} \, .$$

In the settling zone, density will be σ_A; the corresponding conjugate density is σ_B, the density limiting throughput. In a thickener run in the batch mode (with no discharge), this value would equal the interface density just below the discontinuity. The corresponding cylinder-test fluxes are q_A and q_B, respectively.

If the flux in the feed, q'_0, is less than the limiting flux q_k, then density — cf. Part B of Fig. 7.21 — is reduced from σ_A to σ'_A, in the settling zone and from σ_a to σ'_a in the discharge. If, on the other hand, the feed flux is $q'' > q_k$, then the density of the settling zone increases to σ''_A, but that of the discharge remains unchanged at σ_a. The materials balance is upset thereby, and a discontinuity is produced; it rises at a velocity corresponding to the slope of the tangent to the curve through the point $C(q''_0; \sigma''_A)$.

Thickeners may be dimensioned also on the basis of the $q = f(\sigma)$ curve of a dischargeless (cylinder) laboratory test, in which case the interface velocities u_a and settling-zone densities corresponding to different values of the feed flux must be established. The rise velocity of the interface — at a given settling-zone density — corresponds to the discharge velocity of the fully loaded thickener; discharge density can be derived from the relationship

$$q_A + u_a \sigma_A = u_a \sigma_a \, ,$$

where q_A is the feed flux belonging to the density σ_A in the dischargeless thickener (lab cylinder). To each feed flux value there belongs a different pair of values $(u_a; \sigma_a)$. That is, the specification of the discharge density σ_a of an industrial thickener at once fixes its discharge velocity u_a also. The solids feed rate Q m³/h specifies the pulp volume discharge rate U through the relationship

$$U = \frac{Q}{\sigma_a} \, ,$$

and the thickener area F required is provided by the formula

$$F = \frac{U}{u_a} \, .$$

(Anderson and Sparkman 1959; Comings et al. 1954; Cross 1963; Davies 1965; Gaudin and Fuerstenau 1962; Hassett 1958, 1965, 1968; Jaisle 1964; King and Shepman 1962; Moncrief 1964; Robel 1965; Robins 1964; Schubert 1970; Scott 1966, 1970; Shannon 1963, 1966; Speth and Sandrina 1971; Straumann 1968).

If the particles coagulate, three zones (clear liquor, coagulated pulp and compacted bottom sediment) develop in the thickener. It is best for the zone of coagulated pulp to be turbulent, i.e., agitated by vigorous circulation: this generates sufficient shear to make the clusters smaller and more compact, resulting in faster settling. Less of a shear (less of a turbulence caused by a less vigorous circulation) makes for looser, slower-settling, larger clusters; no turbulence (no circulation) at all gives rise to quite large aggregates that settle very slowly indeed: this is when throughput is least.

A vigorous pulp circulation can be realized by replacing the conventional short pulp feed pipes with long ones provided with apertures at suitable points, thanks to the principle of hydrostatic equilibrium.

The least thickener depth H_{min} needed is a function, in addition to the depth of penetration H_1 of the feed pipe and the inclination H_2 of the radial arms rotating at the bottom, also of the time it takes for satisfactory settling to occur (H_3):

$$H_{min} = H_1 + H_2 + H_3.$$

Most often, H_1 equals 0.5 m, but may be greater than that, too,

$$H_2 = Ri,$$

where R is thickener radius and i ($\cong 0.05$ usually) is the inclination of the radial arms ($i = \text{tg } \alpha = H_2/R$). H_3 can be estimated by the following rule of thumb: In the dilute top zone of the thickener, particles will sink rapidly to the layer of critical dilution D_c. With reference to Fig. 7.16, wherever the curve $v = f(D)$ passes above the diagonal line, domains of no settling (stagnation) or, indeed, of reverse circulation will be found in the thickener. If compaction from D_c to D_a in the zone of compression takes t hours, the flux (the flow through a unit of thickener area) is qt m³/m² for the (compact) solids and qtD_{avg} m³/m² for the pulp; the height of the pulp column passing through is

$$H_3 = qtD_{avg} \text{ m}.$$

One may assume

$$D_{avg} = \frac{D_c + D_a}{2}.$$

The substitution

$$q = \frac{V_c}{D_c - D_a}$$

furnishes the formula

$$H_3 = v_c t \frac{D_c + D_a}{2(D_c - D_a)}.$$

The velocity of clarification of the pulp can be increased by installing parallel oblique baffles in the thickener. In the layer between any two baffles, settling makes pulp density increase near the bottom: there is a corresponding decrease at the top of the layer. The pulp flow caused by the resulting density difference makes the clear water move upward and the thick pulp downward. The insertion of oblique parallel baffles or trays will greatly increase thickener throughput even apart from this accelerating effect. The mounting of n conical trays over a height H in the settler, spaced at intervals $h = H/n$, increases throughput by a factor n against that of trayless thickener of equal pulp area. (The same phenomenon is exploited in the parallel-connected multi-compartment Dorr thickener.) Some of the possible baffle and tray arrangements are indicated in Fig. 7.22. The trays mounted on the central tubular shaft which introduces and disperses the feed (as in the middle drawing) may be horizontal also (e.g. in a stack of 50, one below another): the pulp settled on them can be removed by rapidly spinning the shaft at intervals.

The methods of thickener design described so far are all based on the assumption that the relationship linking the velocity of clarification (or settling velocity) of the particles to pulp density (or dilution) is a well-defined, unique one and that a pulp of given density will always settle at one and the same velocity at any depth. In the clarification of fine slimes coagulated by a flocculating agent (a polyelectrolyte), however, this assumption often fails. In such situations, it is the solids weight per unit area of pulp column, G kp/m², that plays the key role: initial dilution D_0 and/or pulp column height H_0 are less relevant. Settling velocity increases as G (or pulp depth) is increased, because the pressure of the solids above the sediment is transmitted through the contacts between flakes flocculated by means of a polyelectrolyte: the flocs will in fact touch even at very great dilutions (starting at pulp densities of 5 g/l or so). As the particles or flocs settle, the liquor exuded by them flows in the reverse direction: this reduces effective pressure on the bottom sediment. In a lab cylinder, bottom pressure gradually increases with time — in step with the gradual decrease of settling velocity — until the full pressure of the solids

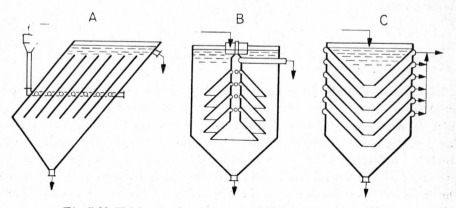

Fig. 7.22. Thickeners featuring oblique baffles or inclined trays

comes to bear. It is this pressure in the final analysis that compacts the flocs of the bottom layer to the ultimate dilution h_a. The ultimate dilution that can be attained in the settling of a flocculated clay pulp accordingly decreases (i.e., pulp thickness increases) as total solids weight G kp/m² in the pulp column increases. In the settling of clay pulps flocculated by means of long-chain polyelectrolytes, then, the throughput of a cylindrical Dorr thickener will depend on its height also, and not only on its plan area, as is the case in the settling of coarser-grained pulps. As another practical implication, in order to achieve a lower ultimate dilution in the settling of such pulps, deep funnels (spitzkastens) should be preferred to cylindrical Dorrs, as this permits the G kp/m² in the pulp column above the discharge outlet to be much greater for a given feed rate.

The ultimate (equilibrium) volumetric solids content of the bottom discharge is given by

$$\sigma = KG^k$$

or

$$\sigma = K'H^{k/(1-k)},$$

where K, K' and k are constants characterizing the material being settled, and G is the weight per unit area measured in water (i.e. the pressure) of the solids in a pulp column of height H. The equations are found to be valid for filters, too, provided G kp/m² is interpreted as the pressure differential. The slow stirring of the bottom deposit prevents the particles from forming bridges and from being locked by static friction to the tank wall: all this helps the flocs to compact, and also contributes to the formation of channels in the sediment and in the zone of compression, respectively. These channels greatly facilitate the upward egress of the liquor. Bridging often prevents attaining the envisaged discharge density, but bridges can be destroyed by slight stirring (Abbott et al. 1973; Dell and Keleghan 1973; Dell and Sinha 1966—1967; Hassett 1968).

7.4. FILTRATION

7.4.1. Fundamentals; filtration equations. In filtration, a porous-permeable partition is used to retain the solids in a pulp but pass the liquor phase (the filtrate). A pressure differential applied to the two sides of the partition helps the liquor exuded by the pulp fed in on the higher-pressure side to seep through the filter. A filter is called a vacuum filter if the high side is under atmospheric pressure and the low side is under depression; it is called a pressure filter if the pressure is atmospheric on the low side and higher on the other side (Ferguson 1971; Szabó et al. 1968; Tamási and Schwartz 1968).

Filtration velocity is

$$u = \frac{\dfrac{dQ}{dt}}{A} = \frac{p}{k\mu l} \; ,$$

where A is filter surface area, Q is filtrate volume, t is time and p is pressure differential, μ is the viscosity of the liquor, l is the thickness of the filter medium and k is its specific resistance. (The medium is made up by the porous-permeable partition plus the cake of filtered material retained by it.) If the cake volume (solids plus pore liquor) retained on the filter is b times the volume of the filtrate, then

$$Al = bQ,$$

implying

$$Q \, dQ = \frac{pA^2}{k\mu b} \, dt \; .$$

In the cake of volume Al, volumetric solids content is σ_l, solids weight is $Al\sigma_l\delta$ and the weight of the liquor trapped in the pores is

$$Al(1 - \sigma_l)\gamma.$$

Let the volumetric solids content of the original suspension (of the feed) be σ; let its solids content by weight be s (which gives liquor content by weight as $1 - s$); then,

$$z = \frac{s}{1 - s} = \frac{\sigma\delta}{(1 - \sigma)\gamma} = \frac{Al\sigma_l\delta}{[Q + Al(1 - \sigma_l)]\gamma} \; ,$$

where the numerator represents the weight of the solids retained by the filter and the denominator represents the combined weight of the filtrate and of the liquor trapped in the cake. Hence,

$$(1 - s)Al\sigma_l\delta = sQ\gamma + sAl(1 - \sigma_l)\gamma \; ,$$

or

$$l = \frac{sQ}{A[(1 - s)\sigma_l\delta - s(1 - \sigma_l)\gamma]} = \frac{Q\sigma}{A(\sigma_l - \sigma)} = \frac{Qb}{A} \; ,$$

where

$$b = \frac{s}{(1 - s)\dfrac{\sigma_l\delta}{\gamma} - s(1 - \sigma_l)} = \frac{\sigma}{\sigma_l - \sigma} \; .$$

If the pressure differential is constant, then

$$Q^2 = \left(\frac{2pA^2}{k\mu b}\right) t = Kt$$

or

$$Q = \frac{Kt}{Q},$$

and

$$l^2 = \left(\frac{2pb}{k\mu}\right)t.$$

The first and third equation is quadratic in Q (or l) vs. t. The second one is linear in Q vs. t/Q; its slope is

$$m = \frac{1}{K} = \frac{k\mu b}{2pA^2},$$

whence specific filter resistance is

$$k = \frac{2pA^2 m}{\mu b}.$$

Specific filter resistance is a constant if the cake is rigid (its pore volume is unaffected by changes in pressure). This is the case e.g. if the particles in the cake are crystalline. If, on the other hand, they are deformable (in clay pulps, for example), then the pore volume of the cake is changed by pressure, and

$$k \simeq k_0 p^z,$$

where $z < 1$. (In a rigid cake, $z = 0$ and $k = k_0$.)

The cake will grow to be inhomogeneous if the liquor, in its approach to the medium of gradually increasing thickness, slows down so that it can no longer carry the coarser particles to the cake and make them stick there. In that case, the empirical formula

$$Q^n = K'p^{n'}A^n t$$

can be used, where $n < 2$ if the cake is inhomogeneous. For rigid (incompressible) cakes,

$$n' = n - 1$$

as a rule.

At great pressure differentials, pore volume may vary even within the cake, decreasing towards the filter. For example, in the filtration of kaolin, at the bottom of the cake,

$$\varepsilon = 47 \quad 50 \quad 53\%$$
$$\text{at } p = 14 \quad 6 \quad 1.4 \text{ bars,}$$

whereas, at the top of the cake, $\varepsilon \simeq 63\%$; for limestone,

the top ε is   72   65%
and the bottom ε is   82   80%
at a pressure of $p =$ 14   50 bars, respectively (Hutto 1957).

The fundamental equation of filtration may be derived also from the Hagen–Poiseuille Law. By that law, the average velocity of a liquid of viscosity μ flowing through a straight capillary of radius r and length l_1 under a pressure drop p is

$$u_1 = \frac{r^2 p}{8\mu l_1} .$$

(The hydraulic radius r_h is the ratio of $r^2\pi$, the cross-sectional area of the liquid, to $2r\pi$, the wetted circumference of the capillary, or — multiplying both the numerator and the denominator by l_1 — the ratio of liquid volume to capillary surface area.) In a cake of unit volume, liquor-filled pore volume is $(1 - \sigma)$; the aggregate surface of the solid particles is $F\sigma$, where F is the specific surface per unit volume of the solid particles. In other terms,

$$r_h = \frac{r}{2} = \frac{1 - \sigma}{F\sigma} .$$

If particulate structure is homogeneous, then the fraction intersecting solid particles of any plane of cross section equals the volumetric solids content σ; the fraction intersecting liquor is accordingly $(1 - \sigma)$. Hence, the rate of filtration referred to the entire cross section is

$$u = u_1(1 - \sigma).$$

In a cake of thickness l, liquor seeps through rambling capillary passages of varying aperture, along paths of length cl longer than l $(c > 1)$ rather than through straight capillaries of length $l_1 = l$. On replacing l_1 by cl and on introducing

$$r = 2\frac{1 - \sigma}{F\sigma} ,$$

the equation

$$u = \frac{(1 - \sigma)^3 r}{2c\sigma^2 F^2 \mu l}$$

is obtained. The coefficient c is a function, in addition to σ, also of the shape, distribution and preferred orientation, if any, of the particles. A fair average value for isometric particles is $c = 2.5$, implying

$$K = 2c \simeq 5(\pm 10\%).$$

The filtration equation is thus obtained as

$$u = \frac{dQ}{A\,dt} \simeq \frac{(1 - \sigma)^3 p}{5\sigma^2 F^2 \mu l} = \frac{p}{k\mu l} ;$$

where

$$k = \frac{5\sigma^2 F^2}{(1 - \sigma)^3}$$

is the specific resistance of the cake. Since

$$F = \frac{\alpha}{x},$$

k varies inversely as the square of particle size. k is proportional also to

$$\frac{\sigma^2}{(1-\sigma)^3},$$

but σ itself is proportional to p if the cake is compressible. Increasing the pressure differential may therefore actually reduce the throughput in certain situations.

In our considerations so far, we have left out of account the resistance of the porous-permeable partition (of the actual filter sheet that carries the cake). If that also is taken into account, then total pressure drop becomes

$$p = p_1 + p_2$$

and

$$u = \frac{dQ}{A\,dt} = \frac{p_1}{\mu k_1} = \frac{p_2}{\mu k_2 l} = \frac{p}{\mu(k_1 + k_2 l)},$$

where k_1 is the specific resistance of the filter sheet and k_2 is that of the cake.

If, in the formula

$$\frac{dQ}{dt} = \frac{Ap}{r},$$

p and r are constant (e.g. early on in filtration on a sand filter of constant thickness l, as long as the filter resistance r ($k\mu l$) may be regarded as constant), then

$$Q = \frac{Apt}{r},$$

and the time it takes for filtrate of volume Q to form is

$$t = \frac{Qr}{Ap}.$$

If the (constant) thickness l of the filter medium is great, then

$$\frac{dQ}{dt} = \frac{A(p + l\gamma)}{r},$$

and

$$p = H\gamma$$

equals the static pressure of a liquor column of height H above the filter medium. Over a time dt, the liquor level sinks by dH, and liquor loss $-A\,dH$

through the filter equals the increase dQ in filtrate volume. We may write

$$\frac{dQ}{dt} = -\frac{A\,dH}{dt} = \frac{A}{r}(H+l),$$

or

$$dt = \frac{-r\,dH}{\gamma(H+l)}.$$

Integration gives

$$t = \frac{r}{\gamma}\ln\frac{H+l}{l};$$

This is the time it takes for the liquor level to sink from a height H down to the level of the filter medium.

It is more usual for the thickness l of the medium to increase as filtration proceeds and for filter resistance to increase along with it. The substitution

$$l = \frac{bQ}{A}$$

then gives the differential equation

$$\frac{dQ}{dt} = \frac{pA^2}{\mu(k_1 A + k_2 bQ)}$$

which, at $p = \text{const.}$, furnishes the relationships

$$t = \left(\frac{\mu k_1}{pA}\right)Q + \left(\frac{\mu k_2 b}{2pA^2}\right)Q^2 = \frac{\mu Q}{pA}\left(k_1 + \frac{k_2 bQ}{2A}\right)$$

or

$$\frac{t}{Q} = \frac{\mu k_1}{pA} + \left(\frac{\mu k_2 b}{2pA^2}\right)Q = \frac{\mu}{pA}\left(k_1 + \frac{k^2 bQ}{2A}\right)$$

or

$$Q = A\left[\sqrt{\frac{2pt}{\mu k_2 b} + \left(\frac{k_1}{k_2 b}\right)^2} - \frac{k_1}{k_2 b}\right].$$

The relationship between t and Q is parabolic; that between t/Q and Q is linear.

In a rotating vacuum filter of continuous operation, filtrate discharge per revolution Q and wet cake volume per revolution

$$L = Al = bQ$$

are obtained by replacing in the formula the full duration t_1 of a revolution by the time actually available for filtration,

$$t = \frac{t_1\varphi}{2\pi} = at_1.$$

(where φ is the central angle of immersion into the pulp, in radians), the reason being that effective passage (suction) of filtrate through any element of the filter surface is confined to the interval thus defined.

Filtrate discharge Q_1 and cake production L_1 per unit of time (during n revolutions) are obtained (neglecting, e.g., k_1) as

$$Q_1 = \frac{Q}{At_1} = \sqrt{\frac{p\varphi}{\mu\pi k_2 b t_1}} = \sqrt{\frac{\varphi p n}{u\pi k_2 b}} = \sqrt{\frac{2apn}{\mu k_2 b}}$$

and

$$L_1 = \frac{L}{At_1} = \sqrt{\frac{pb\varphi}{\mu\pi k_2 t_1}} = \sqrt{\frac{\varphi p b n}{\mu\pi k_2}} = \sqrt{\frac{2apbn}{\mu k_2}},$$

respectively, where $n = 1/t_1$ is the speed of filter rotation. Q_1 and L_1 have the same dimension (e.g. both are in $cm^3/cm^2 \cdot min$ or in $m^3/m^2 \cdot h$, etc.);

$$T_1 = L_1 \delta' \ g/cm^2 \cdot min$$

or

$$T = 600 L_1 \ \delta' \ kg/m^2 \cdot h,$$

where δ' is the s.g. of the wet cake.

The substitution

$$b = \frac{\sigma}{\sigma_l - \sigma}$$

gives rise to

$$T_1 = \delta' \sqrt{\frac{pn\varphi\sigma}{\mu\pi k_2(\sigma_l - \sigma)}} = \delta' \sqrt{\frac{2pna\sigma}{\mu k_2(\sigma_l - \sigma)}}.$$

Here, σ is volumetric solids content in the feed, and σ_l is the same in the cake where it emerges from the pulp.

Let two filtering situations be characterized by

$$k_2, \ \mu, \ \tau, \ \sigma, \ b = \sigma/(\sigma_l - \sigma), \ p, \ t_1, \ n, \ \varphi$$

and

$$k_2', \ u', \ \tau', \ \sigma', \ b' = \sigma'/(\sigma_l - \sigma'), \ p', \ t_l', \ n', \ \varphi'.$$

respectively (where τ is pulp temperature and the other variables have been identified above). In principle (if k_1 is negligible), the ratios

$$\frac{Q_1}{Q_1'} \quad \text{and} \quad \frac{L_1}{L_1'} \quad \text{or} \quad \frac{T_1}{T_1'}$$

all change proportionally, as

$$\sqrt{\frac{k_2'}{k_2}}, \ \sqrt{\frac{\mu'}{\mu}}, \ \sqrt{\frac{p}{p'}}, \ \frac{t_1'}{t_1} \quad \text{or} \quad \sqrt{\frac{n}{n'}} \quad \text{and} \quad \sqrt{\frac{\varphi}{\varphi'}},$$

but Q_1/Q_1' varies as $\sqrt{\dfrac{b'}{b}}$

522

or

$$\sqrt{\frac{\sigma'}{\sigma} \frac{\sigma_l - \sigma}{\sigma_l - \sigma'}} \, ,$$

and

$$\frac{L_1}{L_1'} \quad \text{and} \quad \frac{T_1}{T_1'}$$

vary as

$$\sqrt{\frac{b}{b'}} \quad \text{or} \quad \sqrt{\frac{\sigma}{\sigma'} \frac{\sigma_l - \sigma'}{\sigma_l - \sigma}} \, .$$

For a compressible cake,

$$k_2 = k_0 p^z \, ,$$

where $z < 0.7$ in practice. In that case, p/k_2 in the formulae may be replaced by p^{1-z}/k_0, and the change in pressure differential will entail a change proportional to

$$\sqrt{\left(\frac{p}{p'}\right)^{1-z}}$$

in the ratios Q_1/Q_1' of filtrate output and L_1/L_1' of cake output.

The actual ratios

$$\frac{Q_1}{Q_1'} \quad \text{and} \quad \frac{L_1}{L_1'} \left(\text{or } \frac{T_1}{T_1'}\right)$$

may differ more or less from the theoretical ones. The reason may be e.g. segregation in the filter tank in the case of dilute pulps; in the case of thicker pulps, the flocculation of the particles, the reduction of shear and of effective floc/particle weight in the pulp, the slimming of the water film adhering closely to the particles in the cake as viscosity decreases (the temperature increases) and the resulting increase in effective pore volume may contribute, and so may, on the other hand, the reduction of the angle of contact (and the concomitant increase of the propensity to be wetted) of the particles with non-zero contact angles (bituminous coals, concentrates produced by flotation) and the resulting decrease in effective pore volume as surface tension, a function of temperature, decreases, etc.

On the cake of a vacuum filter, air dissolved in the liquid phase tends to separate out in the form of bubbles (on the hydrophobic particles above all), in quantities increasing as pressure decreases. Bubbles reduce the permeability of the cake. This is one of the phenomena that may impair filter performance under a higher vacuum (Nemeth 1970).

Flow of fluid through the cake under the pressure differential p on a rotating filter represents a force S (a suction) perpendicular to the filter surface. In addition, the vertical force of its weight reduced by buoyancy, G_0, also

523

acts on any particle in the cake, and so does the shear P caused by the velocity differential between the medium and the filter surface, which is tangential to the latter (and opposed to the direction in which it rotates). It is the component perpendicular to the filter surface of the resultant R of these three forces that makes a particle adhere to the filter (or to the cake). Figure 7.23 shows

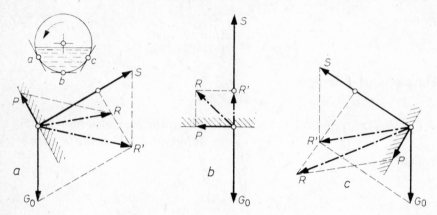

Fig. 7.23. Forces and their resultant acting upon a particle at the cake top in a rotary filter, at three points of a revolution

the resultants R and R' vectorially for three points: one just after immersion (a), the second in the deepest position (b) and the third just before emersion (c), assuming the proportions

$$S : G_0 : P = 3 : 2 : 1$$

and

$$S' : G'_0 : P' = 3 : 2 : 0,$$

respectively. The component perpendicular to the surface is least in the position (b).

S and P are proportional to Stokesian fluid drag, that is, to $xv\mu'$, whereas G_0 varies as $x^3 (\delta - \gamma')$. The velocity v corresponding to the force S varies as the rate of passage of the filtrate: it is great right after immersion and decreases as cake thickness increases. The velocity corresponding to the force P is greater, the greater the drum speed and the thinner the pulp, the reason being that a thick pulp has a tendency to drag along with the filter surface in a thick layer, eliminating shear at the surface (this accounts for putting $P = 0$ in the second set of assumptions). μ' and γ', both proportional to σ, tend to be greatest in the deepest position (at b), provided $\sigma \lesssim 0.45$. (If, on the other hand, $\sigma \gtrsim 0.45$, no segregation by settling occurs, and μ' and γ' are the same at any depth in the pulp.) If there is segregation, then the particles

524

encountered next to the pulp surface (right after immersion and right before emersion) tend to be finer on average than those encountered deeper down: consequently, the middle layer of the cake will be coarser than its top and bottom layers. The volumetric solids content of the cake, σ_l, will also be less (e.g. about 0.57) than in a homogeneous cake taken out of an unsegregated pulp, in which the finer particles fit better into the interstices of the coarser ones (giving a σ_l in the 0.62 to 0.65 range).

On the filtration of a dilute suspension with a low σ, particles do not interfere with one another as they follow the flow lines taking them to the pores of the filter. Depending on the ratio of pore size to particle it can either pass through the pore or clog it up. In the first case, the filtrate will contain some slimes; in the second, the resistance k_1 of the filter will turn out to be relatively great. If, on the other hand, the pulp is a thick one with a high σ, then several particles will be carried towards any one pore at the same time, and they will tend to form bridges above the pore. Filter resistance will in that case remain unchanged while the cake builds up. If bridging does occur, then the pores of the filter may be greater by a factor

$$\sim \frac{600}{x + 15}$$

than the particle size x μm. The cake is the less compact and its unit resistance k_2 the less, the thicker the original pulp (the higher its σ).

If the pressure differential p is constant, both filtrate volume Q and cake thickness l increase as the square root of the time elapsed: steep at its onset, the curve representing the process gradually flattens out, indicating a gradual decline in filtration performance. For crystalline particles, the economic optimum of cake thickness is around 5 to 10 cm; for colloids, it is in the order of 5 to 10 mm. It may be useful to apply a low pressure at the outset and to let it build up gradually as the cake thickens. The lower initial pressure entails the formation of a more porous first cake layer of lower unit resistance; by increasing pressure in step with the thickening of the cake, a constant rate of filtration (Q/t const.) may be achieved. In such a case, a filtration equation

$$t = \frac{\mu Q}{pA}\left(k_1 + \frac{k_2 bQ}{A}\right)$$

will hold; if k_1 is negligible, it will simplify to

$$Q^2 = \frac{pA^2}{\mu k b}t = K't.$$

Here, p is the maximum pressure differential, which builds up by the time t.

In intermittent filtration, the effective duration of a pass is followed by a dead time (time of manipulation) t', during which no filtration takes place. Neglecting k_1, an equation of the form

$$\frac{Q}{t} = \frac{K}{Q}$$

is obtained, provided $p = \text{const.}$ or $Q/t = \text{const.}$ In the first case,

$$K = \frac{2pA^2}{\mu k_2 b} \ ;$$

in the second case,

$$K = \frac{p_{max} A^2}{\mu k_2 b} \ .$$

In intermittent filtration, the filtration equation acquires the form

$$\frac{t_{tot}}{Q} = \frac{t + t'}{Q} = \frac{Q}{K} + \frac{t'}{Q} \ .$$

An optimum (a maximum volume of filtrate) is obtained at

$$\frac{d\left(\dfrac{t_{tot}}{Q}\right)}{dQ} = 0$$

or

$$\frac{1}{K} - \frac{t'}{Q^2} = 0 \ ,$$

implying

$$Q^2 = Kt'.$$

The introduction of this optimum of Q^2 into the general filtration formula

$$t = \frac{Q^2}{K}$$

gives

$$t = t';$$

that is, in intermittent filtration, the effective time of filtration should equal the time of manipulation. If k_1 too is taken into account, then

$$t = t' + k_1 \sqrt{\frac{2\mu t'}{k_2 bp}}$$

is obtained on the assumption that $p = \text{const.}$ and

$$t = t' + k_1 \sqrt{\frac{\mu t'}{k_2 bp_{max}}}$$

on the assumption that $Q/t = $ const.; that is, the optimum duration of filtration somewhat exceeds the time of manipulation.

With reference to Fig. 7.24, the time $t_{\text{opt}} = t'$ giving optimum productivity in intermittent filtration may be determined by a graphic construction also. The curve in the figure is a plot of the function $Q = f(t)$. The tangent to the curve through the point $-t'$ of the axis of abscissae defines by its point of

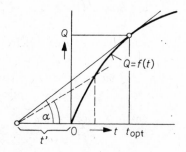

Fig. 7.24. Graph for finding the optimum time of filtration of an intermittent filter

tangency the optimum time t_{opt} and the optimum volume of filtrate Q_{opt}. The point of tangency is where the performance parameter

$$\tan \alpha = \frac{Q}{t + t'}$$

is a maximum.

The fundamental equation of filtration may be written up in a simplified form as

$$\frac{1}{u} = \frac{dt}{dQ} = \frac{k}{p} = \frac{k_1 + k_2}{p} \,,$$

where k_1 and k_2 are the resistance of the filter sheet and of the cake, respectively, and k is total resistance. Time t is then furnished by

$$t = \int \frac{k}{p} \, dQ = \int \frac{dt}{dQ} \, dQ \,.$$

In other terms, if the variation of k/p or dt/dQ as established in a test is plotted against Q, then the area below the curve provides the time t of filtration. The ordinate belonging to $Q = 0$ is k_1/p; that belonging to any other $Q > 0$ is k/p; this being so, cake resistance

$$k_2 = k - k_1$$

can be derived for any instant. If $p = $ const., the curve becomes a straight line. Different pressure differentials generate lines of different slope (give rise to different resistances k_2). If dQ/dt is a constant, then so is p/k, and the pressure differential is to be increased in step with the thickening of the cake. The time needed for filtration is furnished also in this case by the area below the curve between Q_0 and Q:

$$t = \frac{Q - Q_0}{\dfrac{p}{k}},$$

where Q_0 and Q are the filtrate volumes respectively at the beginning and the end of the filtration pass (Dobie 1965).

Part of the liquor filling the pores can be removed from the cake if, after its emergence from the pulp, the pressure differential is used to suck in air, which can drive out the water in the pores before it. For expelling water from a capillary of radius r, a pressure differential $p' > p$ is required, where

$$p = a \frac{\cos \vartheta}{r_h} = \frac{F \sigma_l a \cos \vartheta}{1 - \sigma_l}.$$

Here, $F \ (= \alpha/x)$ is the specific surface of the particles of contact angle ϑ and a is the surface tension of the liquid. The degree to which the cake can be dewatered is accordingly a function of cake porosity σ_l and of the fineness F and contact angle ϑ of the grains making it up, as well as of the surface tension of the liquor and of the pressure differential p'. The ultimate moisture content of the cake for a pressure differential p' is

$$n' = \frac{n_0}{3} \left[1 - \log \left(\frac{p'}{p} - 0.99 \right) \right],$$

where n_0 is the moisture content of the cake with all its pores full of liquor (Kubitza 1962). Increasing the pressure differential, however, may cause the cake to crack. With the cracks short-circuiting the capillaries of the cake, further drying, if any, is of a drastically reduced efficacy. Cracking is easier to avoid if the cake is thinner.

7.4.2. Filtration aids. The ultimate moisture content of the cake can be reduced by the dosage of agents reducing the surface tension of the liquor (frothers, wetters), agents increasing the angle of contact ϑ (collectors), and flocculants affecting cake porosity (the volumetric solids content σ_l). The latter greatly improve filtration performance as well, by reducing the cake resistance

$$k_2 = \frac{5\sigma^2 F^2}{(1 - \sigma)^3}.$$

Flocculants-coagulants have been seen above to play an important role in clarification and thickening also (Dollimore and Horridge 1972; Gieske 1962; Wölfer 1973).

The angle of contact is best increased using non-specific collectors (fatty acids, soaps, amines) which hydrophobize the solids and reduce the surface tension of the liquor at the same time.

The wetters available to reduce surface tension if required include alkyl and aryl sulphates and sulphonates, polyglycol ethers and esters, etc. The sulphates and sulphonates act as collectors *vis-à-vis* certain minerals also (improving the angles of contact of those), but wetters tend to affect the wetting of the particles adversely from the specific viewpoint of filtration technology. Of the frothers, terpene alcohols, phenol derivatives and higher aliphatic alcohols are used in practice to decrease the water content of the cake. Reducing the surface tension tends to reduce the angle of contact also, and so this influence is not always in the right direction. The effect of the decrease in the angle of contact tends to be stronger for finer-grained aggregates (Bolek 1968; Bosenik 1956; Schranz and Menzel 1958).

Warming the water reduces both its surface tension and viscosity, e.g.

at	10	100 °C,
surface tension is	74	59 dynes per centimetre,
and viscosity is	1.32	0.28 cP.

On drying the cake with a slightly superheated steam, the vapour will condense at any point of the cake at the boiling temperature determined by the pressure prevailing there. The front of condensation progresses down the pressure gradient (towards the interior of the cake): it expels cold water by hot. This permits to improve filter throughput by 50 to 100% and to reduce the ultimate moisture content of the cake by 40 to 60% as against air flushing, depending on the nature and granulometry of the solids. For example, in the filtration of a coal slurry containing 27% minus-40 μm and 82% minus-400 μm material, the moisture content of the cake could be reduced to 11% as against the 18% attained with air flushing. Evaporation during the cooling of the cake reduced the moisture content even further, to 8% (Brown 1965; Dahlstrom and Silverblatt 1973; Gathen 1963; Reuter and Lemke 1963; Schoenberger and Burch 1964; Silverblatt and Dahlstrom 1964; Simons and Dahlstrom 1966).

Flocculants or coagulants will be described in more detail in Section 7.5.

7.4.3. Types of filters. Filters may, according to the mode of operation, be of intermittent or continuous type: according to the mode of applying the pressure differential, they may be pressure or vacuum filters, or filters profiting simply by the hydrostatic head of the liquor to be filtered.

The simplest sort of intermittent (batch) filter is the drip filter operating on the principle of the laboratory funnel filter. A "nutsch" is a tank with a false bottom supporting a filter: the filtrate passes through under the influence of a partial vacuum created beneath the false bottom by means of a water-jet

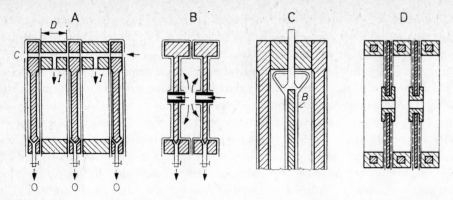

Fig. 7.25. Diagrams of filter presses. A — plate-and-frame, B — chamber, C — AJKO, D — Demeter filter press

vacuum pump. It is a cheap device that is easy to operate and to supervise, but it occupies a great deal of space per unit of throughput, and the removal of the sediment by hand is labour-consuming. Some nutsches are made tiltable with a view to faster and easier emptying.

The filter elements of vacuum-leaf filters are canvas bags totally immersed into the liquor; the filtrate is removed from their interior by suction while the cake deposits outside. The filter leaf is a frame of perforated pipe covered with cloth. The device is recommended for the filtration of liquors containing little solids (less than 3% or so). When cake thickness is judged sufficient, the leaves are transferred, with the vacuum still on, into another tank, where the cake is removed after the vacuum has been taken off. Some leaf filters operate with pressure, in which the pulp is injected by means of a pump or of compressed air into a closed tank which contains the leaves. The filtrate then passes into the leaves as above.

Filter presses of intermittent operation used in mineral processing in the filtration of fine slimes (e.g. kaolin, the clayey tailings of coal flotation, etc.) are of the plate-and-frame or of the chamber type (Fig. 7.25).

A plate-and-frame filter press (Part A) is made up of empty frames and massive plates in alternation. A piece of filter cloth is pressed between each side of a frame and the adjoining plate: it retains the solids out of a suspension pumped in under some pressure (3 to 30 bars) through inlets I branching off a bore C connecting all the elements, whereas filtrate can leave through the outlets O provided with stopcocks. The trickle of filtrate from the outlets tapers off when the chambers are full of cake. Frame thickness D (2 to 15 cm) is to be adapted to the nature and granulometry of the pulp to be filtered, whereas frame number (5 to 90) and surface area (0.1 to 3 m²) are to be adapted to the throughput required. Large filter presses these days have aggregate filtering surfaces of 200 to 250 m² or so. The frames and plates are suspended by outside lugs from horizontal rods along which they are free to move. They are compressed together manually (by bolting) or by a hydraulic press. At the end of the pass, the bolts are undone, the frames pulled apart and the cakes removed.

In chamber-type filter presses (Part B of Fig. 7.25), there are no separate empty frames, only massive rimmed plates: by pressing these together, chambers are formed, which take up the pulp injected into the device. Central apertures connect every chamber of the press: it is through these that the pulp is injected.

Plate-and-frame type filter presses of Hungarian design include the AJKO filter press (Part C of Fig. 7.25) and the Demeter filter press (Part D). The frames of the AJKO filter contain rubber bags B that can be inflated with compressed air after the end of injection. This permits to press further liquor out of the "finished" cake (Juhász and Schumiczky 1966; Schumiczky and Lux 1964—1966). The plates of the Demeter press are sheets covered with a screen cloth and filter canvas; the filtrate may trickle through along the screen cloth in any direction towards the rim; the frames are simple rubber rings, the compression of which after the end of injection permits here also to press further liquor out of the cake.

In filter presses operated in the intermittent mode, the time of manual cake removal and of preparation for the next period of filtration (the dead time) is fairly long as compared with the useful filtration time, especially when thickish pulps and suspensions are being handled. The current trend in filter press design is the development of automatic and semi-automatic devices which eliminate or reduce manual handling (Harper 1956; Niessen and Koppitz 1962; Radford and Smith 1972; Reuter and Beckerath 1974; Teichmann 1959).

The unit throughput (in $t/m^2 \cdot h$ or $m^3/m^2 \cdot h$) of a continuous filter is much greater than that of an intermittent filter press: small wonder that the filters most popular in mineral processing practice are continuous vacuum filters. The most widespread design is the cell-type vacuum filter (drum or disk filter). Figure 7.26 shows diagrams of some of these.

Part A of Fig. 7.26 is the diagram of an outside-drum filter. Space inside the canvas-covered (outer) screen surface of the drum is compartmented into cells: from every cell, a pipe leads to a valve whose seat slowly rotates against a stationary port plate. This arrangement keeps the cells under suction during the best part of each turn. The vacuum sucks filtrate into the cells submerged into the suspension, making a cake of increasing thickness build up on the canvas. For some time after the cell has emerged from the suspension, the vacuum is left on, to suck air through the cake and to expel the liquor from the pores (provided the pressure differential exceeds

$$p \cong 8a\,\sigma_l \frac{\cos\vartheta}{(1-\sigma_l)\,x} ,$$

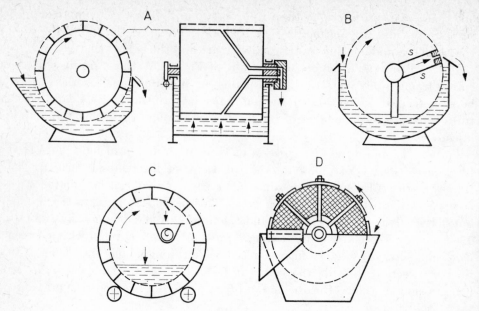

Fig. 7.26. Diagrams of vacuum filters. A — outside-drum, B — cell-less, C — inside-drum, D — disk filter

where a is the surface tension of the liquor, x is the surface average grain size of the particles [cf. Vol. 1, p. 78], ϑ is their angle of contact and σ_l is volumetric solids content in the cake). The air requirement is about 3 m³/min · m². In the chemical industry and in hydrometallurgy, the cake is often sprinkled with wash water after the removal of the filtrate; wash water and filtrate leave through different ports of the rotating valve. Further on in its revolution, the cell is taken off vacuum and blown with low-pressure compressed air at 1.1 to 1.2 bar absolute to loosen up the cake and to free the pores of the canvas. Compressed-air requirement is about two litres per minute per m². The cake is removed by means of adjustable scrapers, a takeoff roll or loops of string guided by rolls which detach themselves from the drum at this point. Cake removal precedes the reimmersion of the cell into the suspension. In the Rotobelt filter, the whole filter cloth is lifted off the drum: the cake drops off it as it passes a discharge roll of small radius (Cornell et al. 1958). Drum filter diameter is in the 1 to 5 m range; the largest units have filter surfaces in the order of 100 m². Speed is 0.1 to 3 rpm.

The small-cell drum filter is a special construction: it has a plurality of cells about 2 cm wide next to its surface, instead of the usual cells of 20 to 30 cm width. This filter produces a drier cake than a conventional drum filter because, when the cake is blown off the latter, some of the water left behind in the suction piping is blown back into the cake. In the small-cell filter, on the other

532

hand, there is not time for that to happen, because the cake immediately lifts off the drum when suction ceases. (Consider that, in a drum filter run at one rpm speed, the time of passage of one cell is reduced from 60/20 = 3 s to 60 : : 400 = 0.15 s if the number of cells is increased from 20 to 400.)

Part B of Fig. 7.26 is the diagram of an uncompartmented (cell-less) vacuum drum filter. The drum rotates here about a tubular stationary shaft into which the vacuum sucks the filtrate appearing inside the drum, without the benefit of any vacuum valve. Compressed air is introduced into a sealed compartment made up of the plates S and leaves it through a thin slot (see the bold arrow); the blast lifts the cake off and throws it onto a scraper blade. The power draft of the vacuum pump can be small because the repeated emptying of a succession of cells is avoided. The moisture content of the cake also tends to be low as there is no opportunity for the cake to be re-wetted during removal (Lemke 1953).

Part C of Fig. 7.26 represents an inside-drum type vacuum filter. The cells are disposed here also about the periphery of a drum open at one end, but the cloth-covered screening surface is on the inside rather than on the outside of the drum. The piping of the cells is attached to a vacuum valve at the other (closed) end of the drum. The pulp to be filtered is fed into the drum: its coarse particles settle out first on the filter, preventing clogging by the fines and keeping the permeability of the cake comparatively high as it forms. The cake is removed near the zenith of the drum by means of a scraper blade or a compressed-air blast, and taken out of the drum by a screw or belt conveyor. The device is recommended for the filtration of pulps containing coarse or heavy particles above all.

Part D of Fig. 7.26 is the diagram of a disk filter. Each of the disks mounted on a tubular shaft is made up of exchangeable sector-shaped units. Both faces of the disks are filter-covered. Each sector is a separate cell, connected first to the vacuum port and then to the compressed-air port of the rotating valve. The phase of blowoff where the cake is taken off by scraper blades precedes the reimmersion of the sector. The pulp tank of a disk filter may be compartmented, in which case it is possible to filter several products (e.g. two or three concentrates) using a single machine. Another advantage over drum filters is that the space taken up is less and the change of filter cloth is fast and easy. Cloth consumption is also less because it suffices to change damaged cloth on one sector only (that is, on one-eighth to one-twentieth only of the entire disk surface). Its drawback is that cake granulometry (and hence also humidity) tends to vary from the outer rim to the central part of the disk.

The revolving-leaf or tray filter is another continuous vacuum cell filter: its filtering surface is a slow-rotating horizontal leaf. Pulp is poured on at one point. Filtrate leaves through a suction conduit installed centrally under the filter. The cake is loosened up and taken off by means of an oblique scraper before its return to the feed point. These devices are best suited for the handling of heavy coarse crystalline stuff (sands) whose particles cannot be picked up against the force of gravity by the vacuum in a drum filter (Schwalbach 1972).

Some other types of continuous filters used in the chemical industry (such as vacuum belt filters, capillary belt filters and some pressure filters) are not used in mineral processing.

The vacuum to be applied to a vacuum filter depends on the size of the solid particles above all. A fine granulate material requires about 0.4 atmosphere;

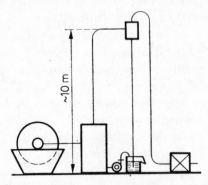

Fig. 7.27. Vacuum filter with filtrate collector, filtrate pump, barometric condenser and piston vacuum pump

a flotation concentrate requires 0.7 to 0.8, and pulps rich in fine slimes about 0.9 atmosphere.

A low vacuum is most often produced by a wet (water-ring) pump, whereas dry reciprocating (piston) pumps are preferred for high vacuum. The filtrate may flow through the wet pump, but no liquid must get into the dry type. In the latter case, the filtrate tank is connected with the piston pump through a "barometric leg" (piping reaching up to a head of 9 m or more, corresponding to the greatest vacuum of 0.9 at). In the upper part of this leg, a barometric condenser is installed as a rule, so as to entrap the vapour separating out in the vacuum. Filtrate may be removed from the collector vessel by means of a centrifugal pump or — if there is sufficient headroom (9 to 10 m) — by means of a barometric drop pipe. In another arrangement, two collector vessels are in alternate use between filter and pump. When a vessel is full, it is opened to the outer atmosphere, whereupon the liquor in it drains off on its own. A frequent type of arrangement is shown as Fig. 7.27.

The throughput of vacuum filters and the degree of dewatering that can be attained on them is a function of all the parameters figuring in the formulae of Q_1, L_1 and T_1, notably filter speed ($n = 0.1$ to 3 rpm in the usual run of filter), the relative duration of immersion and air flushing ($\varphi/\pi = 0.7$ as a rule), the vacuum ($p \cong 150$ to 600 torr), the nature, consistency and granulometry of the feed (the k_2 parameter), the solids content of the pulp (σ), the material and state of the filter surface (the k_1 parameter), etc.

k_1 is a function of the nature of the filter cloth (woven wire, wool, cotton, silk, asbestos; various man-made fibres such as rayon, polyamides [perlon, nylon], polyesters [terylene], polyacrylonitriles [orlon], PVC, polyethylene, polypropylene, etc.), of its pore size and state of clogging (Cunliffe 1971; Nemeth and Sirois 1970; Polke 1956).

k_2, the specific resistance of the cake, can be reduced considerably by the dosage of coagulating-flocculating agents. Coagulation tends to increase output and may reduce the ultimate moisture content in the cake also, because, out of a dispersed pulp on a conventional vacuum filter, it is the fine slimes that are sucked first to the filter cloth, clogging it to some extent. Overcoagulated pulps, on the other hand, are easy to filter but their cakes remain wetter. The high k_2 of fine pulps (such as clays, the tailings of coal flotation, the red mud of alumina refineries, swelling lyophilic hydroxides, gels, etc.) makes them hard to filter; their throughputs on continuous vacuum filters are very low, and the dewateting of the cake is none too efficient, either. Throughput can in these cases be improved by increasing drum speed n, to give a cake thickness of 1.5 to 3 mm only, instead of the more usual 5 to 10 mm. Cakes as thin as these may be taken off by means of a rotating roll to which the cake adheres in preference to the filter.

If both the filter cloth and the solid particles of the pulp are hydrophilic, then both carry thin adhesive films, made up of water molecules which move ceaselessly; liquor can drain off in these films. If, on the other hand, water is adsorbed to the particles less strongly than to the filter cloth, this latter will tend to pull the water films off the particles in contact with it, making the particles adhere strongly both among them and to the cloth: this produces a compact layer of cake next to the cloth, with a high filter resistance k_2 (a low permeability). This situation may be prevented by the use of various filtering aids such as fibres of cotton or asbestos, perlite, diatomite or kieselguhr, activated carbon or montmorillonite, etc., either dosed into the pulp or strewn and sucked onto the filter cloth in a layer more or less thick prior to filtration. (In this case, the scraper blade is approached to the filter by a few tenths of a millimetre per one, two or three turns.)

The specific throughput of coal slurry filtration is furnished by the rule-of-thumb formulae

$$T \simeq 250 \frac{z^2}{hS}$$

or

$$T \simeq z(20 - 0.06h \sqrt{S})$$

if

$$h \sqrt{S} \lessapprox 220,$$

where T is in kg per hour per m², $z\%$ is the solids content by weight of the feed, $h\%$ is the ash content of the minus-200 mesh (minus-74 μm) fraction and S is the weight percentage of that fraction. The second formula holds for disk filters at a speed $t_1 = 3$ minutes per revolution ($n = 0.33$ rpm) and a vacuum $p = 560$ torr, handling a raw slurry. For other speeds and vacuums, an approximate throughput T' is obtained as

$$T' \cong T \sqrt{\frac{3p}{560 t_1}} = T \sqrt{\frac{pn}{560 \cdot 033}} \; .$$

For flotated coal froths and/or $h\sqrt{S} > 220$, actual filter throughput tends to exceed that furnished by the formula. Another vacuum filter throughput formula doing fairly well in practice is

$$T = T_0 \frac{1 - h'\sqrt{S'}}{180}$$

at $t_1 = 3$ min and $p = 560$ torr, where S' is the weight percentage of minus-100 μm particles, h' is the percentage ash content of those and T_0 kg/m² · h is specific throughput at $h'\sqrt{S'} = 0$; the formulae furnishing T_0 for different volumetric solids content ranges are stated in Table 7.4.

Part B of Fig. 7.14 presents graphs of the function $T = f(h\sqrt{S})$, with pulp density $z\%$ as the parameter, at $t_1 = 3$ min and $p = 560$ torr. The graphs plot as straight lines in the bilogarithmic grid are chosen. The full lines refer to settling with no flocculant; the dashed ones refer to a thin dosage of flocculant (5 to 10 ppm).

The ultimate moisture content that can be attained in the filtration of coal slurries on vacuum filters is

$$n\% \cong 14 + \frac{hS}{105}$$

or
$$n\% \cong 12 + 0.27 S (\pm 4\%) \; .$$

A fair average throughput of vacuum filters handling ore flotation concentrates is $T = 300$ to 400 kg/m² · h (Bitter 1965).

Table 7.4. Vacuum filter performance
T_0 kg/m²·h at $h'\sqrt{S'} = 0$, for different
volumetric solids content ranges $\sigma\%$

$\sigma\%$	T_0 kg/m² · h
15—25	$110 + 21\sigma - (25 - \sigma)^{2.5}$
25—40	$110 + 21\sigma$
40—50	$110 + 21\sigma + (\sigma - 40)^{2.5}$

536

The granulometry ranges of application of different dewatering and thickening devices are shown in Fig. 7.28 for coal slurries; the ultimate moisture content $n\%$ of the cakes of coal and ore concentrates vs. the average particle size x_{avg} is shown in Fig. 7.29.

Table 7.5 presents the variation in cake thickness, moisture content and porosity (specific permeability) as a function of various parameters. Throughput is a monotonic function of cake thickness, but speed makes throughput

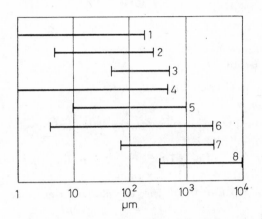

Fig. 7.28. Granulometry ranges of application of thickening/clarification equipment for coal slurries: *1* — thickener or settling pond, *2* — cyclone, *3* — spitzkasten or funnel, *4* — filter press, *5* — vacuum filter, *6* — settling centrifuge, *7* — slime filter centrifuge, *8* — screen centrifuge

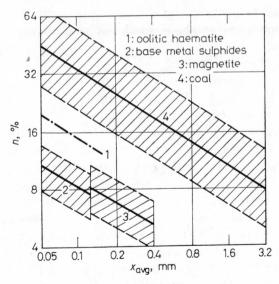

Fig. 7.29. Cake moisture $n\%$ vs. average particle size x_{avg} for ore concentrates and coals

Table 7.5. Variation of cake parameters under the influence of adjustments in operating parameters of vacuum filters

Increase	Thickness	Moisture	Porosity
		of the cake	
Cake thickness	+	+	O
Solids content	O +	− O +	+
Particle size	O − +	−	+
Immersion	+	+	O
Speed	−	+	O
Pressure differential	O +	−	−
Temperature	+	−	−

O unchanged, + increasing, − decreasing.

increase even though the thickness of the cake produced is less (Bolek 1961; Kelsey 1965; Rumpelt 1967).

The total power draft of a 107 m² (11 × 2.7 m dia.) disk filter is typically 90 kW, with 88% consumed by the air pump, 6% by the filtrate pump and 2% each by the motor turning the filter, the stirring device and the blower.

7.5. FURTHER TECHNICAL DETAILS OF DEWATERING

Coagulating reagents. By the dosage of such agents, the clarification of pulps can be greatly accelerated and their filtrability improved.

Coagulating agents include inorganic electrolytes (milk of lime, iron chloride, aluminium sulphate, zinc sulphate, sulphuric acid, etc.), organic ones (poly-carboxyls, polyacrylates, natural glues, etc.) or organic non-electrolytes (such as polyacrylamides or starch, etc.).

The dosage of electrolytes reduces the surface charge (zeta potential) of the particles, which may then be attached together or to the large-molecule poly-mers e.g. by London-van der Waals forces.

London attraction is due to rapid fluctuations in the dipole moment of a neutral atom, which polarizes an adjacent atom. The attraction between two atoms varies inversely as the sixth power of their separation; the attraction V between particles made up of a multitude of atoms varies approximately as the inverse of the square of their separation. Repulsion T between a particle carry-ing a surface charge and an electric double layer also decreases as separation d increases. The situation is illustrated by Part A of Fig. 7.30. The curves in part B of the figure are the resultants of one of three forces of repulsion of different strength, T_1, T_2, T_3 and a force of attraction V. The shape of the T curves is a function of the surface charge on the particles and of the distribution of the diffuse layer on the counter-ions, both of which can be influenced by the dosage of electrolytes.

If the repulsive force is weak (case T_3), the resultant curve (3) remains within the domain of attraction throughout: the particles attract each other, no matter what is their separation; rapid coagulation takes place as a result. If the resultant curve has a maximum in the domain of repulsion (curves 1 and 2), then this barrier must be overcome if the particles are to be brought close enough to adhere together. The overriding force may e.g. be provided by Brownian motion. The mean kinetic energy of fluid molecules in Brownian motion is $1.5kT$, where k is the Boltzmann constant and T is absolute temperature in K. The distribution of the molecules' energies is governed by the Maxwellian distribution function: some are greater than the average, some are less. If the peak of the resultant curve in Part B of Fig. 7.30 is of the same order as kT, a slow flocculation takes place; if it exceeds $20kT$ or so, the suspension remains in stable dispersion, because the collision energy of the molecules in Brownian motion is insufficient overcome the barrier. The energy required for flocculation may be imparted by more or less vigorous stirring or by ultrasonic energy as well.

Slime particles tend to be negatively charged. Their charge can be cancelled more effectively by polyvalent inorganic cationic electrolytes (Al^{3+}, Fe^{3+}, etc.) than by monovalent ones. Instead of producing synergism, the presence of more than one electrolyte may in fact impair settling. In recirculated water, ion concentrations tend to build up to where they may offset the influence of electrolyte dosage.

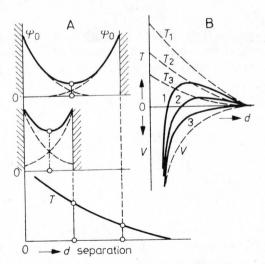

Fig. 7.30. A — Electric potential ψ and repulsion energy T of two charged particles vs displacement d; *B* — the resultant of energy of attraction V and three variants of energy of repulsion T vs. displacement d

539

Organic agents of coagulation may be chosen e.g. from among the petrochemical intermediates. Thread-like compounds of large molecular weight ($5 \cdot 10^6$ to $1.5 \cdot 10^7$) tend to be fair organic flocculants. They may exert strong coagulating action even in minute quantities (0.1 to 5 g/m^3). Referred to the solids to be coagulated, the required dosage seldom exceeds 10 g/t in a neutral, 90 g/t in an acid and 180 g/t in an alkaline medium. In water, polyelectrolyte molecules dissociate into macro-ions and a very large number of counter-ions. Their free charges repel one another: this makes the molecular threads straighten out. In that state, they can react with a multitude of solid particles in the pulp. For example, a polyacrylamide thread of molecular weight $3 \cdot 10^6$, about 10 μm long and 1 nm thick, carries some 40,000 active radicals (elementary acrylamide molecules of molecular weight 72). One gramme of such polyacrylamide contains $2 \cdot 10^{17}$ macromolecules. The total straightened-out length of these, end to end, is about fifty thousand times the circumference of the Earth. Envisaging particles of s.g. 2.5, and a reagent dosage of 10 g/t, the number of macromolecules per particle is

$$5 \cdot 10^6 \qquad\qquad 5 \cdot 10^3 \qquad\qquad 5$$

if the particles are cubical of edge length

$$100 \qquad\qquad 10 \qquad\qquad 1 \ \mu\text{m}.$$

If the solid particles are spherical, the number of molecules per particle is greater by a factor $6/\pi$, giving

$$\sim 10^7 \qquad\qquad 10^4 \qquad\qquad 10.$$

The degree of dissociation of the polyelectrolyte and, through it, its flocculating effect is influenced by the pH. For example, if the macro-ion is anionic, then its dissociation is reduced by any reduction of the pH: it will therefore be less effective as a coagulant in an acid pulp.

Of the artificial organic flocculants, polyacrylamide

$$\left[\begin{array}{c} \text{H} \quad \text{H} \\ | \quad\ | \\ -\text{C}-\text{C}- \\ | \quad\ | \\ \text{H} \ \ \text{CONH}_2 \end{array} \right]_n ,$$

is the most widespread. Pure polyacrylamide is no electrolyte, but some of its amide radicals will spontaneously hydrolyse to form carboxyl radicals in water: this turns the molecule weakly anionic. Deliberate hydrolysis of the amide radicals produces strongly anionic macro-ions: the polymerization of acrylamide in the presence e.g. of quaternary ammonium compounds, on the

540

other hand, gives rise to strongly cationic macro-ions. The "undissociated", the anionic and the cationic polymer structure look as follows:

$$-CH-CH_2-CH-CH_2-CH-CH-$$
$$\quad |\qquad\qquad |\qquad\qquad |$$
$$\quad CO\qquad\quad CO\qquad\quad CO$$
$$\quad |\qquad\qquad |\qquad\qquad |$$
$$\quad NH_2\qquad\quad NH_2\qquad\quad NH_2;$$

$$-CH-CH_2-CH-CH_2-CH-CH_2-$$
$$\quad |\qquad\qquad |\qquad\qquad |$$
$$\quad CO\qquad\quad CO\qquad\quad CO$$
$$\quad |\qquad\qquad |\qquad\qquad |$$
$$\quad NH_2\qquad\quad NH_2\qquad\quad O^-\ldots H^+$$

$$-CH-CH_2-CH-CH_2-CH-CH_2-$$
$$\quad |\qquad\qquad |\qquad\qquad |$$
$$\quad CO\qquad\quad CO\qquad\quad CO$$
$$\quad |\qquad\qquad |\qquad\qquad |$$
$$\quad NH_2\qquad\quad NH_2\qquad R_1-N-R_2$$
$$\qquad\qquad\qquad\qquad\qquad\qquad |$$
$$\qquad\qquad\qquad\qquad\qquad\qquad R^+\ldots Cl^-$$

For example, Separan is polyacrylamide containing $\sim$10% carboxyl radicals and $\sim$15% micromolecular compounds. The polymers available commercially under a variety of trade names such as Sedosan (of Hungarian make), Sedipur, Aerofloc, Superfloc, Praestol, Acrysol, Lacetoll, Ekofan, KMA, PMS, PPA, HPS, PK3, DT120, etc. also have similar structures. Most of them are derivatives of polyacryls, polyvinyls, polyimines, polyglycols, polyoxides or of maleic acid; others are cellulose ethers (e.g. carboxyl methyl cellulose) or mixtures of such. The formulae below represent the monomers out of which the polymers named in the caption are built up.

$$\left[\begin{array}{c} -CH-CH_2- \\ | \\ CONH_2 \end{array}\right]_n$$
polyacrylamide,

$$\left[\begin{array}{c} -CH-CH_2- \\ | \\ COOH \end{array}\right]_n$$
polyacrylic acid

$$\left[\begin{array}{c} -CH-CH_2- \\ | \\ O-CO-CH_3 \end{array}\right]_n$$
polyvinylic acid,

$$[-CH_2-CH_2-NH-CH_2-CH_2-]_n$$
polyethylene imine,

$$[-CH_2-CH_2-O-CH_2-CH_2-]_n$$
polyethylene glycol,

$$\begin{array}{l} CH{=}CH_2 \\ | \\ CONH_2 \end{array}$$
acrylamide,

$$\begin{array}{l} CH{=}CH_2 \\ | \\ COOH \end{array}$$
acrylic acid,

$$\begin{array}{l} CH{=}CH_2 \\ | \\ O{-}COCH_3 \end{array}$$
vinyl acetate,

$$\begin{array}{l} CH_2 \\ | \quad \diagdown NH \\ CH_2 \diagup \end{array} \qquad \begin{array}{l} CH_2 \\ | \quad \diagdown O \\ CH_2 \diagup \end{array}$$
ethylene imine,   ethylene oxide.

On blending the acrylamide with increasing quantities of sodium acrylate, copolymers of increasing viscosity are obtained which have a specific flocculating effect on different suspensions. The viscosity depends, of course, in addition to the molar proportions, also on the molecular weight of the copolymer. For example, the viscosity of one per cent solutions of copolymers containing an alkali acrylate varies with the concentration of the latter as follows:

1	to	7%	50	to	6,000 cP,
7		20	1,000		40,000 cP,
20		40	8,000		50,000 cP,
40		60	20,000		50,000 cP,
60		99	30,000		50,000 cP.

The blend with 1 to 7% alkali acrylate is best suited for the flocculation of uranium, copper and aluminium hydroxides, iron ores, pigments and the fly dusts of metallurgical furnaces: the blend with 20 to 40% is best for slurries of coal, magnesia, diatomaceous earth, whereas the flocculation of kaolin pulps requires a blend with more than 60% alkali acrylate.

Natural glues and gelatine have an amphoteric nature: they do not dissociate about a pH $\simeq$ 5, and are cation-active below and anion-active above that. Depending on the charge on the particles in the pulp, then, they may give better coagulation in acid pulps in certain cases and in alkaline pulps in others.

Starch e.g. is an organic non-electrolyte. Its principal components are amylose and amylopectin. The elementary building blocks of both are molecules of glucopyranose

which connect up into a linear chain to form amylose and into multiple branching chains to form amylopectin. In water under 60 °C, only the lighter amylose fractions are soluble: the other constituents of starch will dissolve only if kept for a prolonged time at or above 90 °C. If the amylopectin found in the shells of the starch grains encounters amyl cellulose, it hydrolyses and loses its flocculating property. Erythroamylose and dextrine, which are formed in the same process, are strong peptizing-dispersing agents that cancel such flocculating effect as there is. Degradation may be prevented by adding the hydrates of certain salts: this results in the formation of a stable-elastic gel on the polymeric cell wall and of hydrophilic colloid micelles of strong positive charge. Boiling with $CaCl_2$ or $ZnCl_2$ stabilizes the starch solution for as long as one year; without that, its effectiveness will markedly decrease within 10 to 15 hours.

In some situations, organic non-electrolytes will exert a flocculating effect only in combination with electrolytes that weaken the negative zeta potential of the particles in the pulp and facilitate thereby the adhesion to their surfaces of the starch-colloid macromolecules or micelles which tend to be of like (negative) charge. Often, however, like charges reduce flocculation but do not prevent it: it is no absolute precondition of adhesion that the opposite charge of the polyelectrolytes or of other ions should cancel the charge on the particle. For example, a suspension with negative charges on it will be flocculated out not only by non-electrolyte coagulants such as starch or other polysaccharides, or cationic polymers, but often — especially after vigorous stirring — by polyelectrolytes of like charge as well.

For the coagulation of clayey pulps (e.g. the tailings or middlings containing less than about 50% ash of coal flotation), starch and lime are often employed in combination. (At ash contents higher than 50%, polyelectrolytes will do better.) The Ca^{2+} ions of the lime get attached to bonds on the clay-particle surface (presumably by ion exchange): the process is accompanied by the release of H^+ ions from the surface layer, which reduces the OH^- concentration in the pulp. The starch molecules attach themselves to the Ca^{2+} ions, which form bridgeheads on the clay particles: the suspension will deflocculate if the Ca^{2+} ions are lacking. The flocs formed under the combined influence of starch and lime can break up at the Ca bonds under strong shear (stirring), but the bonds (and the flocs) are reconstituted at once when the shear ceases or even weakens. (Bonds formed by polyelectrolytes are not reconstituted once they have been broken by stirring because, in their case, it is the polymer chains themselves that get broken, rather than just their attachment to the clay particles.)

In flocculation, the organic polymers tend to attach themselves to the particles by chemisorption, as revealed by the fact that the process is irreversible as a rule. Adsorption proper may involve several bonding types, depending on the chemical nature of the particles' surfaces and of the polymers. Ionic bonds of energy 150 to 200 kcal per mole, hydrogen bonds of 5 to 10 kcal per mole and dipole effects of less than 5 kcal per mole may be involved, depending on the situation.

Polyelectrolytes with anionic radicals: carboxylate, phosphate or sulphonate (such as hydrolysed polyacrylamide) are attached by ionic bonds to solid particles that contain metal ions in their crystal lattices. Neutral polymer molecules such as unhydrolysed polyacrylamide, starch, glue, etc. are attached by weaker bonds. Hydrogen bonds are most likely to occur between non-ionic O, OH or NH_2 radicals of the neutral polymers and the surface atoms (usually oxygen) of the solid particles. Several thousand such bonds may come to exist on a single polymer molecule, so that total bond energy per molecule may be quite great.

Water molecules associate even among themselves by hydrogen bonding; it is the clusters of water molecules attached to the active (NH_2, OH or O) radicals that effect the "dissolution" and straightening out of the macromolecule in the liquor. The hydrogen bond is insensitive within limits even to the presence of acids, alkalis and the salts of polyvalent metals. Clay minerals may adsorb polyelectrolytes by a combination of hydrogen and ionic bonds. Clay suspensions are more sensitive to polycations than to polyanions, although under suitable conditions — as has already been pointed out — the latter may also effect flocculation.

It is important for the dosage of a polymer flocculant to stop short of the quantity that can actually be adsorbed by the particles, because the latter can cluster only if positions permitting adsorption to the polymer remain free on their surfaces. This is the explanation of the empirical finding that effective flocculation is confined to a narrow range of concentrations. An overdose of flocculant exerts a protective influence: it disperses more strongly than it coagulates, by turning the wholly coated particles strongly hydrophilic. Polymers of greater molecular weight do better as flocculants because longer chains may join more particles. It is better in any case to underdose the flocculant than to overdose it. The point of flocculant feeding and the conditions of introduction are also important. The flocculant should be stirred in rapidly and thoroughly, but subsequent turbulence should not be excessive so as not to break up the flocs (Schubert 1964 (1969); Špaldon 1960).

The volume of a flocculated pulp settling in a thickener is greater than that of an unflocculated one: that is, the thickened product will contain more water. This is why flocculants as thickening accelerators may fail if the feed pulp is too thick to start with: the flocs may occupy the entire feed pulp volume, so that no settling at all is possible. In such a situation, the solvate shells on the solid particles can be broken up and the viscosity of the medium reduced at the same time by the addition of wetting agents. (The effective s.g. of the particle is less if taken together with the solvate shell than without it.)

On the filtration of a flocculated feed, large pores remain in the cake between flocs. Moreover, the particles making up a floc are also attached together by their apices or edges, so that the floc itself will have a fairly large internal pore volume; the cake is thus fairly permeable to the filtrate. Dewatering agents (e.g. the collectors of flotation) will increase inter-particle adhesion; collectors act as flocculants also. Wetters too accelerate filtration, provided they reduce the viscosity of the liquor. Organic agents that improve filtrability will lower the ultimate moisture content attainable in pulp centrifuges also (Adorján 1968; Akyel 1966; Beckerath and Wiegand 1970; Bolek 1972; Götte and Flöter 1961; Healy and LaMer 1964; Kuzkin et al. 1964; Linke and Booth 1960; Mackenzie 1964; Matheson and Mackenzie 1962; Michaels 1965; Oliver 1963; Pelser-Berensberg et al. 1956; Pesch and Wiegand 1969; Petersen 1938; Reuter 1970; Slater et al. 1968; Sommer 1966; Wadsworth and Cutler 1956).

7.6. DRYING

7.6.1. Fundamentals. Drying means removing water from a material by evaporation. Natural drying takes place in free air without any deliberate heating, but the latent heat required to evaporate the water has to be supplied also here (out of the heat content of a drying medium such as ambient air). Forced or heat drying (which we shall call drying for simplicity) is achieved by means of a hot drying medium (combustion gases, hot air, steam, etc.). Drying being an expensive operation, it is indicated to reduce the moisture content of the material to be dried to the lowest feasible value by mechanical means prior to actual drying (Krischer and Kröll 1963; Kröll 1962, 1964; Mason 1967; Scheiling 1967).

Water will change from a liquid to a gas (evaporate) if the vapour pressure (vapour tension) of the liquid phase is greater than the partial pressure of water vapour in the gaseous medium in contact with it.

If a liquid (e.g. water) is placed under vacuum, it will evaporate strongly or even boil up. If there is enough liquid, not all of it will evaporate: a state of equilibrium sets in, in which the vapour pressure acting on the wall of the container equals the vapour pressure (tension) of the liquid. This pressure is independent of the volume of the vessel as long as there is some liquid at least left over in it, and depends on temperature only. Once equilibrium has set in (va-

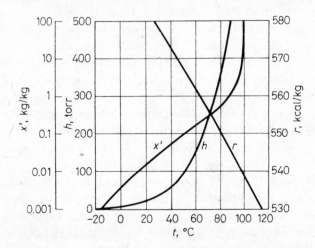

Fig. 7.31. Saturation, x' kg of steam per kg of air, vapour tension h torr and heat of evaporation r kcal/kg of water, vs. temperature t °C

pour pressure has stabilized), the space is said to be saturated with the vapour of the liquid, meaning that any further evaporation of liquid molecules is offset by the condensation of an equal number of liquid vapour molecules.

If a liquid is not under vacuum but in a closed container which, in addition to the liquid's own vapour, contains air and possibly some other gases as well, evaporation will begin at a much slower rate than under the vacuum. In this setup, a different equilibrium is attained; the quantity of the liquid's vapour in the gas space will be (provided the size of the vessel is the same) exactly that which provided the entire pressure in the vacuum; here, however, it merely produces a vapour partial pressure (the liquid's contribution to pressure in the gas space above it), which equals the vapour tension of the liquid phase. Here, it is the air (or some other gas or gas mixture) that gets saturated with the vapour of the liquid. Saturation concentration increases as temperature increases. Figure 7.31 presents saturation concentration x' (in kg of steam per kg of air), vapour tension h torr (mm of mercury) that is, the partial pressure of water vapour in saturated air and heat of evaporation r kcal/kg for water in air, vs. the temperature, t °C. At a fair approximation, the latent heat of evaporation is

$$r \simeq 600 - 0.6t \text{ kcal/kg,}$$

or
$$r' \cong 21\ T\ \text{kcal/kmole},$$

where T is in kelvins. In the $p = 2$ to 6 bars range, the saturated-steam temperature (°C) is furnished by

$$t \cong 100 + 10p;$$

also, in the temperature range from 60 to 130 °C,

$$h \cong \frac{8t^{3.5}}{10^5}$$

gives water vapour tension in mm mercury column (torr).

Even if the liquid is not in a closed vessel but under free air, its evaporation follows the same course in principle: it will evaporate until the air in contact with it becomes saturated (that is, until the partial vapour pressure above it attains the vapour tension of the liquid phase). The rate of evaporation can be increased by increasing the difference between the vapour tension of the liquid and the partial pressure of vapour in the air in contact with it: that is, by increasing the temperature and the vapour-absorbing capacity of the surroundings. (The vapour-absorbing capacity of vacuum is a maximum: this is why evaporation under it is so rapid.) Hot air can absorb more vapour than cold air; this is why a hotter drying medium accelerates evaporation. Partial water vapour pressure is lower in dry than in humid air: this is why the ceaseless agitation of the air above the liquid (e.g. by blowing) also accelerates evaporation.

Evaporation is caused by heat. Heating increases the velocity of the liquid molecules in their disordered motion whose average kinetic energy is a function of temperature. The velocities of the molecules are dispersed about that average: some move faster, some slower. Those moving faster can detach themselves from the other molecules and escape from the liquid surface, so much so that they do not return to it even later on. The higher the temperature, the greater is the likelihood for this to happen.

If at the beginning of the drying process a granular aggregate is covered with what is called surface water (water visible on its surface), its velocity of drying is a constant, as expressed by the formulae

$$u = \frac{dV}{F\,dt} = k(p_w - p_l) = k\,\Delta p$$

and

$$\frac{dn}{dt} = -C(H_w - H_l) = -C\,\Delta H,$$

where V is the quantity of evaporated water, F is the free water-surface area, p_w is the vapour tension of water at the interface, p_l is partial vapour pressure in air at the interface, t is time, and n is the moisture content of the drying aggregate, H_l is the actual and H_w the wet-bulb saturation moisture content of the air: that is,

$$H = H_w - H_l$$

is the dissaturation of the air.

The meniscuses formed by the liquid surface subtended by the particles at the surface of a fine-grained aggregate exert a capillary force

$$p = \frac{2a \cos \vartheta}{r} = \frac{8a\sigma \cos \vartheta}{x(1 - \sigma)}.$$

that sucks water from the interior of the aggregate to the surface. It should be noted that if

σ varies as	0.5	0.6	0.7	0.8, then
$8\sigma/(1 - \sigma)$ varies as	8	12	18.7	32.

On the convex side of the meniscus (from where the radii of curvature diverge), pressure is greater by p than on the concave side, and the vapour tension of the aqueous phase is, accordingly, less at a given temperature than for a smooth surface of water: it is less easy to make water evaporate from a capillary, where its boiling point is also higher. Small droplets of water, on the other hand, evaporate more readily than larger drops or a smooth surface, because pressure in their interior is less and vapour tension at a given temperature accordingly greater: small droplets start boiling at lower temperatures.

Vapour pressure at the surface of a drop of radius r on the one hand and a smooth surface of liquid on the other are related by

$$\ln \left(\frac{g_r}{g} \right) = \frac{2aM}{\varrho RTr} \; ,$$

where M is the molecular weight of the liquid, ϱ is its density, a is its surface tension, R is the gas constant and T is absolute temperature. If the droplet has an electric charge as well, then the relationship modifies to

$$\ln \left(\frac{g_r}{g} \right) = \left(\frac{2a}{r} - \frac{e^2}{8\pi r^4} \right) \frac{M}{\varrho RT} \; .$$

Vapour tension in an electrically charged droplet is accordingly less than in a neutral droplet of the same size, and becomes actually less than that of a smooth surface if the expression in parentheses on the right-hand side becomes negative. In that case, $g_r < g$, and the droplet is in a stable equilibrium of evaporation-condensation with its surroundings. If saturation in the ambient atmosphere increases, the droplet may serve as a nucleus of condensation: it may actually absorb vapour out of its surroundings and swell as a result. (The same phenomenon makes visible the trace of a particle in a cloud chamber, or

548

the contrail of an airplane, which supersaturates the air with the water vapour in its exhaust.)

If the pores of a particulate aggregate are not filled with water (if some of the pores are filled with air instead), then water in the capillaries, invariably moving to where the passages are narrower or the radii of curvature shorter, breaks up into nodoid droplets; the water-covered fraction of the exposed surface gradually shrinks as a result. The rate of drying decreases in step therewith: the equations of this phase of drying are

$$\frac{\mathrm{d}V}{F\,\mathrm{d}t} = k'n\,\varDelta p$$

and

$$\frac{\mathrm{d}n}{\mathrm{d}t} = -C'n\,\varDelta H\ .$$

The rate of drying is reduced further when the particles on the surface are dried out completely; subsequently, the dry layer becomes thicker and thicker, and any water is retained deeper down. Water evaporates and diffuses towards the surface from the isolated nodoids caught between the particles in the interior. During this phase, the temperature of the aggregate increases gradually, to attain ultimately the temperature of the drying medium.

The distribution of moisture in the aggregate is not controlled by diffusion. Capillary forces may move water up the concentration gradient: e.g. if a fine-grained sediment is layered on top of a coarser-grained one, the latter will dry faster than the former, although evaporation is exclusively from the former.

In a layer of monodisperse sand evaporating from its top only, water content $n\%$ varies with time and depth as shown by the curves in Fig. 7.32.

The variation of average moisture $n\%$ in an aggregate is represented vs. drying time by the drying curve $n = f(t)$. The course of this curve is a function of many factors, the most important of which are the nature of the aggregate, the size of its particles, the thickness of the bed, its initial and ultimate mois-

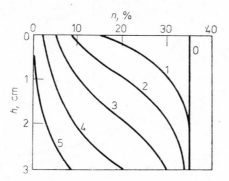

Fig. 7.32. Moisture $n\%$ at depth h below the surface at successive instants $0-1-2\ldots$

ture content, its critical moisture content, the humidity of the drying medium, its temperature, velocity, turbulence, etc. (The critical moisture content is that which separates the phase of constant-rate drying from that of falling-rate drying. The duration of the two phases is different, depending on the nature of the aggregate, the shape of its particles, the shape and size of the heap and other factors.) The rate-of-drying curve is obtained as the derivative of the drying curve:

$$u = -\frac{dn}{dt} = f'(t).$$

The negative sign implies that moisture content decreases in time.

Figure 7.33 is the plot of a drying curve $n = f(t)$ and drying-rate curve $u = f(n)$. The latter curve ends at n_0, the equilibrium moisture content of the aggregate, at which vapour tension at the aggregate surface is at equilibrium with the partial vapour pressure in the surrounding gaseous medium. n_0 is determined by the temperature and relative humidity of the gas. No aggregate can be dried below its equilibrium moisture content: indeed, a hygroscopic material drier than that will take up moisture from its surroundings until it attains the equilibrium.

In the phase of constant-rate drying (between 1 and 2 in Fig. 7.33), vapour pressure above the aggregate equals the vapour pressure of the pure liquid; the temperature of the aggregate does not rise above the boiling point of the liquid phase, and the rate of drying depends neither on bed thickness nor on the initial moisture content but only on the thermal conditions of drying:

$$\frac{dn}{dt} = -C\,\Delta H.$$

In the phase of falling-rate drying, on the other hand (between points 2 and n_0 in Fig. 7.33), the drying rate is determined first and foremost by the rate of

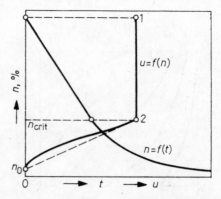

Fig. 7.33. Drying curve $n = f(t)$ and its inverse derivative, the drying-rate curve $u = f(n)$

diffusion of moisture from the interior of the aggregate towards its surface. In that phase, the rate of drying depends on the thickness and moisture content of the bed:

$$\frac{dn}{dt} = -C'n\Delta H\,;$$

it is practically independent of the velocity of passage or humidity of the drying medium. In this phase, the rate of drying gradually declines, to attain zero by

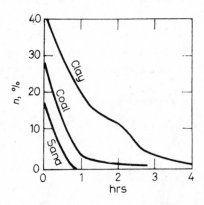

Fig. 7.34. Drying test results on three materials in a steam-drying oven

the time the aggregate attains the equilibrium moisture content n_0. The surface temperature of the material may attain the temperature of the drying medium in the process. In the falling-rate phase, drying can be accelerated by reducing bed thickness, by rearranging the aggregate to prevent or hinder the formation of clots and lumps, and to reduce thereby the distance the water must travel to reach the surfaces accessible to the drying medium. The moisture content at which cohesion into clots and lumps appears is a sensitive function of the nature and granulometry of the aggregate. Porous and fine-grained aggregates attain it sooner than massive and coarse-grained ones. Unsized or long-range aggregates will also dry slower than a short-range one. Figure 7.34 shows drying curves recorded in a steam-drying oven. The flat bottom parts of the curves are indicative of clotting. It invariably takes a disproportionately long time to remove the last traces of removable moisture.

The process of drying is greatly influenced by the nature of the bond between the solids and the moisture. Water can be attached to the solids by adhesion, capillary forces, forces of adsorption, etc. Adhesive moisture tends to be confined to the surface of the body; as it evaporates, it has a well-defined vapour pressure at any temperature, equal to the saturated vapour tension of the liquid. In the case of capillary bonding, the temperature of evaporation is slightly higher than the boiling point at the given pressure. Adsorbed water is the hardest to remove.

Another classification is into free and hygroscopic moisture. Free moisture is practically identical with adhesive moisture. Hygroscopic moisture is made up of capillary and adsorbed water.

The total heat ΣH required for drying is made up of the following components: (1) heat required to raise the solids from the starting to the operating temperature; (2) heat required to raise all the water in the feed to the same temperature; (3) heat required for evaporating the water to be removed; (4) heat making up for the radiative and conductive losses; and (5) heat required to offset losses due to the escape of part of the drying medium and to raise the temperature of the equipment to the operating temperature on startup. The five components may be characterized as follows.

$$H_1 = Gc(t_{\text{out}} - t_{\text{in}});$$

$$H_2 = V(t_{\text{out}} - t_{\text{in}});$$

$$H_3 = V_e r;$$

$$H_4 = Fk\,\Delta t;$$

$$H_5 = 0.1 \quad \text{to} \quad 0.2 \cdot \sum_1^4 H_i.$$

Here, G kg/h is solids feed rate in terms of dry solids; c kcal/kg·°C is the specific heat of the dry solids; t_{in} and t_{out} are the temperatures in °C of the solids fed in and those discharged; V kg/h is total water feed rate, V_e kg/h is the rate of evaporation; r kcal/kg is the heat of evaporation of water at the temperature of discharge from the drier; F m² is the radiating surface area; k kcal/m² · h · °C is unit heat loss through the surface, and Δt °C is the mean temperature differential between its two sides.

If a material of initial moisture content $n_{\text{in}}\%$ is to be dried to an ultimate moisture content $n_{\text{out}}\%$ at the rate of T tph, then

$$G = 1{,}000\,T\,\frac{100 - n_{\text{in}}}{100}\,;$$

$$V_e = 1{,}000\,T\,\frac{n_{\text{in}}}{100}\,;$$

$$V_e = 1{,}000\,T\,\frac{n_{\text{in}} - n_{\text{out}}}{100 - n_{\text{out}}}\,,$$

and

$$r \cong 600 - 0.6 t_{\text{out}}\,.$$

552

Specific heat c in kcal/kg · °C units is between 0.2 and 0.25 for most solids, but below that range for some (e.g. 0.188 for quartz and 0.135 for pyrite); 0.2 is a good working average. The specific heat of coals is grater, however: it is furnished by the formula

$$c \cong 0.24(1 + 0.008i)$$

for moisture-free (bituminous) coals in the 24 to 100 °C range, where i is percentage volatiles content: for example,

| $c \cong$ | 0.26 | 0.28 | 0.30 | 0.32 |
| at $i =$ | 10 | 20 | 30 | 40%. |

The specific heat of bituminous coal increases with temperature also: the average specific heat for the temperature interval from 24 °C to t °C is given by

$$c = 0.21\left[1 + \frac{0.15t}{100} - 0.0008\left(\frac{t}{100}\right)^3\right].$$

The specific heat of moisture-free young (subbituminous) coals and lignites is in the 0.32 to 0.41 range.

An idea of the unit heat loss k kcal/m² · h · °C through the drier wall can be had from the following figures: asbestos, 5 cm thick: 0.6 to 1.4; brick wall, 10 cm thick: about 3.8; concrete, 10 cm thick: about 4.2; sheet steel:

$$\sim 8.3 + \frac{\Delta t}{24}.$$

The drier must be supplied with enough heat to cover all the five items making up ΣH. If the drying medium is combustion gas, then the heat balance is obtained in the form

$$G_F c_F(t_{IN} - t_{OUT}) = \Sigma H,$$

where G_F kg/h is the gas supply rate required, c_F is the specific heat of the gas (that of air, $c_a = 0.23$ kcal/kg · °C, may be used for practical purposes), and t_{IN} and t_{OUT} are the entry and exit temperature of the gas.

If drying is by steam, then the heat balance equation is

$$G_{St} r_{St} = \Sigma H,$$

where G_{St} kg/h is the steam supply required, and r_{St} kcal/kg is its latent heat at the pressure used (at the corresponding saturation temperature). The total heat ΣH includes in that case also a sixth item in addition to the five listed above:

$$H_6 = L c_a(t_{out} - t_{in}),$$

where L kg/h is the air supply required to absorb the evaporated moisture and $c_a = 0.23$ is its specific heat.

553

The thermal efficiency of a drier is given by

$$\eta_{therm} = \frac{H_1 + H_2 + H_3}{\Sigma H}.$$

Drying is the more economical, the greater the temperature drop of the gas passing through the drier ($t_{IN} - t_{OUT}$). Yet at 660 °C sheet steel is already dull red; its strength is one-third only of its cold strength, and its propensity to corrode has greatly increased. The entry temperature of the gas should therefore be slightly less than that, except if the drier is protected at the entry point of the gas by very wet cold feed. In such a setup — in concurrent drying — inlet temperatures up to and above 1,000 °C may be allowed.

The entry temperature of the drying medium may be limited also by the nature of the material to be dried. For example, coking coals tend to soften between 350 and 400 °C; some coals start to give off volatiles around 300 °C, and the risk of the coal igniting also increases as medium temperature rises. The temperatures of ignition of a coal dust cloud of dry minus-74 μm particles and of a bed of the same dust are shown in Fig. 7.35 vs. the volatiles content of the coal.

There is no particular lower limit to the inlet temperature of the drying medium, but it is to be kept in mind that supplying a fixed amount of heat to the drier at a low inlet temperature requires a high gas feed rate; also, heat lost in the discharged medium will be more per unit of evaporated water; moving a larger volume of medium takes more energy; and fly dust losses also increase. Gas exit velocity is to be kept between 0.3 and 0.5 m/s for powdery fines, but may be allowed to attain about 4.5 m/s if the material to be dried is comparatively coarse-grained. Otherwise, if it is desirable to have a higher gas exit

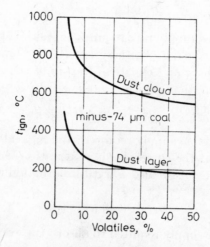

Fig. 7.35. Ignition temperature of minus-74 μm coal as a function of volatiles content

velocity, a dust collector — e.g. a cyclone — must be installed downstream of the drier. On the other hand, a lower inlet temperature results in a reduced radiation loss and a longer drier life.

The exit temperature of the gas should be as low as is consistent with keeping it above the dew point: the optimum should be between 65 and 95 °C. Its degree of saturation may be calculated by adding the water evaporated by it to the water it contained on its entry. By dividing the weight of water thus found by the weight of the dry gas, a ratio x' kg/kg is obtained, which can be compared with the corresponding data in Fig. 7.31. If the saturation temperature (the dew point) belonging to x' in the figure is far below the exit temperature of the gas, then no condensation is liable to take place.

The volume of gas to be moved can be calculated using the ideal-gas laws because the partial pressure of water vapour is just a small fraction of total pressure (Wagener 1973).

7.6.2. Driers. Depending on the drying medium that supplies the drier with heat, driers are usually grouped into gas (combustion-gas) driers and steam driers.

The drying medium may enter into direct contact with the material to be dried (direct-heat drier) or may be separated therefrom by a partition which is called upon to transfer the heat (indirect-heat drier). There are, however, mixed types (direct-indirect heat driers) as well, in which the medium delivers part of its heat direct and part of it through a partition (Kröll 1964; Porter 1963; Roeder 1970).

In driers of continuous operation, the drying medium may flow concurrent, countercurrent or crosswise to the material to be dried.

In concurrent drying, the wet material entering the drier encounters high-temperature, low-humidity gas. The moisture content of the material leaving the drier is low; the humidity of the cooled-down medium is high. In concurrent drying, then, the drying potential (Δp or ΔH) decreases monotonically along the drier; that is, the rate of drying decreases as the moisture content of the material declines. The emerging material, whose temperature may be relatively low, is in contact with a cooled-down medium of high humidity; this circumstance may limit the ultimate moisture content that can be attained. Concurrent drying is a reasonable choice whenever the material will stand intense drying better when wet than when dry and is not hygroscopic or not overly so.

In countercurrent drying, a high-temperature, low-humidity drying medium enters into contact with the emerging hot and dry material; the wet material as it enters the drier encounters in its turn a cooled-down, high-humidity medium. Drying potential is thus more or less uniform along the drier: temperature and humidity differences between medium and material are less than in concurrent drying. Countercurrent drying may be used whenever the material is not sensitive to high temperatures and the ultimate moisture content to be striven for is very low.

In cross-current drying, the high-temperature drying medium flows crosswise to the material being dried. The arrangement permits rapid drying at a high drying potential. It may be applied whenever the material may be dried at a fast rate both when wet and when nearly dry and is insensitive to high temperatures, and rapidity of drying and a low ultimate moisture content are more important than economies of drying medium and heat.

Driers of continuous operation are classed in two groups, according to the nature of solids transport: (1) the solids are transported in the drier by mechanical means: contact with the drying medium may be direct or indirect; and (2) the solids are transported by the medium proper, the two phases being in direct contact. The first group includes rotary and hearth-type (rabble and tray, etc.) driers: the second includes fluid-bed and pneumatic driers.

In current mineral-processing practice, rotary combustion-gas driers are the most widespread. These are long cylinders installed on a slight incline, supported by rollers and driven through gears. The material to be dried is fed at their upper end. They are best fitted for the drying of granular free-running materials containing little dust.

There are concurrent, countercurrent, combined counter- and concurrent, cross-current, direct-heat, indirect-heat and semi-direct-heat rotary driers. The direct-heat types may be concurrent or countercurrent; the indirect-heat ones may be single-shell with steam tubes or double-shell. In the latter, the material may e.g. be fed into the annulus between two cylindrical shells, with the gas leaving the inner shell led back in gas tubes; or the gas and the feed may be separated by the inner shell, each being confined to one of the two spaces and moving either concurrent or countercurrent. Semi-direct-heat rotary driers are either double-shell, with the material advancing in the annulus and the gas first flowing concurrent in the inner space and then countercurrent in the annulus, or single-shell, with the shell enclosed in a housing of brick or the like; here, the gas first heats the shell on the outside and then returns countercurrent through the shell.

Direct-heat and semi-direct-heat rotary driers are usually provided with a ribbing to spread the material. As the shell revolves, the material showers down from each rib in turn onto the rib below.

Speed is typically in the $n = 4$ to 6 rpm range.

When a material prone to clotting (e.g. a flotation concentrate) is to be dried, chain-mail curtain rather than a ribbing is often installed inside the shells of rotary gas driers.

Figure 7.36 shows cross sections of the more usual types of ribbing in gas-heated rotary driers (Frey 1968).

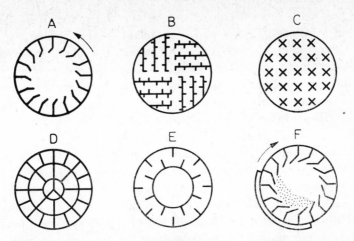

Fig. 7.36. Types of ribbing and compartmentation in rotary combustion-gas driers.
A — scoop, *B* — shelf or quadrant, *C* — X-bar, *D* — flue, *E* — double-shell, *F* — roto-louvre

The most frequent single-shell, concurrent, direct-heat cylinders are shown in cross section in Parts A to C of Fig. 7.36. In types B, C, D, the fraction φ of shell space filled with the material to be dried is in the 0.15 to 0.25 range; it is 0.1 to 0.2 in the type shown as Part A.

Assuming the time it takes to dry a material of loose s.g. δ' t/m³ at a rate T tph to be t hours, shell volume required is

$$K = \frac{Tt}{\varphi\delta'} \; \text{m}^3.$$

Shell length L is typically 5 to 8 times the diameter D: accordingly,

$$K \simeq 4D^3 \quad \text{if} \quad L = 5D$$

or

$$K \simeq 6D^3 \quad \text{if} \quad L = 7.5D.$$

The evaporation performance per unit of shell volume is e.g.

~67 kg/h · m³ when drying fine coal from 10 to 1% moisture,

~98 kg/h · m³ when drying a coal slurry from 25 to 8% moisture.

The approximate power draft of the drive and blower combined is

$$N \simeq 4D^2 \; \text{kW}.$$

The rotary-louvre (roto-louvre) drier is a cross-flow direct-heat gas-heated cylinder. It has a cylindrical shell provided with radial ribbing whose height

557

decreases gradually downstream (towards the dry-material discharge end). Overlapping tangential louvre plates attached to the ribbing reach the full length of the cylinder. The louvres constitute an inner shell whose inside diameter gradually increases downstream. Within the drum, the feed moves along on the louvres. Between the inner and the outer shell, the radial plates and the louvres constitute a number of separate flues whose height decreases downstream. Each of these flues communicates with the interior of the drum by a slot reaching the full length of the cylinder. Gas is introduced through those slots only which are overlain just than by the material to be dried, so that the gas is forced to pass through the material. Near the feed end, where the material is still wet, more gas can pass through the slots than near the discharge end where the bed, dry but thicker, opposes the passage of gas more strongly.

Single-shell concurrent direct-heat drying cylinders will serve for the drying of non-hygroscopic granular materials down to one percent moisture or so. The exit temperature of the dried material (t_{out}) is about 90 °C typically. The thermal efficiency η_{therm} of the drier is 55 to 75% as a rule. Performances and thermal efficiencies of other types of rotary drier are referred to the above by the figures in Table 7.6. (Relative performances refer to identical cylinder volumes and similar temperature distribution conditions.) In actual fact, concurrent rotary driers are also cross-current, what with the material moving spirally in the drum and the gas moving axially. The situation is similar in the fan drier, which appears countercurrent at first sight. The only truly concurrent driers are the pneumatic ones.

Tray type gas driers of the Herreshoff or Skinner type have several annular trays arranged in a vertical stack in a cylindrical container: oblique baffles mounted on the radial arms of a central shaft sweep the material towards apertures alternately on the outer and inner rims of the trays, through which it can drop onto the tray below.

The fan (turbine) drier of the Büttner type is another type of tray gas drier. Its annular trays rotate slowly (at one to three rpm) as they carry the material to be dried: they have a number of radial slots through which the material can drop onto the tray below. The thickness of the bed is regulated and its removal

Table 7.6. Throughput referred to the direct-heat combustion-gas drier and thermal efficiency of different rotary drier types

Type	Relative throughput	η_{therm}
Direct-heat combustion-gas drier	1.0	55—75
Indirect-direct (semi-direct) heat	1.35	75—85
Indirect-heat (double shell) combustion-gas	0.7	50—60
Indirect-heat steam-tube	3.0	75—85
Roto-Louvre	1.5	60—80

onto the tray below is taken care of by adjustable slats fixed above each tray. Combustion gas (or air heated in heat exchangers) enters the cylindrical shell enclosing the drier at its bottom: it is deflected outward by broad fan blades mounted at intervals on a central shaft rotating at $n = 60$ rpm or so and inward again in the gaps between the blades (the gas flow is thus cross-current throughout). Gas velocity is 1 to 2 m/s. (For an example, a fan type tray drier of 9.4 m dia. by 12.2 m height, of weight 50 t, outfitted with 41 trays, having a total heating surface area of 1,270 m², drawing 55 kW for moving the gas and 11 kW for the slow rotation of the trays, was found to reduce the moisture content of 30 tph of pre-dried lignite in 40 min from 16 to 0%, while the hot gas cooled down from 450 to 220 °C. If surface moisture only is to be evaporated, the inlet temperature of the gas can be 600 to 700 °C for an outlet temperature of 150 °C. Evaporation rate is ∼ 8 kg of water per hour and m² of tray area.

Tray driers are direct-heat hearths of great height.

A low, large plan area indirect-heat hearth is the rabble (Lowden) drier. In its long horizontal trough, material is moved along by a series of reciprocating rakes resembling those of the Dorr rake classifier, operating on the bell-crank principle. The plates of the trough are heated by combustion gases from below. The device is used in places for the drying of flotation concentrates. Its thermal efficiency is not above 50% or so.

Contact driers are low-built, direct-heat devices of large plan area. Drying blades mounted on a horizontal shaft dip into the material to be dried. The blades constitute an interrupted spiral which moves the material along as the shaft rotates, similarly to the spiral in an Akins classifier. Gas flowing above the material heats the blades as they emerge from the material. Blades may be replaced by concentric rings of angle steel, with the transporting spiral confined to the feed end of the shaft. Typical shaft speeds are 3 to 4 rpm: plan area is 3 to 4 m², power draft is 1.5 kW h per ton of dried coal.

Screen gas driers are designed much like screen-type classifier separators with the air at ambient temperature replaced by hot gas. The gas passes upward or downward (i.e. cross-current) through the bed on the horizontal or gently inclined screen. The machine is suited for the drying of strongly dripping materials also, in which case the hot gas should pass downward through the bed. The group of screen driers includes designs in which the material to be dried is taken into the drying space by an endless apron conveyor made up of perforated elements rather than by a vibrating or swinging screen. The gas passes through the material and the perforations of the pans either upward or downward (Dwight–Lloyd–Oliver) or alternately up- and downward at different points of the drying space (Heyl and Patterson). Instead of combustion gases, air heated in heat exchangers installed in the drying space proper is often used as the heating medium. The belt and the bed on it are often flushed with cold air for cooling as they emerge from the drying space.

The evaporation performance of screen driers is greatly dependent on the granulometry of the material, on its initial and ultimate moisture content and on the temperature and velocity of the gas or air. For vibrating-screen driers, it is in the 10 to 50 kg/m² · h range for granular, free-running materials of plus-1, minus-25 mm size at gas velocities of 1.5 to 4 m/s, at temperatures exceeding 200 °C. For conveyor driers — at gas velocities about 1 m/s — it is about one-third as much. Thermal efficiencies too are highly variable. The η_{therm} of conveyor driers attains 50 to 70% when drying a very wet material but can be as low as 15% when drying to near-zero ultimate moisture. For vibrating-screen driers, η_{therm} is in the 15 to 50% range.

In pneumatic flash or suspension and fluid-bed driers, the solids are moved along by the hot gas in contact with them, without benefit of any mechanical device. Flash driers are best suited for the drying of fine-grained aggregates and slimes (minus-6 $\sim$ 8 mm ore so). The particles are entrained by hot gas rising in a vertical shaft at a velocity of about $15 + v_0$ m/s, where v_0 is the terminal settling velocity of the coarsest particles in the gas at rest. The top end of the shaft connects to a deflection chamber and a drop pipe: this latter in turn connects to a dust cyclone from which de-dusted gas emerges as a rule through a bag filter or an electro-precipitator, whereas the dry material is tapped off through a dust lock.

In the shaft of the flash drier, coarser particles move upward slower than finer ones; that is, the retention time of the latter in the hot gas is less. The removal of internal water (as e.g. in the drying of air-dry lignites) takes in fact more time for the coarser than for the finer grains; the drying time needed for a given reduction of moisture content is given by the rule-of-thumb formula

$$t \cong x^2,$$

where t is in minutes and x, the particle size, is in cm. For example,

$$\text{if} \quad x = 1 \text{ mm,} \quad \text{then} \quad t \cong 0.1^2 = 0.01 \text{ min} = 0.6 \text{ s;}$$
$$\text{if} \quad x = 3 \text{ mm,} \quad \text{then} \quad t \cong 0.3^2 = 0.09 \text{ min} = 5.4 \text{ s.}$$

At high velocities, considerable wear tends to occur in the shaft. The uniform distribution of wet feed at the cross profile of the shaft is difficult: some of the dry discharge is therefore recycled into the feed in order to reduce its average moisture content. The usual arrangement is to use a fan in the suction mode so as to keep the system under depression rather than overpressure. Drying being concurrent, a high initial gas temperature is admissible. Shaft height, depending on the initial temperature and moisture content of the feed, is between 10 and 30 m. Power draft is comparatively high at 5 to 6 kW h/t: floor space occupied is about 1.5 m² per ton of dry material. (Comparable figures for rotary driers are 3 kW h/t and 7 m²/t or so.)

560

Flash drying is often combined with comminution. For example, the top end of the drying shaft may connect to a pneumatic classifier whose coarse discharge is returned through a grinding mill to the hot-gas stream at the bottom of the shaft, whereas its fine discharge is fed to a dust cyclone. In other cases, an impact-blade fan mill is installed at the bottom end of the shaft for the coarser particles of the feed to drop back into (Chonion 1971; Kröll 1967).

On drying washed coal fines from 11% to 1% moisture at a rate of about 50 tph (corresponding to an evaporation rate of about 5 tph of water), one has for

	rotary	fan	contact	flash driers

a total heat consumption of

	1,130	1,077	1,076	1,075 kcal

per kg of evaporated water, at a thermal efficiency

$$\eta_{\text{therm}} = \quad 71 \qquad 82 \qquad 77 \qquad 76\%,$$

for an inlet gas temperature $t_{\text{IN}} = 700\ °C$ and outlet temperatures

$$t_{\text{out}} = 100 \qquad 150 \qquad 135 \qquad 100\ °C,$$

and with the feed raised from $t_{\text{in}} = 10\ °C$ to a discharge temperature

$$t_{\text{out}} = \quad 75 \qquad 90 \qquad 80 \qquad 75\ °C.$$

Assuming 100 units for the rotary drier, investment cost is 120 units for the fan and about 70 units for the flash drier.

A fluid-bed drier will serve in the 0.07 to 12 mm particle size range. An updraught of hot gas of appropriate velocity passing through a thickish bed lying on a porous distributor sheet (screen) fluidizes the particles, making them move in a turmoil above the sheet without actually entraining them. The distributor sheet and the fluid bed between them cause a fairly great pressure drop, so that a blower of rather great power draft is required. If the fluidizing medium is air heated in heat exchangers, it is indicated to blow from the cold side, where gas volume is small. In this case, the material is to be fed and discharged through rotary airlock valves. Alternatively, a slight depression may be generated in the drier by means of an auxiliary fan run in the suction mode. In the usual run of fluid-bed drier, however, dry material may simply flow out over a weir. Another discharge aperture, installed right above the distributor screen, is required for full evacuation or for the removal of largish lumps. In this type of drier, heat exchange is extremely rapid. One or two minutes of drying have the same effect as half an hour in a rotary drier: the discharge temperatures of the material and of the gas become practically identical. Another considerable advantage is the very small plan area. Investment cost is a mere 30% of that of a rotary drier (Quinn 1963).

Spray driers are modern devices coming increasingly to the fore in the drying of suspensions and pastes (and, in fact, in the evaporation of solutions). In them, a paste or pulp is prayed by means of air or steam out of a nozzle to form small droplets, or a (pumpable) fluid is sprayed by means of a centrifugal or pneumatic pulverizer. In the drying space, these droplets will sink under the influence of gravity. The drying medium (air) also flows downward in most cases but upward in a few designs. Evaporation is extremely rapid: by the time the droplet reaches the tank wall, only the solids (with moisture one percent or less) are left behind. One litre of fluid sprays out into

$$z = 10^6 \, \frac{6}{\pi d^3}$$

drops of diameter d mm: the aggregate surface area of those is

$$F = z\pi d^2 = 10^6 \, \frac{6}{d} \, \text{mm}^2 = \frac{6}{d} \, \text{m}^2 \, .$$

The process was made popular by the Danish firm Niro: that is why it is called "niroing" in places (MacLeod 1972; Masters 1968).

In lignite drying — in connection with binderless briquetting above all — tube- or tray-type steam driers are often employed. Both are of the indirect type. Direct drying with steam is used in lignite ahydration by the batch-type Fleissner method.

The diagram of the tube-type rotary steam drier is shown as Fig. 7.37; that of the tray-type steam drier is shown as Fig. 7.38.

The tube-type rotary steam drier is a sheet steel cylinder of 2.5 to 3.6 m diameter and 6 to 8 m length, installed on a gentle incline (5 to 6°), rotating at 4 to 6 rpm. Into its two opposite head walls, a large number (420 to 720) of tubes of about 10 cm dia., open at both ends, are fitted. There is a thick perforated tube along the shaft. Drying steam is introduced into the drum through

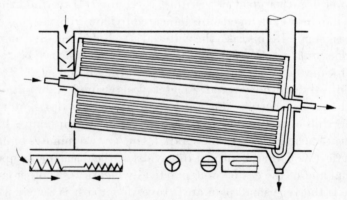

Fig. 7.37. Tube-type rotary steam drier

its upper trunnion, whereas condensate leaves through a spiral piping attached to its bottom trunnion. The material to be dried is introduced by a special feeder into the upper ends of the tubes in the upper head plate; it is transported downward by the rotation of the drum, to drop dry out of the pipe ends at the lower head plate.

By combining the feeder with a blower, a better filling of the tubes may be achieved. The internal surfaces of the tubes are often increased by means of

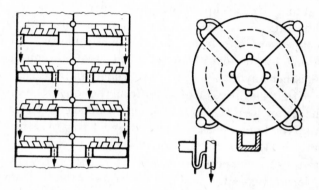

Fig. 7.38. Tray steam drier

ribbing or compartmentation as shown in the three small insets at the bottom of the figure, in order to ensure a better transfer of heat. In other cases, transporting-choking spirals are fitted loosely into the tubes, in which they can roll freely. The thread of the upper (transporting) section is opposite to that of the lower (choking) section. The short transporting section near the feed end is a fairly close fit in the tube. The choke spiral is a much looser fit: its purpose is to retain coarser particles longer in the tubes (see bottom left-hand inset).

In the tray-type steam drier (Fig. 7.38), steam is introduced through a pair of opposite risers into annular, hollow trays of 4 to 5 m outside and 1 to 2 m inside diameter, each made up of four sectors. Condensate leaves through another pair of opposite upright pipes. The trays, of about 5 cm height, are mounted on consoles fixed to these four hollow uprights. Their number is 25 to 30; their vertical separation is 20 to 25 cm. The drier is in a steel sheet housing which communicates with an outside stack. (The stack serves as an outlet to the water vapour removed from the material and also creates the updraught necessary to remove it.) Blades mounted on the radial arms of a slowly revolving central shaft move the material drying on top of the hollow trays to apertures alternately at the inner and outer rims of those, through which it can drop onto the tray below.

Typical drying steam is saturated and has a pressure of $p = 1.5$ to 4.5 bars absolute; specific rates of evaporation are furnished by

$$q = 1.45 + 0.7p \text{ kg of water per m}^2 \text{ per hour.}$$

The area to be taken into account is the aggregate tube surface area for the tube-type drier and the top and bottom surface area of each hollow tray for the tray-type one.

Fleissner ahydration. If a gel coal (a lignite or young brown [subbituminous] coal) is heated in air, it falls apart because its heating proceeds gradually from the outside inward: its outside may have become quite hot while its core is still cold. Water evaporates from an outer shell while the core is still moist: the shell, shrunk by the loss of moisture, spalls off the unshrunk core. The essence of Fleissner ahydration is to heat whole lumps of coal to the desired temperature so that the diffusion of water from the core to the surface may keep step with the water loss, thereby avoiding shrinkage and local stresses that would break up the lumps. This is achieved by heating in saturated steam at a high temperature (170 to 211 °C, corresponding to 8 to 20 bars pressure). Doing so forestalls the evaporation of gel water. Part of the water (20 to 50% of the total, depending on the colloidal structure of the coal) will nevertheless be exuded as a liquid, a phenomenon due to the reduction of the surface tension and viscosity of water by heating. Gel water in the normal state of the coal exerts a certain pressure upon the walls of the capillaries in the micelles; it is counteracted by forces of molecular attraction. The decreased surface tension of hot water reduces capillary pressure: as a result, the molecular forces gain the upper hand, compressing the capillaries until a new equilibrium sets in. A volume of water equal to the reduction of pore volume is thus pressed out of the coal. Exudation is promoted by the reduced viscosity of hot water. In lamellar micelle structure a given reduction in surface tension results in a greater reduction of pore volume than is the case with more isodimensional micelles.

Steaming entails minor chemical changes in the coal also: at the surfaces of the micelles, part of the humic acids is converted into humins; the contact angles and the propensity to wetting of the capillaries are changed in the process; a fraction of some of the inorganic ash minerals is leached out of the coal, etc. Thanks to the irreversible alteration of the gel, ahydrated coal does not swell and recover its original water content when immersed in water. Its net calorific value is greater and its ash content less than should be expected simply on account of the reduction in moisture content: coal is upgraded by ahydration.

After steaming for a long enough time, pressure is taken off, whereupon some more water escapes in the form of steam, including some 20% of the water exuded as a liquid. Afterdrying with hot air is then performed in much the same way as in the conventional processes of drying. A vacuum may be pplied also to accelerate afterdrying and cooling. On ahydration, the lumps of coal shrink but undergo no other deformation: their strength often actually ncreases in the process.

In order to rationalize the process, several of the autoclaves of ahydration can be hooked up together in rational programme. The phases and their approximate duration may be as follows: (1) filling the autoclave with coal — 15 min; (2) steam injection — 30 min; (3) ahydration proper — 90 to 120 min; (4) blowoff — 30 min; (5) afterdrying — 60 to 90 min; (6) emptying the autoclave — 15 min. If e.g. the autoclaves are run in pairs, blowoff in one unit of the pair may coincide with steam injection in the other — that is, steam can be transferred from the one into the other; furthermore, ahydration proper (3) in one vessel may coincide with the aggregate duration of afterdrying, emptying and filling (5 + 6 + 1) in the other.

The useful volume of an autoclave may be between 5 and 40 m³ (3.5 to 30 t of raw lignite).

In Hungary, ahydration by the Fleissner method is used at Várpalota for upgrading plus-20 mm lignite. At Rózsaszentmárton, according to a Hungarian patent, hot water at a suitable temperature used to be employed instead of saturated steam. At Várpalota, the steam used is at a temperature of 211 °C (20 bars); it turns raw lignite of a gross calorific value of 2,720 kcal/kg with an average water content of 43% into a fuel of 4,160 kcal/kg on average, containing 19% moisture. The total heat consumption of removing one kg of water is about 570 kcal, in contrast to the usual heat requirement of $\sim$800—1,000 kcal/kg of water removed. There are 16 autoclaves of 2.5 m dia×6.2 m in operation. The full cycle takes 220 minutes at Várpalota, with 120 min for steaming, 30 min for blowoff and 30 min for evacuation. No hot-air afterdrying is applied because the ahydrated coal of Várpalota is prone to self-ignition if so treated.

7.7. LITERATURE ON SEPARATION OF SOLIDS FROM LIQUIDS

ABBOTT, J. (et al.): Die Behandlung von Flotationsbergen in tiefen Spitzen. 6. *IMPC*, Paris 1973, 20 D.
ADORJÁN, L. A.: Some aspects of flocculation. *Coal Preparation* 1968, 125—134, 171—176.
AKYEL, H.: Neue Erfahrungen mit hochmolekularen polymeren synthetischen Flockungsmitteln zur Klärung von Trüben und zur Entwässerung von Schlämmen. *Glückauf* 1966, 364—368.
AKYEL, H.—M. NEVEN: Hochmolekulare organische synthetische Flockungsmittel in der modern Aufbereitungstechnik. *Chem. Ing. Tech.* 1967, 172—178.
ANDERSON, A. A.—J. E. SPARKMAN: Review sedimentation theory. *Chem. Eng.* 1959, 75—80.
BATEL, W.: Vorausberechnung der Restfeuchtigkeit bei der mechanischen Flüssigkeitsabtrennung. *Chem. Ing. Tech.* 1955, 497—501.

BATEL, W.: Menge und Verhälten der Zwischenraumflüssigkeit in körnigen Stoffen *Chem. Ing. Tech.* 1961, 541—547.

BATTAGLIA, A.: Some problems of designing closed washery circuits. *J. of mines, metal. and fuels (India)* 1964, 6/2, 97—100.

BATTAGLIA, A.: Some aspects of the closed circuit theory. *Coal Preparation* 1966, 142—147.

BECKERATH, H.—G. WIEGAND: Die Entwässerung von Kommunalschlämmen auf Voll mantelschneckenschleudern unter Einsatz von synthetischen Flockungsmitteln. *AT* 1970, 229—231.

BITTER, J. H.: Über die Filtration von Flotationskonzentraten. *AT* 1965, 11—17.

BÖHM, H.—H. GAMMERLER: Neuentwickelter Krählwerks-Eindicker. *AT* 1972, 183—185

BOLEK, M.: Beziehungen zwischen Kuchendicke und Leistung von Filterpressen. *Berg bauwissenschaften* 1961, 85—87.

BOLEK, M.: Möglichkeiten zur Verbesserung der Ergebnisse bei der Vakuumfiltration. *AT* 1968, 494—499.

BOLEK, M.—J. LOCHMANN: Zur Flocking von Flotationsabgängen in der Steinkohlen aufbereitungsanlage Paskov und Möglichkeiten zu ihrer Automatisierung. *AT* 1972, 147—150.

BOSENIK, G.: Die physikalische und chemische Beeinflussung von Feststoff-Flüssigkeits Gemischen zur Erhöhung der Filterleistung. *Chem. Ing. Tech.* 1956, 761—763.

BROWN, J. H.: The mechanism of dewatering by steam filtration. *Can. M. M. Bull.* 1965 315—319.

COE, H. S.—G. H. CLEVENGER: Methods for determining the capacities of slime-settling tanks. *Trans. AIME* 1916, 356—384.

CHONION, J.-P.: Pneumatische Luftstrahltrocknug. *AT* 1971, 627—630.

COMINGS, E. W.—C. E. PRUISS—C. DeBORD: Continuous settling and thickening. *Ind Eng. Chem.* 1954, 1164—1172.

CORNELL, C. F.—R. C. EMMETT—D. A. DAHLSTROM: The Rotobelt filter. *Min. Engng* 1958, 253—257.

CROSS, H. E.: A new approach to the design and operation of thickeners. *J. S. Afr. Inst Min. Met.* 1963 Feb., 271—298.

CUNLIFFE, B. J.: Filter cloth in the mining industry. *Can. Min. J.* 1971 June, 76—79

DAHLSTROM, C. D.: Closing coal preparation plant water circuits with clarifiers, thickener and continuous vacuum filters. *2nd Symp. Coal Prep.*, Leeds 1957, 151—189.

DAHLSTROM, D. A.: Processing and disposal of coal flotation tailings. *Min. Congr. J* 1962, 50—55.

DAHLSTROM, D. A.—C. E. SILVERBLATT: Herabsetzung des Wassergehaltes durch Fil tern mit dem Ziel, die thermische Trockung zu vermeiden. 6. *ICPC*, Praha 1973, 5D

DALE, L. A.—D. A. DAHLSTROM: Design and operation of thickening equipment for close water circuits in coal preparation plants. *Trans. AIME* 1965, 141—149.

DAMGAARD-IVERSEN, J.: Spray drying converts wet to dry process. *Rock Products* 197 May, 114—116.

DAVIES, E.: Selection of equipment for solid-liquid separation. *Trans. ICE* 1965, 256—259.

DAVIES, R.—B. H. KAYE: Experimental investigation into the settling behaviour o suspensions. *Powder Tech.* 1972 Jan., (5/2), 61—68.

DELL, C. C.—T. H. KELEGHAN: The dewatering of polyclay suspensions. *Powder Tech* 1973, (7), 189—204.

DELL, C.C.—J. SINHA: Experimental study of the behaviour of flocculated clays in thicken ing. *Trans. IMM* 1966, C139—C146; 1967, C135—C141, C219—C224.

Dobie, W. B.: A review of recent filtration theory. *Trans. ICE* 1965, 225—227.

Dollimore, D.—T. A. Hollidge: The filtration of beds of china clay flocculated by poly-acrylamide. *Powder Tech.* (5/2) 1972 Jan., 111—114.

Fejes, G.: *Centrifugálás.* (Centrifuging.) Műszaki Könyvkiadó, Budapest 1967.

Fejes, G.—G. Tarján: *Vegyipari gépek és műveletek.* (Machines and operations of the chemical industry.) Tankönyvkiadó, Budapest 1973.

Ferguson, W. C.: Filtration in the mining industry. *Can. Min. J.* 1971 June, 76—79.

Ferney, F. X.: Coarse coal centrifuging. *Min. Congr. J.* 1966 Sep., 57—59.

Fitch, B.: Sedimentation process fundamentals. *Trans. AIME* 1962, 129—137.

Fitch, B.: Current theory and thickener design. *Ind. Eng. Chem.* 1966 Oct., 18—28.

Fitch, B.: The design of intermittently fed thickeners. *Ind. & Eng. Chem.* 1968 July, 8—14.

Frey, H.: Kreutzeinbauten in Trockungstrommeln. *AT* 1968, 331—338.

Gathen, R. von der: Entwässerung von Flotationskonzentrat auf einem Dampfhauben-filter. *Glückauf* 1963, 1374—1380.

Gaudin, A. M.—M. C. Fuerstenau: On the mechanism of thickening. *IMPC*, London 1960, 115—127.

Gaudin, A. M.—M. C. Fuerstenau: Experimental and mathematical model of thicken-ing. *Trans. AIME* 1962, 122—129.

Gieseke, E. W.: Flocculation and filtration of coal flotation concentrates and tailings *Trans. AIME* 1962, 352—358.

Gillmore, D. W.—C. C. Wright: Drainage behavior and water retention properties of fine coal. *Min. Engng* 1952, 886—894.

Götte, A.—W. Flöter: Untersuchungen über neuzeitliche Flockungsmittel und ihre Einwirkung auf Flotation und Entwässerung feiner Steinkohle. *Aachener Bl.* 1961, 89—148.

Graf, B.: Betriebserfahrungen mit der Entwässerung von Mittelkohle und Feinkohle im Zonenschragbunker. *Glückauf* 1955, 40—43.

Harper, W. G.: Entwässerung von Flotationsabgängen in Filterpressen. *Schlägel und Eisen* 1956, 392—396. (Or 2. *IMPC*, Essen 1954, AIV.)

Harris, C. C.—H. G. Smith: The moisture retention properties of fine coal. A study by permeability and suction potential methods. *2nd Symp. Coal Prep.*, Leeds 1957, 57—97, 211—249.

Hassett, N. J.: Design and operation of continuous thickening. *Ind. Chem.* 1958, 116—121, 169—172, 489—494.

Hassett, N. J.: Mechanism of thickening and thickener design. *Trans. IMM* 1965, C627—C656; 1966, C188—C191.

Hassett, N. J.: Role of depth in continuous thickening of flocculated suspensions. *Trans. IMM* 1968, C227—C228.

Healy, T. W.—V. K. LaMer: Flocculation of mineral dispersions by polymers. 7. *IMPC*, New York 1964, 359—365.

Hoffmann, E.: Bauart und Anwendung nass arbeitender Zentrifugalabscheider in der Kohlenaufbereitung. *Glückauf* 1953, 105—120.

Hutto, F. B., Jr.: Distribution of porosity in filter cakes. *Chem. Eng. Progr.* 1957, 328—332.

Jaisle, J.: Berechnung von Kläreindickern. *Chem. Ing. Tech.* 1964, 1127—1133.

Juhász, Á.—I. Schumiczky: Filtering of finest sludges with an air-chamber filter press. 5. *IMPC*, Pittsburgh 1966, G5.

Kelsey, G. D.: Some practical aspects of continuous rotary vacuum filters. *Trans. ICE* 1965, 248—255.

KENNEDY, G. H.—H. E. CRINER: Application of the cyclone thickeners to preparation plant water circuits. *Min. Engng* 1951, 259—261.

KING, D. L.—B. A. SHEPMAN: New concepts in thickener design, underflow pump arrangement, and automatic controls. *Trans. AIME* 1962, 337—343.

KÖHLING, R.—W. PLATE—W. SIMONIS: Zur Fliehkraftentwässerung von Steinkohle. *AT* 1972, 543—550.

KRISCHER, O.—K. KRÖLL: *Die wissenschaftlichen Grundlagen der Trocknungstechnik.* (2. Auflage.) Springer, Berlin—Göttingen—Heidelberg 1963.

KRÖLL, K.: Das Trocknen formloser Güter und seine Grundlagen. *AT* 1962, 57—68.

KRÖLL, K.: Klassifizierung der Trockener. *AT* 1964, 287—295.

KRÖLL, K.: Förderluft-Trockener. *AT* 1967, 312—321. 357—364.

KUBITZA, K. H.: Der Entwässerungserfolg bei der Filterung von Steinkohlenschlämmen in Abhängigkeit von der wirksamen Druckdifferenz. *Glückauf* 1962, 832—841. (Or: 4. *IMPC*, Harrogate 1962, 381—388.)

KUZKIN, S. F.—W. P. NEBERA—S. N. ZOLIN: Aspects of the theory of suspensions flocculating by polyacrylamides. 7. *IMPC*, New York 1964, 347—357.

KYNCH, G. J.: A theory of sedimentation. *Trans. Faraday Soc.* 1952, 166—176.

LEMKE, K.: Betriebsergebnisse eines zellenlosen Trommelfilters. *Glückauf* 1953, 322—324.

LEMKE, K.: Neue Entwässerungsschleudern. *Glückauf* 1954, 47—53.

LEMKE, K.: Neue Möglichkeiten zur Entwässerung feinster Schlämme in der Steinkohlenaufbereitung. *Glückauf* 1959, 293—298.

LINKE, W. F.—R. B. BOOTH: Physical-chemical aspects of flocculation by polymers. *Trans. AIME* 1960, 364—370.

LYONS, O. R.: An approximative method of predicting and comparing expected results when dewatering coal by centrifuges. *Min. Engng* 1951, 417—425.

MACKENZIE, J. M. W.: Relationships between rheological and flocculating properties of polymer flocculants. *Trans. AIME* 1964, 44—48.

MACLEOD, J.: Spray drying of mineral concentrates. *Canad. Min. J.* 1972 June, 96—98.

MASON, G. A.: Dewatering and drying of coal. *Coal Prep.* 1967, 185—189, 237—243.

MASTERS, K.: Spray drying. *I. E. Chem.* 1968 Oct., 53—63.

MATHESON, G. H.—J. M. W. MACKENZIE: Flocculation and thickening: coal washery refuse pulps. *Coal Age* 1962 Dec., 94—100.

MEERMAN, G.: Die physikalisch-technischen Grundlagen der Entwässerung, Klärung und Eindickung. *Glückauf* 1954, 955—964.

MICHAELS, A. S.: Polyelectrolyte complexes. *Ind. Eng. Chem.* 1965 Oct., 32—40.

MICHAELS, A. S.—J. C. BOLGER: Settling rates and sediment volumes of flocculated kaolin suspensions. *I & EC Fundamentals* 1962 Feb., 24—33.

MONCRIEF, A. G.: Theory of thickener design based on batch sedimentation tests. *Trans. IMM* 1964 July, 729—759.

NEMETH, N.: Filtration: basic mechanisms and the medium. *Can. Min. J.* 1970 June, 71—76.

NEMETH, N.—L. L. SIROIS: Role of the filter medium in continuous-vacuum filtration. An intracular approach. *Trans. AIME* 1970, 104—108.

NIESSEN, R.—K. KOPPITZ: Grundsätzliche Überlegungen zur Auslegung von Filterpressen für die Entwässerung von Steinkohlen-Flotationsabgängen. *AT* 1962, 345—360.

NOWAK, Z. A.—H. ALESKA: Mathematisches Modell eines Wasser- und Schlämmkreislaufs. 6. *ICPC*, Paris 1973, 24D.

OLIVER, R. H.: Guide to the use of flocculants in mineral processing plants. *E/MJ* 1963 June, 193—203.

PAUL, H.: Der Wasserkreislauf mit den Einrichtungen für Klärung und Eindickung. *Der deutsche Steinkohlenbergbau. Bd. 5:* Aufbereitung der Steinkohle. Verlag Glückauf, Essen 1966, 109—172.

PEČINKA, D.: Kennwerte linearschwingender Entwässerungssiebmaschienen. *AT* 1968, 289—291.

PELSER-BERENSBERG, B. V. (et al.): Verbesserung der Waschwasserklärung durch Zusatz von Flockungsmitteln. *Aachener Bl.* 1956, 65—88.

PESCH, K.-H.—G. WIEGAND: Zur Entwässerung von Schlämmen in Vollmantelschneckenschleudern unter Einsatz synthetischer Flockungsmittel. *AT* 1969, 263—267.

PETERSEN, W.: Der Einfluss von Flockungsmitteln auf die Entwässerung von Steinkohlenschlämmen. *Glückauf* 1938, 493—503.

POLKE, R.: Filter-Entwässerung von Anthrazit-Schlamm unter Verwendung verschiedener Werkstoffe für die Filter-Bespannung. *Aachener Bl.* 1956, 169—195.

PORTER, S. J.: The design of rotary driers and coolers. *Trans. ICE* 1963, 272—280.

PRICE, J. D.—W. M. BERTHOLF: Modernisierung der Schlämmaufbereitung und Wasserklärung in einer Wäsche. 3. *ICPC*, Liège 1958, E-11.

QUINN, M. F.: Fluidized bed dryers. *Ing. Eng. Chem.* 1963 July, 18—24.

RADFORD, B. C.—N. P. SMITH: Slimes treatment by filter press at Manton Colliery. *Mine and Quarry* 1972 Oct., 45—52.

REUTER, H.: Sedimentation in der Überlaufzentrifuge. *Chem. Ing. Tech.* 1967, 548—553.

REUTER, J.: Die Verwendung synthetischer, makromolekularer Flockungsmittel bei der Steinkohlenaufbereitung. *Glückauf* 1970, 943—952.

REUTER, J.—H. VON BECKERATH: Schlämmentwässerung mit kontinuierlichen Pressfiltern. *AT* 1974, 253—259.

REUTER, J.—K. LEMKE: Entwässerung von Steinkohlenschlämmen auf einem Druckfilter, Bauart Fest, mit Hilfe von Dampf. *Glückauf* 1963, 1380—1387.

REUTER, J.—K.-H. PESCH—G. WIEGAND: Probleme der maschinellen Entwässerung organischer Schlämme mit Hilfe von Vollmantelschneckenzentrifugen. *AT* 1972, 157—164.

RICHARDSON, J. P.—W. N. ZAKI: Sedimentation and fluidisation. *Trans. ICE* 1954, 35—52.

ROBEL, H.: Vergleich der Berechnungsmethoden zur Bestimmung der Absatzfläche kontinuierlich arbeitender Klärgefässe und Eindicker. *Chem. Tech.* 1965, 392—397.

ROBINS, H. H.: The theory of the design and operation of settling tanks. *Trans. ICE* 1964, 158—163.

ROEDER, H.: Trockner. (ACHEMA 1970.) *Chem. Ing. Tech.* 1970, 1394—1398.

RUMPELT, H.: Besondere Probleme bei der Anwendung von Drehfiltern in der Aufbereitungstechnik. *AT* 1967, 640—645.

SCHARMER, W.: Entwässerungs-Schwingsiebmaschinen in der Aufbereitungs- und Verfahrenstechnik. *AT* 1967, 593—595.

SCHEILING, A.: *Szárítás.* (Drying.) Műszaki Könyvkiadó, Budapest 1967.

SCHMIDT, O.: Klären von Feinstkorn-Kohlenschlämmen in einem neuartigen Rundeindicker. *Glückauf* 1967, 784—788.

SCHNEIDER, F. W.: Schubzentrifugen — Konstruktiver Aufbau, Anwendung und Leistungsberechnung. *AT* 1967, 630—636.

SCHOENBERGER, R. W.—E. F. BURCH: Improved dewatering of coal by steam filtration: Continuous pilot-scale filter tests. *Trans. AIME* 1964, 379—383.

SCHRANZ, H.—W. BERGHOLZ: Die Ermittlung des Erfolges von Entwässerungseinrichtungen und die rechnerische Erfassung von Wasserkreislaufen. *Bergbauwiss.* 1954, 242—250.

SCHRANZ, H.—R. MENZEL: Der Einsatz von grenzflächenaktiven Mitteln beim Filtern von Steinkohlenschlamm. *Bergbauwiss*. 1958, 134—143.

SCHUBERT, H.: Über die Wirkungsweise von Flockungsmitteln in wässrigen Trüben. *AT* 1964, 175—182; 1969, 175—182.

SCHUBERT, H.: Sedimentationtypen und deren Bedeutung für die Dimensionierung von Schwerkrafteindickern. *Bergakademie* 1970, 603—606.

SCHUMICZKY, L.—A. LUX: Das AJKO-Druckfilter, eine neuartige automatische Filterpresse für die Entwässerung von Kohlenschlämm. *Glückauf* 1964, 1272—1274. (Or: 5. *ICPC*, Pittsburgh 1966, G.5. Cf. also: Anonymus: New Hungarian filter press. *Canad. Min. J.* 1963 March, 63—68.)

SCHWALBACH, W.: Das Planfilter zur Feinsandentwässerung. *AT* 1972, 147—150.

SCOTT, K. J.: Mathematical models of mechanism of thickening. *I & EC Fundamentals* 1966 Feb., 109—113.

SCOTT, K. J.: Significance of critical settling point in settling of flocculated slurries. *Trans. IMM* 1967, C71—C72.

SCOTT, K. J.: Theory of thickening: factors affecting settling rate of solids in flocculated pulps. *Trans. IMM* 1966, C85—C97.

SCOTT, K. J.: Continuous thickening of flocculated suspensions. *Ind. Eng. Chem. Fundamentals* 1970, 422—427.

SCOTT, K. J.—L. ALDERTON: Maximum solids handling capacity of continuous thickeners. *Trans. IMM* 1966. C201—C210; 1967, C135—C141, C219—C224.

SHANNON, P. T. (et al.): Batch and continuous thickening. *I & EC Fundamentals* 1963 Aug., 203—211; 1964 Aug., 250—260.

SHANNON, P. T.—E. M. TORY: The analysis of continuous thickening. *Trans. AIME* 1966, 375—382.

SILVERBLATT, C. E.—D. A. DAHLSTROM: Improved dewatering of coal by steam filtration: Experimental bench scale tests. *Trans. AIME* 1964, 341—347.

SIMONS, C. S.—D. A. DAHLSTROM: Application of steam to the dewatering of metallurgical concentrates. *Can. M. M. Bull.* 1966, 961—967.

SLATER, R. W.—J. R. CLARK—J. A. KITCHENER: Chemical factors in the flocculation of mineral slurries with polymeric flocculants. 8. *IMPC*, Leningrad 1968, C-5.

SMIDTH, O.: Mechanischen Entwässern von Flotationsbergen in sieblosen Vollmantelschleudern. *Glückauf* 1965, 41—45.

SOMMER, H.: Bunker für Entwässerung feinkörniger Güter. *AT* 1965, 101—103.

SOMMER, O.: Die Auswirkungen des Einsatzes von Flockungsmitteln auf die Entwässerungstechnik bei der Steinkohle. *AT* 1966, 207—213.

ŠPALDON, F.: Ein Flockungsmittel in der Erzaufbereitung. *Freib. Fh. A163* 1960, 85—100.

SPETH, S.—W. SANDRINA: Dimensionierung und Optimierung von Kläreindickern — Die Sinkgeschwindigkeitanalyse und ihre praktische Bedeutung für die Dimensionierung und den Betrieb. *Verfahrenstechn.* 1971, 1—8.

ŠPETL, F.—G. ŠEBOR: Erkenntnisse aus der Entwässerung der Schlämme in Vollmantelzentrifugen. *AT* 1966, 576—579.

STERN, H.: Untersuchungen für Turmentwässerung von Feinkohle. *Glückauf* 1952, 1037—1046.

STRAUMANN, R.: Zur Berechnung kontinuierlich arbeitender Eindicker und Klärapparate. *Chem. Ing. Tech.* 1968, 383—390.

STREHL, R.: Schlammentwässerung mit Zentrifugen. *AT* 1970, 546—550.

SZABÓ, Z.—M. CZIRFUSZ—G. FEJES: *Szűrés.* (Filtration.) Műszaki Könyvkiadó, Budapest 1968.

Szantho, E. von—H. Mathiak: Entwicklung der Schwingsiebschleuder und Einsatzmöglichkeiten zum Entwässern von Aufbereitungsprodukten. *Z-VDI* 1966, 493—499.

Talmage, W. P.—F. B. Fitch: Determining thickener areas. *Ind. Eng. Chem.* 1955, 38—41.

Tamási, A.—S. Schwartz: *Szűrés.* (Filtration.) Műszaki Könyvkiadó, Budapest 1968.

Teichmann, E.: Die Feinstkornentwässerung in der Steinkohlenaufbereitung und die Anwendungsmöglichkeiten der Druckfiltration. *Bergfreiheit* 1959, 73—87.

Ternes, P.: Entschlämmung und Vorentwässerung von gewaschener Feinkohle auf Resonanzsieben. *Aachener Bl.* 1956, 143—154.

Trawinski, H.: Zentrifugen, Trenngeräte mit höchster Abschiedewirkung. *Chem. Ing. Tech.* 1954, 189—201; 1958, 393—399.

Trawinski, H.: Kapazität, Trenneffekt und Dimensionierung von Vollmantelschleudern. *Chem. Ing. Tech.* 1959, 661—666.

Trawinski, H.: Die unwollständige Klärung von Kreislauf-Waschwasser unter Gleichgewichtsbedingungen. *Glückauf* 1961, 991—996.

Trawinski, H.: Zentrifugen, Hydrozyklone, Kläreindicker. (ACHEMA 1970.) *Chem. Ing. Tech.* 1970, 1445—1453; 1964, 1276—1285.

Trawinski, H.: Mechanische Trennverfahren für Suspensionen und Schlämme. *AT* 1966, 709—719.

Trawinski, H.: Filter für Nassprozesse. (ACHEMA 1970.) *Chem. Ing. Tech.* 1970, 1453—1456.

Wadsworth, M. E.—I. B. Cutler: Flocculation in mineral suspensions with co-precipitated polyelectrolytes. *Min. Engng* 1956, 830—833.

Wagener, W.: Der Betrieb und die Plannung von Heisslufttrocknern für rieselfähriges Gut. *AT* 1973, 265—271.

Wersch, B.: Der Anteil der natürlichen Verdunstung der Feinkohlenentwässerung in Nachentwässerungstürmen verschiedener Bauarten. *Aachener Bl.* 1954, 194—200.

Wölfer, E.: Der Einsatz eines neuartigen polymeren Flockungshilfsmittels bei der Filtration eines Zinkblende-Konzentrates. *Erzmetall* 1973, 482—484.

Woodhead, R. C.: The capital and operating cost of typical closed water circuits. 5. *ICPC*, Pittsburgh 1966, F3.

Wuhrmann, K.: Einige Gesichtspunkte zur Klärschlämmeentwässerung mittels Zentrifugen. *AT* 1969, 256—259.

8. SEPARATION OF SOLIDS FROM GASES: DUST COLLECTION

8.1. GENERAL REMARKS

Gas (or air) carrying a load of dust is collected into a pipe as close as possible to the site of dust generation, through hoods attached to the suction inlet of a fan. It is better if the source of dust can be boxed in more or less hermetically and a depression applied to it, again by attachment to the suction inlet of a fan. The typical gas velocity of dust collection is one m/s: that is, if the effective aggregate inlet area of the dust hoods and/or the openings on the boxed-in space is F m², then the fan should have an intake rate of F m³/s. Air velocity in the piping should be 20 m/s or so to forestall the settling of the dust. (A velocity higher than 20 m/s causes superfluous erosion in the piping and an unjustified excess power consumption.) The separation of the solids from the gas in the piping is a further task akin to water clarification, the single major difference being that the phase to be separated from the solids is a gas (air) rather than a liquid (water). This is why methods analogous to those of water clarification (classification by joint settling, coagulation plus settling and filtration) are encountered in the de-dusting of gases also.

The viscosity of air is roughly one-sixtieth of that of water: the s.g. of air is negligible against that of water. The particles that will remain suspended in air are, therefore, depending on their s.g., one-eighth to one-sixteenth the size of the particles that will remain suspended in water for the same space of time. One may write notably

$$v_0 = x_w^2 \frac{\delta - \gamma_w}{18\mu_w} = x_a^2 \frac{\delta - \gamma_a}{18\mu_a},$$

whence

$$\frac{x_w}{x_a} = \sqrt{\frac{\mu_w}{\mu_a} \frac{\delta - \gamma_a}{\delta - \gamma_w}} \simeq \sqrt{\frac{60\delta}{\delta - 1}},$$

implying

$$\frac{x_w}{x_a} = 16.1 \quad 9.9 \quad 8.7$$

if

$$\delta = 1.3 \quad 2.6 \quad 5.0.$$

Slimes that will remain suspended for very long periods in stagnant water tend in practice to be finer than 10 μm; particles up to 100 μm or so will remain in suspension for shorter periods. The implication is that the dust particles suspended in air at rest are finer in practice than about 1 to 10 μm. Physiologically — as regards the silicosis hazard — quartz particles of 0.4 to 5 μm size are the most harmful. Air in motion — just as water in motion — will keep in suspension coarser particles also, thanks to its turbulency. In mechanical dispersions, the bulk of the dust particles is in the plus-5 to minus-50 μm range.

8.2. DUST COLLECTION EQUIPMENT

The devices of dust collection rely for their operation on (1) gravity, (2) inertia, (3) the centrifugal force, (4) electric forces, (5) filtration and (6) wet capture (Brown 1968; Gösling and Himmen 1970; Hirsch 1964; John 1968; King 1967; Koglin 1964; McKibbon 1962; Meldau 1956/1958; Nagel and Ibing 1961; Stairmand 1968; Strauss 1967; Tuma 1966). Different as to their operating gas resistance (pressure drop), these several devices are suited for the collection of dust loads of different granulometry. Figure 8.1 presents the approximate fields of application of dust collection equipment in granulometry terms. Parts A to C of Fig. 8.2 state typical fractional efficiencies or dust recoveries $m\%$ (or $100 - m\%$ parameters) vs. average particle size x or terminal settling velocity in air, v_0.

For designing a dust-collecting system and calculating its power draft, an idea of the pressure drop involved is required. In turbulent flow (e.g. in dust collectors relying on inertial or centrifugal forces), pressure drop p varies as the square of gas velocity:

$$\Delta p = \frac{\zeta u^2 \gamma}{2g} = \frac{\zeta u^2 \varrho}{2} \ ;$$

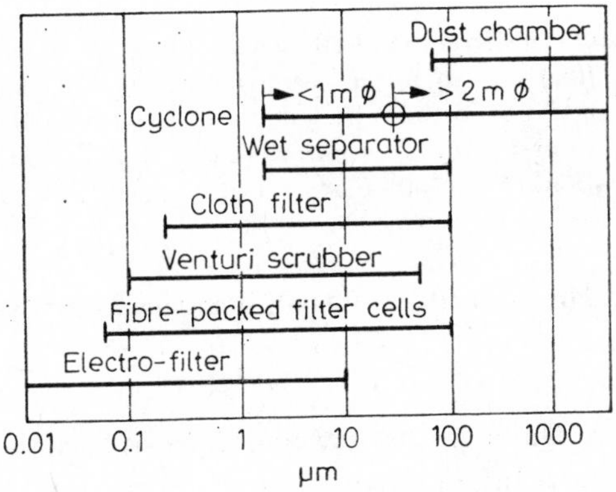

Fig. 8.1. Approximate granulometry limits of application of dust-collecting equipment

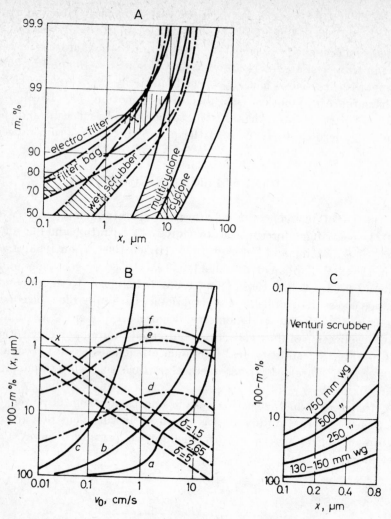

Fig. 8.2. A — dust recoveries (fractional efficiencies) $m\%$ vs. x, the average particle size, *B* — $(100 - m\%) = f(v_0)$ curves for a — a cyclone or multiclone of poor efficiency, b — of middling efficiency, c — of fair efficiency; and electrostatic collection of a dust of resistivity 10^{13} ohm · cm in d — direct separation, e — dry separation after conditioning, f — wet separation. *C* — $(100 - m\%) = f(x)$ curves of Venturi scrubbers

in laminar flow (e.g. through filter cloths), it varies as gas velocity proper:

$$\Delta p = \zeta \mu u,$$

where γ, ϱ and μ are the s.g., density and viscosity of the gas, respectively; u is gas velocity in the intake pipe or in front of or behind the filter cloth; and ζ is a drag coefficient.

In gas approaching a d-dia. cylinder (wire, thread) or sphere in a straight line at relative velocity u, only the dust particles contained in a core zone of width $b < d$ will collide with the cylinder (sphere): particles outside this zone will bypass the obstacle by following the flow lines of the gas. The ratio

$$r = \frac{b}{d}$$

varies as the dimensionless expression

$$k = \frac{uv_0}{gd} \; ;$$

at high values of k, the ratio r tends towards unity. Corresponding pairs of k and r are listed in Table 8.1.

The gas volume which entrains the dust particles colliding with the obstacle is stated by the formula

$$\frac{\partial Q}{\partial t} = dl \frac{b}{d} u = Fru$$

for cylinders (e.g. the threads of a filter cloth), or

$$\frac{\partial Q}{\partial t} = \frac{d^2 \pi}{4} \left(\frac{b}{d}\right)^2 u = Fr^2 u.$$

for a sphere (e.g. the droplets of water in a wet dust collector).

Both for very small droplets ($d \to 0$) and very large ones ($b/d \to 0$), the gas volume Q that can be swept (de-dusted) by one droplet of diameter d is minute: there is an optimum droplet size at which the efficiency of dust collection is greatest. Another implication of the formulae is that a great relative velocity u is to be striven for, by accelerating either the droplets or the gas (Sell 1931).

The resistance of some dust collectors (e.g. of filters) changes in the course of their operative life. Increased drag reduces gas velocity and the gas throughput rate of the system. This not only limits the efficiency of dust collection but causes deposits to form in the ducts as well, which may get completely clogged up after a while (Brown 1968).

Table 8.1. Corresponding pairs of values of $k = uv_0/gd$ and $r = b/d$

$k = uv_0/gd$		0.1	0.2	0.5	1.0	2.0	5.0	10.0
$r = b/d$	for cylinders	0.2	0.13	0.39	0.56	0.72	0.86	0.93
	for spheres	0.08	0.20	0.43	0.62	0.77	0.90	0.95

v_0 is the settling velocity of the dust particle in the gas at rest; the condition for two flows to be similar are v_0/u and uv_0/gd ($= k$).

575

8.2.1. Dust chambers. Settling chambers are dust collectors relying on gravity. Dust-laden gas passes through them at a low velocity (0.4 to 0.8 m/s), so that the larger particles (plus-50 or plus-100 μm) may settle out. A dust particle of terminal settling velocity v_0, moving in a horizontal gas flow of velocity u, travels over a time t a horizontal distance $L = ut$ and a vertical distance $H = v_0 t$. In other terms,

$$\frac{L}{H} = \frac{u}{v_0}.$$

Putting

$$u = \frac{Q}{BH}$$

and

$$F = LB,$$

(where Q is the gas flow rate, B is the width and F the horizontal cross sectional area of the dust chamber), the relationship called the area principle,

$$v_0 = \frac{Q}{F},$$

presented earlier in connexion with the dimensioning of classifiers (Vol. I, p. 499) is obtained. Particles whose settling velocity is less than v_0 will, during the time t of their passage through the dust chamber, fall a vertical distance $h < H$: for these, the ratio h/H states the fractional efficiency of dust collection.

If the dust chamber is divided up by horizontal baffles into shallow zones of 4 to 10 cm height, the dust has to sink less before it can settle out. The dimensions of the chamber can thus be reduced and its efficiency improved at the same time. There is an analogy here with the compartmented Dorr thickener.

Dust chambers are of low resistance: their drag factor referred to the inflow velocity is in the $\zeta = 1$ to 2 range. It is indicated to use them as roughers upstream of the more delicate devices of dust collection.

8.2.2. Baffle collectors rely for their operation on the forces or inertia generated by abrupt deflections of flow. The dust particles with their greater mass have a greater inertia than the gas molecules. They cannot therefore follow the deflections of the gas molecules completely: driven to the baffles that cause the deflections, or rolled along those, they get separated from the gas stream.

The baffle collectors shown in Fig. 8.3 serve for the separation of comparatively coarse-grained, free-running dust. Through the outlet marked D, a fraction (5 to 10%) of the total gas flow takes out the bulk of the dust: this split-off stream can then be de-dusted e.g. in a cyclone. It is usual to let the split-off gas be returned to the intake of dust-laden gas by means of an auxiliary fan. Baffle collectors of this type tend to have an inflow velocity u in the 15 to 25

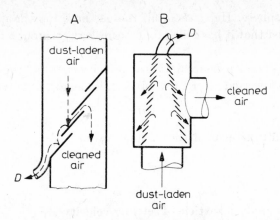

Fig. 8.3. Diagrams of baffle-type dust collectors

m/s range and a drag coefficient $\zeta = 2.5$ to 3.5. Comparatively small, simple and cheap, these devices can be installed in the duct that conveys the dusty gas. The design shown in Part B of the figure, with the baffles forming a cone, has a better efficiency. Fractional efficiencies are about 50% at 10 μm, 90% at 30 μm and 98% at 50 μm (Weber 1969).

8.2.3. Dust cyclones and **vortex tubes** rely on the centrifugal force for dust separation.

The principles of the dust cyclone (aerocyclone) are the same as those of the hydrocyclone. The dust particle is driven outward by a centrifugal force

$$C = \frac{x^3 \pi \delta v_t^2}{6gr}$$

opposed by a fluid resistance

$$S = 3\pi\mu x(v_r - V).$$

Here, V is the absolute radial velocity of the particle as it approaches the cyclone axis. $V = 0$ means that the particle circulates about the axis on a radius r that can be calculated by equating C with S, until it is taken out of the cyclone by the axial component of the flow. A radius of circulation r is assigned to any particle size x by

$$x = k\frac{\sqrt{r}\sqrt{v_r}}{v_t}.$$

Particles whose r is greater than the cyclone radius are driven to the cyclone wall: they discharge through the apex (spigot) of the cyclone into a closed dust collecting tank or through a dust lock that separates the cyclone interior from the outer atmosphere. Here, then, all the gas entering the cyclone, together with the fine dust that it has failed to deposit, leaves through the vortex finder (top) aperture.

A sheet of gas of width B circulating at velocity v_{t1} round the cyclone cylinder of diameter r_1 is released after z revolutions; its length of travel is accordingly

$$2\pi r_1 z,$$

and its retention time against the cyclone wall is

$$\frac{2\pi r_1 z}{v_{t1}}.$$

During this time, a dust particle of settling velocity

$$v_r = \frac{x^2 \delta v_{t1}^2}{18\mu g r_1}$$

must travel a distance B in order to settle out from the gas stream onto the cyclone wall, implying

$$t = \frac{B}{v_r} = 2\pi \frac{r_1 z}{v_{t1}}.$$

In other terms,

$$v_r = \frac{B v_{t1}}{2\pi r_1 z} = \frac{x^2 \delta v_{t1}^2}{18\mu g r_1}$$

and

$$x = \sqrt{\frac{9\mu g B}{\pi \delta z v_{t1}}} = K\sqrt{\frac{B}{\delta v_{t1}}},$$

where B is the width of the (rectangular) inlet of the cyclone. (Typically, z is between 1.5 and 3.)

The particle size x_T corresponding to the Tromp value of 50% is obtained by writing $B/2$ instead of B. This furnishes for conventional cyclones, run with air at about 15 °C,

$$x_T \cong 7.1 \sqrt{\frac{B}{\delta v_{t1}}},$$

where x_T is in μm, B in cm and v_{t1} in m/s (Leineweber 1967). In a gas whose viscosity μ deviates from the viscosity μ_{15} of air at 15 °C, x_T varies as $\sqrt{\mu/\mu_{15}}$. Recovery (or Tromp percentage or fractional efficiency) is approximately

	96	80	50	30	4%
if $\dfrac{x}{x_T} =$	5	2	1	0.5	0.2.

For the fractional efficiencies of dust cyclones of different design, the relationship

$$m_x = 1 - e^{-cx}$$

often proves valid. Here, x is particle size and c is a cyclone-design parameter.

Parts A and B of Fig. 8.4 are diagrams of conventional cyclones. Part C is that of a Van Tongeren cyclone. The double vortex in the cylindrical part of the conventional cyclone takes a lot of dust up near the lid, and the dust cloud collecting there is driven by the radial flow towards the vortex finder outlet. In the Van Tongeren cyclone, this dust cloud can escape through strategically placed ports a into a vortex-free bypass N, in which it can fall to where axial flow next to the cyclone wall is downward. (Using a Van Tongeren cyclone of 90 cm diameter in one case, gas at 188 °C flowing at a rate of 800 m³/min laden with 150 g of dust per m³, with 27% of the dust minus-5 μm and 21% plus-20 μm, could be cleaned at a dust recovery of 84% at the price of a pressure drop of about 70 mm water gauge.)

Part D of Fig. 8.4 is the diagram of a double cyclone. Dust-laden gas is introduced into a large cylindrical collector, tangentially along its whole height. Rolling along the cylinder shell, the dust with the gas entraining it is split off into an auxiliary cyclone through a side slot, whereas the bulk of the gas undergoes further de-dusting by passing through the louvered cylinder and then leaving axially. The vortex finder outlet of the auxiliary cyclone joins the axial outlet of the main cylinder.

The centrifugal force

$$C = \frac{mv_t^2}{r}$$

acting on the particles is the greater, the greater is v_t and the smaller is r. For example, given an inlet velocity $v_{t1} = 20$ m/s, the centrifugal force next to the shell of a cyclone of radius r_1 is related to the force of gravity, $G = mg$, as

$$z = \frac{C}{G} = \quad 41 \quad 82 \quad 204 \quad 408 \quad 815 \quad 2{,}040$$

if $\qquad\qquad r_1 = 100 \quad 50 \quad 20 \quad 10 \quad 5 \quad 2 \text{ cm.}$

In the interior of the cyclone, tangential velocity v_t increases as the radius of circulation r decreases:

$$v_t = v_{t1} \left(\frac{r_1}{r}\right)^n.$$

n is in the 0.5 to 0.9 range. The greater the centrifugal force, the finer are the dust particles that can still be separated from the gas stream. This is the rationale of the multiclone and of the vortex tube with its spin-generating spiral baffles.

The multiclone is a bank of many small cyclones (of 15 to 25 cm diameter) run in parallel to replace one large cyclone. In one case, collecting dust of s.g. g, of granulometry

plus-20 μm	20 to 10	10 to 5	minus-5 μm
43%	21	10	26%,

n concentrations of 70 to 170 g/m³ in cyclones of different diameter at a pressure drop of 100 mm water gauge, a cyclone of 15 cm diameter recovered almost all (98%) of the plus-5 μm and 66% of the minus-5 μm fraction; a cyclone of 23 cm diameter recovered 99% of the plus-10 μm and 60% of the minus-10 μm fraction, whereas a cyclone of 60 cm diameter recovered only the plus-20 μm fraction "fully" (at a recovery of 98%) but only half (47% in fact) of the minus-20 μm fraction.

Vortex tubes are small cyclones (of 6 to 25 cm dia), axially blown, in which spin is imparted to the injected air by spiral baffles installed in an annular space (cf. Parts E and F of Fig. 8.4). They are excellently suited for the collection of dry, free-running dust. In the design of Diagram E, clean gas is discharged oppositely to the injected dust-laden gas; in that of Diagram F, it is discharged in the same direction. Vortex tubes, being as small as they are, will handle comparatively small gas flows only; complexes of great throughput can be made up by installing a large number of units in parallel, as shown in Part G of Fig. 8.4. Depending on the space available, these banks can be installed obliquely or horizontally also.

The drag coefficient of a cyclone is a function of its design, size and geometry: it is typically in the $\zeta = 1.5$ to 10 range. Large simple cyclones of 65 to 400 cm

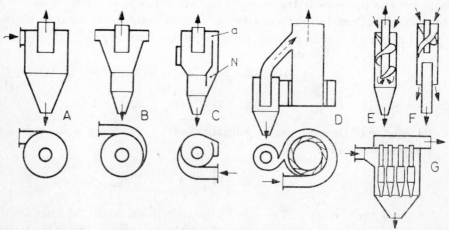

Fig. 8.4. Diagrams of dust cyclones (aerocyclones). A and B — conventional designs, C — Van Tongeren cyclone, D — double cyclone, E and F — vortex tubes (axial-injection cyclones, G — vortex-tube bank

diameter (Parts A and B of Fig. 8.4) have a low drag coefficient ($\zeta = 1.5$ to 2.0); their inlet velocity is in the order of 15 m/s, and their corresponding pressure drop is $p = 25$ to 30 mm water gauge. For a Van Tongeren cyclone (Part C), $\zeta = 4$ to 6; the usual range of inlet velocities is 18 to 22 m/s; for a multiclone, $\zeta = 7$ to 9 and the inlet velocity is 15 to 20 m/s. For vortex tubes (Parts E and F), $\zeta = 10$ to 20 and inlet velocity is about 10 m/s. In the design shown as Part D, the diameter of the main cylinder is 70 to 300 cm; $\zeta = 2$, and inlet velocity is about 30 m/s. (One such device of diameter 200 cm, run at an inlet velocity of 18 m/s, recovered 50% of the minus-5 μm fraction and 99.5% of the plus-40 μm fraction of a dust of s.g. 20). (Shepherd and Lapple 1939).

It is to be pointed out that the recoveries stated above or read off the relevant curves and bands in Fig. 8.2 refer to disperse dust at comparatively low concentrations (<170 g/m³) collected in a cyclone. In practice, dust concentration in the gas entering the cyclone is often greater: in such cases, the particles exhibit a tendency to clot. At higher dust concentrations, some of the fine particles are removed by the suction in the "lee" of the larger particles for purely mechanical reasons, without the benefit of any agglomeration. Both effects tend to improve the efficiency of dust collection above the theoretical value deduced from the granulometry of the dust (Koehle 1970; Kriegel 1968; Nagel and Ibing 1961; Rosin et al. 1932; Stairmand 1951).

8.2.4. In electro-precipitators, gases are de-dusted using the forces generated by an electric field. Solid particles (or droplets of a liquid) dispersed in a gaseous phase and endowed with an electric charge move in an electric field towards the electrode whose charge is unlike their own. The force acting is

$$P = Eq_0,$$

where E is field intensity and q_0 is the charge on the particle.

$$q_0 = kFE = k'x^2E$$

if $x \gtrsim 1$ μm and

$$q_0 = k'x$$

if $x \lesssim 1$ μm. F is the surface area of the particle of size x; k and k' are coefficients depending on particle shape and the dielectric constant ε or permittivity

$$1 + 2\frac{\varepsilon - 1}{\varepsilon + 2}$$

of the particle.

By equating the force

$$P = k'x^2E^2$$

or

$$P = k'xE$$

581

with fluid resistance

$$S = 3\pi\mu x v_e,$$

the velocity of the particle's motion towards the unlike electrode is obtained as

$$v_e = k'' E^2 x,$$

provided $x \gtrsim 1$ μm, and

$$v_e = k'' E,$$

provided $x \lesssim 1$ μm. Velocity is thus seen to be independent of particle size for particles smaller than about 1 μm and to vary as particle size (in theory at least) for particles larger than that. In a field of gravity or of centrifugal force — in mechanical dust collectors, that is — settling velocity varies as x^2, meaning that it decreases rapidly as particle size decreases, and vice versa. This is why, in the minus-10 μm and especially the minus-5 μm particle size range, electrical precipitation is so much more efficient than mechanical dust collection (cf. also Part A of Fig. 8.2).

In fact, even at $x \gtrsim 1$ μm, particle velocity v_e does not increase linearly: it is kept quasi-constant over a broad particle size range by the electric wind arising in the electric field, as shown by the dashed curve in Fig. 8.5. In practice, depending on field intensity E, v_e varies in the 4 to 20 cm/s range.

In electro-precipitators, particles acquire their charge from a corona electrode, negatively charged to a potential of 30 to 70 kV, installed at a distance of 5 to 25 cm from the grounded collecting electrodes. The current in the corona is 0.1 to 0.5 mA per metre of corona electrode: charge density in the field is 10^7 to 10^8 ions per cm³. Electrode potential and spacing are to be chosen as a function of the ionizability of the gas and of the nature of the dust. Field intensity E is to be the greater, the greater the impressed voltage U, the less the electrode separation R and the smaller the radius of the corona electrode.

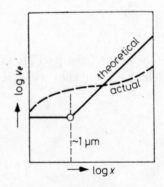

Fig. 8.5. Approximate variation vs. particle size of the drift velocity v_e of dust particles in electrofilters towards the oppositely charged electrode

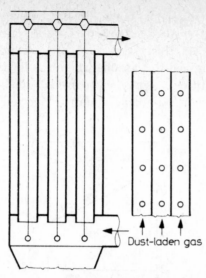

Fig. 8.6. Diagrams of the pipe-type and of the plate-type electrofilter (from left to right)

For example, if the electrodes are concentric cylinders,

$$E = \frac{U}{R} \ln \left(\frac{r_c}{r_s} \right),$$

where r_c and r_s are the radii of the collecting and of the spraying (corona) electrode, respectively. The spraying electrodes are made of fine wire as a rule. The collecting electrodes may e.g. be vertical tubes of 1.8 to 4.5 m length, with a spraying electrode running along the axis of each. They may also be parallel sheets of 1.3 to 1.8 by 5.4 m size, with spraying electrodes strung between them. Figure 8.6 shows diagrams of the operative sections of pipe- and plate-type electro-precipitators, respectively (the latter in top view).

No corona discharge arises below a critical field intensity. Above another, higher field intensity threshold, however, sparkover (electrical breakdown in the medium separating the electrodes) occurs, and that is to be avoided. The smaller the radius r_s of the spraying electrode, the greater the voltage interval separating the critical corona voltage from the sparkover voltage. The two come very close if

$$\frac{r_c}{r_s} \lesssim 10$$

(cf. Fig. 8.7).

The reason why the corona electrode in an electro-precipitator is invariably charged negative is that sparking always starts on the positive electrode, which in such a setup is the collecting electrode. Now for reasons of geometry, field intensity on this latter is much smaller. The difference between the corona voltage and the sparkover voltage is about twice as great in this setup than with the polarities reversed. (In a correct design, sparking in the inhomogeneous electric field will be confined to the zone where the field is strongest. The rest of the gas, not sparked through, serves as an insulator helping to prevent sparkovers amounting to a short circuit between the electrodes.)

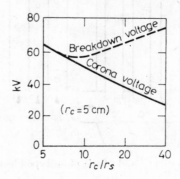

Fig. 8.7. Corona threshold voltage and breakdown (sparkover) voltage vs. the ratio of collecting to spraying electrode radius, r_c/r_s

Dust is recovered from the collecting electrodes by shaking or rapping at intervals. The dust falling off them at those times is sufficiently agglomerated as a rule. In another arrangement, the collecting sheets may be provided with louvered apertures: the dust falling behind the sheet through the louvre has no opportunity to reenter the gas stream.

The emission by the corona electrode is affected among other factors by the nature of the gas, its temperature and relative humidity. High humidities hamper the corona emission or, what is the same, they raise the corona voltage threshold and the voltage required to drive an emission current of a given intensity. For a given voltage, the same operating conditions can be maintained by raising the temperature in step with increasing relative humidity. In Fig. 8.8, Part A shows typical current vs. voltage characteristics of electro-precipitators for different gases; Parts B and C show them for air at different temperatures and relative humidities, respectively; Part D compares dust-free with dust-laden air. Part E is a plot (for a given electrical dust precipitator) of the threshold corona voltage vs. temperature and relative humidity in air.

The correct operation of an electro-precipitator depends greatly on dust resistivity. For a substance to be readily separable, its resistivity should be in the 10^6 to 10^{12} ohm · cm range; the optimum is between 10^8 and 10^{10}. Dusts whose resistivity is below 10^4 are good enough conductors to pass their charge on to the collecting electrodes rapidly enough and, being recharged by it, to be

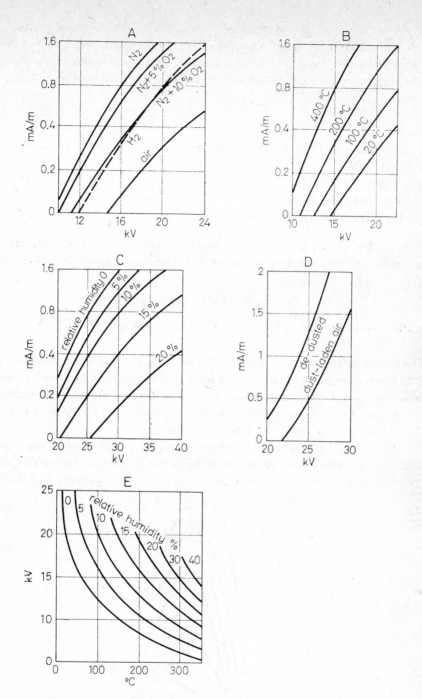

Fig. 8.8. A, B, C, D — typical voltage-current characteristics of electro-filters; E — corona threshold voltage vs. temperature and relative humidity

repelled back into the gas stream. Dusts whose resistivity exceeds $\sim 10^{12}$ ohm · cm on the other hand, may form a coherent insulating layer on the collecting electrode: being negatively charged, this layer repels the particles of like charge approaching it. Approximate resistivities of some dusts in ohm · cm units are

pyrite:	10^3;
chromite, magnesite, quartzite, burnt fireclay:	10^9;
zinc oxide, talc:	10^{10};
clay, marble, iron oxides:	10^{11};
lead oxide, bituminous coal:	10^{12};
gypsum, magnesium oxide, cement:	10^{13}.

At a high dew point, however, the resistivities of cement dust, iron sulphate, lead oxide and clay all drop to about 10^9. The approximate resistivity of fly ash is

$$10^9 \quad 10^{10} \quad 10^{11} \quad 10^{12}$$

at carbon contents of   20   15   10   5%.

Dust may settle on the corona electrode also, provided the dielectric force due to the convergence of the lines of force is stronger than Coulomb repulsion. This is the case with dust particles of high dielectric constant (permittivity) moving close to the corona electrode. In such cases, the latter electrode must also be cleaned at intervals by rapping or shaking.

On the dust settled on the collecting electrodes, potential may build up sufficiently to cause local discharges resulting in the expulsion of ions. The critical current density of emission, I mA per m² of collecting surface, and the resis-

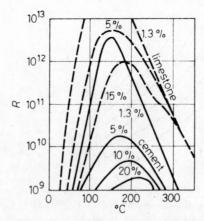

Fig. 8.9. Resistivity of cement and limestone vs. temperature and relative humidity

tivity, R ohm $\cdot$ cm, of the dust are related by

$$\log I = 10.6 - 0.925 \log R$$

Resistivity is a function of dust temperature and surface moisture content also. Operating conditions can be influenced by conditioning the dust-laden gas. The conductivity of dust of a given nature can be influenced by modifying its relative humidity: moisture adsorbed on the particle surfaces reduces apparent resistivity. The way the resistivity of cement and limestone dust is affected by the temperature and relative humidity of air is shown in Fig. 8.9. In cement factories employing the wet process, where the relative humidity of the gas is high, conditions may be stable at any temperature; in dry-process plants, on the other hand, wetting may be necessary, either by simple spraying or by the insertion of a scrubbing tower into the flowsheet. Dust collection out of the flue gases of blast furnaces and other metallurgical furnaces, sinter plants, etc. also requires, more often than not, the wetting of the gas in order to bring the resistivity of the dust within the range of electro-precipitation.

Sulphur contained in the fuel is burnt to SO_2 and constitutes sulphurous acid escaping in the flue gas with the water formed on combustion. The resistivity of fly ash, which is a maximum between 150 and 200 °C, is affected by the presence of sulphurous acid as follows:

	10^{12}	10^{10}	10^9 ohm $\cdot$ cm
with	0	0.2	0.6% H_2SO_3 present;

that is, it is shifted from the hard-to-precipitate zone to the optimum range (Sproull and Nakada 1951).

Dust recovery out of a gas spending a time t between the plates of a plate-type electro-precipitator is

$$m = 1 - e^{-v_e t/R} = 1 - e^{-v_e L/Ru} = 1 - e^{-v_e f} = 1 - e^{-t/t'} = 1 - K^{-t}.$$

In a pipe-type device, t is to be replaced by $2t$. In the formula, v_e (which is in the 4 to 20 cm/s range) is the velocity of the dust particles' travel towards the collecting electrode; $R = 5$ to 25 cm is the separation between the spraying and the collecting electrode; $L = 200$ to 500 cm is the length of the precipitator (more precisely, of the field in the direction of the gas flow), and $u = 100$ to 400 cm/s is gas velocity.

$$f = \frac{L}{Ru} = \frac{t}{R} \quad \text{s/cm}$$

is the specific retention time of the particles in the field;

$$t = \frac{L}{u}$$

is the retention time of the gas in the field, and

$$t' = \frac{R}{v_e}$$

is the travel time of the dust particles in the field. The relationship

$$f = \frac{t}{R_h} = \frac{F}{Q}$$

also holds, where R_h cm (surface area over circumference) is the hydraulic radius (applicable to both pipe and plate type precipitators) of the collecting surface; F cm^2 is the surface area of those; Q cm^3/s is the gas flow rate and $K = 0.05$ to 0.5 is a constant characterizing a given dust in a given electro-precipitator. In practice, f is in the 0.0115 to 0.035 s/cm range. (In the formulae, centimetres may be replaced by metres; this changes the other units to m/s, m^3, m^2/s, etc.)

The formula is furnished by the following consideration. It takes the gas flow a time element dt to travel a distance dL. During the time dt, dust concentration decreases by dc. If electrode distance is R and the third dimension of the electric field is B, then the amount of dust removed the while from the volume $BR\,dL$ is $BR\,dL\,dc$. On the other hand, during the time element dt, the dust particles travel a distance $v_e\,dt$ towards the collecting electrode. In other words, all the dust will be removed from a volume $Bv_e\,dL\,dt$ defined by the distance $v_e\,dt$ from the collecting electrode. The quantity of dust removed is thus given by the product $cBv_e\,dL\,dt$. Hence, the differential equation

$$-R\,dc = cv_e\,dt$$

may be written up; it integrates to

$$\ln\left(\frac{c}{c_0}\right) = -v_e\frac{t}{R}$$

or

$$m = 1 - \frac{c}{c_0} = 1 - e^{-v_e t/R}.$$

If the precipitator is of the pipe type, the cross section BR perpendicular to the gas flow is to be replaced by $R^2\pi$ and the area element $B\,dL$ by $2R\pi\,dL$, giving

$$\ln\left(\frac{c}{c_0}\right) = -2v_e\frac{t}{R}.$$

Dust recovery m vs. f,

$$m = 1 - e^{-v_e f},$$

588

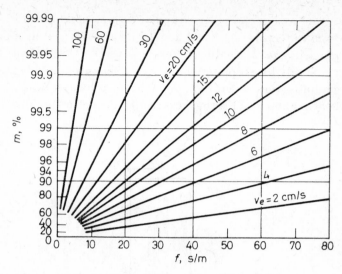

Fig. 8.10. Dust recovery in an electro-filter vs. $f = F/Q$, specific retention time in the field, with travel velocity v_e as the parameter

with the cross velocity v_e as the parameter, has been plotted in Fig. 8.10. The exponential form of the recovery formula implies that improving recovery from 90% to 99% (or from 99% to 99.9%) requires the same length of precipitator L or the same retention time t as recovering the first 90%. It is thus greatly indicated to use a rougher collector to remove the coarser dust fractions upstream of the electrical precipitator (Masuda 1966). In systems where gas flow is horizontal, several (two to five) electrically independent devices are often connected in series.

The pressure drop in an electro-precipitator is low at about 5 to 15 mm water gauge; hence, so is power draft (0.1 to 0.3 kW h per 1,000 m³ of gas); the device requires no maintenance, except for its shaking or rapping unit. Its principal advantage over other dust collection systems is that it permits to remove the finest dust at almost the same efficiency as the coarser fractions. It can be used to handle acid or otherwise corrosive gases even at high temperatures. Its investment cost and space requirement are fairly great, however (Arras 1972; Czibók 1968; Heinrich 1961; Jákli 1973; Koglin 1964, 1965; Masuda 1966; McKibbon 1971; Norman 1970; Raschovszki 1968, 1974; Rose and Wood 1956; Sayers 1960).

8.2.5. Cloth filters are efficient devices, but they are expensive and delicate as well, and take up a great deal of space. Filter elements in a bag filter are tubular bags of 2 to 4 m length and 12 to 25 cm diameter, attached to a moveable frame with their top (closed) ends and to the round ports of a dust tank with their bottom (open) ends. Their tubular form is maintained by wire rings fixed (sewn in) at intervals of 0.5 to 1.2 m. Clean air is sucked by a fan through the bags arranged in parallel; dust is retained on the cloth. Captured dust is removed at intervals by stopping the fan and shaking and/or stretching the bags. In larger units, these operations are performed by a suitably programmed automatic device. Figure 8.11 is the cross section of such a bag filter (the BETH

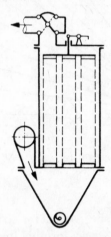

Fig. 8.11. Diagram of a BETH cloth filter

filter). Groups of bags are installed in this device in several separate chambers. The chambers are connected by a butterfly valve each to the suction manifold of the fan. At intervals of 5 to 15 min, the butterfly valve is turned so as to open the chamber to the ambient air. During these periods of reversal, air flows through the bags from the outside inward; simultaneously, the shaker is also turned on: the pores of the filter cloth are unclogged by this double action. The air let in escapes towards the fan through the neighbouring chambers.

Hand-shaken bag filters are best suited for the cleaning of air containing one to two grammes of dust per m^3: the BETH filters with their automatic cleaning can be used up to 50 g/m^3, at gas flow rates in the 1 to 4 $m^3/min \cdot m^2$ range. At greater dust loads, it is usual to insert a rougher stage. Filter cloth is made of wool, cotton, various man-made fibres, etc. The finer the threads of the cloth, the finer are the dust particles the cloth can take out of the gas. There are cloths that permit to recover about 99.5% even of minus-0.5 μm dust ! Gas in its passage through the cloth is deflected repeatedly, so that the dust particles in it can collide with and adhere to the fibres. The attachment between particles and threads may be mechanical and/or electrostatic. Once the particles settled out have bridged the pores of the cloth, it is the dust layer on the cloth that functions as the actual filter.

The relationship

$$m = 1 - k_1 e^{-k_2 Q}$$

or

$$m = 1 - k_1 e^{-k_2' t}$$

holds, where Q is the weight of dust adhering to the filter and t is the duration of the filtration run. Q varies as t. The logarithm of $P = 1 - m$, of dust in the cleaned gas, decreases linearly as Q (or t) increases; $\log k_1$, the ordinate intercept at $Q = 0$ (or $t = 0$), is a function of cloth quality and gas velocity u through the filter:

$$k_1 = Au + B.$$

Dust recovery can be expressed in terms of other parameters also. Consider a unit area of filter sheet, of porosity $1 - \sigma$, made up of threads of diameter d, whose specific dust-capturing capability is b/d. The effective dust-capturing area of the threads being σ for a total length of σ/d, the amount of dust that can be recovered will vary as

$$\frac{\sigma}{d} \cdot \frac{b}{d}.$$

Dust recovery on the other hand equals the loss of dust from the gas passing through, where c_{in} and c_{out} is the entry and exit concentration of dust in the gas flowing at velocity u. Hence,

$$c_{in} - c_{out} = \frac{k}{u} \cdot \frac{\sigma}{d} \cdot \frac{b}{d},$$

and

$$m = \frac{k}{c_{in} u} \cdot \frac{\sigma}{d} \cdot \frac{b}{d}.$$

The formula holds only until the pores of the sheet are bridged by dust. Even before, however, the porosity and dust-capturing capability of the sheet will gradually change as the pores are clogged up. (m increases monotonically because both δ and b/d increase.)

Electric charges affect the agglomeration of dust particles among them, their adhesion to the filter cloth, and, through those, also the efficiency of dust collection and the ease or otherwise of de-clogging the filter cloth. The different types of filter cloth differ as to the sign and magnitude of the charges they acquire by friction. Of the filter-cloth materials most widespread in industrial practice, the one with the highest positive charge is wool ($\sim +20$ V), whereas the one with the highest negative charge is polyethylene (-20 V). Usual frictional charges are $+15$ V for glass fibres, $+5$ to -10 V for dacron and orlon, and -10 to -15 V for polypropylene (Dick 1970; Frederick 1961; Funke 1971;

Löffler 1966; Schlegel 1969; Silverman et al. 1955; Stafford and Smith 1951; Winkel 1964).

The porosity of the layer of dust deposited on the cloth has a tendency to increase as average particle size decreases. (For example, the porosity, $\varepsilon = 1 - \sigma$, of the layer forming on the cloth was found to be 0.94 for fly dust of 0.25 μm, 0.81 for talc of 1.5 μm, 0.70 for clay of 4.6 μm, 0.75 for fly dust of 5.6 μm, 0.66 for flour of 12 μm and 0.56 for flour of 33 μm average particle size.)

The resistance of a filter bag is expressed by the formula

$$\Delta p = \frac{\zeta \varrho}{2}\, u^n \text{ mm water gauge,}$$

where u m/s is gas velocity referred to the entire filtering surface, $\varrho = \gamma/g$ is gas density, ζ is a resistance coefficient determined by the nature of the filter cloth and the extent of its clogging, and n is a function of the flow behaviour of the gas flowing in the filter (of the Reynolds number): it is in the 1 to 2 range. ζ is about 8,000 e.g. for clean filter bags of wool, and many times that value for bags made of man-made fibres. For example, taking a woollen cloth and a gas flow rate of 3.6 m³/min · m² giving

$$u = 0.06 \text{ m/s,}$$

we have

$$\Delta p = 8,000 \frac{1.3}{19.6}\, 0.06^{1.5} = 7.5 \text{ mm wg}$$

for an exponent of 1.5 and

$$\Delta p = 30 \text{ mm wg}$$

for an exponent of $n = 1.0$.

The specific resistance of the filter sheet is k_s mm water gauge times seconds per metre; that of the dust layer is k_r mm wg · sm/kg, and total resistance in laminar flow is

$$\Delta p = (k_s + k_r Q)u \text{ mm wg,}$$

where Q is in kg/m² and u is in m/s or (or m³/m² · s). The average operating parameters of dust-covered filter cloths tend to fall between $u = 0.005$ and 0.03 m/s and $\Delta p = 50$ and 150 mm water gauge.

There are tubular bag filters operated under pressure as well. In these too, dust settles on the inner face of the cloth, but the tubes do not have to be boxed in to create a depression: clean air can emerge from the bags direct into the ambient air.

Instead of filter tubes, flat pillowcase-like elements can also be used: in this way, a larger filter surface can be accommodated in the same space.

Cloth filters, if undamaged, can achieve almost 100% dust recovery, so that the air leaving them may be returned to any work space. This is a great advantage in wintertime, when recycling permits a considerable economy of heat. Further advantages include a comparatively small resistance. Their drawbacks include a propensity to clogging if the air or the dust is moist. They also damage rather easily. Combustible filter cloths represent a fire hazard too (Funke 1971).

8.2.6. Ultrasonic dust precipitation. Rapid agglomeration of dust particles in a gas can be achieved by creating standing sound waves that make the particles vibrate. In gas of viscosity μ, vibrating at a frequency ν and an amplitude λ, particles of diameter x and s.g. δ will vibrate with an amplitude

$$A = \frac{\lambda}{\sqrt{\left(\dfrac{\pi x^2 \delta \nu}{9\mu C}\right)^2 + 1}},$$

where $C > 1$ is the Cunningham correction coefficient that accounts for the free paths of the gas molecules in the settling of fine particles (the medium friction $P = 3\pi\mu x \nu$ in Stokes's formula is to be divided by it). For example, with $\delta = 1$, the Stokesian settling velocity in air of particles of size

$$x = 20 \quad 5 \quad 1 \quad 0.1 \ \mu\text{m}$$

is increased by

$$<1 \quad 5 \quad 17 \quad 300\%\ !$$

If

$$A \cong 0.8\lambda,$$

then

$$x^2 \frac{\delta \nu}{C\mu} = 2.16;$$

the particles finer than the critical size c_{crit} thus defined will practically vibrate together with the gas. Critical size is accordingly a function of frequency: e.g., the frequency corresponding to $x_{\text{crit}} \lesssim 7 \ \mu\text{m}$ is practically ultrasonic.

8.2.7. Spray washers. In order to improve the efficiency of dust collection, spray washers add to the dust-laden gas a wetting fluid (water in most of the cases). Spray washers tend to have less of a resistance and to occupy less space than dry devices of identical dust collection performance. Sprayed dust collects in the form of a pulp. This is an advantage in that pulp discharge gives rise to no secondary dusting, but a drawback also in that the pulp requires further handling (Mallozzi 1970, 1971).

The extent to which dust particles will wet depends on their contact angle (their hydrophilic or hydrophobic nature). Wetting can be direct (by spraying) or indirect (by condensation). The dust particles may carry some adsorbed gas as well on their surfaces. Angle of contact is determined by the surface tensions or surface energies E of the solids (S), water (W) and air (A) in combination.

(Of all the types of free energy that may be at work, we shall confine the enquiry here to surface energies only.) A droplet of water in air will adhere to a solid particle if

$$A = E_{WA} + E_{SA} - E_{SW} > 0.$$

The substitution

$$E_{SA} = E_{SW} + E_{WA} \cos \vartheta$$

restates the condition of adherence between the solid and the droplet as

$$A = E_{WA}(1 + \cos \vartheta) > 0.$$

The angle of contact being invariably less than 180°, a droplet of water would invariably adhere to any solid particle it encounters, if surface energy were the only energy at play. The propensity to adhere together is the greater, the less is ϑ. As E_{WA} decreases, $\vartheta < 90°$ decreases along with it; in practice, agents reducing the surface tension of water (wetters) are sometimes used to reduce the angle of contact and thereby to promote adhesion between the water droplets and the particles of large angle of contact (such as the dust of bituminous coal).

The wetting of hydrophobic dust particles may often be hindered by films of gas adsorbed on their surfaces. This may be circumvented by taking the dusty air first through a hot humid space and then through a cooler one. Water vapour diffusing into the gas films on the particles will condense in the cool chamber; the droplets of mist thus formed will open up the surface of the solid particle to the water (Cheng 1973; Weber 1968).

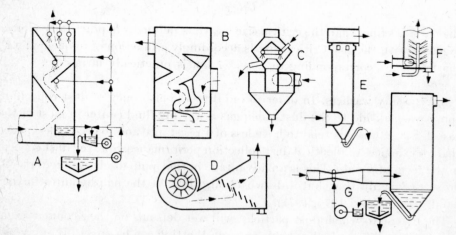

Fig. 8.12. Diagrams of wet dust collectors. A — simple spraying tower, B — an inertial device (roto-clone scrubber), C — a wet dust collector combined with a dry cyclone, D — coaxial-nozzle dynamic collector, E and F — wetted-wall dust collectors (cyclone scrubbers), G — Venturi scrubber

Wet dust collectors may be static scrubbers, dynamic disintegrators and wetted-surface devices (Dullien and Murro 1973; Lapple and Kamack 1955; Quitter 1966). Some of the possible designs are shown in Fig. 8.12.

Part A of the figure shows a static spray washer. In it, a rain of spray falls on the upward-moving gas; the sludged dust is collected, the water is clarified and the clear water is returned to the sprayers. The process is more economical if, as shown in the diagram, water is recycled without removing the slimes and an excess buildup of slimes is prevented by clarifying a part-stream of water in a bypass circuit.

A jet of water of diameter D will spontaneously change into a droplet of diameter d if the surface of the latter (more precisely, the surface multiplied by the surface tension) is less. In other words, a jet of volume

$$LD^2 \frac{\pi}{4}$$

change into a droplet of volume

$$d^3 \frac{\pi}{6},$$

provided

$$\pi d^2 a \leq DLa,$$

that is, if

$$d \geq 1.5D.$$

If droplets finer than that are to be generated, energy (kinetic energy in partic-ular) must be imparted to the system, so as to deform the large droplet and break them up into smaller ones. The drops formed on spraying are not all of the same size. Their diameter is related to the number z of droplets by a sto-chastic relationship, with the number of droplets a maximum in the proximity of some diameter d. The distribution is a lognormal one as a rule. For practical purposes, it is best to use the surface-area average droplet size

$$d_f = \frac{\Sigma d_i^3 \, \Delta z}{\Sigma d_i^2 \, \Delta z}.$$

(This is the size at which surface area stands in the same ratio to volume as the aggregate surface area of the actual droplets with their different diameters stands to their aggregate volume.) (Troesch 1954.)

Dust-laden gas moves at a relative velocity u against the falling or scattered droplets. The flow lines of the gas are deflected by the droplets: the condition of a collision taking place between a droplet and a dust particle is that the lat-ter, passing through the gas flow at a crosswise velocity u, attains the droplet.

38*

The Stokesian fluid resistance hindering the dust particle of size x is

$$\frac{m \, du_x}{dt} = \frac{\delta \pi x^3}{6g} \frac{du_x}{dt} = -3\pi \mu x u_x.$$

μ here is the viscosity of the *gas*. Hence,

$$\frac{du_x}{u_x} = -\frac{18\mu g}{\delta x^2} \, dt = -K \, dt.$$

Integration gives

$$u_x = u_0 e^{-Kt},$$

where u_0 is the initial velocity of the droplet perpendicularly to the gas flow. The distance travelled by the dust particle is

$$s = \int u_x \, dt = \frac{u_0}{K} (1 - e^{-Kt}) = \frac{u_0 - u_x}{K}.$$

The radius of action is a maximum at $u_x = 0$:

$$s_{max} = \frac{x^2 u_0 \gamma}{18\mu g}.$$

The maximum radius of action as measured from the surface of the droplet, b, relates to the diameter of the droplet as

$$b = \frac{s_{max}}{d}.$$

Dust particles within a distance s_{max} will collide with the droplet but will not necessarily adhere to it on every collision. The probability of adherence is expressed by the formula

$$p = a\sqrt{b} = ax \sqrt{\frac{u_0 \delta}{18\mu g d}},$$

where a is a constant characterizing the system under examination. Hence, scrubbing efficiency increases, the greater the velocity differential u_0 between droplet and gas, the larger the size x of the dust particle, the greater its s.g. and the smaller the diameter of the droplets.

Figure 8.13 presents the probability $p\%$ of adhesion per collision of dust particles of different size to the droplets in a static scrubber relying on Earth gravity, vs. droplet diameter d. It emerges that, in such scrubbers, where the relative velocity of collision equals by and large the terminal settling velocity of the droplets, optimum droplet size is about 0.5 mm. Moreover, p is seen to be very small for dust particles smaller than about 2 μm. The deflection of these fine dust particles from the flow lines of the gas is due to weak forces of diffusion and of electrostatic attraction rather than to the even weaker forces of inertia.

Part B of Fig. 8.12 is the diagram of a wet roto-clone. The bottom part of this "inertial" device is a tank provided with a specially designed air deflector, which serves also for the storage of the retained dust. Gas flowing at a high velocity through the narrow passage just above the water level raises foam and spray, the deflection of which creates a water curtain. This fills out completely the cross section leading into the clean-gas compartment. Dust attachment is

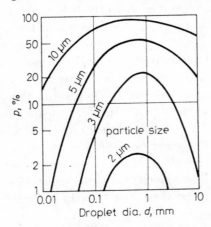

Fig. 8.13. Probability of adhesion $p\%$ of dust particles of different size vs. water droplet size in static dust collectors relying on gravity

brought about partly by the reduction of velocity on the air intake side, partly by the intensive mixing and deflection of mist- and dust-laden gas (by forces of centrifugal inertia), and partly by further deceleration on the clean-gas side. On the Tromp curve of a roto-clone (handling a quartz dust), the particle sizes corresponding to the Tromp values

$T =$	25	50	75	90	99%
are	1	2	6	16	50 μm.

In the pressure drop formula

$$p = \frac{\zeta \varrho u^n}{2} = A u^n \text{ mm water gauge,}$$

$\zeta \cong 70$ (or $A = 4.4$) and $n \cong 1.22$ if u is in m/s.

The spray washer is often combined with a dry roughing cyclone, as shown in Part C of Fig. 8.12.

Part D of the figure is the diagram of a dynamic spray washer in which a rotary nozzle coaxial with the impeller of a fan creates a finely dispersed veil of droplets. This mixes thoroughly with the gas and wets the dust particles in it. Further along the path, the gas is deflected by baffles to which the droplets of slimy water adhere.

In another type of mechanical (dynamical) spray washer, water is broken up into a fine mist and mixed thoroughly with the gas by a disintegrator. The disintegrator (Vol. 1, p. 330) incorporates three or four concentric rows of impact pegs on a disk rotating about a horizontal axis. Blades mounted on the rim of the rotating disk serve partly to remove the water from the gas and partly for creating the pressure that moves the gas along. Disintegrators deliver a remarkable de-dusting performance at comparatively low power drafts (5 to 6 kW h per 1,000 m³ of gas). The water requirement is 0.5 to 1.5 m³ per 1,000 m³ of gas.

Parts E and F of Fig. 8.12 represent wetted-surface devices. Both are essentially wet-wall aerocyclones into which dust-laden gas is introduced tangentially at the bottom. Cleaned gas emerges axially at the top (or tangentially, after passing some spin-reducing baffles). In Diagram E, the cylinder wall is wetted with water sprayed in at the top: a water film tricking down the shell picks the dust particles coming into contact with it out of the gas spiralling upward in the cylinder. Diagram F, the cyclone scrubber, has a multi-nozzle spraying pipe installed centrally at its bottom. Water consumption is 0.4 to 1.4 m³ per 1,000 m³ of gas. Axial gas flow velocity in these spraying cyclones is 6 to 8 m/s. The drag coefficient ζ referred to inlet velocity in their formula

$$\Delta p = \frac{\zeta \varrho u^2}{2}$$

equals about 2.5.

Part G of Fig. 8.12 is the diagram of a throat-nozzle Venturi scrubber. In it, a Venturi tube is inserted into the inlet pipe bringing the dust-laden gas. Where the passage is narrowest and gas velocity is accordingly greatest at 60 to 90 m/s, water is sprayed in at 0.3 to 2.0 bars gauge, at a rate of 0.4 to 1.4 m³ per 1,000 m³ of gas. The spray breaks up into a very fine mist which adheres to the dust particles. These can be taken out at a very high efficiency in the wet cyclone attached to the Venturi tube. The resistance of the entire setup is fairly high at 300 to 500 mm water gauge, but it performs well even when handling particles in the minus-2 μm range (Ekman and Johnstone 1951).

The straight lines in Fig. 8.14 show the optimum droplet sizes d_{opt} corresponding to different dust particle sizes x μm vs. air velocity u in the Venturi tube. The dashed curve, on the other hand, presents mist particle size vs. gas velocity. The surface-area average diameter of the droplets is given by an empirically established formula as

$$d_l \simeq \frac{a}{u} + b \left(\frac{q_l}{q_g} \right)^c,$$

where q_l/q_g is the ratio of the volume velocities of liquid and gas, and a, b and c are constants. Mist particle size will be optimally matched to given dust particle size at a unique air velocity only (where the curve and the appropriate line, intersect). It emerges from the figure that only the finest dust particles require high gas speeds.

A droplet of diameter d travelling a distance dL sweeps a volume

$$\frac{d^2\pi}{4}\,dL.$$

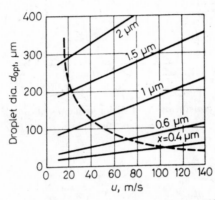

Fig. 8.14. Optimum water droplet size d_{opt} corresponding to different dust particle sizes x vs. air velocity u out of the nozzle in a Venturi scrubber. The dashed curve shows the variation of droplet size on leaving the nozzle

Liquid sprayed in at the volume rate q_l breaks up into $6q_l/\pi d^3$ droplets: that is, the total gas volume swept by the droplets is

$$dq_g = \frac{6q_l}{d^3\pi}\frac{d^2\pi}{4}\,dL = 3q_l\,\frac{dL}{2d}.$$

Dust contained in this volume is cdq_g; if the probability of attachment is $p < 1$, then the amount of dust that can be removed is $pcdq_g$. The same amount of dust is obtained by multiplying the gas volume q_g with the decrease in dust concentration, $-dc$: that is,

$$-q_g dc = 3q_l pc\,\frac{dL}{2d}.$$

Integrating between the limits of initial and final dust concentration, c_0 and c_1 one finds

$$\ln\left(\frac{c_1}{c_0}\right) = -3p\,\frac{q_l}{q_g}\,\frac{L}{2d}.$$

The ratio $L/d = b$ is a constant under given operating conditions for the nozzle; p varies as the square root of b; that is,

$$\frac{c_1}{c_0} = e^{-K\frac{q_l}{q_g}\sqrt{b}},$$

599

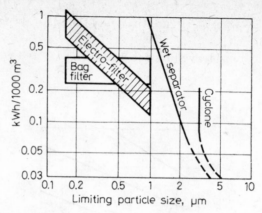

Fig. 8.15. Specific energy consumption of different types of dust collecting equipment vs. the limiting particle size

and dust recovery is

$$m = \frac{c_0 - c_1}{c_0} = 1 - e^{-K\frac{q_l}{q_g}\sqrt{b}},$$

where K and b are constants characteristic of the given setup.

The power draft per unit of gas throughput of different types of dust collecting equipment is shown vs. the limiting particle size in Fig. 8.15.

The expenses of using different types of dust collecting equipment, broken down into operating costs and depreciation, with those of the cyclone taken as unity, are shown in Table 8.2, and so is the approximative particle size range of application of each. The middle values of the size data in μm (in the parentheses) indicate the usual, safely reliable ranges of application, whereas the outer values indicate the extremes regarded as still feasible.

Table 8.3 provides information concerning the operating parameters ($m\%$, Δp), investment cost and operating costs of certain types of dust collecting equipment at a rate of gas throughput of $\sim$30 m³/s ($\cong$10⁵ m³/h). The dust

Table 8.2. Cost of operation of different types of dust-collecting equipment referred to that of the cyclone and breakdown into operating cost and depreciation

	Depreciation ($\sim\mu$m)	Relative cost	Oper.	Depr.	Depr. %
Cyclone	5 — (15 — 60) — 100	1.0	0.6	0.4	40
Vortex tube	0.5 — (5 — 20) — 50	1.6	0.8	0.8	50
Roto-clone	0.5 — (1 — 50) — 200	2.4	1.4	1.0	42
Electro-filter	0.01 — (0.5 — 20) — 50	4.9	1.4	3.5	72
Bag filter	0.01 — (0.5 — 10) — 50	5.4	2.9	2.5	46
Venturi scrubber	0.1 — (0.5 — 50) — 100	6.6	4.3	2.3	35

600

Table 8.3. Approximate investment costs (I) and operating costs including depreciation (O) and percentage breakdown of those for different types of dust collecting equipments

Dust-laden gas throughput 30 m³/s	$m\%$	$\dfrac{\Delta p}{mm\ wg}$	$\dfrac{I}{10^3\ £}$	$\dfrac{O^*}{sh/10^4\ m^3}$	Percentage breakdown at total cost			
					depreciation	energy	water	others
1 Inertial dust collectors	59	45	11	0.47	55	40	—	5
2 Average cyclones	65	95	8	0.62	31	66	—	3
3 Cyclones of high efficiency	84	125	15	0.94	39	59	—	2
4 Vortex tubes	94	110	17	0.91	45	53	—	2
5 Electro-filters	99	25	74	2.14	84	11	—	5
6 Bag filters	99.7	65	52	2.52	51	18	—	31
7 Wet aerocyclone	91	100	19	1.15	40	43	14	3
8 Rotoclone	94	150	21	1.30	40	53	2	4
9 Disintegrator	98.5	—	43	6.86	15	81	3	1
10 Average Venturi scrubber	99.7	500	34	3.54	24	66	8	2
11 High-energy Venturi scrubber	99.9	800	37	4.90	18	74	6	2

Referred to 10,100 m³ of gas/h (0.8 Ft kW h, 8,000 h/year)	$m\%$	$\dfrac{\Delta p}{mm\ wg}$	Water m³/h	$\dfrac{I}{10^6\ Ft}$	$\dfrac{O^{**}}{10^6\ Ft/year}$
1 Cyclone	65	90	—	0.5	270
Cyclone	75	105	—	9.7	320
Cyclone	85	120	—	0.8	360
Multiclone	90	120	—	1.1	350
Multiclone	93	140	—	1.2	430
1a Wet cyclone	91	100	64	1.0	500
2 Scrubber	94	150	10	1.2	500
Scrubber	98	160	48	1.4	640
3 Bag filter, wool	99	120	—	2.5	760
Bag filter, glass	99.3	120	—	3.0	900
4 Electro-filter, dry	85	10	—	3.0	240
Electro-filter, dry	90	10	—	3.2	250
Electro-filter, dry	95	10	—	3.7	260
Electro-filter, dry	99	10	—	5.5	340
4a Electro-filter, wet	99.5	10	35	6.0	400
Electro-filter, wet	99.7	10	40	6.2	430
5 Disintegrator	99.5	—	80	3.0	1,980
6 Venturi scrubber	98.2	410	110	1.9	1,570
Venturi scrubber	99.4	550	110	2.0	1,960
Venturi scrubber	99.8	660	110	2.8	2,290

* Without the cost of pulp handling for wet dust collectors.

** Without depreciation.

sh/10⁴ m³: UK shillings per 10,000 m³.

recovery data $m\%$ in the top part of the table, taken from an English-language publication, refer to dust of s.g. 2.7 and granulometry

$x\ \mu m$:	2.5	5	10	20	40	80	120
$s_F\%$:	12	20	30	45	65	92	98.

The investment and operating costs of the equipment figuring in the table are plotted in Fig. 8.16. Dry collectors are somewhat more economical than wet ones. The least economical of the items figuring in the list is the disintegrator (Gilbert 1961).

Further to be mentioned are packed filters, in whose filter elements zigzagged or corrugated sheets force the gas moving between them to change direction every so often. The dust particles colliding with the walls lose their velocity. These filters are operated wet: their surfaces of collision are coated with a film of some high-viscosity liquid suited for trapping the dust (e.g. viscin oil). Clogged-up filters are removed and washed out at intervals. The corrugated or zigzagged sheets may be replaced by similarly bent wire netting (screening) or glass fibres or a loose heap of metal cylinders of 5 to 10 mm diameter and about

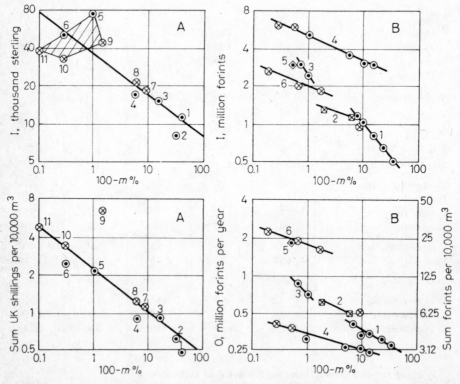

Fig. 8.16. Investment (I) and operating (O) costs of different types of dust collecting equipment vs. $(100 - m\%)$: cf. Table 8.3

the same height (Raschig rings). Filter elements are 3 to 7 cm thick. Depending on the packing, the drag coefficient of the cell, referred to gas velocity over the entire cross section of gas flow (a velocity of 1 to 1.5 m/s as a rule), is in the $\zeta = 50$ to 300 range. It increases as dust builds up on the filter elements.

Wet filters appropriately packed with lamellae, labyrinths, Raschig rings, pressed fibres, etc. are suited for the removal even of very fine dust. Their principal drawback is that they will serve at fairly low dust concentrations only, and even then they must be cleaned fairly often to prevent their resistance becoming excessive. Automatic cleaning has been devised: cells are combined into an endless chain moving crosswise to the gas flow. The bottom flight of the chain dips into an oil tank which washes out and regenerates the cells (Kangro 1961).

8.3. LITERATURE ON SEPARATION OF SOLIDS FROM GASES

ARRAS, K.: Elektrofilter für die Entstaubung von Zementmühlen. *Zement—Kalk—Gips* 1972, 610—615.

BROWN, R. L.: Which dust collector is right for you. *Rock Products* 1968 Feb., 76—80.

CHENG, L.: Collection of airborne dust by water sprays. *I & EC Process Des. Develop.* 1973, 221—225.

CZIBÓK, E.: Elektrofilterek szerkezete és üzeme. (Design and operation of electrofilters.) *MTI 4646*, Budapest 1968.

DICK, G. A.: Fabric filters. *Can. Min. J.* 1970 Oct., 72—80.

DULLIEN, F. A. L.—T. S. MURRO: Fractional mass efficiency measurements on a wet dust scrubber. *Powder Tech.* (8) 1973, 57—68.

EKMAN, F. O.—H. F. JOHNSTONE: Collection of aerosols in a Venturi scrubber. *Ind. Eng. Chem.* 1951, 1358—1363.

FREDERICK, E. R.: How dust filter selection depends on electrostatics. *Chem. Eng.* 1961 June, 107—114.

FUNKE, G.: Faserstoff-Filter für Zementwerke. *Z-K-G* 1971, 327—337.

GILBERT, N.: The cost of wet scrubbing. *Chem. Eng. Progr.* 1961, 112—114.

GÖSLING, C.-E.—U. HIMMEN: Entstauber. (ACHEMA 1970.) *Chem. Ing. Tech.* 1970, 1457—1459.

HEINRICH, D. O.: Study on electro-precipitator performance in relation to particle size distribution, level of collection efficiency and power input. *Trans. ICE* 1961, 145—163.

HIRSCH, L.: *Porelszívás, porleválasztás.* (Dust removal and de-dusting.) Táncsics Kiadó, Budapest 1964.

JÁKLI, E.: Villamos porelválasztók nagyfeszültségű energiaellátó berendezései. (High-voltage power supplies for electric dust precipitators.) *Műszaki Élet* (28) 1973 Oct., No. 22, 4.

JOHN, P.: Zur Entstaubungstechnik bei Aufbereitungsprozessen. *AT* 1968, 399—409.

KANGRO, C.: Theorien über die Abscheidung von Aerosolen in Faserfiltern. *Staub* 1961, 275—280.

KING, D. T.: Dust collection in coal preparation plants. *Min. Engng* 1967 Aug., 64—69.

KOEHLE, H.: Basic information on dry centrifugal collectors. *Can. Min. J.* 1970 Oct., 85—88.

KOGLIN, W.: Entstaubung mit Elektrofiltern. *AT* 1964, 580—605.

KOGLIN, W.: Abschiedgrad eines Elektrofiltern in Abhängigkeit von der Leistungsaufnahme und der Staubkörnung. *AT* 1965, 484—489.

KOGLIN, W. (ed.) *BETH-Handbuch Staubtechnik*. (2. Aufl.) Selbstverlag Maschienenfabrik BETH GmbH, Lübeck 1964.

KRIEGEL, E.: Einfluss der Staubbeladung auf den Durchsatz und Druckverlust von Zyklonabscheidern. *AT* 1968, 1—8.

LAPPLE, C. E.—H. J. KAMACK: Performance of wet dust scrubbers. *Chem. Ing. Progr.* 1955, 110—121.

LEINEWEBER, L.: Auslegung von Zyklonabscheidern nach vorgegebenen Werten für Grenzkorn, Druckverlust und Durchsatz. *Staub* 1967, 123—129.

LÖFFLER, F.: Untersuchung der Haftkräfte zwischen Feststoffteilchen und Faseroberflächen. *Staub* 1966, 274—280.

MALLOZZI, F.: Wet collectors. *Can. Min. J.* 1970 Oct., 80—85.

MALLOZZI, F.: Wet collectors control dust and air pollution. *CIM Bull.* 1971 Oct., 77—84.

MASUDA, S.: Statistische Betrachtungen über den Abscheidegrad des Elektrofilters, *Staub* 1966, 459—463.

McKIBBON, J. H.: Developments in dust collection equipment. *Can. M. M. Bull.* 1962, 713—715.

McKIBBON, J. H.: Selection of electrostatic precipitators to meet new pollution codes. *CIM Bull.* 1971 Sep., 82—84.

MELDAU, R.: *Handbuch der Staubtechnik*. Bd. I: Grundlagen; Bd. II: Staubtechnologie. VDI-Verlag, Düsseldorf 1956/58.

NAGEL, R.—R. IBING: Welche Betriebswarte muss der Besteller eines Entstaubers (spez. Fliehkraftentstaubers) dem Lieferer geben und welche Gewährleistung kann er erwarten. *Staub* 1961, 8—15.

NORMAN, G. H. C.: Electrostatic precipitation. *Can. Min. J.* 1970 Oct., 69—72.

QUITTER, V.: Untersuchungen an dynamischen Nassabscheidern des Abscheidegrades. *Staub* 1966, 468—472.

RASCHOVSZKI, L.: Elektrosztatikus leválasztók. (Electrostatic precipitators.) *Építőanyag* 1963, 348—352.

RASCHOVSZKI, L.: Elektrofilterek elmélete és villamosberendezései. (Theory and electric installations of electrofilters.) *MTI 4642*, Budapest 1968.

RASCHOVSZKI, L.: Korszerű elektrofilterek folyamatai. (Processes in modern electrofilters.) *Építőanyag* 1974, 139—148.

ROSE, H. A.—A. J. WOOD: *An introduction to electrostatic precipitation in theory and practice*. Constable, London 1956. (2nd ed.)

ROSIN, P.—E. RAMMLER—W. INTELMANN: Grundlagen und Grenzen der Zyklonentstaubung. *Z-VDI* 1932, 433—437.

SAYERS, J. E.: Electroprecipitators: Practical design aspects. *J. Inst. Fuel* 1960, 542—550.

SCHLEGEL, H.: Einsatz von neuen Filtermedien in der Entstaubungstechnik. *AT* 1969 505—508.

SELL, W.: Staubabscheidung an einfachen Körpern in Luftfiltern. *VDI-Forschungsheft* 1931, No. 347.

SHEPHERD, C. B.—C. E. LAPPLE: Flow pattern and pressure drop in cyclone dust collectors. *Ind. Eng. Chem.* 1939, 972—984.

SILVERMAN, L.—E. W. CONNORS—D. M. ANDERSON: Mechanical electrostatic charging of fabrics for air filters. *Ind. Eng. Chem.* 1955, 952—960.

SPROULL, W. T.—Y. NAKADA: Operation of Cottrell precipitators: effects of moisture and temperature. *Ing. Eng. Chem.* 1951, 1350—1358.

STAFFORD, E.—W. J. SMITH: Dry fibrous air-filter media; performance characteristics. *Ind. Eng. Chem.* 1951, 1346—1350.

STAIRMAND, C. J.: The design and performance of cyclone separators. *Trans. ICE* 1951, 356—383.

STAIRMAND, C. J.: Report on the removal of grit, dust and fume from effluent gases. *Chem. Eng.* 1968, 257—261.

STRAUSS, W.: *Industrial gas cleaning.* Vol. 8. Pergamon Press, New York 1967.

TROESCH, H. A.: Die Zerstäubung von Flüssigkeiten. *Chem. Ing. Tech.* 1954, 311—320.

TUMA, J.: Eigenschaften des Staubes, die seine Abscheidung beeinflussen. *Staub* 1966, 455—459.

WEBER, E.: Der Einfluss der Benetzbarkeit von Stauben bei der Nassentstaubung. *Staub* 1968, 462—467.

WEBER, E.: Die Abtrennung von Feststoffteilchen am Gasen durch Massenkräfte. *Verfahrenstechnik* 1969, 51—58.

WINKEL, A.: Elektrische Polarisation der Staube und ihre Bedeutung für die Elektrofilterung. *Z-VDI, Beiheft Verf.* 1964, No. 2, 25—28.

9. AGGLOMERATION

9.1. FUNDAMENTALS

Agglomeration, as an operation opposite to comminution, is used to reduce the specific surfaces of material aggregates. Unintentional aggregation of fine particles (clotting) may occur during storage, transportation, air classifying, screening, mixing and grinding: processes of intentional agglomeration include briquetting, pill-making, granulation, pelletization, extrusion and sintering. Agglomeration may be due to bonding by (1) solid bridges, (2) the surface and capillary forces of freely moving liquids, (3) adhesive and cohesive forces of captive binders (binders unable to move freely), (4) forces of attraction between solid particles, (5) suitable (interlocking) shape configurations (Knepper [ed.] 1962; Rumpf 1958).

(1) Solid bridges may be formed by sintering, chemical reactions, the hardening of binders or crystallization out of a solution.

(2) On the concave side of a meniscus in a freely moving liquid, where the radii of curvature (assumed to issue from the corresponding centres of curvature) diverge, pressure is greater by

$$\Delta p = a \left(\frac{1}{R_1} + \frac{1}{R_2} \right)$$

than on the convex side, where they converge. a is the surface tension of the liquid; R_1 and R_2 are the two principal radii of curvature of the meniscus. If a cluster of particles contains little enough liquid, liquid bridges only are formed where the particles touch. These bridges exert capillary suction thanks to their surfaces' surface tension. Both forces tend to pull the particles closer together. This pendular state is superseded as the quantity of liquid increases by the funicular state in which the connected phase in the interstices of the particles is the liquid rather than the gas, and the surfaces of the particles are wetted everywhere, but the gas still forms isolated bubbles in the pores. The capillary state sets in when the interstices of the particles are completely filled with liquid but the surface of the aggregate still exhibits concave meniscuses between particles. This gives rise to capillary suction,

$$\Delta p = \frac{6ka\sigma \cos \vartheta}{(1 - \sigma)x},$$

derived in detail in section 7.1; this suction is operative throughout the whole liquid volume, so that the agglomerate acquires a tensile strength

$$\sigma_z \cong \Delta p.$$

(For roundish sand grains, $k \cong 1.33$; $6k \cong 8$.) The tensile strength provided by the liquid bridges of the pendular state is only about 30% of capillary Δp; this can be derived, using the laws of agglomeration by localized bonds, as follows (Pietsch and Rumpf 1967; Rumpf 1970).

If a lump of agglomerate is broken in two, a particle next to the surface of fracture remains in that part of the lump which contains its centre of gravity. Assuming the particles to be spherical, the volume of that part of the particle sticking out of the fracture surface may vary between zero and a hemisphere: the particles' average cross section in the fracture surface is

$$f_m = \frac{\pi x^2}{6},$$

and their average fracture surface area (where the bonds have snapped) is

$$F_m = \frac{\pi x^2}{4}.$$

The particle count per unit fracture surface area is

$$n_F = \frac{\sigma}{f_m} = \frac{6\sigma}{\pi x^2},$$

and the average number of bonds in the fracture surface is

$$z_1 = \frac{z F_m}{\pi x^2} = \frac{z}{4};$$

σ is volumetric solids content ($\sigma = 1 - \varepsilon$ if ε is porosity); x is average grain diameter, and z is the number of the points of contact of a particle with other particles. Tensile strength is provided by the components perpendicular to the fracture surface of the bond forces. Assuming the orientation of the points of contact (of the bond forces) to be uniformly random over the aggregate, the projection onto a line normal to the fracture surface of these bond forces, uniformly distributed over the surface F_m of a spherical segment, is

$$\sin^2 60° = \frac{3}{4}$$

times the average bond force at any point of contact.

The number of bonds per unit fracture-surface area is

$$N_F = n_F z_1;$$

that is, tensile stress is

$$\sigma_z \cong 0.75 N_F H,$$

where H is the bond force at one point of contact. Substitution yields

$$\sigma_z = \frac{9\sigma z H}{8\pi x^2}.$$

Tests have established $\sigma \cong 0.55$ and $z \cong 7$ for loose aggregates, $\sigma \cong 0.65$ and $z \cong 8$ to 9 for aggregates compacted by rapping, and $\sigma \cong 0.75$ and $z \cong 12$ for a stamped charge. That is, approximately,

$$z(1 - \sigma) \cong 3.1 \cong \pi,$$

and hence,

$$\sigma_z \cong \frac{1.1\sigma H}{(1 - \sigma)x^2}.$$

For example, if $\sigma = 0.65$, then

$$\sigma_z = \frac{2H}{x^2}.$$

If the bridges are constituted by a liquid, then

$$H = axf(\vartheta, \beta) = Kax,$$

where a is surface tension, ϑ is the angle of contact and β is the central angle subtended by the liquid ring, as seen from the centre of the particle. The variation of K vs. b/x at $\vartheta = 0$ is shown in Fig. 9.1 for different values of

$$B = \frac{V_w}{2V_s}.$$

Here, b is the separation of the spheres of diameter x and volume

$$V_s = \pi \frac{x^3}{6};$$

V_W is the volume of the liquid bridge. As separation b increases, K and, along with it, the adhesive force H decreases, whatever the liquid volume, albeit less abruptly for larger than for smaller liquid bridges. Adhesion has a maximum at $b = 0$ (that is, when the particles touch). In that case, K is in the range 2.0 to 2.5 if $B \cong 0.0001$ to 0.2 (that is, $\beta = 15$ to $80°$).

Putting $H \cong 2.25 \, ax$ gives

$$\sigma_z \cong \frac{2.5\sigma a}{(1 - \sigma)x},$$

which is approximately

$$100 \cdot \frac{2.5}{8} \simeq 30\%$$

only of the capillary suction,

$$\Delta p \simeq \frac{8\sigma a}{(1 - \sigma)x},$$

arising at $\vartheta = 0°$, with the entire pore volume liquid-filled. Liquid filling in the pores is funicular between $\beta = 20$ and $80°$ and pendular at $\vartheta \lessapprox 20°$. In the

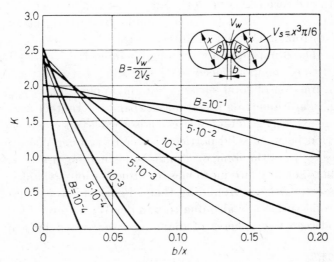

Fig. 9.1. $K = f(\vartheta, \beta)$ vs. b/x with $B = V_w/V_s$ as the parameter

funicular state, part of the liquid constitutes bridges; the rest fills out certain pore domains entirely; tensile stress is accordingly somewhere between that of capillary suction (Δp) and that of the pure pendular state ($\sim 0.3\ \Delta p$).

If a cluster of solid particles gets fully covered with liquid, the hollow meniscuses in the pores coalesce into the convex surface of a drop of liquid; capillary cohesion between particles disappears, and the particles are held together exclusively by the surface tension of the convex drop.

(3) Adhesive binders which constitute coatings of more or less thickness on the solid particles behave as captive viscous liquids, provided the energy needed to deform them exceeds the reduction of surface energy due to the deformation.

In such a situation, it is the adhesion between the solid and the liquid and the internal cohesion of the binder that hold the solid particles together. In practice, the adhesive component of the bond force is almost invariably stronger than the cohesive one, so that the strength of the agglomerate is determined by the latter. In order to facilitate its spreading on the particle surfaces, a viscous binder is often diluted with water or some other solvent (or liquefied by heating). The viscous binder is then left in place as the diluent evaporates. Some binders that are liquid when hot jell into strong solid bridges on cooling (e.g. pitch in briquetted coal). Binders dosed in aqueous solution in industrial practice include glue, gelatine, starch paste, etc.; those dissolved in organic solvents include shellac, waxes, varnishes, etc. Often, a binder making up much less than one percent of total volume may be sufficient to endow an agglomerate with satisfactory strength.

Liquid films adsorbed on the surfaces of solid particles may also be classed as captive. In the case of water, for example, no capillary condensation (formation of meniscuses) takes place if the capillary radii are smaller than about 3 nm (30 ångströms). Contact or interpenetration between adsorbed water films thinner than 3 nm provides a strong bonding. It is confined as a rule to the prominences of rough-surfaced particles, which between them make up a small enough fraction of total surface, but the application of a great enough pressure (e.g. in a briquetting press) may expand the contact area sufficiently to let the more extensive contact between adsorbed layers create a strong bond.

(4) Attraction between solid particles is due to van der Waals forces above all. Much weaker than the ionic or atomic bonds making up the crystals, such forces arise between any two molecules (or atoms or ions), thanks to the interaction of the force fields surrounding them. Physical adsorption of gases and vapours by solid surfaces is also due to van der Waals forces. van der Waals attraction between two spheres of diameter x separated by a distance b is

$$H = \frac{Cx}{b^2},$$

provided $b \lesssim 100$ nm, where C (in ergs) is a material constant, a function of polarization, of the number of atoms per unit of volume, etc. Its approximate values in 10^{-14} erg units are,

for plastics,	~ 2.7;
ionically bonded crystals,	~ 3.2;
quartz glass,	4.0;
hard minerals,	5 to 10;
semiconductors: e.g. Si,	~ 11.2;
metals: Au,	~ 14.4.

Let e.g. $C = 8 \cdot 10^{-14}$ erg and $\sigma = 0.65$; then,

$$\sigma_z \cong \frac{1.1 H \sigma}{(1 - \sigma)x^2} \cong \frac{2H}{x^2} \cong \frac{16}{10^{14}b^2 x} \text{ dynes per cm}^2 \cong \frac{16}{10^{20}b^2 x} \text{ kp/cm}^2,$$

if b and x are in centimetres. If a sphere of diameter x is separated by b from a plane surface rather than from another sphere, then the values C, H and σ_z

610

are to be doubled. In that case, then,

$$\sigma_z = 0.32 \text{ kp/cm}^2$$

if $b = 1$ nm $= 10^{-7}$ cm and $x = 1$ μm $= 10^{-4}$ cm.

Polar radicals such as —OH or —COOH possess van der Waals dipole forces: mutual attraction between two dipoles is

$$H = \frac{6M^2}{b^4},$$

where M is the dipole moment and b is the separation of the charge centres. For example, if

$$b = 200 \qquad 20 \qquad 2 \text{ nm,}$$

then $\sigma_2 \simeq$ 1 dyne   10 ponds   100 kiloponds per cm².

Adsorbed liquid films 0.3 to 3 nm thick are — as we have seen — strongly bonded to the surfaces, smoothing out the micro-roughness of those, reducing the separation b and increasing the adhesive force H in the process. (If mobile liquid in films thicker than 3 nm is present in the interstices of the particles, then interparticle attraction is confined to capillary forces, with no van der Waals forces in play.)

The behaviour of solid surfaces (adhesion, wetting, friction, etc.) depends greatly on the films adsorbed by them. This may be a drawback as far as the mutual adhesion of solid particles is concerned. Adhesion is confined as a rule to clean surfaces of solids; even then, though, one of the participating particles must be thin or small enough to be readily deformed. A film of moisture thicker than 3 nm adsorbed from the atmosphere or a trace of grease from one's finger may completely cancel the propensity of particles or objects to stick together. Many metals grow oxide coatings: such coatings must be removed by pressure or rubbing if metal particles are to be made to adhere together.

For the van der Waals forces to become relevant, a major part of the interparticle gap must be reduced to below 10 nm. For example, a van der Waals bond of tensile strength 10 kp/cm² will arise in a cross section of a briquette if the interstices in that cross section are less than

	0.5	1	1.75 nm wide
over	2.4	19	100% of the surface

(Rumpf 1958, 1970; Turba and Rumpf 1964).

Electrostatic forces between particles give bonds weaker by several orders of magnitude (e.g. about 10^{-4} kp/cm²) than the other forces of agglomeration; they may play a role nevertheless in the constitution of the clusters' initial nuclei. In an aggregate of oppositely charged spheres bearing the charges

$\pm Q$ (e.g. in a cubic ionic lattice), electrostatic attraction is less by a factor of about 0.3 than between two isolated spheres:

$$H = 0.3 \frac{\left(1 - \dfrac{2b}{x}\right) Q^2}{x^2}$$

if $b \ll x$.

Magnetic attraction likewise provides a small enough tensile strength, less e.g. than 0.2 kp/cm^2 in a cluster of magnetic magnetite particles.

Adhesion due to solid bridges formed by crystallization is

$$H \cong np\sigma_{cr}(1 - \sigma)x_2 \frac{\varrho}{\varrho_{cr}},$$

where n is the initial (pendular) moisture content of the granulate; p is the mass fraction (abundance by weight) of the crystallizing substance; σ_{cr} and ϱ_{cr} are the tensile strength and s.g. of the crystal, respectively; x is the grain size, σ the volumetric solids content and ϱ the s.g. of the granulate. The formula holds after the total evaporation of the solvent (with all the bridge-forming substance crystallized). In the case of hardening binders, n represents the binder content of the mix; $p = 1$; and ϱ_{cr} and σ_{cr} represent the tensile strength and s.g. of the hardened binder. In sintering, solid bridging between particles may be caused, depending on the nature of the aggregate, by phenomena of viscous or plastic flow, evaporation and re-condensation, and diffusion within and between the particles. The cross-sectional area q of such bridges increases in time according to the formula

$$q = Ct^i$$

(provided temperature is constant), where C is a constant and the exponent i is about 1/2 for fluids (e.g. glass), about 1/3 for volatile materials (e.g. rock salt) and about 1/5 for products with a strong propensity to diffuse (e.g. Ag, Cu, Ni, Al$_2$O$_3$ ...). The adhesive force consequently increases in time,

$$H = q\sigma_{br} = C\sigma_{br}t^i,$$

where σ_{br} is the tensile strength of the solid bridges in the sinter. (The sinter contracts because its pores shrink at the same time.)

(5) Fibrous and ramifying (dendritic) particles can be made to interweave and to lock together by suitable agitation and pressing. This interlocking, however, is confined to few materials, and its role in agglomeration tends to be subordinate.

The maximum tensile strength σ_z that can be lent to an agglomerate by the different bonding forces is shown in Fig. 9.2 vs. particle size x. The domains of briquetting and salt precipitation are separated by a horizontal (dashed)

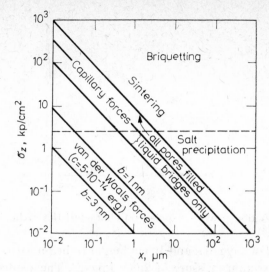

Fig. 9.2. Tensile strength σ_z of agglomerates vs. particle size x

line, independent of particle size. The oblique lines represent the types of bond whose strength varies inversely as particle size (capillary forces, van der Waals forces, etc.) (Rumpf and Hermann 1970).

9.2. PROCESSES

9.2.1. Briquetting. Applying sufficient pressure to an aggregate filled into a mold (with or without a binder) produces briquettes, pills, blocks or bricks. The pressure required depends on the nature of the material to be briquetted: it is typically

70 to	140 bars for clay bricks,	
150 to	250 bars for coal briquettes with a binder,	
250 to	500 bars for ore briquettes,	
300 to	400 bars for dry-pressed clay bricks,	
350 to	700 bars for iron ore blocks,	
1,000 to	2,000 bars for binderless coal briquettes,	
about	1,500 bars for metal bearings made by powder metallurgy,	
about	3,000 bars for other products of powder metallurgy.	
about	7,000 bars for permanent magnets.	

Plastic materials can be agglomerated by extrusion through an orifice as well as by compression in a mold.

The compaction (travel-vs.-pressure) characteristics of different materials tend to be widely different. The characteristics of lignite and sawdust, loosely

613

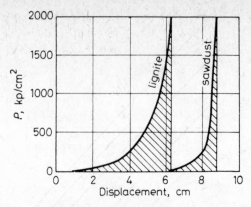

Fig. 9.3. Compaction (travel-vs.-pressure) characteristics of lignite and sawdust

rapped in a mold of 6 cm dia. and 10 cm height to begin with, are shown in Fig. 9.3, up to a maximum pressure of 2,000 kp/cm². The shaded area under the curves represents the work input required by the briquetting process: it is seen to be greater for lignite than for sawdust. At a fair approximation,

$$p = A' \left(\frac{1 - \sigma_0/\sigma_p}{e^{0.4343B'} - 1} \right),$$

where p is pressure in the press and A' and B' are material parameters (the dimension of A' being the same as that of p — e.g., both may be stated in kp/cm² units); σ_0 is the initial volumetric solids content (the one belonging to zero pressure); σ_p is that belonging to the pressure p. (σ is the ratio of bulk density to s.g.)

Table 9.1. Volumetric solids contents σ in % (100% minus porosity ε) of different materials in the loose, compacted ($p = 0$) and compressed state at various pressures

Material		Loose	$p = 0$	1,000	2,000	4,000	8,000
					kg/cm²		
Roasted pyrite residue		14.4	26.5	40.8	44.7	49.2	54.2
Sponge iron		23.8	31.0	43.8	51.0	60.0	70.6
Ferrosilicon		53.6	65.1	76.0	79.0	82.5	84.8
Glass		45.0	56.8	74.6	79.6	85.0	89.3
Limestone	0—1 mm	46.3	71.8	81.6	84.7	88.5	93.4
Limestone	1—3 mm	52.0	63.0	81.7	85.3	89.4	93.1
Limestone	0—6 mm	58.4	74.0	86.1	88.9	91.6	93.2
Rock salt	0—1 mm	45.6	67.0	85.5	92.3	98.6	102.6
Rock salt	1—3 mm	50.7	65.2	86.7	94.0	99.8	102.1
Rock salt	0—6 mm	59.0	72.1	88.6	94.2	98.3	102.8
Clay	0—1 mm	44.2	85.2	97.6	99.5	101.2	104.7
Clay	1—3 mm	40.3	86.0	91.0	93.7	97.2	102.7
Clay	0—6 mm	48.3	84.5	92.9	95.4	98.8	103.6

Table 9.1 states σ_p values obtained on testing various aggregates in the loose state and at different pressures of agglomeration. In the case of rock salt and clay, the σ_p values exceeding 100% are due to the expansion of the briquettes after the release of pressure, but the comparability of the compaction figures is not impaired by these deviations (Rieschel 1971).

Compression and pressure distribution in a briquette of powdered $MgCO_3$ of approximate Mohs hardness $M = 4$ is presented in Fig. 9.4 for different pressures. Around the upper rim of the test solid, pressures greater than that of the (single-acting) piston are seen to arise in the compressed material. At piston pressures less than about 500 bars, pressures in the test solid gradually decrease downward, whereas, at stronger compressions, the pressures arising along the axis of the test solid exceed piston pressure even in the bottom half of the mold. The volumetric solids content σ of the material compressed at a piston pressure of 2,040 bars was found to be about 64% in the pressure domains of 1,400 to 1,600 bars and about 70% in the domains of 2,200 to 2,500 bars (Heckel 1961).

The compaction (s.g.) and strength of coal briquettes (and of briquettes made of other semi-plastic materials) can be greatly increased by applying shear

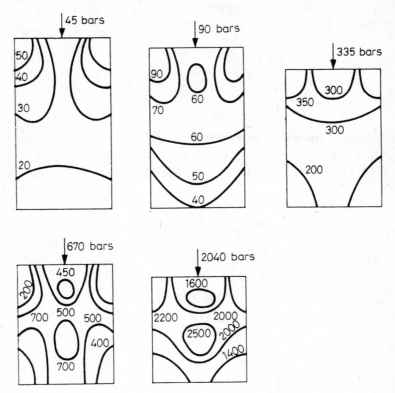

Fig. 9.4. Isobars in test solids of compressed magnesite at different pressures

simultaneously with compression, e.g. by turning an oblique-faced piston in a round cylinder. Shear activates interparticle bonding mechanisms (e.g. welding by friction) which would not enter into play under simple compression. The marked reduction of pore volume by shear generates strong van der Waals forces of adhesion and adsorption between the particles.

The work of friction $\mathrm{d}N$ required to bring about a volume change $\mathrm{d}V$ by irreversible compression (neglecting the work of elastic compression) varies as the pressure increment:

$$\mathrm{d}N = -p\,\mathrm{d}V = k\,\mathrm{d}p.$$

Integration yields

$$\log p = -\frac{cV}{V_t} + C,$$

where V is actual volume and V_t is the (theoretical) volume referred to the poreless state:

$$\frac{V}{V_t} = \frac{1}{\sigma},$$

and c and C are constants. $V/V_t\,[1/\sigma]$ varies as $\log p$; the slope c of the line is a modulus of compaction that depends on the shape, size, etc. of the particles; it is constant up to middling pressures. The relationship

$$c = \frac{\log\left(\dfrac{p_1}{p}\right)}{\dfrac{V}{V_t} - 1} = \frac{\sigma}{1-\sigma}\log\left(\frac{p_1}{p}\right) = Kx^n$$

may be written up, where p_1 is the extrapolated pressure corresponding to $V/V_t = 1$, x is particle size, and K and n are material constants.

If plastic deformation occurs (e.g. in the compression of metal powders), the empirical formula

$$\ln\left(\frac{1}{1-\varrho}\right) = Ap + B$$

holds, where ϱ is the relative apparent s.g. of the aggregate compressed at pressure p, and A and B are constants.

For monodisperse or short-range powders,

$$\frac{\varepsilon}{\varepsilon_0} = e^{-ap},$$

where

$$\varepsilon = 1 - \sigma$$

is porosity at pressure p, ε_0 is initial porosity (at zero pressure) and a is a material constant. At low pressures, the substitution

$$\frac{\varepsilon}{1 - \varepsilon} = \frac{\varepsilon}{\sigma}$$

is to be performed. Up to middling pressures, the formula

$$\varepsilon - \varepsilon_0 = bp^{1/3}$$

also gives fair results. b is a material constant.

In briquetting, pressure is used to bring the particles of the aggregate into a contact so intimate that the bond forces so established persist even after the removal of the pressure, endowing the briquette with sufficient strength. A material is suitable for briquetting if its particles can be deformed by pressure sufficiently to fit together practically poreless. If this is not the case, a plastic binder must be added or the material itself must be rendered plastic by suitably changing its physical state. Plastics can be so transformed by heating; clays by the addition of water; older (non-plastic) coals are heated and briquetted with a binder that is plastic at higher temperatures. Younger brown (subbituminous) coals and lignites of sufficient plasticity can be briquetted binderless at a high enough pressure, and so can the products of many other industries.

The tailings of some copper ore concentrators in the US are dry-pressed into bricks with a calcium lignosulphate binder and sold as a building material. A mixture of glass shards and rubble (stone, brick, concrete, etc. recovered from pulled-down buildings), heated to the softening point of the glass in suitable molds, gives high-strength construction panels, e.g. of 3.6 by 1.2 by 0.15 m size. From the incineration residue of city rubbish, part of the broken glass can be recovered and returned to the glass factories; the rest, ground and mixed with about 30% plastic clay (or a little binder of some other nature) can be made into bricks using one of the conventional methods of brickmaking (dry compression, plastic extrusion, etc.). The glass present in these bricks permits burning at lower temperatures than those usual at the brickyards.

The remainder of this chapter will concentrate on the briquetting of coals with and without a binder (Stilman 1923; Wüster 1958).

9.2.1.1. Briquetting of coals using a binder (Franke and Kraushaar 1909; Stilman 1923). Older coals (bituminous coals) are hydrophobic: not readily wetted by water, they are wetted well enough by organic liquids (e.g. oils) or molten tar or pitch, bitumen, asphalt, etc. The above are the most widespread binders of coal briquetting, together with starch paste which is usually dosed in combination with one of the above substances. A drop of molten tar or pitch will spread out into a thin film on the surface of a hydrophobic coal particle. The fine-grained (e.g. minus-3 mm) coal is blended with the binder (e.g. with 5 to 10 weight percent pitch) and introduced into the press at a temperature exceeding the binder's softening point (80 to 100 °C in the case of pitch). Being readily deformable at a comparatively low pressure (100 to 250 bars), the binder fills out completely all the voids among the coal particles making up the briquette. The binder hardens on cooling, constituting solid bridges among the coal particles. Other binders, used more seldom, include molasses, resins, viscose, sulphite leach and inorganic materials such as clay, marl, cement, lime, etc. which although cheaper, increase the ash content of the briquettes.

Pitch is the distillation residue of black (bituminous) or brown (subbituminous) coal tar or petroleum tar. Depending on the temperature at which distillation is terminated, the residue obtained is asphalt, soft pitch, medium-hard or hard pitch. The s.g. of these increases in the same sequence: that of soft pitch is less than 1.09 and that of hard pitch is greater than 1.12. Pitch is not chemically homogeneous: it is a mixture of a number of different hydrocarbons. It includes some heavy tar oils (anthracene, etc.), but its bulk is bitumen. It is a black brittle material of conchoidal fracture.

	Soft	medium-hard	hard pitch
has a softening point about	40	60	90 °C
and a fusing point about	60	90	170 °C
(plus or minus 10 to 20%).			

A briquette made of non-caking black or brown coal falls apart in the fire if the binder burns faster than the coal. This can be helped by adding a few per cent of caking (coking) coal. Falling apart in the fire may be due to the use of the wrong kind of pitch also, e.g. one that gives a swelling coke whose expansion cracks the briquette.

Pitch is added to the coal to be briquetted either in the solid or in the liquid state. For solid dosage, hard pitch is usually chosen because it does not soften on comminution to clog up the insides of the mill (which may e.g. be a disintegrator). Pitch dust is a health hazard: it may cause cancer and inflammation of the eyes. No person must be employed on a pitch comminution job beyond a certain period of time (e.g. two years). The softer the pitch, the less harmful it is physiologically. For molten dosage, medium-hard pitch is used. Hard pitch can be made medium-hard e.g. by adding low-grade oils.

Preparing the ingredients for briquetting usually involves comminution and blending, which may be combined with the drying of the coal. Usual briquette feeds are the minus-6 to minus-10 mm fractions of some non-coking coal. Plus-3 mm coal, however, is not best for briquetting: the briquettes made of it tend to be low-strength because the larger particles will break apart in the press, where their fresh fracture surfaces can no longer acquire coatings of pitch. If the minus-10 mm coal fraction is not particularly high-strength, it tends to comminute spontaneously in the course of handling, to the extent that, by the time it is fed to the press, it will contain hardly any plus-3 mm particles; however, if the coal *is* of exceptional strength, its plus-3 mm fraction should be comminuted (using e.g. a disintegrator).

As pointed out above, the pitch also must be comminuted when it is added solid to the coal. Pitch is sold in large cylindrical blocks (in drums): these are broken into lumps manually, with hammers, then crushed in a ball race (to about 2 cm) or in a jaw crusher. The output is fed to a hammer mill or — more seldom — to a disintegrator. (The disintegrator does not lend itself to the comminution of medium-hard pitch or resin, because the material tends to soften and to stick to the impact pegs.) It is usual for pitch to be ground to a granulometry of 5 to 8% plus-2 mm and 6 to 10% minus-0.6 mm.

The coal to be briquetted and the ground pitch are fed into separate hoppers which dose them to a blending spiral or a blending disintegrator. Pitch dosage is 5 to 10% (most often 6 to 8%) of finished briquette weight. The briquetting of hydrophilic, damp coals or coals of a large specific surface (rich in fines) requires more pitch than the briquetting of hydrophobic or dry coals or coals of small specific surface.

Coal and pitch blended together are fed to a steam-heated kneading machine, a malaxator, which kneads the blend thoroughly and heats it to the required temperature. The malaxator is a vertical cylinder open at the top, with spirally bent kneading-mixing arms mounted on its central shaft which rotates at $n \simeq 30$ rpm. Nozzles installed at suitable vertical intervals inject into it super-saturated steam at 300 to 450 °C (or saturated steam at 150 to 170 °C) so as to melt the pitch and heat the whole blend above the softening point thereof. Steam demand is 3 to 5% of feed weight. The blend fed in at the top traverses the malaxator in 10 min or so. It is discharged at the bottom through a sliding gate, either directly into the briquetting press or onto a spiral conveyor leading to it. The essential criterion is that, when introduced into the press, the blend should be hotter than the softening point of the pitch.

If liquid pitch is used in briquetting, it will blend more readily and more uniformly with the coal; this reduces the necessary pitch dosage by 0.5 to 1%. The cost of comminuting the pitch and the formation of pitch dust with all its harmful physiological consequences are also avoided thereby.

In the Fohr–Kleinschmidt process, pitch is usually transferred molten, in insulated containers, from the tar works, and tapped into a storage bin. It is lifted therefrom — e.g. using compressed air — into a standby boiler whence it is injected at a well-regulated rate through a nozzle into a blending drum (of, say, 2 m dia. × 10 m size, rotating at 9 rpm) using a pitch pump, a steam jet or a mixture of steam and compressed air. It meets the coal to be briquetted in the blending drum. The injected pitch cools down in the drum sufficiently to solidify and to rain down upon the coal in the form of fine droplets resembling soot. Its granulometry tends to be about 2% plus-1 mm and 4 to 8% minus-0.1 mm when handled by means of a pitch pump and less than 1% plus-1 mm and about 20% minus-0.1 mm when injected in a steam jet. From the blending drum, the blend is fed to the malaxator and thence to the press.

Briquettes discharged from the press attain their ultimate strength only after some cooling, when the binder, which is soft when hot, has had time to solidify. Briquettes may be cooled e.g. on the screen-cloth conveyor belts which take them to the railcar loading points. (Brick-shaped briquettes should be arranged lengthwise on the belt, as otherwise the radiation of any one brick will be absorbed by the adjacent ones and no cooling will take place.)

Pitch is the most popular briquette binder world-wide. Of the other organic binders, bitumen and the heavy fuel-oil residuals of petroleum refining should be mentioned. In Hungary, briquetting with a bitumen binder is predominant. Bitumen is a black, hard or semi-hard thermoplastic material at room temperature: it is made up of large-molecule hydrocarbons (asphaltenes, resinoid substances and aromatic or aliphatic oils). Deep green or brownish-black residual fuel oil is the distillation residue of petroleum about 300 °C; its further distillation gives mineral lubricants on the one hand and black, pitch-like bunker C oil on the other. Asphalt pitch is the distillation residue of raw asphalt.

Naphthalene ($C_{10}H_8$), sometimes used as a binder blended with pitch, is made out of coal tar. One percent naphthalene replaces three percent pitch. The presence of naphthalene fumes increases the vapour tension of water: water evaporates more readily through the top aperture of the malaxator while the naphthalene fumes condense in the cooler spots of the machine. (Naphthalene softens at 179 °C and sublimates at 216 °C.) The addition of naphthalene, then, permits to reduce the dosage of pitch on the one hand and to briquette a damper coal without pre-drying, on the other.

Flour (or starch) paste is another organic binder. On wetting flour and hotting it up to about 80 °C, its starch content turns into a good adhesive. Briquettes made with flour only, however, are not water-resistant: this is why flour is used in combination with pitch as a rule. Starch paste is a better adhesive than pitch, so that their combined use permits a substantial reduction of bituminous binder dosage, as also of smoke and soot formation on combustion. In fact, pitch and flour combined give briquettes of greater strength, less prone to crumble and also cleaner (less messy) to handle. Often, flour, added to the coal in the form of an emulsion, is the essential binder, with the finely dispersed pitch or bitumen merely serving as a waterproofing substance (Müschenborn and Schinzel 1965).

Further organic binders include molasses, cellulose pitch, cellulose xanthate or viscose, sulphite leach, etc.

Viscose (sodium cellulose xanthate, $NaSSCOC_6H_9O_4$) is a viscous liquid when dissolved in water. Gradually shedding NaSSC radicals, it changes into a compound of the form $NaSSCO(C_6H_9O_4)_n$ which gradually jells if warmed or if the caustic-soda concentration decreases. Finally, it is turned by water intake into "wood" cellulose $(C_6H_{10}O_5)_n$. This latter stage sets in immediately on the dosage of an acid. 0.3 to 0.7 percent of wood cellulose is sufficient for the production of strong and water-resistant briquettes.

Sulphite leach is a practically valueless by-product of paper mills using the sulphite route. Thickened to 31 to 33 degrees Baumé, it is delivered to briquetting works as a binder. Thick sulphite leach contains about 50% organic solids, with lignin and pentosan as its principal ingredients. It is used in two different ways in briquette making. Either its water content is removed prior to pressing, by drying the mixture of coal and sulphite leach in a rotary drier, or the briquettes are dried after pressing; this latter process may again employ either slow drying at 270 °C or combustion-gas drying and coking at 450 °C. Durable, water-resistant briquettes can only be made by the latter route which, however, requires some special equipment. Briquettes made with sulphite leach are smokeless and sootless. Sulphite leach is used also in combination with pitch: this permits to avoid the follow-up treatment with combustion gas at 450 °C. It is usual to replace about half the pitch required with about twice the weight of thick sulphite leach: this gives sufficient durability and resistance to water, but the briquettes fresh from the press must be air-cured for some time to attain the strength of the briquettes made exclusively with pitch.

Briquettes made with pitch or bitumen are water-resistant as a rule if enough binder (more than 5 or 6%) is added to a coal of suitable granulometry (160 to 240 cm²/g of specific surface) and the technology used produces briquettes with uncracked surfaces. In that case, a continuous surface layer of binder will protect the interior of the briquette from the infiltration of water, so that it may be kept under water for days on end without suffering any harmful physical alteration.

In the briquette, the surfaces of the coal particles are partly or entirely coated with a thin film of binder, and their interstices are filled partly or entirely with a "mortar" of binder and fine coal. High-grade briquettes contain few air-filled pores if any, and certainly no networks of cracks. (Cracks may lead water into the interior of the briquette.) Whether the binder, forming films 3 to 8 μm thick, will cover the coal particles' surfaces adequately depends on the hydrophobia or otherwise of the coal particles and on the viscosity of the binder after meeting the hot steam in the malaxator. The quantity of mortar made up of coal dust and binder is a function of the temperature of the coal to be briquetted and of the degree and duration of kneading. If the temperature is above the softening point of the binder, then a great deal of mortar will form even if binder dosage is comparatively lean, provided kneading is satisfactory. The larger coal particles may embed themselves in the mortar so that compression in the press may produce a more or less pore-free "concrete texture" without breaking up the larger particles and forming fresh fracture surfaces uncoated with binder in the process.

If a connected network of pores and/or cracks remains in the interior of the briquette, then water seeping, or sucked by capillary forces, into its interior through the surface cracks is liable to make the briquette crumble, the more so, the more hygroscopic (hydrophilic) the coal and the greater the abundance of coal particles uncoated with binder. However, the briquette may crumble even if all the coal particles are fully binder-coated if it is traversed by cracks which can take up capillary water. Atmospheric agencies (fluctuation of temperature and humidity, frost, etc.) make the cracks expand and contract, breaking up the briquette by a process analogous to weathering.

The several constituents of a briquette (the binder, the different grades of coal and their inorganic ash minerals) differ more or less as to physical characteristics (including strength — brittleness, plasticity, hardness, etc. — and thermal properties — absorption of sun rays, thermal conductivity, thermal expansion, specific heat), hydrophilia and hygroscopicity. The individual, inhomogeneous constituents differ as to rates and magnitudes of changes in thermal state and hygroscopic humidity, expansion and contraction in their interiors, let alone at their interfaces; as a result, local tensions arise and, when they exceed the strength of the constituents (or their bonding), crack up the briquette. Possibly, in a first phase, only microfissures form, into which capillary water can get absorbed; it is this latter phenomenon which, in the final reckoning, is responsible for the breakup of the briquette. The local tensions reduce the strength (point hardness or drum strength) even of apparently sound briquettes: in the presence of such tensions, even a comparatively weak external force will be sufficient to shatter the briquette.

Let e.g. the quantity of binder in the briquette be 10 weight percent, or, referred to the weight of coal,

$$\frac{10}{0.9} = 11.1\%.$$

Let further the s.g. of the binder be 1.11 and that of the coal, 1.6 g/cm³. In that case, in a pore- and fissureless briquette, the volume percentage of binder is

$$\frac{\dfrac{0.1}{1.1}}{\dfrac{0.1}{1.1} + \dfrac{0.9}{1.6}} = 13.9\%,$$

and that of the coal particles is 86.1%. For example, in the case of a coal of specific surface 200 cm²/g, the binder forms coatings of average thickness

$$\frac{\dfrac{0.111}{1.1}}{200} = 0.000505 \text{ cm} = 5.05 \ \mu\text{m}$$

on the loose coal particles. In the briquette, the average thickness of binder between any two coal particles is twice that, 10.1 μm. In the solid-disperse system which a good-grade, pore- and crackless briquette is, the solidified binder is the dispersant and coal is the dispersed phase. Assuming always a specific surface of 200 cm^2/g, at binder dosages of

	7	10	13%,
coal-particle spacing is	7.07	10.10	13.13 μm and
the coal's volume percentage is	90.0	86.1	82.2%.

If, on the other hand, the specific surface of the coal is 150 cm^2/g, then, volume percentages being equal, average coal-particle spacing becomes

	9.41	13.45	17.50 μm,
and, for a specific surface of 250 cm^2/g,	5.66	8.09	10.50 μm.

The quantity of binder required to give a good "concrete texture" and to make durable, water-resistant briquettes of satisfactory strength thus depends fairly sensitively on the hydrophobia and the granulometry of the coal used, as well as on whether binder and fine coal dust together constitute enough of a mortar of adequate quality. (These conditions are easier satisfied if the coal is subjected to suitable thermal pretreatment and the coal and binder are thoroughly mixed and kneaded together.)

The binder is to be chosen so as to have a strong propensity to adhere to the particles to be briquetted; in that case, the molten binder will form thinner coatings on the particles, meaning that less of it will completely coat all particle surfaces. Pitch adheres less well to younger, more hydrophilic coals: in briquetting those, the use of starch paste or sulphite leach may be reasonable and more economical. The required quantity of binder is — as we have seen — a sensitive function of coal granulometry also. The best granulometry is the one with the least pore volume. Granulometries developed for concrete making such as the Bolomey or the Fuller curve are best. In the case of the Fuller curve, about 31 weight percent is minus-$x_{max}/10$, and the granulometry graph in a bilinear system of coordinates is a straight line between 31 and 100 weight percent.

9.2.1.2. Binderless briquetting (Franke and Kraushaar 1930; Kegel 1948; Kegel and Rammler 1959).

Hydrophilic lignites and young brown (sub-bituminous) coals dried sufficiently (to a water content of 12 to 18%) can be briquetted binderless. Pressure in the press should be great enough to expel any water left behind after drying in the micelles of these gel coals. In the briquette, it is the capillary suction of this exuded water, combined with intermolecular forces (interpenetrating films of adsorbed water and other van der Waals forces simultaneously arising) that keeps the particles of the briquette together. Between the polar radicals of the coal micelles ($-OH$, $-COOH$), hydrogen bonds may also form. Briquette strength is impaired by non-optimal water content. Strength will not be increased in the presence of too much water by applying more pressure: water being incompressible, the pressure increment will not reduce the pore volume. In the presence of too little water, on the other hand, capillary action cannot be sufficiently pervasive; the internal friction of the overdried particles is too great; their plasticity is too low. The greater the pressure of which the press is capable, the lower is the optimum water content. In a lignite to be dried to 21% water content, pore volume was found to be

	65	36	34%
at pressure of	0	1,000	3,000 bars,

the aggregate volume of minus-4 μm			
pores being	36	31	14%
and that of minus-3 μm pores being	0	2	5%

Hence, the minus-4 μm pores made up	55	58	41%
and the minus-3 μm pores	0	5	15%.

respectively, of total pore volume.

Soft young brown coals and lignites can be briquetted rather well at the optimum water content even comparatively coarse-ground (to minus-4 to minus-6 mm) and at comparatively low pressures (800 to 1,200 bars).

Briquettes intended for coking or semi-coking are pressed at 1,500 to 2,000 bars, after drying to below the optimum water content (to about 8%) and grinding to minus-0.5 or minus-1 mm. Harder dull brown coals can at their optimum water content still be briquetted economically in the same pressure range when ground to minus-1 as minus-2 mm; glossy brown coals or black (bituminous) coals, on the other hand, can be briquetted binderless only as very fine powders and at pressures above 3,000 to 4,000 bars, hard to realize on a large scale. Such coals can be briquetted more economically using a binder.

Brown coals can be separated into organic components by means of solvents. Bitumens (wax and resins) dissolve in acetone or in a mixture of benzene and alcohol; humic acids dissolve in alkalis (caustic soda, caustic potash, soda ash). Residual coal is that part of the organic matter which is insoluble in both; it includes humic acids condensed to high molecular weight, neutral humins, bitumen polymers, lignin and cellulose (xylite).

Plant lignin condenses to humic acids (fulvoic acid, hymatomelanic acid, humoligninic acid, etc.) as coalification progresses: those in turn condense into neutral humins, while the aromatic hydrocarbons and the hydrophilic radicals of those ($-OH$, $-COOH$, $-CH_3O$, $=CO$, etc.) gradually disappear, to be replaced by alkyl hydrocarbons with their hydrophobic radicals.

Fair binderless briquettability depends primarily on the abundance and nature of free humic acids. (Bound humic acids are those combined into humate salts with a variety of metals: Ca, Na, Al, Fe, etc. Those salts with their inorganic, ash-forming constituents cannot, using the methods of mineral processing, be separated from the organic part of the coal.) Condensed humic acids present in the residual coal have a propensity to exchange bases: they can form Ca. Na, etc. humates. Calcium humate is a colloidal substance with a great propensity to swell which, on the one hand, greatly impairs the briquettes' resistance to water; on the other, it renders coal hard, thereby impairing its briquettability also.

The humic acids' molecular weights tend to be in the 700 to 1,500 range: the molecules are disks of about 2.5 nm diameter, 0.15 nm thick. Three to five disks separated by interstices 0.1 to 0.2 nm thick combine to form a crystallite about one nm thick. Four or so crystallites cluster together to form a micelle of edge length 5 to 6 nm and thickness about 1 nm, thanks to the van der Waals forces located on their rims. These micelles are coated with a strongly bound liosphere-type water film of 0.3 to 0.6 nm thickness. The capillary interstices of 1 to 100 nm diameter between the micelles that make up the soft raw brown coals in disordered heaps are also water-filled. Both the hair cracks of a few μm width and the coarser fissures in the coal are of course also filled with capillary water. Capillary porosity makes up 50 to 60% and more of the total volume of the coal: this is why young brown coals can contain so much water (45 to 60%). Such coals are essentially colloidal liogels, in which the solids constitute the dispersed phase and water is the dispersant. The strength of a brown coal gel, such as it is, is due to the capillary and intermolecular (van der Waals) forces bonding the micelles together: it is these same forces that keep coal particles compressed together in a briquette.

Humic acids — free ones in particular — are readily briquettable; bitumen is poorly so; residual coal may be readily or less radily briquettable, according as it is made up in its bulk of condensed humic acids and humates or polymerized bitumens. The briquettability of two coals of identical elemental composition may differ widely if their nature, degree of coalification or condensation, ageing and compaction differ. It is these features that are mainly responsible for the consistency of the coal, its hardness, elasticity, plasticity, etc. A coal is readily briquettable if it is plastic (not hard and not elastic). Harder coals can also be briquetted in a more finely comminuted state, at a higher pressure and temperature, but their strength will not attain that of the softer, more plastic coals.

For each coal, an optimum water content can be established (it is e.g. between 12 and 20% for the brown coals of the GDR), which, at a given pressing force, temperature and granulometry, furnishes briquettes of the greatest strength. This is the water content at which the plasticity and compressibility of the coal material is greatest and its elasticity is least.

In the interior of a coal particle, the micelles are coated with adsorbed water; the capillaries of 1 to 100 nm diameter and the finer or coarser cracks forming a network in the coal particle are filled with capillary water; the outer surface of a wet lump of coal may carry a sheet of thicker — less strongly bound — water; the smaller voids among lumps of coal loosely dumped together in a stockpile may also be filled with water. This latter water will drip off when the dump is reclaimed; the other types, attached to the coal with forces that grow weaker in the above order of enumeration, accordingly evaporate in reverse

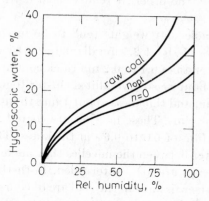

Fig. 9.5. Hygroscopic water content in samples of a lignite, raw and dried to different moisture contents, vs. relative humidity

order upon drying. Adsorbed and capillary water in the interior of the coal is hygroscopic water whose vapour tension is less than normal. Its abundance, a function of relative humidity (and of temperature), can be represented as a function of those by the hygroscopicity curve (the vapour pressure isotherm). The water content of air of a given relative humidity (and temperature) read off this curve is the air-dry equilibrium moisture content of damp coal. If the coal or briquette contains less moisture than that, it will absorb water from the atmosphere and swell; if it contains more, it will lose water and shrink, until the moisture stipulated by the hygroscopicity curve is attained.

Drying reduces the hygroscopicity of gel coals irreversibly: the vapour pressure isotherm and/or hygroscopic moisture content of coal dried to the optimum water content remains permanently below that of the raw coal. The curve of a coal dried to zero water content passes below all the other curves, as shown in Fig. 9.5. The method and intensity of drying also influence the outcome. On drying with hot combustion gases, the residual hygroscopicity of the coal will be less than one gentle drying with steam. In the first case, the contact angle of the coal also increases, owing to the activation of the bituminous constituents. The attendant saturation of the coal with inert gases may also contribute.

In Hungary, the mean relative humidity of air is 80 to 85% in the winter and about 70% in the summer. Under these conditions, the air-dry equilibrium hygroscopic moisture content of the fairly broad variety of Hungarian coals

626

(most of them brown coals and lignites) equals about two-thirds of their as-mined moisture content on a very rough average, provided no heat drying has taken place. [As-mined moisture content is 42 to 48% for Hungarian lignites, 25 to 35% for the Miocene brown coals of Borsod County, 20 to 25% for those of Northern Nógrád County, 14 to 17% for the Eocene brown coals of the Dorog and Tatabánya regions (and for the Miocene coals of Southern Nógrád County also), 25% for the Cretaceous brown coals of Central Transdanubia (Dudar, Ajka, Balinka, etc.) and 4 to 6%-for the Liassic bituminous coals of the Pécs – Komló range of Southern Transdanubia.] In order to improve the durability and storability of the binderless briquettes sold to households and industry, it is indicated — in view of the lower average relative humidity — to dry the coal to be briquetted to a moisture content lower by 1 to 1.5% in the summer than in the winter, provided the resulting reduction in the strength of the briquettes, due to the deviation from the optimum water content, remains within tolerable limits. It is best if the hygroscopic and the optimum water content are close together. The fine-grained (minus-3 to minus-1 mm) raw material of briquettes intended for low-temperature carbonization ("Schwelen"), gasification and coking is dried to a much lower water content as a rule than the minus-6 mm raw material used in the normal run of commercial briquettes, in order that the higher-grade briquettes may stand without cracking the drying to zero water content by which the process in the oven begins (the higher the water content from which the briquettes are dried to zero, the greater is their shrinkage). Hygroscopicity plays no role here, because the briquettes are transferred hot to the appropriate oven, without any intermediate storage.

The moisture content of a brown coal spread out thinly so as to be readily accessible to ambient air is reduced to the equilibrium level by evaporation. The heat of evaporation is furnished by the atmosphere. This process of evaporation is the quicker, the less the relative humidity of ambient air, the higher its temperature and the higher its velocity. Heat drying accelerates this natural process by inputs of excess heat, by efficient guidance of the air flow and by causing evaporation to take place at a higher temperature.

The moisture-vs.-time curve is convex in the beginning (while the coal is being heated up to the temperature of drying), linear thereafter, and concave below the point of hygroscopicity. Over most of the drying process, water escaping from the particles' interiors makes up for surface evaporation: the liquid–steam interface is at the particles' surface and intra-particle temperature remains equal to the temperature of evaporating water. Once the hygroscopic point has been passed, water must travel to the surface from ever narrower capillaries: the liquid–steam interface penetrates into the particles, and the surface temperature of those increases.

Over a given span of drying time, finer particles dry out more than coarser ones. The difference between the moisture contents of the finest and the coarsest fraction, called the moisture gap, may attain as much as 20%. The moisture gap is highly relevant to the storability and strength in the fire of the briquettes, on account of the swelling and shrinking connected with the equalization of moisture. The finer-grained the coal to be briquetted and the lower its average (optimum) moisture content, the smaller the moisture gap and, hence, the better-grade the briquette. On drying the coal to a lower moisture, more and

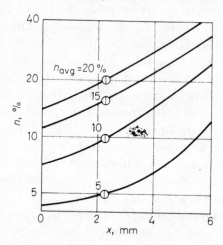

Fig. 9.6. The $n = f(x)$ function (the moisture gap) in lignites dried to different average moisture contents

more of its fine particles pass below the hygroscopic point, where drying is slower, while the original drying rate is maintained in the coarser particles. Moisture distribution vs. particle size, $n = f(x)$, is shown in Fig. 9.6 for lignites different as to average moisture n_{avg}. The fine-grained material intended for briquettes to be fed to the low-temperature carbonizing and coking ovens is dried to a lower moisture than that which is intended for normal commercial briquettes; the idea is to let the strength under heat of the former be increased also by the reduction of the moisture gap.

It would, however, be wrong to assume that the best briquettes are obtained at zero moisture gap: in fact, a gap less than 6% tends to impair briquette strength as a rule. The reason is that the processes and phenomena involved in briquetting are largely confined to the surface layers of the particles. Now a moisture gap exists also within every particle, its surface being drier than its interior. This kind of moisture gap is the greater, the larger the particle. If the average moisture content of the particles in the 5 to 6 mm range were to be the same as that of the particles in the 0 to 1 mm range, then the surface layer of the particles of 5 to 6 mm size would have to be strongly overdried, rendering them hard, overaged and insufficiently plastic, all of which would make for reduced briquette strength.

Even individual particles of one and the same size may differ as to moisture owing to differences in petrographic composition. Further differences may be due to the non-uniform loading of drying elements in the tube-type steam or other driers or to the coal being taken from fresh or partly dried parts of the coal seam or dump. But whereas differences in average moisture between different grain size fractions are established readily enough if one wants to find the apparent moisture gap, it is not possible without excessive effort to determine differences in moisture between the individual particles making up one and the same grain size class; hence, this latter moisture gap is liable to remain a latent one.

On drying, coal particles shrink as their moisture content decreses to between 5 and 10%, shrinkage ceases beyond that. For very wet lignites, shrinkage may attain 30 to 35% of original volume. Stresses arising between the outer shell and the core of the coal particles heated and dried from the outside inward leads to cracking, the spalling off of outer layers and further comminution. Furthermore, in its passage through the drier, coal is subjected to mechanical wear as well, which also reduces its particle size.

Water resistance in binderless briquettes is greatly varied. Some such briquettes tolerate immersion in water for 3 to 4 days without losing any of their strength (as e.g. those from the Niederlausitz region of the GDR), whereas others (e.g. those from the Geiseltal in the GDR or from Hidas in Hungary) may be so sensitive to water as to render their marketing something of a problem.

In brown coals, bitumen is hydrophobic but the bulk of the ingredients is hydrophilic to a greater or smaller extent, and water will adhere to those. If water molecules can find their way into the interstices between the coal particles pressed together to form the briquette, they will tend to pry the interstices apart (to make the briquette swell): the weakening of the capillary and intermolecular forces of cohesion will result in a reduction of briquette strength. The rate at which this reduction proceeds is a function of the hydrophilia (wettability) of the coal particles and of the relative magnitude of the forces of cohesion. In a second phase, water molecules penetrate into internal capillaries in the individual coal particles, right in between the micelles: the separation of the colloidal particles themselves that make up the macroscopic particle is increased thereby. This makes the individual particles swell in their turn. (In the first phase, only the separation of the coal particles is increased; the particles themselves do not swell.) Total swelling in a briquette is a combination of phase-1 and phase-2 swelling. Briquettes made of coals of great enough hardness will often crumble into particles under phase-1 swelling even before phase 2 can begin. The fracture surfaces of the particles of such harder coals tend to be smooth where those of softer coals are rough and ragged: these latter surfaces are likely to carry a gas film that reduces their hydrophilia. Water penetrates more easily between the smoother faces which are held together by comparatively weaker forces of cohesion. The briquettes of some hard coals fall apart within minutes of being immersed in water.

Phase-2 swelling depends greatly on the nature of the coal. Calcium humate, for example, is much more hygroscopic than free humic acids are, and its swelling is also very strong. Sodium humate behaves similarly. There may be some calcium metahumate with its strong propensity to swell even in the residual coal. Swelling clay minerals also reduce the water resistance of the briquette, partly because they themselves swell and partly because they swell differently from the coal; the tensions generated by differential swelling crack the briquette up. The presence of clay makes it more difficult to make non-cracking briquettes in any case.

Briquettes fresh out of the press may also crack if their moisture content deviates greatly from the hygroscopic point or if the moisture gap is excessive.

Briquette strength goes hand in hand as a rule with water resistance: in a stronger briquette, the cohesive forces are stronger as related to the disruptive ones. (The high resistance to water of the Niederlausitz briquettes is due not only to the limited swelling of the coal used but also to its fair briquettability, whereas, in the Geiseltal and Hidas briquettes, strength is reduced not only by the strong swelling of the calcium humate that they contain but also by the great hardness of that compound, much greater than that of the free humic acids; all this impairs briquettability and hence also the strength of the briquette.)

On preparing briquettes out of a given coal at different moisture contents, overdried coals were found to give briquettes of very poor water resistance, whereas resistance improved as the optimum moisture content was approached. In brown coal briquettes, optimum water content (the water content which gives the greatest strength) gives the greatest water resistance also, the connection being that the pore volume of the briquette is least at this moisture content. This rule is not all-embracing, however: in some brown coals, the moisture giving the best resistance to water is 2 to 6% above the optimum (the moisture giving the greatest strength). If water resistance at the optimum is not satisfactory, it may be indicated to split the difference and press the briquettes at a moisture 2 to 3% above the optimum.

Given a certain moisture content, a briquette is likely to be the more water-resistant, the finer-grained the coal used and the higher the temperature of pressing. This latter effect is more conspicuous in harder coals and/or coals richer in bitumen. The impact of the piston and friction against the mold heat the briquette, which was fairly hot to begin with, above the softening point of bitumen in the surface layer. The surface sealing provided thereby reduces both the permeability and the hydrophilia of the surface layer.

Water resistance in a briquette is a function of both the apparent and the latent moisture gap. The wider is either of these, the more readily will the sealed texture of the briquette be pried apart by water. Resistance to water can be improved by overdrying the coal somewhat, removing the fines (the minus-1 or minus-2 mm fraction) and returning them to the coarser fraction after judicious wetting. The spraying of the overdried fine fly dust caught in the dust collecting system of the briquetting works with a fairly thick coal sludge and its subsequent introduction into the coal to be briquetted has also been recommended. (Dry dust is difficult to wet with clear water, even if the water is hot, whereas a thickish sludge will wet it readily. The process has the double advantage of simplifying slurry handling and increasing the quantity of briquette feed.)

In another approach, the entire briquette feed, somewhat overdried, may be sprinkled with the thick coal sludge, without removing the fines first. The specific surface of both the fine particles and the dust exceeds that of the coarser fraction by orders of magnitude: hence, the uniform spraying of the dried coal augments the moisture content of the finer fractions above all. The coarser particles with their greater heat content will in fact evaporate the thin water films adhering to their surfaces. The removal by screening of the wet coarse fraction (plus-4 mm), its comminution to minus-1 mm and recombination with the fines or with the overdried dust has also been recommended. The process was found to improve both the strength and the resistance to water of the briquettes, even though it greatly increased the latent moisture gap in the fine dust. This suggests that the different moisture contents of the fine-grained ingredients will undergo a fairly rapid homogenization thanks to their large specific surfaces. It is a fact in any case that storage of the briquettes made by this process eliminates the latent moisture gap without any cracking or crumbling.

Combustion-gas drying of the coal gives more water-resistant briquettes than steam drying. Closed grinding-drying circuits feeding a briquetting unit with fine-grained coal have been found to be specially advantageous. In these, coal particles in suspension, encountering combustion gas at 900 to 1,000 °C, lose their water content by explosive evaporation: a comminution of the coarser particles also takes place. A fan mill may be inserted at the bottom of the drop stack to further comminute the coarser particles dropping into it. Under the usual run of conditions, gentle steam drying provides the best briquettes overall: the high temperature of the combustion gas tends to reduce the adhesive strength of coal. If, however, the coal is strongly oxidized, combustion-gas drying may make for greater briquette strength as well. Water resistance, on the other hand, is improved, especially in coals rich in bitumen polymers, by the activization of those at the particle surfaces by the hotter combustion gases.

The briquettes of greatest resistance to water can be made out of finely comminuted xylite. Next best are soft, young brown coals rich in humic acids

(Niederlausitz), in which the intermolecular forces of cohesion greatly exceed the wetting effect of hygroscopicity. As the abundance of calcium humate increases, the coal becomes harder and the resistance to water of the briquettes made out of it deteriorates, partly owing to the swelling of the calcium humate and partly to the poor briquettability of the coal. At the other end of the spectrum, hard dull brown coals tend to give the poorest resistance to water. (The harder the coal, the greater the liability that the forces of wetting gain the upper hand over the forces of cohesion: the more probable is phase-1 swelling and the more the briquette texture is open to phase-2 swelling.)

The greater the propensity of the coal to swell, the less is it possible to endow the briquettes with sufficient strength by adjusting the usual variables of briquette manufacturing. Special measures must then be taken to improve resistance to water. These fall under three headings in principle: (1) a treatment of the coal particles which changes their entire mass: (1a) chemical ash removal by acids, (1b) heat treatment, (1c) a combination of the two; (2) surface treatment of the particles; (2a) with the gases of low-temperature carbonization (2b) by impregnation with oil, (2c) with carbon dioxide gas; (2d) Plochmann process; and (3) treatment of the ready briquettes: (3a) heat treatment in a humid atmosphere; (3b) giving the briquettes a hydrophobic protective coating; (3c) protecting the briquettes with tarpaulin or paper. Let us consider these methods one by one.

(1a) If poor resistance to water is due to the calcium humate content of the coal, that constituent can be decomposed by the dosage of an acid into free humic acids and $CaCl_2$ (using hydrochloric acid) or $CaSO_4$ (using sulphuric acid). The inorganic $CaCl_2$ salt thus formed can be washed out of the coal with water before drying, entailing a reduction in ash content. (This method has not yet been applied in industrial practice.)

(1b) Coals rich in calcium humates can be dried to zero moisture with combustion gases and heated to 200 to 250 °C in the process. The result is the rapid ageing of the coal as a whole. The point is that calcium humate ages even more rapidly: its hygroscopicity and propensity to swell are reduced irreversibly. If coal so treated is re-wetted before briquetting to the usual water content of 12 to 16%, the resistance to water of the briquettes eventually obtained is greatly improved thereby. For example, using Geiseltal coal dried to zero moisture and subsequently heated to

$$105 \qquad 160 \qquad 200 \qquad 220 \text{ °C,}$$

the briquettes obtained were found to absorb

$$20 \qquad 13 \qquad 4 \qquad 2\%$$

water when immersed in water for 24 hours; without the prior heat treatment, they absorbed 36%.

The process is applied in Geiseltal practice. Coal pre-dried in a steam drier to 16% moisture and 75 °C is dried to zero moisture and 220 to 250 °C in a combustion-gas fan drier. It then passes into a wetting drum and so on to a fan cooler whence it is fed to the press at 16% moisture and 45 °C. Remarkably enough, re-wetting produces practically no moisture gap. It has not been clarified whether heating to 200 to 250 °C decomposes the calcium humate more or less. Some $CaCO_3$ may be formed under the influence of the carbon dioxide in the combustion gas, but calcium humate is known not to undergo bulk decomposition below 275 to 300 °C. (Such a temperature, however, also hardens the coal appreciably, and therefore reduces the strength of the briquettes. Coals that are fairly hard to start with do not as a rule tolerate this sort of strength reduction.)

High-temperature steaming, e.g. by Fleissner ahydration as described in Chapter 8, will also reduce the swelling of the coal and improve its water resistance. Ahydration likewise involves an irreversible process of ageing in the surface layers of the colloidal material, which partly transforms humic acids into neutral humins. As a result, capillary walls grow less hygroscopic, less wettable: this in turn reduces the coal's propensity to swell.

Coal dried by the Fleissner ahydration process usually requires some after-drying, but the briquettes made of such coal are often much more water-resistant than if the coal had been dried in the usual way. For example, Geiseltal coal dried "normally" (in a tube-type steam drier at 135 °C) gave briquettes that swelled by 22% on immersion in water for two hours, whereas steam-drying at a pressure of 20 bars and 214 °C and subsequent afterdrying to 16% reduced swelling to 12%.

High-temperature steaming affects the briquettability of different coals differently. The strength of Geiseltal briquettes with their high calcium humate content was found to increase monotonically as steaming pressure was increased:

$$170 \qquad 200 \qquad 280 \text{ kp/cm}^2 \text{ (strength)}$$

at

$$5 \qquad 10 \qquad 25 \text{ bars} \qquad \text{(pressure),}$$

whereas that of the Niederlausitz briquettes was found to decline beyond 10 bars:

$$220 \qquad 224 \qquad 140 \text{ kp/cm}^2.$$

The water resistance of Geiseltal briquettes made of steamed coal greatly exceeded that of the briquettes made of coal dried in the usual way: the bending strength of briquettes made after steaming at

	0	5	10	15	20 bars
was	11	13	16	17	17 kp/cm²;

it was reduced to

$$3 \qquad 10 \qquad 14 \qquad 16 \qquad 14 \; kp/cm^2$$

by immersion into water for two hours and to

$$0 \qquad 0 \qquad 2 \qquad 3 \qquad 8 \; kp/cm^2$$

by immersion for four hours. The coal is to be steamed raw rather than dried, as otherwise its briquettability is impaired intolerably.

(1c) A combination of chemical ash removal and heat treatment has been suggested for the strongly swelling, poorly water-resistant brown coals of the Halle region (GDR) with their high NaCl, Na humate and Ca humate contents. In the Lissner process, coal is first treated with dilute hydrochloric acid and stored for 24 hours in a dump. Then, filled into autoclaves, it is exposed to steam at 5 to 10 bars pressure. Water is injected into the autoclaves at the same time. Hydrochloric acid converts the Na and Ca humates into free humic acids on the one hand and NaCl and $CaCl_2$ on the other: the latter are exuded by the coal together with the capillary water, and washed out by the injected water. The briquettes made of the coal so de-salted are highly water-resistant; they also have greater strength than the briquettes made of untreated coal, presumably thanks to the free humic acids formed on humate decomposition. A pilot plant using this process has been in operation for some time.

Most of the ash of the Miocene brown coal of Hidas, Southern Hungary, is CaO: almost all of the Ca is in the form of humates. Treatment in autoclaves with hydrochloric acid and leaching the $CaCl_2$ would permit to make low-ash, high-strength briquettes of unexceptionable water resistance out of Hidas coal.

(2a) Briquettes made of hard brown coals tend to have a low resistance to water. The particles of such coal have smooth, hydrophilic surfaces of fracture; water can penetrate the briquettes readily along those surfaces. If the process used manages to endow these surfaces with a film of oil or tar prior to briquetting, then the particles are turned hydrophobic, the penetration of the briquette by water is hindered thereby. In the process devised by Plochmann and Andersch, 15% or so of the coal is dried to 5% moisture and fed to low-temperature carbonization; the remaining 85% is cured using the "smoulder gases" ("Schwelgase") of carbonization while cataracting in a rotary drum. In the process, a fine film of tar condenses on the surfaces and in the cracks and pores of the coal particles, turning those hydrophobic. The smoulder gases enter the drum at 200 to 300 °C and leave it at 90 to 100 °C. The entry and exit temperatures of coal are about equal at 95 to 100 °C: the adsorption of the tar augments coal weight by about 2%. The surface layer of the coal particles is presumably softened up a little, which also improves briquettability. (Briquettes made by this process of the hard North Bohemian brown coals

634

have high strength and very good resistance to water. Kept under water for one hour, they absorb one percent water, whereas briquettes made of untreated coal fall apart in water in a few minutes.)

(2b) Admixing one to two per cent oil to the dry coal at the temperature of briquetting has also been recommended as a means of endowing the coal particles with oil films. This did improve the water resistance of the briquettes to some extent, but reduced their strength rather substantially. It seems preferable to let the films form out of the smoulder gases of the coal proper, by condensation out of vapour phase above 100 °C onto coal heated to about 100 °C (as in the Plochmann process).

(2c) Flushing the coal with sulphur dioxide gas improves the briquettes' resistance to water. The treatment of a Geiseltal coal slurry with sulphurous acid has also been attempted, followed by the flushing-out of the acid. True, briquettes made out of coal thus treated did absorb much less water, but the improvement was not so great as using hydrochloric or sulphuric acid: comparatively weak, sulphurous acid was unable to completely decompose the calcium humates.

(2d) One drawback of the Plochmann process is that 15% or so of the coal suited for briquetting must be used for the production of smoulder gases and vapours and that a distilling oven must be built for the purpose. With a view to avoiding this inconvenience, the process of Hock and Jeckel intends to mobilize the bitumens in the outer layers of the coal particles by a high-temperature flash treatment, in order that they may form hydrophobic films on the particles' surfaces and fill out their pores. Some smoulder evaporation will probably also take place in the surface layer, contributing to a better resistance to water. Coal dried to a moisture of 3 to 6% is ground to minus-0.3 mm and then brought into contact with a comparatively small volume of combustion gas at 700 to 900 °C (0.2 to 0.5 kg of gas per kg of coal). The simple and polymerized bitumens next to the coal particles' surfaces are mobilized thereby, coating the particles with hydrophobic films. Incipient smoulder evaporation softens up the surface layer as a whole, improving briquettability, although the particles' interiors remain hard the while. This is another factor contributing to a better resistance to water. Coal powder emerging from the heat treatment at about 130 °C is immediately fed to a briquetting press delivering 1,800 bars pressure. The process is being used with a fair success on North Bohemian brown coals.

(3a) On storage in air at 55 °C and 85% relative humidity, the water resistance of briquettes made of a swelling coal was found to improve substantially in as little as two hours. The limit of improvement was attained in five hours. Even broken-up lumps of the briquettes so treated did not crumble in water, which suggests that exposure to hot moist air reduces phase-2 swelling, possibly as a result of a homogenization of capillary water contents all over the briquette.

A similar storage of the coal prior to briquetting did not, on the other hand, improve the water resistance of the briquettes.

(3b) Some German (GDR) briquette factories employ the Albert emulsion process. The emulsion is made up as to nine parts of bitumen or tar oil and one part of ozokerite, colophonium and a fatty acid: the emulsifiers are alkalis and a soap. The composition is adjusted to the incoming coal grade. One part emulsion is diluted with five parts warm (40 to 50 °C) water: the briquettes are immersed hot into the liquid. They emerge from the bath carrying a dirty grey-brown coating which in 1.5 to 2 minutes turns into a gleaming black dry non-sticky film. The consumption of emulsion is about 1.6 kg/t for household briquettes but may attain 3.3 kg/t for the smaller-sized industrial briquettes. The cost of such sealing in the 1950s used to be in the 0.45 to 0.70 DM/t range.

(3c) The simplest way of protecting briquettes of low water resistance is to cover railcars with a tarpaulin or with paper, with or without a wire mesh embedded in it. Paper will stand one journey only; a tarp may stand up to 75. Briquettes of low water resistance must in any case be stored under cover.

The standard technology of binderless briquetting used in the production of household and industrial briquettes is as follows.

Raw coal is comminuted to minus-6 mm and dried to the optimum moisture content (e.g. 15 to 16%). Cooled to about 40 °C, it is then briquetted in an Exter rod press. The loose bulk density of the coal fed to the press is about 0.65 g/cm³; its granulometry must be such as to keep pore volume low (e.g. 40 to 60% minus-1 mm, 65 to 80% minus-2 mm, 80 to 90% minus-3 mm and 90 to 95% minus-4 mm). Coal in the finer particle-size range (minus-4 or minus-3 mm) is usually dried to a lower moisture (e.g. 12%) and fed into the rod press without cooling. The coal for briquettes intended for coking or semi-coking is ground even finer (minus-1 to minus-0.5 mm), dried even more thoroughly (e.g. to 8%) and briquetted without cooling e.g. in a ring press. In such a setup, it is indicated to combine grinding with drying: raw coal pre-crushed to minus-20 to minus-6 mm is dried with combustion gas at about 1,000 °C in a pneumatic drier: this makes its moisture escape explosively. The coal particles are further comminuted by decrepitation. Any coal of plus-1 (or plus-0.5 mm) size left behind is comminuted in some grinding unit, e.g. a fan mill installed at the bottom of the pneumatic drier shaft.

Those components refractory to briquetting, poorly briquettable or impairing briquette quality (fibrous-woody lignite, pyrite nodules, clay, etc.) should if possible be removed from the raw coal. In a favourable situation, simple selective comminution will help. For example, a material crushed in a hammer mill or a toothed roll may be separated into two fractions, e.g. at 12–16 and 80–100 mm. The coarse fraction is likely to consist largely of fibrous-woody matter that can be used as an in-plant boiler fuel after the removal of the lumps of clay and nodes of pyrite. The middle fraction may be fed e.g. to a disintegrator and a screen of 12 to 16 mm aperture size; here too, the retained fraction is diverted for use as in-plant boiler fuel, whereas the passed fraction and the fines of the original separation are used as the briquette feed, to be introduced into the presses after drying and suitable grinding.

Coal for conventional briquetting is most often dried in tube-type steam driers. The discharge of those is screened at 6 mm; the retained fraction is ground to below 6 mm and (in order to reduce the moisture gap) afterdried in a smaller tube-type steam drying unit.

If a tray-type steam drier is used, it is usual to install a tray suitable for screening and grinding about the middle of the stack of trays. This tray has three concentric annular screening surfaces, with apertures e.g. of 3 mm on the innermost one and of 6 mm on the two others. Crushing cones of adjustable pressure roll in races between the screens. The finished fraction passed by the 3-mm screen is driven shaftward by the baffles. The fractions passed by the 6-mm screens undergo further drying on the trays below; the retained fractions consist — provided the adjustment of the cones is right — of the fibrous, woody stuff. This is removed from the drier to be used as in-plant boiler fuel. The two or three bottom trays are not steam-heated in order to let the coal cool to 40 to 60 °C before it leaves the drier. (In case a drying column is being used, it is usual to cool the coal to be briquetted in a separate cooling house where it slides down some louvered cooling baffles.)

In the GDR, the moisture of earthy brown coals is reduced before briquetting from 53% on average (50 to 60%) to 13.5% on average (to between 9.5 and 19.5%). Making one ton of briquettes thus requires about 2.33 tons of raw coal, breaking down to

43% or 1.00 t briquettes,

36% or 0.84 t evaporated water,

21% or 0.49 t boiler fuel for drying and driving the presses.

The coal prepared to a suitable granulometry, moisture and temperature is usually pressed into briquettes in an Exter type rod press at 600 to 1,800 bars or in a ring press at 1,500 to 3,000 bars.

9.2.1.3. Press types are classed by form and operation into piston presses with closed or open molds, cylinder and ring presses.

(A) Closed-mold piston presses. Machines of this type are encountered among the brick presses, including those making coal briquettes, the various presses of the silicate industry, the cube presses of the sugar mills, various pill-making machines, presses for thermosetting plastics, etc.

The material to be pressed is filled into a mold placed horizontally or vertically and compressed by the piston fitted into it. The press tool performs a reciprocating motion in a form shaped to fit its cross section. The motion is made up of two symmetrical strokes, one of which is the compression stroke. During the other, the piston draws back while the briquette is removed and a new dose of loose granular material is introduced by a suitable feeder into the working space. If briquettes thicker than the usual run are to be made, it is indicated to use dual-action presses in which a piston is pressed into the mold from either side. This reduces the buffering effect which, in single-action pressing, reduces the useful pressure in the interior of the briquette where direct pressure is confined to one face and friction among the feed particles and against the mold takes up a major part of the pressure force. If the brick is too thick even for dual-action briquetting, its two faces will be hard but its strength will be less in between, where it is difficult for the pressure to work through.

Closed-mold piston presses are divided into stationary- and rotary-tray types. The stationary-tray ones may be hand, moving-feeder and hydraulic presses.

Hand presses are made without force multiplication for small pressures (0.5 to 2 t) and with a multiplier linkage for greater ones (up to 30 t).

Moving-feeder presses may be of the impact, toggle, angle-lever and excenter type. The moving feeder moves around a stationary tray; it also serves to remove the finished briquettes from the forms.

Impact presses are most often used for the semi-dry pressing of clay and lime-sand bricks. Toggle presses are used for semi-dry pressing in the silicate industry.

One typical representative of angle-lever presses is the Tigler press, which simultaneously presses eight large brick-shaped briquettes or 48 maller cubes, as shown in Part A of Fig. 9.7. The upper connecting rod of the press is fixed to an upper cross bar. This is connected by tie rods to a lower cross bar to which the lower piston is fixed. The press is dual-action in that the two pistons move simultaneously. The upper piston, however, is not directly fixed to the lower connecting rod: only its guide bar, against which the piston is free to move, is attached to the connecting rod. The upper piston can thus be lifted up regardless of the phase the press is in. The lower crossbar can also be moved relative to the press frame. The upper piston can be coupled to or uncoupled from its guide bar by means of an angle lever. The angle lever is actuated by a cam. The upper piston proper can be lifted by a pin controlled by a double cam whenever it is not coupled to its guide bar. A third cam lifts the lower piston and crossbar independently of the phase of the press.

The feeder frame serving to fill the mold and to remove the finished briquettes from the stationary table is controlled by a coulisse which — similarly to the crank and the three cams — is fixed to the main shaft of the machine. As long as the pin moves in the small arc of the coulisse, the frame is immobile; this is when pressing takes place. After the termination of pressing, the two pistons move apart. Next, the lower crossbar together with the lower piston rises up in the mold, popping the ready briquette out of it. The coulisse then moves the frame forward until it comes to lie above the mold, pushing the ready briquette in front of it, onto an inclined chute. Subsequently, the lower piston sinks so that the material contained in the frame can fall into the mold. Meanwhile, the upper piston has been lifted by the pin: it now drops back through the frame, compressing the material somewhat and completing the filling of the mold. The upper piston is then lifted by cam 2, and the frame is retracted; the upper piston thereupon drops again onto the material, giving it a first blow. The upper piston is keyed to its guide bar by the pin: pressing can now begin with a slow buildup of pressure.

Some ten pressings or so can be performed in a minute. Output is the number of briquettes made at a time multiplied by briquette weight: it is e.g.

$$8 \cdot 4 \cdot 10 \cdot \frac{60}{1,000} = 19.2 \text{ tph}$$

when making eight four-kilogramme briquettes per stroke or

$$48 \cdot 0.4 \cdot 10 \cdot \frac{60}{1,000} = 11.5 \text{ tph}$$

when making 48 cubes of 0.4 kg weight each per stroke.

Excenter presses are used in the ceramic industry for the afterpressing of refractory bricks pre-formed in an extruder (a belt press). One type of moving-feeder excenter press is the pill-making machine widespread in the pharmaceutical and plastics industries. (In the pharmaceutical industry, it is used to give the final product its definitive shape and consistency; in the plastics industry, it is used to facilitate the dosage of plastics to extruders and presses.) The pill press cold-compacts a powder of s.g. 0.5 g/cm^3 on average to a s.g. of 1 to 1.2 g/cm^3. Pills permit a more accurate and more rapid dosage: weighing can be dispensed with, and no dust loss is incurred.

Stationary-table hydraulic presses have the advantage over the types described so far that they can be run with a longer stroke; the pressure required can be applied at any point of the stroke and maintained up to its end; idling and operating speeds can be easily adjusted and modified, even with the press running. There are two-column, four-column and frame-type machines. The frame-type machine has the advantage that it guides the piston with greater precision, whereas two-column machines permit better access from all sides.

Revolving-table presses. In these, the successive operations of pressing (filling the mold, pressing, the extrusion of the finished briquette and its removal) which are performed in a time sequence on the stationary-table machines are performed simultaneously at different points of the table. The number of pressings per unit of time can thus be augmented rather substantially. Revolving-table piston presses — suitably designed to fit the intended purpose — are in use in many fields such as the briquetting of coals with a binder, semi-dry stamping in the silicate industry, sugar cube making in sugar mills, etc.

The essential element of a revolving-table press is a round pressing table which, at suitable intervals, is turned by a given sub-multiple of a full circle. The molds are radial cavities in the table. Pressing is usually performed by two countermoving pistons (dual-action pressing).

The Couffinhal press, whose diagram is shown as Part B of Fig. 9.7, is used in coal briquetting. The two opposite pistons are moved by swinging levers. A pin at the end a of the upper lever can move in a slot in the shaft which joins the two levers. The shaft carries at its top end a hydraulic pressure-regulating cylinder. This device permits to pre-set the maximum pressure permissible in the course of pressing. The con-rod of the piston in the cylinder is connected to the pin of the upper lever. The shaft is attached by its bottom end to the linkage that moves the lower piston; the lever c of the lower piston is normally kept depressed by a spring. The only fixed point of the entire upper and lower linkage is the fulcrum f of the lower lever. The system is kept in motion by a crank which actuates the right-hand end of the upper lever through a con-rod and a universal joint u.

While the universal joint moves downward, the fulcrum of the upper lever is the peg at its far end, which is blocked at the bottom of the slot until the pressure-regulating piston permits it to move. The upward force acting upon the piston in the equalizer strives to raise the slotted shaft and the cylinder with it, but is prevented from doing so by the spring which holds the lower lever depressed. Early on in the pressing phase, only the upper piston penetrates the mold to compress the material as its pressure builds up gradually. At a given pressure threshold, however, the upward force upon the regulating piston overcomes the force of the spring, and the slotted shaft together with the cylinder starts to rise, actuating the lower piston which then starts to compress the fill from below. In this phase, the upper piston is already immobile, with its fulcrum transposed to b (into the piston bearing). The pressure regulator is activated when the pressure buildup exceeds a pre-set maximum. Valve n, loaded by a strong spring, opens, so that liquid may escape from the piston space, and the piston may move upward independently of the cylinder and the slotted shaft. (It is in order to permit this relative displacement that the rod is slotted.) As the universal joint moves upward on the next stroke, the pistons retract from the mold. The pressing table is now rotated by a certain angle until the next mold, filled with loose material to be pressed, comes to lie between the pistons. The ready briquette is pushed out by a removing piston r actuated by the upper lever. The table is rotated by a forwarding cylinder whose surface has a slot machined into it: the slot, circular on two-

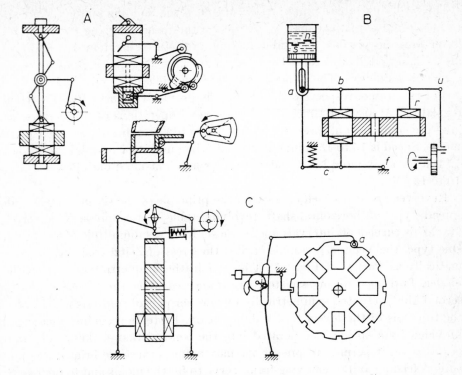

Fig. 9.7. Diagrams of closed-mold piston presses used for briquetting coals with a binder
A — the Tigler (stationary-tray angle lever) press, *B* — the Couffinhal press, *C* — the
Yeadon or revolver press

thirds of the cylinder's circumference, passes at either end into a spiral covering
one-third of the circumference. A small running cone projects from the bottom
of the table under each mold. (There are eight to ten molds in the table.) The
table is immobile as long as the cone is engaged in the straight segment of
the slot; this is when pressing takes place. When the cone enters the spiral
part, the table is moved on. The cone under the next mold simultaneously
engages the spiral at the other end of the slot and slides in it up to the circular segment.

The output of the machine can be calculated in terms of the number of
pressings ($n = 36$ to 40 tpm) and the number and weight of the briquettes
pressed simultaneously. Putting e.g. $n = 40$, and 6 kg per mold, output is

$$6 \cdot 40 \cdot \frac{60}{1,000} = 14.4 \text{ tph.}$$

Power draft is about 15 kW at a pressure of 200 to 250 bars.

The revolving-table "rapid press" current in the building materials industry rotates about a vertical shaft integral with the frame carrying the upper and lower pressing pistons. The table incorporates six or eight molds, and there are as many pairs of pistons. The lower pistons are actuated by rollers pressing against a guide rail. The upper pistons are controlled by cams and the guide rail of the frame, respectively. The press is provided with hydraulic pressure regulation. At any one time, one of the several operations of briquetting (filling, pre-compression, pressing, extraction, etc.) is going on in each of the molds. Speed is 13 to 15 rpm; output, e.g. when making 2.5-kg bricks, is about 12 tph for a six-mold table and 16 tph for an eight-mold one. Power draft is 10 to 13 kW.

Revolver presses, which operate on the principle of the six-gun, are a widespread type of horizontal-shaft revolving-table piston press. The vertical "table" is turned at intervals about the shaft by a submultiple of a full circle. One type, the Yeadon press, also called the press of Zeitz, is shown diagrammatically as Part C of Fig. 9.7; it is used in the briquetting of coals with a binder. Two opposite press pistons are connected by con-rods to levers of the second kind, actuated symmetrically by another pair of con-rods which attach the top ends of the levers to a walking beam. Protection against breakage is provided by a spring incorporated into the con-rod that makes the walking beam move: it permits to pre-set the maximum permissible briquetting pressure. A feeding and a removing frame serve to fill the molds and to remove the finished briquettes. The turning of the table at the proper intervals is controlled by a coulisse-and-lever combination. The coulisse is actuated by an auxiliary shaft perpendicular to the main shaft. During pressing, the table is fixed by a pawl engaging a notch. Meanwhile, the coulisse moves to the right, so that the roller at the end of the linkage can move out of the depression forming a catch in the rim of the table and come to rest in the next one. When the coulisse starts its journey to the left, the roller gets caught in the catch and turns the table, by 45° if the table is an eight-mold one. The number of pressings is 15 to 25 per minute, less than in the Couffinhal press whose design is simpler. The output is proportionately less.

The pharmaceutical industry uses revolving-table presses in pill-making. Their output is much greater than that of the excenter-type pill-making press. Their advantages are most evident when mass-producing large pills of more than about 13 mm diameter. Table speed is 6 to 10 rpm. Output may attain 12,000 pills per hour even with a single-stamp tool. By multiplying stamps, output can be increased to 80,000 per hour and beyond.

(B) Open-mold piston presses. The prototype is the Exter press (Fig. 9.8), used in the binderless briquetting of young brown coals and lignites above all. The mold is a channel about one metre long, open at both ends; its cross section corresponds to that of the briquette to be made. One end of the channel is penetrated by a reciprocating piston, every forward stroke of which, generating 800 to 1,800 bars pressure, presses one briquette out of the loose fine coal fed in.

Feed coal is introduced through a funnel, by means of a feeder roll. The rate of coal flow onto the feeder roll can be adjusted by means of a slide gate. From the funnel, the coal drops through a vertical feed chute onto the bottom

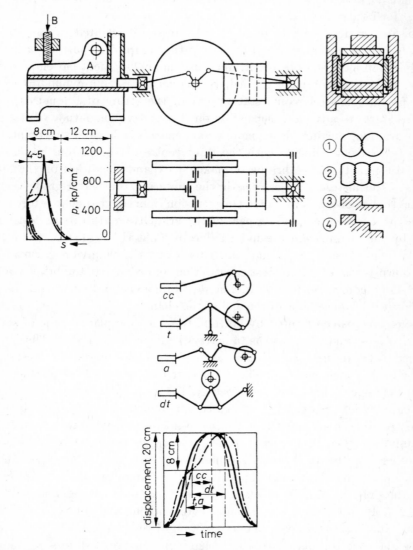

Fig. 9.8. Diagram of the Exter open-mold rod press showing the cross section of the channel (the piston), the $p = f(s)$ (pressure-vs.-displacement) and the $s = f(t)$ (displacement-vs.-time) diagrams of the crank-and-con rod (cc), toggle (t), angle-lever (a) and dual-toggle (dt) type presses

plate of the press channel when the piston is in the fully retracted position. On its forward stroke, the piston shoves the coal on the plate into the channel. Its 20 to 25 cm stroke ensures the compaction of the loose feed. The counterforce needed to generate pressure is provided by the string of pressed briquettes in the channel as it advances the size of one briquette per stroke. The channel tapers towards its discharge end: it is the deformation and the increasing friction caused by the taper that resist the piston. The taper is 3 to 10 mm, greater for harder coals.

Pressure vs. displacement in the Exter press is illustrated by the $p = f(s)$ diagram in the lower left-hand corner of the figure. The piston pushes the freshly fed-in loose stuff before it, until the channel segment left empty by its last retraction is completely filled. Subsequently, pressure buildup begins. Once pressure has overcome static friction, the string of briquettes in the channel starts to advance. Depending on the relative magnitude of static vs. sliding friction, pressure drops more or less markedly beyond this point. Zero pressure does not coincide with the dead centre of the piston, because the residual elasticity of the briquette makes it expand somewhat on the return stroke of the piston. The less elastic the material, the better-grade the briquettes that can be made out of it. On extrusion from the channel, the forces arising in the emerged, expanding part of the briquette and in its part still confined by the channel are the more liable to burst the briquette, the greater the elastic expansion of the material. This is why the channel is given a slight flare downstream of its greatest constriction, in order that the briquette may expand in a controlled fashion to assume its final shape. Every stroke pushes one finished briquette out of the end of the channel.

The channel is constituted by bottom, top and side plates made of steel of great hardness and shaped so as to marry the form of the piston. The top and bottom plates lie up against other steel plates called nests. The nest plates can be heated and/or cooled. The lower nest rests on the base casting of the press; the upper is fixed to press block A. The nests are provided with lengthwise bores which between them constitute a connected passage. The inlet end of this passage is attached to a source of steam or cold water, as required. Heating is necessary before and during startup; cooling must be provided at any other time because pressing generates intense heat. The upper, shorter nesting plate that keeps the top plate of the channel in place is removable from the press block. The block is a heavy piece of iron whose shape recalls a tongue. It can be tilted to a small extent about a massive pivot passing through its flat part above the entry section of the channel. The force that it exerts upon the top plates (nest and channel), which contributes to the pressure in the channel, can be adjusted by means of a hand wheel on screw B. (In more recent makes, the screw is replaced by a hydraulic press.) The pressing element of the piston and the channel are shaped to give the desired shape and size of briquette. The so-called "seven-inch parlour briquette" has a size of 180 by 60 by 54 mm; its weight is roughly 500 grammes.

The piston is most often driven by a crank and con-rod. The crankshaft is driven in turn by a piston-type steam engine in the steam press or an electric motor in the electric press. Large flywheels are keyed to the ends of the crankshaft beyond the bearings, so as to smooth out the abrupt load peaks. Press speed tends to be in the 70 to 130 rpm range, but may attain 200 rpm when making small industrial briquettes with a stepped or split piston (cf. insets 1 to 4). Throughput is

$$\frac{60nG}{1,000} \simeq 0.03n = 2.1 \text{ to } 3.9 \text{ tph}$$

when making seven-inch parlour briquettes of weight $G = 0.5$ kg each at a specific power consumption of 22 to 25 kW h/t and a pressure of 800 to 1,200 bars, out of coal of "standard" minus-6 mm granulometry. The briquetting of finer-grained coal at 1,500 to 2,000 bars requires 30 to 40 kW h/t.

Pressure buildup in the press may be altered by choosing some other type of linkage than the simple crank-and-con rod (cc) shown in Part A of Fig. 9.8. Below it, the toggle (t), angle-lever (a) and dual-toggle (dt) arrangements are shown diagrammatically. The bottom part of the figure shows hodographs (time-vs.-displacement graphs) for all of these. In the first phase of pressing, when the piston just shoves the loose feed before it, t, a and dt give — for a given stroke and drive speed — a greater piston velocity than cc: this is offset by slower motion near the end of the stroke. The time available for pressing in the strict sense is thus longer, which is an advantage in terms of briquette strength. Effective pressing time — during which the piston advances the last eight centimetres of its forward stroke — is

for	cc	t	a	dt
	20	27	27	30%

of the full piston cycle. This is why an angle-lever or toggle press can make fair-grade briquettes even out of coals for which a simple crank-and-con-rod press will not do.

Let e.g. $n = 100$ rpm, $N = 25$ kW h/t and $T = 3$ tph. The power draft of the press then is $25 \times 3 = 75$ kW. Since one kW equals 102 mkp/s, the work done by the press is

$$60 \cdot 102 \cdot 75 = 460,000 \text{ mkp per minute}$$

and 4,600 mkp per cycle. Let the mechanical efficiency of the press be $\eta = 0{,}87$; actual briquetting work is then obtained as

$$0.87 \cdot 4,600 \simeq 4,000 \text{ mkp per briquette.}$$

The briquetting phase of the forward stroke being $s = 0.08$ m, average briquetting force is

$$\frac{4,000}{0.08} = 50,000 \text{ kp.}$$

The face area of the conventional half-kilogram parlour briquette being ~ 110 cm², the average pressure,

$$p_{avg} = \frac{50,000}{110} \simeq 455 \text{ kp/cm}^2.$$

The ratio of peak to average pressure is shown by the hodographs to be 2 to 3 or so: hence, p_{max} is at a fair approximation in the 900 to 1,350 kp/cm² range.

Most of the work input into briquetting is used to overcome friction (that is, to generate heat). 4,000 mkp per briquette equals

$$\frac{4,000}{427} \simeq 9.3 \text{ kcal.}$$

It may be assumed that 90% of this,

$$0.9 \cdot 9.3 \simeq 8.4 \text{ kcal,}$$

goes to heat the briquette. The briquettes' specific heat being about

$$c = 0.4 \text{ kcal/kg} \cdot {}^\circ\text{C,}$$

pressing would raise briquette temperature by

$$\Delta t = \frac{8.4}{0.5} \cdot 0.4 = 42 \ {}^\circ\text{C}$$

if the whole mass took up heat evenly during the brief period of actual pressing. Assuming on the other hand that all the heat is absorbed by an outer shell weighing about 0.1 kg, we find

$$\Delta t \simeq 5 \cdot 42 = 210 \ {}^\circ\text{C.}$$

Given a starting temperature of 40 °C, this implies that average shell temperature will rise to 250 °C, and actual briquette-surface temperature even higher, high enough to coke it. This must be prevented by cooling the channel. In-plant recordings have shown that cooling water flowing at a rate of 24 litres per minute is warmed up from 14 to 28 °C, which takes

$$24 \ (28 - 14) = 336 \text{ kcal/min}$$

or 3.36 kcal per cycle. Since

$$\Delta t = \frac{8.4 - 3.36}{0.1 \cdot 0.4} = 126 \ {}^\circ\text{C,}$$

the average temperature of the outer shell of 0.1 kg weight of the briquette gets heated to $\sim40 + 126 = 166$ °C under such cooling.

(C) Roll presses incorporate a pair of rolls, counter-rotating at equal speed, with suitable depressions (half-molds) shaped in their surfaces. It is the closure of these that compresses the loose feed into egg-shaped briquettes (Fig. 9.9). The peak pressure that can be attained is a function of the degree to

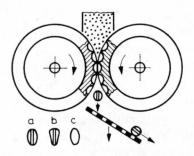

Fig. 9.9. Diagram of a roll press

which the half-molds can be filled. The feed drops down from a hopper above the rolls, to be nipped by them. Uniform feeding is important. The feed rate is usually regulated by means of a feeder tongue developed as a slide gate by means of which the hopper aperture can be regulated. In another setup, feed rate is regulated by means of raising or lowering a vertical baffle installed in the plane of symmetry of the feed shaft. Trouble may ensue if the feed sticks to the shaft wall. The usual preventive measure is to water-cool the wall.

The original application of roll presses, still going strong today, is in the briquetting of coal, with a binder in most cases. Seventy to hundred bars pressure may suffice to make small egg briquettes because, the feed having no opportunity to slide against the mold, no friction loss occurs, and the buffering effect of interparticle friction is insufficient to attenuate pressure between the surface and the centre of the briquette to any significant extent. Rolls are set a few mm apart: briquettes accordingly acquire narrow brims around their equators, which crumble off on release from the mold. The fines thus formed pass the oblique grate below the press and are returned thence to the malaxator.

By increasing the feed rate, pressure can be increased to the 1,000 to 2,000 bars required for binderless briquetting. A pair of half-molds having symmetry of rotation (inset a in Fig. 9.9) will, however, tend to produce split briquettes at such pressures; excess fill is extruded upward from between the closing half-molds; the briquette develops as a result a "beak fissure" between its two halves. This can be avoided by shaping the half-molds so as to prevent this extrusion (inset b) or by using asymmetrical half-molds (inset c) or, indeed, molds on one roll and stamps on the other The molds in the rolls invariably have their major axes parallel to the roll shafts.

Roll presses making egg briquettes with a binder have a diameter of 0.8 to 1.4 m for a length of 30 to 60 cm; their peripheral speed is in the 0.3 to 0.8 m/s range. Briquette weight is 20 to 100 grammes. Throughput is 10 to 15 tph for a 84 cm dia. $\times$ 50 cm press at a peripheral speed of 0.3 m/s, or about 5 tph of 20-gramme nut briquettes or 35 tph of 50-gramme egg briquettes for a 140 cm dia. $\times$ 60 cm press run at a peripheral speed of 0.78 m/s. Twin presses have two rolls keyed to each shaft. This doubles output also.

Toothed rolls of a variety of profiles are used for the dry pressing of powdery materials, e.g. to make tiles 2.5 to 3 mm thick and 100 to 200 mm wide, which are subsequently broken up to the desired size in splitters. The s.g. of the input material is augmented considerably by such pressing. The procedure may be applied e.g. to drugs prior to pill-stamping.

(D) Ring presses feature an annular channel: the feed introduced into it is pressed into a curved bar by an eccentrically installed pressing disk. The Apfelbeck press used in the binderless briquetting of coal is shown diagrammatically in Fig. 9.10 (Holik 1934; Thau 1929). The annular channel is constituted by a pair of large-diameter steel rings rolling on external rollers. At the nadir, the rings are pressed together by conical rollers acting on their sides: at the zenith, they are pried apart by disk D. Motion is imparted to the system by

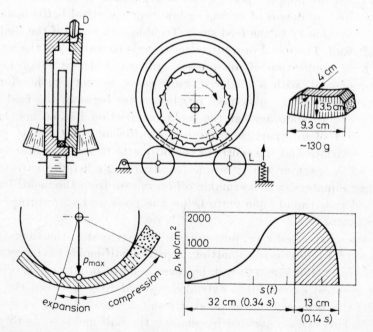

Fig. 9.10. Diagram of a ring (Apfelbeck) press complete with $p = f(s)$ diagram

the friction of the driven support rollers. The pressing disk, pressed down hydraulically into the channel, is rotated in its turn by the friction of the briquette bar forming in the channel. The bearings of the disk are mounted in consoles operating as levers of the second kind. (In another setup, the one actually shown in Fig. 9.10, the pressing disk rotating in fixed bearings is driven, and the support rollers are pressed hydraulically against the rings by levers L of the second kind.) Maximum useful pressure is in the 1,800 to 2,000 kp/cm^2 range. The press disk is provided with cutting wedges which notch the briquette bar of rectangular cross section: the bar, which is removed by a scraper from the pried-apart annular channel, breaks apart at the notches.

Ring diameter is 2 to 3; disk diameter is 1 to 2 m; the peripheral velocity of the disk is 0.3 to 1.0 m/s. Output is a function of speed and briquette cross section. For example, at a peripheral velocity of one m/s and a cross section of 3.5 by 4 cm, as shown in the inset, output is 6 to 7 tph: it is 13 to 15 tph at a cross section of 5 by 5.5 cm. Specific power consumption is 8 to 12 kW h/t, less than in the Exter press (because the motion of the feed relative to the channel and the considerable friction accompanying it are absent). The Exter press, however, has advantages too: friction, combined with the fact that the briquette is shaped in a number of successive pressure peaks (20 to 25, albeit of diminishing height) rather than in a single peak, provides the briquettes with a better-sealed, more durable and water-resistant shell polished to a gleam. This is why Exter briquettes are called "parlour briquettes".

9.2.2. Extrusion. The pressing (extrusion) of a material of sufficient plasticity through a suitably shaped orifice (a die) can produce practically endless lengths of products whose cross section is the same as that of the die aperture. These can be cut down to the desired size by a suitable cutting device. The machines performing this type of pressing are extrusion or band presses. Plasticity is adjusted to the desired value by heating (in the plastics industry) or by an admixture of water (in the silicate industry). The pressure driving the material through the orifice may be transmitted by a piston, a spiral or a pair of rolls.

The predecessor to the piston-type extrusion press is the hydraulic press used to make metal rods, bars, pipes and angles; its piston presses a pre-heated billet of metal through a suitably shaped die. The length of the profile thus obtained is limited by the size of the billet, which is limited in its turn by the stroke of the piston. The operation takes place at a high temperature and pressure. The force actuating the piston may, depending on the size of the machine, vary from 500 to 55,000 tons. Useful pressure is 200 to 400 bars as a rule, but may attain even 7,000 bars in special cases.

In the plastics industry, piston extruders are used to handle thermosetting materials. It is indicated to pre-heat the material prior to extrusion. The material is introduced into a heated press chamber at a temperature between 80 and 100 °C or so, where it acquires optimum plasticity at 100 to 130 °C, depending on its nature. The piston drives the plasticized or semi-plasticized material towards the die. Thermosetting plastics are taken through four zones, each hotter than the preceding one, on their way to the die. Three-dimensional bonding in the plasticized material proceeds in step with the rise of temperature, increasing its strength, so that the extruded product, leaving the die at a temperature of 160 to 180 °C, is practically finished, except that it has to be cut up by a power saw after its emergence from the cooling tunnel.

Spiral extruders are used in the processing of thermoplastic materials into pipes, rods, bars and angles, sheet and foil, in the plastic-coating of wire, in forming sandwiches with paper, etc. The material is plasticized in a heated cylinder and extruded as an endless product through the die. Modern extruders have an automated continuous feed system which provides an adjustable, uniform feed rate. The plastic material is introduced first into a cylinder with a feeder spiral in it. The cylinder is divided into segments, each of which has its own electrical (resistance) heating provided with a thermostat. The design, length, pitch and blade height of the spiral depend on the material to be handled. Modern devices are provided with a suitable tensioning device which pulls the finished product emerging from the die with a constant force until it cools down to where it can be coiled up. The diameter of the spiral is in the 25 to 200 mm range; its output is 2.2 to 450 kg/h. It moves the solid polymer resin, which has no plasticity when cold, from the feed throat into the body of the cylinder, where it is plasticized by heating and converted into a uniform, homogeneous melt, and so on to the die through which it is extruded. The cylinder used in the extrusion of plastics should be long enough to provide a large heat transfer surface and a better homogenization. The length-to-diameter ratio is in the 16 : 1 to 24 : 1 range as a rule.

In extrusion, it is often necessary to let certain volatile substances (water, some organic solvent, etc.) escape before the die, in order to prevent their forming bubbles in the extruded product. One way of doing so is to insert into the spiral, close to the die where blade height is least, a vacuum section where the core of the spiral is thinner (blade height is greater, by a factor of about four): the gases escaping under the pressure drop so generated can be removed by suction at the end of the vacuum segment. The compressive segment downstream of the vacuum segment is again of low blade height.

Spiral presses are used in the silicate industry also, to make bricks, tiles, sewerage pipes, drain-pipes, etc. The lumps of clay dumped into a hopper (the mud box) are moved by the spiral to the cylinder head containing the die, from which the material emerges as an endless band. The size and shape of the product are determined by the die. The clay in the hopper is pressed in between the blades of the spiral by a feeder roll. The cylindrical housing of the spiral is rifled on the inside so as to prevent the material progressing towards the head from being rotated by the spiral. The grooves of the rifling are packed with clay when the press is being operated, thus increasing the resistance to rotation. Counterblades or preventer bars may also be built in to minimize feed rotation. The pitch of the spiral may be constant or changing. The spiral end next to the die is made conical so as to forestall cracking in the extruded product.

Pressing in the strict sense takes place in the tapering cylinder head at the discharge end of the cylinder. Friction is reduced there by lubrication with water. The orifice which gives the product its shape is mounted onto or into the head. When making hollow products, cores fixed to braces inside the cylinder are installed in the orifice. Their size and shape must correspond to the hollows in the intended finished product. In its outward motion, the extruded material flows around the core(s) so that the finished ware preserves only the imprint of its (their) free ends.

These spiral presses too have the drawback that any air entrained into the cylinder together with the feed, unable to escape, reduces the cohesion of the material being extruded. This drawback is eliminated in the vacuum press which extrudes de-aerated material to start with.

Roller presses are similar in conception to a ball race. The rollers press the material fed to them through conical apertures in a die: the extruded bar is cut up by a suitable cutter. Product size is determined by die size and the spacing between die and cutter. Presses of this type are used e.g. at sugar mills to compact the leached-out and dried beet slices. Pressing gives a product of greater s.g. that is easier to handle. The dry s.g. of the cake, 200 to 300 kg/m³, can be increased to about 650 kg/m³, considerably reducing storage space requirement in the process.

9.2.3. Pelletizing. On adding a little water or other liquid to a mass of dry powder being stirred, some of the powder particles aggregate into balls (pellets) while the bulk of the powder remains dry. As more and more liquid is being added, more and more pellets form at the expense of the powder phase, and the aggregate acquires an increasingly coarse-grained consistency. The pellets do not clot together: in fact, stronger agitation gradually reduces their size. The addition of still more liquid results in a qualitative change: the pellets in contact stick together; the granular nature of the mix gives place to semi-plasticity: the material will fracture under a strong impact but flow without fracture when exposed to a slow buildup of force. More liquid gives a paste which does not fracture in any circumstances and is prone to adhere to solid surfaces. Finally, with still more liquid added, the mix starts to flow under its own weight. In the semi-plastic state, the power draft of stirring is greater by a factor of about ten than at either extreme (powder-dry or fluid).

Pellets can be made out of fine dusts by rolling as well as by stirring: rolling is in fact the process current in industrial practice. As the pellet rolls over a particle newly adhered to it, its centre of gravity is deflected at a high acceleration, perpendicularly to the direction of its progress: the resulting inertial impact hammers the new particle into the pellet surface and gives the rolling pellets their more or less regular spherical shape.

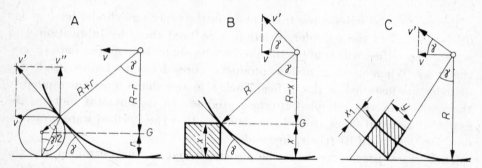

Fig. 9.11. A pellet rolling at velocity v overrides (A) a sphere, (B) a prism, (C) a prism partially embedded in it at a velocity of direction and magnitude v'

Let a pellet of radius R roll at angular velocity ω. The velocity of progress of its centre of gravity, $v = R\omega$, is not changed by its overriding a particle, provided the pellet is large enough (or the particle is small enough). A velocity

$$v' = \frac{v}{\cos \gamma}$$

is added at the beginning of the override; it initially includes an angle γ with the base plane. The radius about which the pellet starts to turn is $R + r$ for a round $2r$ dia. particle and R for a prismatic one of size x: cf. Parts A and B of Fig. 9.11. Centripetal acceleration accordingly is

$$a = \frac{v^2}{(R + r) \cos^2 \gamma}$$

for a sphere and

$$a = \frac{v^2}{R \cos^2 \gamma}$$

for a prism. Introducing

$$\cos \gamma = \frac{R - r}{R + r}$$

for the sphere and

$$\cos \gamma = \frac{R - x}{R}$$

for the prism, one has

$$a = v^2 \frac{R + r}{(R - r)^2}$$

in the first case and

$$a = v^2 \frac{R}{(R - x)^2}$$

in the second. Multiplication by the mass G/g of the pellet gives the magnitude of the inertial impact as

$$P = \frac{Ga}{g}.$$

Its direction is along the radius that connects the point of contact with the centre of gravity of the pellet. For a pellet of radius R,

$$G = 4\pi\delta \frac{R^3}{3};$$

that is,

$$P = 4\pi\delta v^2 R^3 \frac{R + r}{3g(R - r)^2} = 4\pi\delta v^2 R^3 \frac{\dfrac{R}{r} + 1}{3gr\left(\dfrac{R}{r} - 1\right)^2}$$

for a spherical particle, and

$$P = 4\pi\delta v^2 \frac{R^4}{3g(R - x)^2} = 4\pi\delta v^2 \frac{R^4}{3gx\left(\dfrac{R}{x} - 1\right)^2}$$

for a prism, where δ is the bulk density of the pellet; P is in ponds if δ is in ponds per cm³, R, r and x are in cm and v is in cm/s. $g = 981$ cm/s².

An inertial impact arises also when the pellet is deflected from a straight-line trajectory by an irregularity (lack of sphericity) in its own shape, e.g. by a bulge or ellipticity of dimension x_1, rather than by the nipping of a free particle of size x or by a particle jutting to a height x from the pellet surface into which it has been pounded earlier on. It is this inertial force that fattens, compacts and rounds the pellet. In the case shown as Part C of Fig. 9.11,

$$\cos \gamma = \frac{R}{R + x_1},$$

$$v' = \frac{v}{\cos \gamma} = v \frac{R + x_1}{R},$$

$$a = \frac{v'^2}{R + x_1} = v^2 \frac{R + x_1}{R^2},$$

$$m = 4\pi R^3 \frac{\delta}{3g},$$

$$P = ma = \frac{4\pi\delta}{3g} v^2 R(R + x_1) = k\delta v^2 \frac{R^2}{\cos \gamma},$$

with

$$F = cy^2$$

and

$$y = \frac{R}{b},$$

the force acting on a unit surface area of the particle

$$P_1 = \frac{P}{F} = \frac{kv^2b^2}{c \cos \gamma}.$$

Here,

$$k = \frac{4\pi}{3g} = 0.00426;$$

the value of b and c depends on the size of the particle and its position on the pellet. With v high and b great, P_1 may be very great, up to several thousand bars !

R/x_1 is related to $1/\cos \gamma$ as follows:

if $R/x_1 = 2 \quad 5 \quad 10 \quad 20 \quad 50 \quad 100$, then

$1/\cos \gamma \cong 1.5 \quad 1.2 \quad 1.1 \quad 1.05 \quad 1.02 \quad 1.01$.

Assuming $\cos \gamma \to 1$ and $c \cong 1$,

$$P' \to k\delta v^2 R^2$$

and

$$P_1' \to k\delta v^2 b^2.$$

Table 9.2 lists P_1 kp/cm^2 for different values of v and b, on the assumption that $\delta = 4$ ($k\delta = 0.017$).

Table 9.2. Inertial impact P_1 kp/cm^2 arising on a pellet overriding a particle, at different values of velocity v and $b = R/y$, for given values of δ and c

v m/s	P_1' kp/cm^2				
	$b = 10$	20	40	80	160
0.5	4.25	17	68	272	1,088
1	17	68	272	1,088	4,352
3	68	272	1,088	4,352	17,408
4	272	1,088	4,352	17,408	69,632

654

Some materials such as soot and pigments can be pelletized air-dry, but a moisture content of 10 to 20% gives stronger, harder and shinier pellets of any fine-grained aggregate, thanks to stronger capillary action. Pelletizing methods are frequently used to agglomerate chemical fertilizers or powdered iron ore. Too moist a feed gives large pellets rapidly: those, however, remain fairly soft; too dry a feed gives hard brittle pellets that are readily breakable. Optimum moisture is that which gives maximum strength: it corresponds to the water content that is just sufficient to fill out the pores among the compacted particles making up the pellet.

Pellets are made in rotary drums of diameter $D \simeq 1.8$ to 2.8 m with

$$L \simeq 3D$$

and

$$n \simeq \frac{10}{\sqrt{D}} \text{ to } \frac{20}{\sqrt{D}},$$

or

$$K = \frac{r\omega^2}{g} = 0.05 \text{ to } 0.16$$

and

$$\alpha = 2 \text{ to } 5°,$$

or in oblique-axed trays with $D = 1$ to 6 m, $\alpha = 10$ to $60°$ and

$$H = \frac{D}{5} \text{ to } \frac{D}{4},$$

$$n \simeq \frac{22}{\sqrt{D}} \text{ to } \frac{40}{\sqrt{D}},$$

or

$$K' = \frac{R\omega^2}{g \cos \alpha} \simeq 0.3 \text{ to } 0.5$$

and

$$N = (1.0 \text{ to } 1.2) \cdot D^2 \text{ kW},$$

or in the cone granulator which may be regarded as a combination of tray and drum, a truncated cone rotating about an oblique shaft, with $D = 1.6$ to 6.1 m and $N = 2.5 \, D^2$ kW.

Pelletizing drums need a great deal of space: their filling factor is very small at $\varphi = 2$ to 3%; retention time in the drum is long; it takes a long time for any deliberate adjustment of fortuitous change to work through to the discharge. In the tray pelletizer, changes work through more rapidly; regulation is easier. Output is more uniform with fewer undersize pellets, because pellets in the tray tend to segregate by size: the smaller ones which need to grow further roll along the bottom, whereas the big finished-size ones collect at the top, to overflow the rim of the rotating tray.

It is important for the material to roll rather than slide on the drum shell or the tray. If the surface in question is not of suitable texture, no pelletizing will take place, and no adjustment of moisture, speed or inclination will help. Too wet a material will cling to the wall in large dollops that work loose at intervals. A smoothing device (a reciprocating rod with cutting blades) produces an adhesive layer of a given thickness (3 to 6 mm). A continuous scraper is no good because it gives rise to an overly smooth, slippery surface on which the charge tends to slide rather than roll (Pietsch 1968, 1970).

Throughput formulae include

$$T \simeq CnR^3$$

for drum pelletizers,

$$T \simeq C_1 R^2$$

or

$$T \simeq C_2(V + 2)$$

for tray pelletizers, where T is in tph, n in rpm and R in m;

$$V = \pi R^2 H \text{ m}^3,$$

and C, C_1 and C_2 are constants depending on the other parameters of the machine (α, L, n ...) and on the nature of the feed (its s.g., friction coefficient, etc.). For instance, for iron ore, $C \simeq 1.9$ and $C_1 = 2.5$ to 3.2; C_1 is about 4.5 for superphosphate, 5.0 for bauxite or hydrate of lime and 6.3 for cement; C_2 is about 0.65 for phosphorite, 0.8 for apatite from the Kola peninsula and 2.1 for cement ($\pm 20\%$).

The pelletization of iron ores requires a Blaine fineness of

$$F \simeq 1,900 \ (\pm 500) \text{ cm}^2/\text{g},$$

with a minimum of plus-0.1 mm particles, giving an average particle size of

$$x = \frac{6}{\delta F} = \frac{6}{5 \cdot 1,900} = 0.00063 \text{ cm}.$$

The nucleation of the pellets takes a comparatively long time, so that pellet growth is a non-linear function of retention time (Kapur and Fuerstenau 1964; Rausch 1964). A clayey binder — e.g. bentonite — is sometimes added in a dosage of one or two percent (Kortmann and May 1970), because pellets made with water tend to crumble on drying if they contain no natural or artificial binder. Grains ground very fine (e.g. soot or pigments) acquire a property of adhesion, presumably thanks to small quantities of moisture adsorbed out of the atmosphere on the particle surfaces. It is this pendular water that constitutes bonds at the points of contact of these fine grains. Pellet strength due to liquid bonding varies inversely as particle size; even very small quantities of liquid may, therefore, provide satisfactory strength if the particles are very fine. The strength of green pellets bound together by capillary forces is not great as a rule; it is increased many times over if the liquid is replaced by solid bridges. Iron ore pellets e.g. are burnt (sintered) to this end at a high temperature. According to a Swedish patent, however, pellets can be endowed with the necessary strength also in a cold process in which the fine iron ore powder is mixed with about 10% portland cement to give green pellets, which are then rolled in iron ore dust to prevent their sticking together. They are subsequently discharged continuously into a container for a retention time of 30 hours; this is succeeded by storage in other containers for five more days. The pellets of about 12 mm diameter attain a breaking strength of about 30 kg by the end of the first 30 hours and of 120 kg by the end of six days. Their Micum-drum cohesion is about 94% plus-6 mm.

In chemical-fertilizer pellets, it is the dissolved salts crystallizing out of the evaporating liquid phase that constitute solid-bridge bonds (Wenzel and Gudenau 1969).

Superphosphate fertilizer contains as a rule enough liquid for pelletizing. (When the superphosphate emerges from the digester, it contains free phosphoric acid and water in fair abundance. Curing makes its water content decrease; it thus attains the optimum for pelletization after a while. If pelletization is begun too early, many lumps and large pellets will form; if, on the other hand, curing is unduly prolonged, some water must be added to the material before pelletization.)

9.2.4. Sintering, an operation of agglomeration at high temperature (1,100 to 1,700 °C), forms shapeless large lumps rather than pebbles of uniform size out of the fine particles in contact. The sintering temperature of materials of heterogeneous composition may remain far below the melting point of the principal component if a component of lower melting point is present in sufficient abundance: hence, when sintering materials of high melting point, the dosage of some sintering aid may be indicated. For example, the addition of about 15 percent limestone reduces the sintering temperature of iron ores from about 1,400 °C to about 1,150 °C. However, solid-bridge bonds may be constituted at high temperatures also without any melting, simply by solid-state diffusion and/or other chemical reactions. Even on the contact of two grains of one and the same mineral, the one having the lower energetic potential will start growing at the expense of the other far below the temperature of fusion; the result is a solid-bridge bond between the two. In the case of iron ore, a phase different as to energetic potential may be introduced e.g. by adding iron ore powder burnt and reduced beforehand (Hedvall 1926; Fischmeister and Exner 1964; Wenzel and Gudenau 1967).

Sintering may be performed in rotary kilns or shaft furnaces, on stationary grates or conveyors. On grates or conveyors, sintering takes place with the material at rest, with no relative displacement between particles; rotary drums act at the same time as pelletizing devices.

Cement clinker is made e.g. in countercurrent rotary kilns. Material caked onto the wall of the kiln is removed at intervals by means of a water-cooled drill pushed in from the firing side.

On the stationary grates, the material to be sintered, mixed with a fuel, is spread out in a layer of uniform thickness and ignited by means of a burner slowly moving above the grate. During burning, a fan blows or sucks air through the bed. The sinter is then removed by hand or mechanically. One cycle takes about half an hour.

Operation can be rendered continuous by using a travelling (conveyor) grate: loading, drying, pre-heating, ignition and burning follow in succession as the grate moves along. The operator regulates conveyor speed so as to obtain a fair grade finished product at the discharge end. (For a bed 25 to 30 cm thick, using a suction of 800 to 1,200 mm water gauge, burning rate is in the 1.2 to 1.5 cm/min range.) Further means of regulation include bed thickness (15 to 30 cm), fuel dosage (coke breeze, 3 to 9 weight percent) and moisture. The travelling grate can be stopped at any time, so that its one-shift operation is perfectly feasible and possibly viable.

Overmuch fines in the feed reduce the permeability of the bed; large lumps cannot absorb enough heat from the hot gas passing through. Upper limiting size is thus 8 to 10 mm for ore and 4 to 5 mm for coke. Pre-pelletizing the sinter feed may also be indicated; this attaches the fine particles in the aggregate to the surfaces of the larger ones, providing a fair permeability. A travelling grate sintering e.g. 0.225 $t/m^2 \cdot h$ of a material 98% of which was minus-0.2 mm at a suction of 800 mm water gauge gave an output more than three times higher (0.93 $t/m^2 \cdot h$) at a suction of only 600 mm water gauge when the feed was ground to 90% minus-200 mesh and pre-pelletized into balls of 3 to 8 mm size.

Fuel dosage should also be limited. If the material to be sintered is thermo-chemically inert (if it produces no endothermic reaction), 2.5% coke (or 150 kcal of heat per kg) may be sufficient to attain the sintering temperature. Coke consumption can be greatly reduced by pre-heating the feed and the air.

Travelling grates are used outside iron ore sintering also, e.g. in the roasting of sulphide ores (the sulphur content of which serves as the fuel), in the production of aluminium sulphate, the calcination of limestone, the burning of portland cement clinker, etc.).

Figure 9.12 presents examples of operating a travelling-pellet-sintering grate passing over 28 suction boxes of 1.83 by 1.83 m size each, giving an aggregate active grate area of

$$28 \cdot 1.8 \cdot 1.8 \cong 93 \text{ m}^2.$$

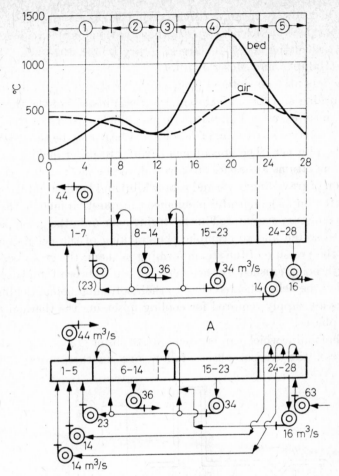

Fig. 9.12. Two possible modes of operation (hookups) of the fans of a 28-box travelling-pellet-sintering grate of 93 m² aggregate active grate area, showing the air flow rates in the fans in m³/s and the arrangement of the successive phases of sintering (*1* — drying, *2* — pre-heating, *3* — ignition, *4* — burning, *5* — cooling)

(The largest pellet-sintering grate in use in 1971 was 3.5 m wide and had an aggregate surface area of 460 m². Today's largest are 4 m wide, with an aggregate surface area of 720 m².) The figures written against the fans represent air throughputs in m³/s units, for the sintering of green pellets of 10% moisture content in a bed 33 cm thick. The top graph shows gas temperature in the bed and in the suction boxes in the successive phases of (1) drying, (2) pre-heating, (3) ignition, (4) burning and (5) cooling, with the numbering on the axis of abscissae corresponding to the numbering of the fans (Ban 1957).

Figure 9.13 shows the grate-kiln system, a widespread combination of travelling grate and rotary drum used in the burning of green pellets. The green pellets with their low strength are dried and pre-heated on a grate conveyor: having thus gained sufficient strength, they are then burnt in a rotary kiln and cooled on a revolving tray. The largest rotary kiln in 1970 was 6.6 m dia. by 46 m size (Halupka and Moser 1970).

Green pellets may be sintered (the successive operations of drying and pre-heating, burning and cooling can be performed) instead of the three machines connected in series, as in Fig. 9.13, also in a single one, e.g. a travelling grate (as in Fig. 9.12) or a shaft kiln. (The source of heat may be the combustion gas of a gas or oil burner.) The phenomena harmful to pellet quality arising in the successive operations are easiest to forestall in the most expensive setup (the combination of travelling grate and rotary kiln) and hardest in the cheapest one (in the shaft kiln). The harmful phenomena in question include the condensation of the moisture evaporated in the drying zone onto the green pellets, causing those to soften and to crumble; the cracking of the pellets on too rapid drying by the pressure of the steam forming in them; the green pellets of very low strength being crushed by the overlying bed between the phases of drying and burning; the pellets heated close to their softening point sticking together; the copious air supply required for cooling upsetting the thermal balances of the other phases.

In the shaft kiln (which can be used only to sinter green pellets of magnetite concentrates), the critical phases follow one another in rapid succession.

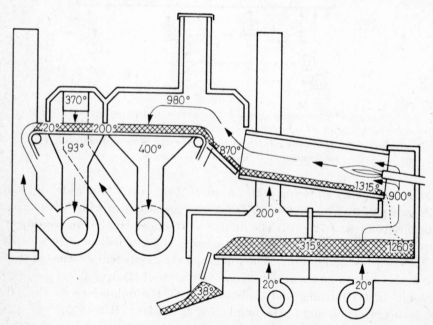

Fig. 9.13. Diagram of a grate kiln, a combined travelling-grate-plus-rotary drum, used in pellet burning

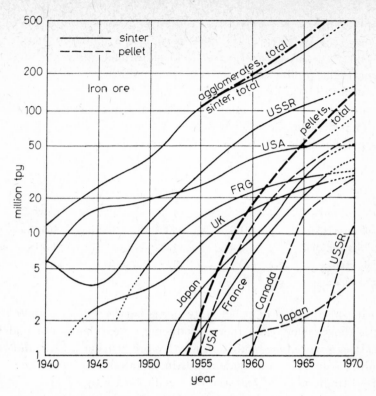

Fig. 9.14. Rise of the production of agglomerated forms of iron ore (pellet and sinter) in selected countries

On the travelling grate, the duration of each successive operation can be optimized by confining it to a suitable segment of the conveyor. The pellets remain immobile throughout in a bed which is about a foot thick; the gas can be led repeatedly through different parts of the bed, alternately on an up- and a down-draught; even should the pellets cake together, the operation of the conveyor will not be affected. Drawbacks include incomplete sintering near the edges of the conveyor (involving some 3% of all pellets on the broader conveyors of 2.4 to 3.5 m width); the peak temperature of sintering must not be applied longer than about 2 min, in order to protect the rods of the grate; hence, the setup is less suited for pellets of more than about 1.5 cm diameter. Both drawbacks can be avoided by covering the grate and especially its edges with a sheet of recirculated burnt pellets before laying on the green-pellet bed. In the grate-kiln system, on the other hand, the maximum temperature may be applied over the full length of the rotary kiln, and rolling down the kiln prevents the pellets from caking together. This is the system best suited for sintering pure haematite concentrates. (The sintering of haematite is no exothermic process, as contrary to the oxidation of magnetite into Fe_2O_3.)

The rapid world-wide spreading of sintering and pelletizing of iron ore is revealed by Fig. 9.14. The world in 1964 consumed 573 million tons of iron ore, of which 49% was introduced into the blast furnaces in sinter and 5.6% in pellet form. Pellet production amounted to 30 million tons in 1965, 129 million tons in 1969, and 150 million tons in 1975; the forecast for 1980 was 300 million tons. Figure 9.15 shows a breakdown by production technology of the total quantity of pellets produced. The figures refer to haematite pellets made in 1965, when the equipment in operation comprised

	shaft kilns	travelling grates	grate kilns	total or average
number:	83	35	12	132;
total annual capacity:	21.6	46.1	17.8	85.5 million t;
annual capacity per kiln:	0.26	1.32	1.27	0.65 million t;
total annual output:	19	21	9	49 million t;
average utilization:	88	67	50	69%.

The heat consumption of pellet sintering is between 200 and 300 kcal/kg if the feed is thermochemically inert, producing no exothermic or endothermic reaction. It can be reduced substantially by pre-heating the air and the feed. The theoretical (loss-free) heat demand (in the absence of any chemical reactions) of heating one kg of material of specific heat c by t °C is

$$H = ct \text{ kcal.}$$

Let e.g. $c = 0.26$ and $t = 1,500$ °C: in that case, $H = 390$ kcal/kg. This exceeds the 200 to 300 kcal/kg actually needed by a factor of 1.95 and 1.3, respectively. Thanks to the exothermic reaction of magnetite, the heat demand of sintering

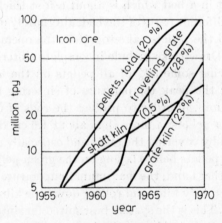

Fig. 9.15. Rise of pellet production in time; distribution over the types of pellet-making equipment

magnetite pellets can be as low as 120 to 170 kcal/kg. Sintering a non-pelletized sinter feed takes two to three times as much heat as the sintering of pellets.

Since 1965, only pelletizing facilities but no sintering ones have been built in the US for aggregating iron ores, even though the fine grinding needed to obtain a fair grade pellet feed in itself requires an additional power draft of 20 to 25 kW h/t (whereas rough grinding to minus-14 mesh demands only 3 kW h/t). The reason for this choice was that the softer sinters, which are readily reduced in a blast furnace, tend to crumble a great deal over longer hauls. (Cold pellets made with about 10% cement binder are lower in Fe and higher in SiO_2 content than the original ore !)

In a blast furnace, the unit cost of producing pig iron decreases about linearly as d, the percentage plus-10 mm fraction in the burden, increases: assuming operating cost O to be 100% at $d = 56\%$, the two variables are related by

$$O\% \simeq 112 - 0.2d.$$

The investment cost of the blast furnace and of the accessory facilities needed for its operation varies as

$$I\% \simeq 116 - 0.286d,$$

with $I = 100\%$ assigned to $d = 56\%$. Total cost including depreciation, to be written up e.g. as $O + 0.2I$, varies as

$$C_T \simeq 113 - 0.233d.$$

For example, if $d = 90\%$, the savings

in	O	I	$T = O + I$
are	6.0%	9.7%	8.0%

against $d = 56\%$.

Assuming a slag basicity of 1.3, the quantity of slag formed in the blast furnace is about 2.3 times the quantity of SiO_2 fed in: removing silica in slag form costs about three times as much as removing it beforehand by mineral-processing methods (with the metal losses in the course of the mineral-processing operations included).

Coke consumption in the blast furnace per ton of pig iron, K, is related to slag output (S kg per ton of pig) or to total (cokeless) burden weight D (per ton of pig), approximately by

$$K_1 \simeq 500 + 0.2S$$

(on feeding a lumpy sinter) or $K_1' \simeq 500 + 0.55$ (on feeding non-agglomerated ore) or

$$\log K_2 \simeq 0.17D + 2.45$$

663

or
$$K_3 \simeq \alpha D + \beta;$$

the parameters used in the formula are $\alpha = 250$ and $\beta = 160$ in the UK and $\alpha = 200$ and $\beta = 250$ on average in France. The values obtained are

	K_1	K_2	K_3
at $D = 1.5$	507	535	550
$= 3.25$	1,000	973	900 kg/t.

As sinter content in the burden $s\%$, increases up to about 60%, the output of the blast furnace increases by about

$$t \simeq 0.065s(0.1s - 1) + 3\%;$$

coke consumption decreases by about

$$k \simeq 0.3s\%;$$

operating costs per ton of pig decrease by

$$O \simeq 0.18s \left(1 + \frac{s}{200}\right) \%$$

and investment cost (per ton of pig) decreases by

$$I \simeq 0.25s \left(1 + \frac{s}{200}\right) \%.$$

Any further increase of sinter percentage in the burden is less beneficial. A ten percent increase of s in the low range (up to 50 or 60%) increases output by 3.5% and reduces coke consumption by 3%, whereas both improve by only 1.4% above $s = 60\%$ or so. If the fines of the ore are sintered separately, giving, say, $s = 20$ to 40%, then coke consumption decreases by about 180 to 200 kg/t. An all-sinter burden compared with a no-sinter one improves output and coke consumption by $\sim 20\%$ each, and reduces the concentration of fly dust in the blast furnace gas by $\sim 40\%$. The same change for pellets, from $p = 0\%$ to $p = 100\%$, about doubles output and reduces coke consumption by 20% (the same as in the case of sinter). Some authors, however, have stated the situation to be different, proposing e.g. for a blast furnace in the US a formula

$$K = 940 - 4.4p$$

for coke consumption and

$$P = 200 - 1.3p$$

for dust in the blast furnace gas. (Here, K is kg of coke per ton of pig; P is kg of dust per ton of pig, and $p\%$ is pellet percentage in the burden. For example, $K = 500$ kg/t and $P = 70$ kg/t at $p = 100\%$.) In the Ruhr, blast furnace out-

Table 9.3. Iron ore pellet production
of selected countries in 1968
and 1972

Country	Million tpy	
	1968	1972
USA	50.1	60.5
Canada	22.9	26.7
USSR	3.3	15.3
Sweden	3.6	7.9
Holland	—	3.3
Norway	0.6	1.8
Australia	7.1	8.3
Japan	2.0	5.5
India	0.6	1.6
China	—	1.1
Peru	3.5	3.4
Brazil	—	2.0
Mexico	—	1.1
Liberia	2.4	4.1
Altogether	98.0	145.0

put is 40 to 55 tons of pig per m^3 using pellets and 30 to 35 t/m^3 without. French sources state the reduction in coke consumption, $k\%$, and the increase in output, $t\%$, at sinter percentages $s\%$, compared with a sinterless burden, $s = 0$, to be

$$k = 20 \quad 25 \quad 30\%$$
$$t = \text{n.d.} \quad 50 \quad 30\%$$
$$s = 18 \quad 50 \quad 63\%$$

as an average for different facilities.

The saving in coke consumption just about covers the cost of sintering: it is the increase in output (as well as the reduction of sulphur content in the sinter !) that improves the economics of the process above all.

Table 9.3 presents the iron ore pellet production of a number of countries in 1968 and 1972.

9.3. LITERATURE ON AGGLOMERATION

ANONYMUS: *Der deutsche Steinkohlenbergbau*. Bd. 3: Brikettierung der Steinkohle. Verlag Glückauf, Essen 1958.
ANONYMUS: *100 Jahre Braunkohlenbrikettierung*. VEB W. Knapp Verlag, Halle 1958.
BALL, D. F. (et al.): Effect of additives on the strength of fired ore pellets. *Trans. IMM* 1974, C47—C58.

BALL, D. F.—P. R. DAWSON—J. T. FITTON: Additives in iron ore pelletizing. *Trans. IMM* 1970, C189—C196.

BAN, T. E.: Agglomeration of hematite concentrates using updraft grate-firing techniques. *IMDC*, Stockholm 1957, 363—392.

BURGHARDT, O.: Fragen der Mahlung und Pelletierung von Eisenerzen und Möglichkeiten der Beeinflussung. *Verfahrenstechnik* 1967, 485—492.

BURGHARDT, O.: Untersuchungen über die Eigenschaften von Sintern in Abhängigkeit von der Körnung eines magnetischen bzw. eines hämatitischen Eisenerzes. 9. *IMPC*, Praha 1970, 383—410.

CAPES, C. E.: The correlation of agglomerate stength with size. *Powder Tech.* (5/2) 1972 Jan., 119—125.

CAPES, C. E.—P. V. DANCKWERTS: Granule formation by the agglomeration of damp powders. *Trans. ICE* 1965, 116—130.

DELIĆ, D.—B. ŽIVANOVIĆ—M. M. RISTIĆ: Polidiszperz oxidporok sajtolása. (Dressing of polydisperse powders.) *Építőanyag* 1972, 308—312.

DOR, A. A. (et al.): Design trends and operating experience in iron ore pelletizing plants. 9. *IMPC*, Praha 1970, 173—238.

EGAN, H. N.: Pelletizing fine coal recovered from pumped refuse. *Min. Engng* 1967 Nov., 73—75.

FISCHMEISTER, H.—E. EXNER: Theorien des Sinters. *Metall* 1964, 932—940; 1965, 113—119, 941—946.

FRANKE, G.—O. KRAUSHAAR: *Handbuch der Brikettbereitung. Bd. I*: Das Brikettieren der Braunkohlen. F. Enke, Stuttgart 1930. *Bd. 1*: Die Brikettbereitung aus Steinkohlen, Braunkohlen und sonstigen Brennstoffen. F. Enke Verlag, Stuttgart 1909. *Bd. 2*: Brikettierung aus Erzen, Hüttenerzeugnissen, Metallfällen und dgl. einschliesslich der Agglomerierung. F. Enke, Stuttgart 1910.

GOOSENS, W.: Die Heissbrikettierung von Steinkohlen nach dem Verfahren des Eschweiler Bergwerk-Verein. *Glückauf* 1973, 521—254.

HALUPKA, H. A.—I. A. MOSER: Grate pelletizing — An operating report and process comparison. *CIM Bull.* 1970, 1395—1405. (Cf. also: ANONYMUS: Circular grate: new tool for pelletizing iron ore. *E/MJ* 1970 June, 102—106.)

HÄSSLER, B.—P. G. KIHLSTEDT: Grundlagen zur Gestaltung des COBO-Prozess als Agglomerierungsmethode für Mineralkonzentrate. *AT* 1973, 811—817.

HECKEL, R. W.: Density-pressure relationship in powder compaction. *Trans. AIME* 1961, 671—675.

HEDVALL, I. A.: Über die physikalisch-chemischen Prozesse beim Zusammenwachsen von ungeschmolzenen Pulvern. *Z. Phys. Chem.* 1926, 33—40.

HERRMANN, W.: The effect of water vapour on the shear strength of briquettes. *Powder Tech.* (5) 1971/72, 25—30.

HOLIK, J.: Die bindemittelfreie Brikettierung nach Apfelbeck. *Glückauf* 1934, 385—393.

KAPUR, P. C.—D. W. FUERSTENAU: Kinetics of green pelletization. *Trans. AIME* 1964, 348—355.

KEGEL, K.: *Brikettierung der Braunkohle*. Teil 1, Bd. 4: Aufbereitung und Brikettierung. Verlag W. Knapp, Halle (Saale) 1948.

KEGEL, K.—E. RAMMLER: Brikettieren. Lehrbrief 1—9. Bergakademie Freiberg, *Fernstudium* 1959.

KIHLSTEDT, P. G.: Agglomeration of iron ore concentration into cold-bound balls. 9. *IMPC*, Praha 1970, 307—317.

KNEPPER, W. A. (ed.): *Agglomeration*. Interscience Publ., J. Wiley & Sons, New York—London 1962.

KORTMANN, H. (et al.): Bedeutung der Gangart für das Schwellverhalten von Eisenerz-pelletts. *Stahl und Eisen* 1973, 463—472.

KORTMANN, H.—O. BURGHARDT: Qualitätsmerkmale von Eisenerzpellets und Möglich-keiten der Beeinflussung bei Verarbeitung hämatitischer Erze. *AT* 1973, 803—810.

KORTMANN, H.—A. MAY: Untersuchungen über die Eigung verschiedener Bentonite für den Einsatz der Eisenerzpelletierung. *AT* 1970, 251—256.

LINDER, R.—D. THULIN: Cold-Pelletieren von Eisenerzkonzentrat. *AT* 1973, 799—802.

MÜSCHENBORN, W.—W. SCHINZEL: Verbesserung der Pechbrikettierung mit Hilfe einer Emulsion. *Glückauf* 1965, 421—425.

NEWITT, D. M.—J. M. CONVAY-JONES: A contribution to the theory and practice of gran-ulation. *Trans. ICE* 1958, 422—440.

NICOL, S. K.—Z. P. ADAMIAK: Role of bentonite in wet pelletizing processes. *Trans. IMM* 1973, C26—C33.

PIETSCH, W.: Die Beeinflussungmöglichkeiten des Granuliertellerbetriebes und ihre Aus-wirkungen auf die Granulateigenschaften. *AT* 1966, 177—191.

PIETSCH, W.: Stand der Welt-Eisenerzpelletierung. *AT* 1968, 201—214.

PIETSCH, W.: Die Bedeutung der Walzenkonstruktion von Brikettier-, Kompaktier- und Pelletiermaschinen für ihre technische Anwendung. *AT* 1970, 128—138.

PIETSCH, W.: Anwendung der Brikettierung in Umweltschutz am Beispiel der Rückfüh-rung von Filter- und Erzstäuben in metallurgischen Anlagen. *AT* 1973, 818—821.

PIETSCH, W.—H. RUMPF: Haftkraft, Kapillardruck, Flüssigkeitsvolumen und Grenzwin-kel einer Flüssigkeitsbrücke zwischen zwei Kugeln. *Chem. Ing. Tech.* 1967, 885—893.

RAUSCH, H.: Pelletisieren feinkörniger Eisenerze. *Chem. Ing. Tech.* 1964, 1011—1019.

RIESCHEL, H.: Über den Verdichtungsvorgang beim Brikettieren. *AT* 1971, 691—698.

RUMPF, H.: Grundlagen und Methoden des Granulierens. *Chem. Ing. Tech.* 1958, 144—158, 329—336.

RUMPF, H.: Das Granulieren von Stäuben und die Festigkeit der Granulate. *Staub* 1959, 150—160.

RUMPF, H.: Zur Theorie der Zugfestigkeit von Agglomeraten bei Kraftübertragung an Kontaktpunkten. *Chem. Ing. Tech.* 1970, 538—540.

RUMPF, H.—W. HERMANN: Eigenschaften, Bindungsmechanism und Festigkeit von Agglomeraten. *AT* 1970, 117—127.

SCHÜTTE, G.: Kriterien für den Vergleich von Pelletieranlagen — Systemvergleich der Erzvorbereitung von Pelletieranlagen mit Trockenmahlung. *AT* 1973, 365—376.

SEIDEL, H.—W. STIEGER—G. VON STRUVE: Bau von Sinter- und Pelletieranlagen für grosse Leistungen. 9. *IMPC*, Praha 1970, 155—171.

SIRONI, G. (et al.): Improved properties of the sinter for its use in blast furnace. 9. *IMPC*, Praha 1970, 355—381.

STILMAN, A. L.: *Briquetting.* Chemical Publishing Co., Eaton—London 1923.

STONE, R. L.: Relation between the zeta potential of bentonite and the strength of un-fired iron ore pellets. *Trans. AIME* 1967, 284—292.

STONE, R. L.—D. S. CAHN: How ultrafine particles affect unfired pellet strength. *Min. Engng* 1970 Apr., 86—87.

STRUVE, G. VON: Grundlegende Betrachtungen über das Pelletisieren von Erzen. *Chem. Ing. Tech.* 1964, 1019—1027.

STRUVE, G. VON: Neue Entwicklungen des Lurgi-Verfahrens des Eisenerzpelletierung. *AT* 1973, 783—788.

TAKÁCS, P. (et al.): Verbesserung der Qualität eines feinkörnigen Kokskohlenkonzentrats durch Brikettierung mit Bindemittel. 6, *ICPC*, Paris 1973, 3D.

667

Tarján, G.: A pelletezés erőhatásai. (Forces operative in pelletizing.) *Koházati Lapok* 1963, 529—533.

Tarján, G.: Mass impact in the field of crushing and pelletizing. *Acta Geodaet., Geophys. & Mont.* 1971, 6 (3—4), 355—375.

Thau, A.: Die Brikettpresse von Apfelbeck. *Glückauf* 1929, 1605—1606.

Turba, E.—H. Rumpf: Zugfestigkeit von Presslingen mit vorwiegender Bindung durch van der Waals-Kräfte und ihre Beeinflussung durch Adsorptionsschichten. *Chem. Ing. Tech.* 1964.

Wada, M.—O. Tsuchiya: The role of hydrophile colloid in iron ore pelletization. 9. *IMPC*, Praha 1973, 23—52.

Wenz, L.—H. J. Feik: Technisch-wirtschaftliche Gesichtspunkte zur Auswahl des Mahlverfahrens vor der Pelletierung. 9. *IMPC*, Praha 1973, 89—124.

Wenzel, W.—H. W. Gudenau: Das Pelletieren von Eisenerzen mit vorgebranntem Gut. *Stahl und Eisen* 1967, 933—938.

Wenzel, W.—H. W. Gudenau: Pelletforschung. *AT* 1969, 167—174.

Wüster, I.: *Brikettierung der Steinkohle.* Der deutsche Steinkohlenbergbau. (Bd. 3.) Essen 1958.

10. HOMOGENIZATION

Homogenization is the process opposite to separation (Bemelman 1968; Dettweiler 1971; Erni 1971; Klein 1971).

The utilization of rated capacity, the economics and often the quality of output of plants processing large volumes of basic materials (mineral processing mills, alumina refineries, coking plants, blast furnaces, plants making bulk chemicals) tend to benefit from the physical and chemical homogeneity of their respective feeds because, with a homogeneous feed the plant as a whole and every one of its units may be run at full rated load, with the chemical reactions optimally adjusted. If, on the other hand, the physical feed parameters (granulometry, moisture, s.g., etc.) are expected to vary, the process has to be adjusted to the worst contingency of resonable probability; hence, except for brief spells, rated capacity will not be fully utilized. Whenever chemical composition (e.g. metal content in an ore) changes, feed (burden) composition in the metallurgical or chemical works must be adjusted accordingly. In order to avoid too frequent adjustments, safety margins are broadened, a method which increases the unit consumption of auxiliary materials and the unit production of waste and reduces the productivity of the facility.

Homogenization can be effected in a variety of ways. Deliveries of different-grade feed may be stacked in an open-air dump according to various layering patterns: the feed so mixed may be reclaimed according to some other pattern, always different from the pattern of stacking. Stacking may be done by manual shovelling, by a crane with a grab, a bulldozer, a conveyor belt with a travelling tripper, etc. Reclaiming may be by manual shovelling, a crane with a grab, a power shovel, etc. Large stacker-reclaimer machines using belt or bucket conveyors, bucket wheels, etc. are used to handle large volumes of material (Wedding 1971).

If the dump is a cone or a long barrow of triangular cross section, with the material to be stacked being cascaded onto its apex or ridge, large lumps will roll down the slope, so that granulometry will be finer centrally than peripherally. In a barrow divided into four zones of about equal width between its edge and its axis, the segregation presented in Table 10.1 could be observed. ($\Delta Fe\%$ is the deviation of the individual zones' Fe contents from the stack average.)

669

Stacks like these are to be reclaimed according to a programme which attacks the individual zones in alternation, in order to obtain a fair homogenization. At Magnitogorsk in the USSR, for example, the iron ore output of five days is stacked in a long barrow of 15.2 m height: it is reclaimed by power shovel into

Table 10.1. Segregation by ore grade in an iron ore barrow divided in four zones of equal width, Zone I being bounded by the foot of the slope and Zone IV by the ridge of the barrow

Zone	ΔFe%	Granulometry, %			
		plus-25 mm	25—10 mm	minus-10 mm	total
I	+1.5	43.5	41.5	15.0	100.0
II	+1.0	41.5	40.0	18.5	100.0
III	0.0	33.2	40.2	26.6	100.0
IV	−0.7	22.3	41.8	35.9	100.0

railroad cars. The reclaiming programme in terms of the zone numbering in Table 10.1 is as follows:

$$1 \times I, \quad 1 \times II, \quad 2 \times III, \quad 3 \times IV, \quad 1 \times I, \quad 2 \times IV, \quad 1 \times II, \quad 2 \times III.$$

The accurate blending of large volumes in a dump of large capacity is permitted by the Robins–Messiter process. A stacker moving to and fro at uniform speed forms long barrows of considerable length (100 to 300 m), made up of several hundred layers. A reclaiming machine then takes small slices out of the finished barrow: each slice contains each of the layers in unchanged proportion, except for the two half-cones at the ends of the barrows, whose composition is not the correct average. (The extreme ends of the barrow are made up practically of the last layer only.) In a short barrow, the volume of the two half-cones (of the unsatisfactorily homogenized material) may make up a substantial percentage of the whole mass. The length of the barrow should accordingly not be less than about six times the width of its base.

In this arrangement, the stacker travelling at velocity v_1 up and down the barrow is fed by a conveyor moving at velocity v to one side of the barrow. The stacker discharges onto the ridge of the barrow. If the conveyor and the stacker move in the same direction, stacking rate is

$$q' = q \left(\frac{v}{v_1} - 1 \right);$$

if they move in opposite directions, stacking rate is

$$q'' = q \left(\frac{v}{v_1} + 1 \right),$$

670

where q is the material on one metre of conveyor length. In other terms,

$$\frac{q'}{q''} = \frac{1 - \frac{v_1}{v}}{1 + \frac{v_1}{v}}.$$

For example, if $v = 90$ m/min and $v_1 = 6$ m/min, then $q' = 14\,q$, $q'' = 16\,q$ and

$$\frac{q'}{q''} = \frac{7}{8}.$$

If the cross section of the barrow is F m², stacker speed is v m/min and stacking rate is Q m³/h, then the number of layers making up the barrow will be

$$z = 60v\,\frac{F}{Q}.$$

Let e.g. the barrow have a length $L = 300$ m, a height $M = 10$ m, and a base width $A = 28$ m, giving a slope of

$$\varrho = \arctan \frac{2M}{A} = 35.5°.$$

In that case,

$$F = \frac{AM}{2} = 140 \text{ m}^2,$$

and

$$V = LF = 42,000 \text{ m}^3.$$

Let conveyor speed, $v = 90$ m/min, average delivery rate, $Q = 360$ m³/h; the number of layers making up the dump of 42,000 m³ volume (or 70,000 t weight, assuming a s.g. $\delta' = 1.6$) will then be

$$z = 60 \cdot 90\,\frac{140}{360} = 2,100.$$

The weight of one layer is

$$\sim \frac{70,000}{2,100} = 33.3 \text{ t;}$$

one metre of barrow weighs

$$F = 140 \text{ m}^3 = 234 \text{ t,}$$

and it takes

$$\frac{V}{Q} = \frac{42,000}{360} = 116 \text{ h} \simeq 4.9 \text{ days}$$

to build the barrow. Assuming a five-day working week upstream of the dump and continuous (seven-day) operation downstream of it, the barrow is to be reclaimed in one week (168 hours); reclaiming rate is then to be

$$Q' = \frac{42,000}{168} = 250 \ \text{m}^3/\text{h} \simeq 400 \ \text{t/h},$$

and reclaimer progress will be

$$v' = \frac{Q'}{F} = \frac{250}{140} = 1.79 \ \text{m/h} = 3.0 \ \text{cm/min}.$$

The reclaiming of 2,100 kg of material takes

$$\frac{3,600 \cdot 2.1}{400} = 18.9 \ \text{s}.$$

The reclaimer discharges onto another belt conveyor. Assuming the speed of that conveyor to be e.g. 1.5 m/s, the 2,100 kg, which is made up of one kg of each layer, that is, one kg per 33.3 tons of dump, is spread on

$$1.5 \cdot 18.9 = 28.35 \ \text{m}$$

of belt.

The setup has the drawbacks of requiring a great deal of space and of consuming rather much energy (the reclaimer alone draws 40 to 50 kW); if the ore is hard and abrasive, reclaimer wear is considerable; if it is soft, on the other hand, crumbling is a problem.

Bins and tanks may also be used for homogenization. In one solution, tanks built side by side are filled layer by layer of presumably different grades of material by the travelling tripper of a belt conveyor passing above them. In the upshot, the average grade in each tank will be the same, but grade may vary in the process of emptying any one tank. In another solution, material different as to grade is stored in different hoppers and blended by discharging at different rates onto a conveyor passing below all of those. A precondition for this latter arrangement is that the material must run readily and uniformly out of the hoppers.

Some segregation by particle size and grade will take place in any tank or hopper. On emptying, the finer material closer to the hopper axis is discharged first, and the material to be discharged last will be coarser than the average. The situation can be improved by filling the hoppers along two parallel lines rather than a single central one (Böttger 1960; Denny and Harper 1962; Grosskraumbach and Kellerwessel 1961; Holz 1969; Ion 1965; Sommer 1960; Tanaka and Kawai 1962).

The standard deviation

$$S = \sqrt{\sum_{i=1}^{n} \frac{(p_i - \bar{p})^2}{n - 1}}$$

of n samples taken at suitable intervals from the flow of reclaimed material (or from different points of the dump) may serve as a measure of homogenization performance. Here, p_i is some parameter established by testing the i-th sample;

$$\bar{p} = \sum_{i=1}^{n} \frac{p_i}{n}$$

is the arithmetic average of that parameter over all the samples. The standard deviation may be decomposed in two parts,

$$S^2 = S_v^2 + S_h^2,$$

where S_v is the variation due to the insufficiency of samples taken (the probability of random error) and S_h is the variation due to the inadequacy of homogenization. If homogenization performance is excellent,

$$S_h \to 0$$

and $S \cong S_v$ (Stange 1964).

10.1. LITERATURE ON HOMOGENIZATION

AHRENS, N.: Tendenzen der Rohmaterial-Homogenisierung. *Zement—Kalk—Gips* 1973, 1—5.

BEMELMAN, W. A.: Das Mischen von Schüttgütern — besonders von Eisenerzen. *AT* 1968, 229—234.

BÖTTGER, E.: Vergleichmässigung der Wäscheaufgabe durch Verwendung eines Misch-bunkers. *Aachener Bl.* 1960, 105—120.

CROSLAND, R.—M. K. LAVERICK: A survey of present and future coal blending systems. *Coll. Engng* 1965, 9—15.

DANIELS, B.: Kennzeichnung der Mischgüte von Mischeinrichtungen in der Steinkohlen-aufbereitung. 2. *ICPC*, Essen 1954, A-IV 1.

DENNY, R. J.—W. G. HARPER: The homogenization of raw coal. 4. *ICPC*, Harrogate 1962, A-1, 19—26.

DETTWEILER, G.: Vermengen und Entmengen loser Massen. *AT* 1971, 212—223, 347—354.

ERNI, H.: Rohmaterialaufbereitung und Homogenisierung. *Z—K—G* 1971, 487—496.

GERSTEL, A. W.—E. LUTTCKES: Homogenisieren in Mischbetten. *Z—K—G* 1973, 6—13.

GRAPENGIESSER, J. C.: Grossraumsilos mit Mischeffekt. *Z—K—G* 1971, 512—514.

GROSSKRAUMBACH, F.—H. KELLERWESSEL: Die Vergleichmässigung der Rohwaschkohle durch einen in zehn Zellen unterteilten Mischbunker. *Glückauf* 1961, 631—635.

HAMPEL, M.: Vergleichmässigen der Kokskohleneigenschaften unter besonderer Berück-sichtigung des Aschegehaltes. *Glückauf* 1965, 1351—1359.

HOLZ, H.: Planung, Bau und Betrieb eines Orgelpfeilenbunkers. *Glückauf* 1969, 243—250.

ION, P.: Stapel-, Dosier- und Mischbunker für Rohkohle. *AT* 1965, 84—89.

KLEIN, H.: Verbesserung bei der Chargen-Homogenisierung. *Z—K—G* 1971, 515—517.

KLEINSTEUBER, R.: Physikalische Zusammenhänge bei Mischvorgängen. *AT* 1960, 83—85, 385—387, 532—533.

KRISTENSEN, H. G.: Statistical properties of mixtures, I. *Powder Tech.* (7) 1973, 249—257.

LEMKE, K.: Ein Beitrag zur Vergleichmässigung von Rohkohle. *Glückauf* 1963, 1149—1160.

LEMKE, K.—F. ISENHARDT—H. KELLERWESSEL: Massnahmen und Einrichtungen zum Vergleichmässingen des Rohkohlenstromes und der Aufbereitungserzeugnisse. *Der deutsche Steinkohlenbergbau.* Bd. 5: Aufbereitung der Steinkohle. Verlag Glückauf, Essen 1966, 240—290.

PARKER, N. N.: Mixing. *Chem. Engng* 1964, 165—220.

PAUL, H.—F.-W. MEHRHOFF: Vergleichmässigung des Aschegehaltes der Kokskohle auf dem Verbundbergwerk Bergmannsglück-Westerhof. *Glückauf* 1970, 1137—1145.

RIES, H. B.: Mischtechnik und Mischgeräte. *AT* 1969, 1—30.

RIES, H. B.: Mischprobleme bei der Aufbereitung von Kalksandsteinmassen. *AT* 1974, 32—46.

SOMMER, O.: Statistische Untersuchungen über die Bemessung von Vergleichmässigungsbunker. *Bergbauarchiv* 1960, No. 2, 59—71.

STANGE, K.: Zur Beurteilung der Güte einer Mischung aus körnigen Stoffen bei bekannter Siebdurchgangslinien der Komponenten. *Chem. Ing. Tech.* 1964, 296—302.

TANAKA, T.—S. KAWAI: Hoppers can be used as mixers. *Rock Products* 1962 Apr., 120—134.

WEDDING, H.-J.: Methoden des Auf- und Abbaues von Schüttguthalden. *AT* 1971, 328—336.

WEISLEHNER, G.: Bau und Betrieb einer Mischbettanlage für Mergel. *Z—K—G* 1971, 61—65.

11. AUXILIARY OPERATIONS

These include storage, transportation, feeding/dosage, sampling, monitoring, control, etc. The operations and the equipment for performing them are fairly standard in any industrial plant, no matter how unique its special equipment may be. They have important functions in the flowsheets of the plants, in joining together the special equipment, etc. Their costs of investment and operation may make up a substantial part (up to 60% in some instances) of total cost, although they do not change any physical or chemical property of the materials handled (except, possibly, for changing its potential energy).

11.1. STORAGE

Storage or stockpiling is required if the feeding of inputs or the removal of outputs is discontinuous, if two successive operations are not connected direct, or if it is intended to isolate an operation or a group of operations from shutdowns that may occur elsewhere in the facility.

11.1.1. It is most usual **to store dry or dewatered materials** in tanks, hoppers or bins. The size of those is determined by their purpose. For example, a surge bin inserted between a primary and a secondary crusher may be fairly small if the two crushers are run on the same schedule. If, on the other hand, crushing is single-shift and grinding is three-shift, then the bin installed upstream of the mill must be able to hold at least 24 hours' throughput. As a general rule of thumb, the aggregate storage capacity available at a plant should not be less than two days' throughput (Mirani 1968; Schwedes 1969).

In a tall bin, dumping height is great when the bin is empty; on the other hand, the pressure of the tall column of material gives rise to considerable friction of discharge when the bin is full. If the material is friable, it will suffer comminution in both cases. In a wide tank, on the other hand, coarse material will roll to the walls while the fines remain near the centre: its discharge will accordingly be variable as to granulometry and possibly as to grade as well (cf. Chapter 10 also) (Denburg and Bauer 1964).

Granular aggregates have an internal friction, $\mu = \tan \beta$. Sticky materials tend to form vertical bluffs of height

$$h_{\max} = \frac{k(1 + \sin \beta)}{\delta' \cos \beta},$$

where δ' is the bulk density of the dump forming out of the cascading material. Sticky or adhesive materials will often refuse to run smoothly out of the discharge gate of the bin: they will tend to form a vertical bluff (hang-up) or a dome (bridge) above it instead. No bridging will occur if the diameter of the discharge aperture,

$$d_m \geq 2k \frac{1 - \sin \beta}{\delta'}.$$

The angle of repose ϱ of the cone forming when the granular material is poured onto a horizontal sheet is greater as a rule than the angle of friction β. In adhesive materials, $\varrho \cong \beta$ if the height of the cone is greater than about 30 times $h_{\max}$.

If a tank is filled with an electrically non-conductive material, a frictional charge that may attain several thousand volts may build up between the material and the (unearthed) tank wall, giving rise to sparking.

In a vertical-walled bin that contains an aggregate of loose bulk density δ' and height h, of hydraulic radius $r_h = F/K$ (where F is cross sectional area, K is circumference), pressure acting on the bottom is

$$p_b \cong \frac{\delta' r_h}{f} (1 - e^{-Ch/r_h}),$$

and pressure acting on the wall is

$$p_w \cong p_b \frac{f}{C},$$

where f is the friction coefficient between the aggregate and the bin wall and

$$C = \frac{1 - \sin \beta}{1 + \sin \beta} = \tan^2 \left(\frac{\pi}{4} - \frac{\beta}{2} \right).$$

C equals 0.3 at a fair approximation. The formulae tend to exaggerate p_b and p_w if $h \approx 8r_h$.

For fine-grained aggregates,

$$p_b = \delta' C A \frac{1 + 2A}{(1 + A)^2}$$

and

$$p_w = \frac{\delta' A}{1 + \dfrac{A}{h}},$$

where

$$A = \frac{r_h}{fC}.$$

In other words, the p_b/p_w ratio is in this case no constant equalling C/f, but is a function of depth h: p_b is about twice as much as the value furnished by the original formula for small values of h but tends to the original value as h increases. On discharge, p_b exceeds the "rest value" furnished by the formulae by 10 to 20%.

The approximate boundaries of the zones forming above the discharge aperture of a flat-bottomed bin are shown in Fig. 11.1. Particles roll down the surface of zone A; in its turn, zone A as a whole slides down the boundary of zone B, and zone B itself — albeit more slowly — moves inward and downward against the boundary of zone C, which is at rest. Zone D is made up of a mixture of particles derived from Zones A and B: their velocity increases downward and inward. The particles in zone E move vertically, at speeds much lower (by a factor of about 1/100) than the velocity of free fall. This zone alternately expands and contracts: it may on occasion reach up to the A-zone boundary. The quantity of material running freely out of the bottom aperture varies as the 2.5th to 3rd power of aperture diameter.

In order to avoid doming, an elongate rectangular discharge aperture should have a short side at least four times, a circular aperture a diameter at least seven times the size of the largest lumps. Outflow velocity is independent of bin diameter if bin diameter is more than three times the diameter of the discharge aperture. The height to which the bin is filled does not affect the discharge rate, either. As opposed to liquids, the pressure that a granular aggregate exerts on the vertical wall is practically independent of column height. If the fill is in motion, its friction coefficient f is less and, hence, the force of friction which holds the material against the wall is weaker, but the pressure p_b acting upon the bin bottom is increased. (It varies inversely as the internal friction of the

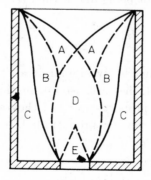

Fig. 11.1. Zoning in a granular aggregate draining out of a bin

material: C is small, and so is p_b, if β is great.) (Doeksen 1970; Fowler and Glastonbury 1959; Jenike 1964; Kneschke 1968; Kott and Kramer 1966; Lee 1963; Williams 1965.)

11.1.2. Agitating or conditioning tanks are used to store watery suspensions of fine-grained aggregates (pulps) if it is intended to let some chemical reaction take place or run its course in the suspension. Aims are to prevent the suspension from settling and to ensure a sufficient retention time for it in the tank. Tanks may be used also to stabilize pulp composition.

The energy demand N of flow is given by the formula

$$N = K\mu d^3 n^2$$

for viscous flow, and by the formula

$$N = K'\gamma d^5 n^3$$

for turbulent flow, where γ and μ are the density and viscosity, respectively, of the liquid (pulp), d is impeller diameter, n is impeller speed, and the constants K and K' are functions of tank and impeller geometry.

A relationship of general validity is

$$N = QH,$$

where N is energy of flow, Q is pulp volume in the tank (throughput rate) and

$$H = H_k + H_s + H_p$$

is the sum of velocity (kinetic), pressure (static) and elevation (potential) heads.

$$H_k = \frac{v^2 + v_1^2}{2g},$$

where v is velocity in the principal direction and v_1 is velocity normal to it, $H_s = p/\gamma$. If the liquid is not being lifted, then $H_p = 0$, implying

$$H = \frac{v^2 + v_1^2}{2g} + \frac{p}{\gamma}.$$

Two situations are geometrically similar if all their respective geometric dimensions are proportional; they are also kinematically similar if, in addition, velocities in them are also proportional; and they are dynamically similar if, furthermore, the forces in them are proportional, too, and the two dimensionless parameters, the Reynolds number

$$\text{Re} = d^2 n \frac{\varrho}{\mu}$$

678

Table 11.1

	N	d	n	Q	H	Q/H
N const.	$\left\{\begin{array}{l}-\\-\end{array}\right.$	$n^{-3/5}$ $-$	$-$ $d^{-5/3}$	$n^{-4/5}$ $d^{4/3}$	$n^{4/5}$ $d^{-4/3}$	$n^{-8/5}$ $d^{8/3}$
d const.	n^3	$-$	$N^{1/3}$	n	n^2	n^{-1}
n const.	d^5	$N^{1/5}$	$-$	d^3	d^2	d

and the Froude number

$$\mathrm{Fr} = \frac{dn^2}{g}$$

are equal in the two situations. One has

$$\varPhi = \frac{Ng}{\varrho n^3 d^5} \left(\frac{dn^2}{g}\right)^{-b}$$

if the flow has non-zero vorticity and

$$\varPhi = \frac{Ng}{\varrho n^3 d^5}$$

if its vorticity is zero. One may write

$$Q \propto nd^3; \quad H \propto n^2 d^2; \quad N \propto Qn^2 d^2.$$

If either N, or d or n is constant, and flow is turbulent, the relationships stated in Table 11.1 hold. For example, let N be a constant. Then, if impeller speed n is doubled, then

$$\frac{Q_2}{Q_1} = \left(\frac{1}{2}\right)^{4/5} = 0.575;$$

that is, the flow rate is reduced to 57.5% of the original; pressure is increased at the same time by a factor of

$$\frac{H_2}{H_1} = \frac{1}{0.575} = 1.74.$$

Turbulence varies as pressure. That is, when an impeller of smaller diameter is being run at higher speed but the same rate of energy input, pulp will move more slowly at higher turbulence in the same tank. Now some chemical reactions are sensitive to pulp flow rate; others are more sensitive to turbulence. By choosing the correct impeller size and speed, both may be accommodated (Siemes et al. 1957; Ullrich 1971). Cf. also Section 2.5.1.

11.1.3. Material of no special value is often stockpiled (stored in dumps) in the open, especially if its storage is intended to last long. If dumped from a tall tower, the stockpile will form a cone: in the possession of the angle of repose and bulk density of the material, the tonnage that can be stored in a conical dump of given height can be calculated. The material in the dump can be reclaimed by manual shovelling or by means of some loading machine (a grab, a scraper, etc.; cf. Chapter 10 also).

11.1.4. Water is usually stored in ponds. In many beneficiation plants (or other industrial plant), the quantity of fresh water available locally is insufficient, so that used water must be recirculated. In some areas, shortage and superabundance of water alternate. Elsewhere, water may be of unsatisfactory quality: it must be improved by clarification or by the dosage of chemical reagents.

Pyrite oxidation in the presence of moisture and air produces sulphuric acid and ferrous sulphate. The ongoing oxidation of this latter produces ferric sulphate, which in turn hydrolyses into some more sulphuric acid and ferric hydroxide. Pyrite oxidation is greatly accelerated by certain bacteria such as *Thiobacillus ferrooxidans*. The intensity of the process can be characterized in terms of dissolved Fe. In a given setup where sterile water dissolved 15 mg/l of Fe in 30 days, bacterial leaching was found to dissolve

	200	500	900	1,250	1,450 mg/l
in	10	15	20	25	30 days.

The pH of acid mine waters is seldom less than 2 because in the pH range between 2 and 4, the buffering effect of ferrous sulphate enters into action. Typical mine waters have the following parameters:

	sulphide ore mine with a quartz gangue	coal mine
pH	3 to 5	2.8 to 6.2
total dissolved matter	1,100 to 5,000 mg/l	900 to 9,000 mg/l
of which, Fe	200 to 600 mg/l	150 to 720 mg/l
SO_4	630 to 2,500 mg/l	660 to 6,700 mg/l.

On neutralization with lime, $\sim$2.5 parts $CaSO_4$ (gypsum) form out of one part CaO. (The solubility of gypsum is about 2,000 mg/l, so that its presence augments the lime hardness of water.) Where ferrous sulphate is abundant, it is usual to aerate the water in order to accelerate the formation of indissoluble ferric hydroxide precipitate, which is then removed from the water in settling tanks.

In beneficiation plants, water storage is often solved by shaping the tailings dump into a dam behind which stored water can form a pond or lake. It is usual to pump the water from the lake into a high, comparatively small tank whose water level is maintained constant; water is led from the tank through appropriate piping by gravity to the points of consumption. The tank is to be dimensioned so as to hold about eight hours' water: that time should be sufficient to repair the pump or piping in the case of a breakdown or puncture.

11.2. WATER RECIRCULATION

A striving that has come to the fore recently in mineral processing operations is to design closed water circuits with no external storage pond: water is clarified in thickeners and the thickened pulp is dewatered on filters (vacuum filters as a rule for raw pulps, and flotation concentrates; filter presses for flotation tailings); the clear water and the filtrates are then reintroduced into the circuit. Fresh water is used only for the indispensable makeup (Kennedy and Criner 1951; Nowak and Aleska 1973; Paul 1966; Price and Bertholz 1958; Schranz and Bergholz 1954; Trawinski 1961; Woodhead 1966).

If clarification is not complete, the slimes content of the water in the circuit builds up to a certain threshold, depending on the rate of makeup water dosage. Let the quantity of suspended slimes that cannot be removed from the water by the system of clarification be z, and let v be the percentage of water recovered by clarification: $v < 1$. The quantity of water lost to the thickened pulp equals makeup water; accordingly, $s = 1 - v$. If the water is entirely clear at the start, and the thickened pulp takes all the coarser particles plus a fraction

$$zs = z(1 - v)$$

of the slimes out of the circuit, the recirculated clear water will retain slimes in the quantity zv in the first cycle; the slimes content of the feed is increased thereby to

$$z_2 = z + zv = z(1 + v)$$

in the second cycle. In the third cycle, a fraction $z(1 + v)v$ of this is added to the slimes content z of the fresh feed, so that

$$z_3 = z + zv + zv^2 = z(1 + v + v^2),$$

and, by the n-th cycle, the geometric progression extends to

$$z_n = z(1 + v + v^2 + \ldots + v^{n-1}) = z\,\frac{1 - v^n}{1 - v}\,.$$

v^n tends to zero as n tends to infinity, so that slimes concentration after a large enough number of cycles tends to

$$z_v = \frac{z}{1 - v} = \frac{z}{s}\,.$$

For example, if $z = 25$ g/l and $s = 0.15$ ($v = 0.85$), then

$$z_v = \frac{25}{0.15} = 166 \text{ g/l.}$$

If total solids in the cycle is to be found, the coarser particles of the pulp must, of course, be added, too.

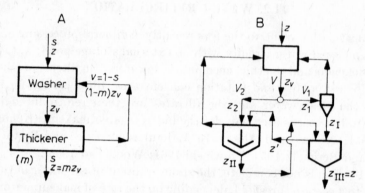

Fig. 11.2. Regeneration of wash water A — in a single thickening line; B — in a thickener and a hydrocyclone in parallel

If z is defined as the quantity of the slimes that cannot be removed from the water, then the fraction s of water retained in the thickened product is numerically equal to the recovery m of dry fine slimes; that is,

$$\frac{z}{z_v} = s = m.$$

This formula holds also if z and z_v are defined to mean the initial and ultimate total solids in the water, and not just the slimes in suspension, as revealed by a simple inspection of Part A of Fig. 11.2.

If two systems of clarification different as to performance (e.g. a hydrocyclone and a thickener) are hooked up in parallel as in Part B of Fig. 11.2 and the quantities of water fed to them are V_1 and V_2 (with $V_2/V_1 = w$), and the quantities of solid slimes fed in are z_1 and z_2, respectively, and if the thickened pulp they produce is filtered, and the filtrate containing slimes in quantity z' is returned to the thickener, then, assuming solids recoveries to be m_1, m_2 and m_3, respectively then, since in steady-state operation the pulp output z_{III} of the filter must equal the quantity z of feed pulp (plus the pulp forming in the washery), the following relationships may be written up:

$$\frac{z_v}{V} = \frac{z_1}{V_1} = \frac{z_2}{V_2};$$

$$\frac{V_2}{V_1} = \frac{z_2}{z_1} = w;$$

$$z_{\mathrm{I}} = m_1 z_1; \quad z_{\mathrm{II}} = m_2(z_2 + z'); \quad z_{\mathrm{III}} = m_3(z_{\mathrm{I}} + z_{\mathrm{II}}) = z;$$

$$z' = \frac{z_{\mathrm{III}}}{m_3} - z_{\mathrm{III}} = z_{\mathrm{III}}\left(\frac{1}{m_3} - 1\right).$$

Introducing the expressions for z_{I} and z_{II} into the formula for z_{III}, the relationship

$$\frac{z_1}{z} = \frac{1 - m_2(1 - m_3)}{(m_1 + wm_2)m_3}$$

is obtained.

A quantity z of fresh solids in a quantity V of water gives a primary pulp density z/V; the solids quantity z_1 is contained in water of volume V_1.

$$\frac{z_1}{V_1} = \frac{z_v}{V}$$

is the ultimate pulp density. The ratio

$$k = \frac{\dfrac{z_v}{V}}{\dfrac{z}{V}} = \frac{z_v}{z}$$

of these densities is obtained by multiplying the ratio z_1/z by the expression

$$\frac{V}{V_1} = \frac{V_1 + V_2}{V_1} = 1 + w$$

$$k = \frac{z_v}{z} = \frac{(1 + w)[1 - m_2(1 - m_3)]}{(m_1 + wm_2)m_3}.$$

If the filtrate produced by the filter is clear water, then $m_3 = 1$, and

$$k' = \frac{1 + w}{m_1 + m_2 w};$$

if the overflow of the thickener is clear water (thanks, say, to the dosage of a flocculant), then $m_2 = 1$, and

$$k'' = \frac{1 + w}{m_1 + w};$$

and if there is only one clarification line, then we have $w = 0$ and $m_2 = 1$ and

$$k''' = \frac{1}{m_1}$$

results. For example, if $w = 0.5$, $m_1 = 0.6$, $m_2 = 0.8$, $m_3 = 0.9$, then $k = 1.53$ ($k' = 1.50$, $k'' = 1.364$, $k''' = 1.666$) (Battaglia 1964, 1966).

The solid slime content of circulating water may be obtained also using the formula

$$z_v = \frac{z_s(f + s - fs)}{1 + z_s(f + s - fs - 1)} ,$$

where z_v is solids content by weight in the circulating water and z_s is the same in the thickened pulp; f is the fine slimes fraction (e.g. minus-10 μm) in the solids of the thickened product, and s is the water fraction finding its way into the thickened product. For example, if

$$z_s = 0.4, \quad f = 0.10, \quad s = 0.15,$$

then

and

$$f + s - fs = 0.235,$$

$$z_v = \frac{0.4 \cdot 0.235}{1 - (0.4 \cdot 0.765)} = 0.136.$$

(Dahlstrom 1957; Dale and Dahlstrom 1965).

11.3. MILL TRANSPORT

In a beneficiation plant, transportation includes the feeding of solids, water, pulps, etc., their transfer from one machine to another and their final removal as solids or pulp. Stationary chutes or launders operate under the force of gravity, consuming no energy from outside sources, whereas shaken chutes, screw conveyors, pneumatic tubes, diaphragm pumps or centrifugal pulp pumps, airlifts, elevators, etc. need a supply of external energy.

11.3.1. Chutes and launders. Chutes used to transport solids by gravity have an inclination of 35 to 55° depending on the granulometry and moisture content of the material, on the nature of the chute bottom, etc. To be on the safe side, they are typically installed on a slope of 40 to 45°, even when intended to transport dust-free dry material, regardless of what the chute bottom is made of (wood, steel, rubber, etc.). Sliding velocity, a function of the friction coefficient and of inclination, has defied calculation so far.

Launders serve for the transportation of fluids (of water or of solids in water). Their inclination is small, but is somewhat greater for pulps than for clear water; for coarse-grained material than for fine sand; for materials of high s.g. than for lighter ones; for dense than for dilute pulp. In pulp transportation, a greater depth of water is an advantage because it entails a greater pulp velocity; too great a depth, however, is a drawback if the solids roll or slide on the bottom. Launders in which a given pulp cross section is combined with a minimum of wetted circumference tend to have the greatest pulp throughput.

In water or pulp flowing at velocity v in a straight launder, loss of head is

$$H = H_1 + H_2,$$

where

$$H_1 = \frac{v^2}{2g}$$

and

$$H_2 = \frac{fL\gamma'v^2}{2gR_h}. \tag{1}$$

Here, v is flow velocity;

$$R_h = \frac{F}{K}$$

is hydraulic radius (F is the cross sectional area of the fluid and K is the wetted circumference of the launder wall), γ' is the gravity of the fluid, f is a friction factor, a function of the Reynolds number and of the roughness of the launder wall, and L is launder length;

$$\frac{H}{L} = \tan \alpha,$$

and

$$i = 100 \tan \alpha \text{ cm/m}$$

is the inclination of the launder against the horizontal. f is ~ 0.005 ($\pm 10\%$) for water and pulps of volumetric solids content $\sigma < 8\%$ and s.g. $\delta \lesssim 2.7$ on sheet steel, it is in the 0.01 to 0.026 range for magnetite ($\delta = 5$) suspension (lower values of f correspond to higher values of v and γ'). For launders of slope i cm/m, the approximate formulae

$$i \simeq K\sqrt{\sigma}$$

and

$$i \simeq K'\sqrt{x}$$

have been established, where x is upper limiting particle size, and K and K' are coefficients depending on the s.g. and granulometry of the solids. For example, $K = 19$ for a fine-grained slimeless placer sand with $x = 0.2$ to 0.4 mm and $\delta = 2.6$. (Slimes reduce friction and K along with it.) $K' = 5.8$ for monodisperse aggregates of s.g. 2.6 to 2.8 if x is in mm.

The H_2 formula (1) holds for pipes also: if the pipe is smooth, then

$$f = \frac{0.32}{\sqrt[4]{\text{Re}}}$$

if flow is turbulent, that is,

$$\mathrm{Re} = \frac{vD}{\nu} \gtrsim 4{,}000;$$

and

$$f \simeq \frac{64}{\mathrm{Re}}$$

if flow is laminar, that is

$$\mathrm{Re} \lesssim 2{,}300.$$

If a pipe of diameter D is filled entirely with pulp, then

$$R_h = \frac{D}{4}.$$

The friction head (the head loss due to friction), H_2, is made up of friction loss in the pure liquid, H_2', and the friction of the solid particles, H_2'', where

$$H_2' = \frac{\lambda L \gamma v^2}{2gD} = \lambda L \gamma \frac{\mathrm{Fr}}{2}$$

and

$$H_2'' = \lambda' L (\delta - \gamma) \frac{\Delta v^2}{2gD}.$$

Here,

$$\mathrm{Fr} = \frac{v^2}{gD}$$

is the Froude number, Δv is the velocity differential (slip) between the liquid and the solid particles,

$$\lambda = f(\mathrm{Re})$$

with

$$\mathrm{Re} = \frac{vx}{\nu},$$

and

$$\lambda' = f(\mathrm{Re}, \mathrm{Fr}, \sigma, \ldots).$$

Part A of Fig. 11.3 presents head loss H_2 vs. the Froude number for three volumetric solids contents ($\sigma_1 < \sigma_2 < \sigma_3$). The zones (1) to (5) are defined as follows: (1) is a settled bed at rest; (2) is a dune (a moving bed of rolling-leaping particles); (3) is a heterogeneous suspension; (4) is a quasi-homogeneous suspension and (5) is a dilute homogeneous suspension. Part B shows profiles of velocity v and relative volumetric solids content σ_{rel} in each zone of the pipe or launder. Part C of the figure shows the domains of state as a function of pulp velocity for a monodisperse aggregate of particle size x, s.g. 2.6. It indicates that the velocity required to prevent the settling of particles of size

	$x =$	0.4	1	3 mm
is about	$v =$	1	2.2	3 m/s;

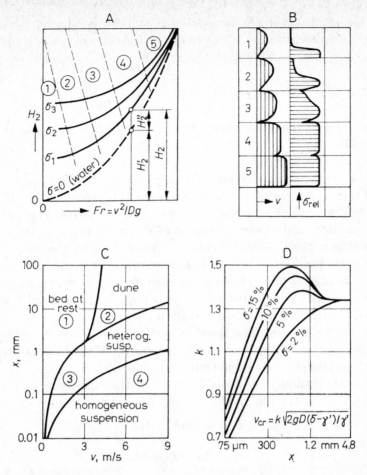

Fig. 11.3. A — head loss H_2 in a pulp flowing in a pipe or launder, vs. the Froude number Fr; B — Profiles of velocity v and relative solids content σ_{rel} in the five zones of Part A; C — domains of the pulp consistencies 1 to 4 in the x vs. space; D — coefficient k of the critical velocity C_{cr} needed to maintain a No. 3 type suspension vs. particle size x, with σ as the parameter

on the other hand, particles of 3 mm size — if no finer particles are present — are taken up into suspension by a velocity $v \geq 4.2$ m/s only. Part D of Fig. 11.3 provides the k coefficient in the formula

$$v_{cr} = k \sqrt{2gD \frac{\delta - \gamma'}{\gamma'}}$$

giving the least (critical) velocity required to constitute a zone-3 (heterogeneous) suspension (with no settled-out fraction) in a pipe of diameter D. In the formula, γ' is "medium gravity", obtained as the s.g. of the liquid and the minus-200 μm slimes suspended in it.

The transportation in the homogeneous state of a pulp of volume V and volumetric solids content σ, made up of particles of size x, s.g. δ and terminal settling velocity v_0 in a horizontal pipe of diameter D, takes energy

$$N = kV(\delta - \gamma)v_0\sqrt{\frac{D\sigma}{(1 - \sigma)x}}$$

(Condolios and Chapus 1963; Kriegel and Bauer 1965; Tonjes and Wasp 1970; Smith 1955).

11.3.2. Conveyors and elevators. The machine most widely used in the mechanical transportation of dry materials is the belt conveyor. It will serve for upward and downward as well as horizontal transportation. The feeding point may be variable, and so may the point of discharge if a travelling tripper is used. Maximum permissible inclination is determined by the friction between the transported material and the belt: it is typically in the 15 to 20° range. It may be as high as 25° in favourable cases (for dry granulate materials) but should not exceed even 15° for wet slippery materials. The usual belt speed of horizontal transportation is 1 to 3 m/s; the higher value belongs to finer-grained materials on wider belts. The speed of inclined conveyors should be reduced as inclination increases, by about 1.7% per degree. If the belt is to be used for hand sorting, its speed should not exceed 0.2 to 0.3 m/s.

Belt transportation rates are a function of the cross section F m² of the material on the belt, its loose bulk density δ' t/m³ and belt speed v m/s:

$$T = 3,600 F v \delta' \text{ tph}$$

or

$$Q = 3,600 F v \text{ m}^3/\text{h}.$$

Under average conditions, the cross section of the bed on a flat belt of width B m has a parabola-like shape of base $B - b$ and height

$$h \cong \frac{B - b}{8},$$

whence

$$F \cong 2h\frac{B - b}{3} = \frac{(B - b)^2}{12}$$

and

$$Q \cong 300\,(B - b)^2 v.$$

The free margins on either side of the belt may be narrower if belt speed is less and the material is finer; $b = 0.1$ m in the normal run of things.

The minimum width B to be chosen for a flat (non-troughed) belt is a function also of the upper limiting particle size of the material to be transported. Relationships for sized and unsized aggregates, as well as belt speeds v m/s cor-

688

responding to a given throughput Q m³/h and belt width B cm, are shown in Fig. 11.4. For example, let

$$Q = \frac{T}{\delta'} \simeq 200 \text{ m}^3/\text{h};$$

then the least belt width B_{min} needed to transport an unsized aggregate of ∼45 cm limiting particle size is 90 cm or so, and belt speed is to be $v = 1.0$ m/s.

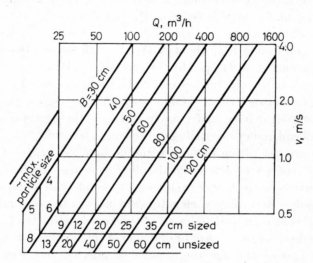

Fig. 11.4. Belt conveyor throughputs $Q = f(v)$ vs. v with belt width B as the parameter

If the limiting size is reduced to 20 cm, then $B = 60$ cm at a speed of 2.0 m/s will do at $Q = 200$ m³/h.

The throughput of a troughed belt supported by triplets of idlers is about three times that of the flat belt of the same width: that is,

$$Q \simeq 900 \, v(B - 0.1)^2.$$

The power draft of a belt is given by the rule-of-thumb formula

$$N \simeq T \left(fL + \frac{H}{370} \right),$$

where N is in kW, T in tph, L m is the horizontal component of the transportation path, and H is its vertical component (negative for downward transportation). The coefficient of friction f is about 0.0007 for idlers with roller bearings and about 0.0015 for grease-lubricated idlers with simple sliding bearings.

For the transportation of a heavy load of lumpy material over short distances (less than about 30 m), pan conveyors made up of pans fixed onto articulated endless chains may be used. Pan bottoms overlap so that the upper, carrying run of the conveyor presents no slots for the material to drop through. The speed of such conveyors is less as a rule than 0.25 m/s. They are most often used horizontally, to feed lumpy granulate materials flowing out of hoppers (apron feeders), but they do well in inclined duty also. Using suitably shaped pans, such conveyors may be given a greater inclination than smooth rubber-belt conveyors, but their power draft is much greater (Wehmeier 1967).

A bucket elevator is a smooth belt or an articulated chain provided with suitable buckets, run at an inclination of 60 to 90°. The head sprocket or pulley is the driven one. Material is fed direct into the buckets on the rising flight, next to the tail end; if the material is finer than, say, 5 or 6 mm, the buckets may scoop it up from a tank (boot) under the tail pulley. The material is discharged as the buckets are tipped by the head pulley. If the buckets are mounted close together (continuous-bucket elevator), the usual speed is about 0.5 m/s; if there are gaps between them, speed must be high enough to permit the combination of centrifugal force and gravity to throw the contents of each bucket clear of the head pulley (centrifugal-discharge elevator).

Elevators are the lifting devices with the broadest range of possible uses: they will lift coarse- or fine-grained solids or coarse- or fine-grained pulps. Yet belt conveyors are better at lifting dry solids and pumps are better at lifting fine pulps. Accordingly, elevators are more or less confined nowadays to the lifting of coarse-grained pulps or of thickened products of some viscosity.

The throughput of an elevator or of a bucket conveyor (buckets tiltable about an axis not passing through their centre of gravity, mounted on an endless drag chain) is given by the formula

$$Q = 3.6v\varphi \frac{i}{a},$$

where Q is in m³/h, v m/s is elevator or conveyor speed, φ is the filling factor of the bucket, i is the volume of one bucket in litres, and a is bucket spacing in m. The filling factor tends to equal about 0.4 to 0.6 for coarse-grained materials and 0.6 to 0.8 for finer-grained ones (Strube 1954).

A less widespread device, the shaken chute permits the horizontal or gently rising transportation of dry materials. Screw conveyors and flight conveyors are suited for the transportation over short distances of dry or wet fine-grained materials (they need little space but suffer very strong wear). Dry fine-grained materials can be transported in any direction in pneumatic tubes, entrained in a stream of air of sufficient speed.

11.3.3. Feeders are short conveyors of regulated throughput. The performance of comminuting, sizing and classifying, concentrating, etc. equipment is a sensitive function of feed rate: satisfactory performance presupposes a uniform supply of feed. The conveying element of the feeder usually passes under a small hopper, provided with a slide gate, which may or may not be integral with a large bin. Figure 11.5 presents diagrams of some of the more widespread feeder types (*a* — chain, *b* — roll, *c* — rotary-tray, *d* — vibrating, *e* and *f* — conveyor).

Belt and rotary-tray feeders are best at coping with sticky materials; for materials coming in very coarse boulders, steel-element (apron) or chain feeders

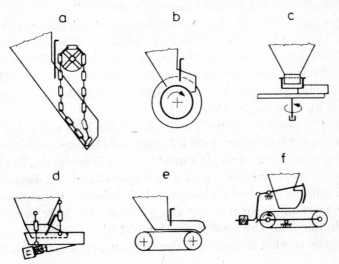

Fig. 11.5. Diagrams of various feeder types

can be used. The size of hopper aperture should be C times the upper limiting particle size, C in turn being a function of the abundance $S\%$ of the largest lumps, as follows:

$S\%$:	5–10	20–30	40–60	60–80	95–100;
$\sim C$:	1.5	2	2.5	3	3.5

The feeders most frequently used for the dosage of chemicals in flotation were described in Section 2.6.

Splitting a stream of solid particles into two or more part-streams can be achieved by means of baffles or devices exploiting the principles of mechanical sampling devices. A pulp stream can be split e.g. by letting the lateral spout of a rotating tank discharge into the successive compartments of a compartmented tank, each of which has a separate outlet of its own.

11.3.4. Pumps. Centrifugal pumps are the most widespread in the pumping of pulps, water and clear liquors. The effective head of pulp pumps seldom exceeds 15 m, although types with heads up to 30 m are also being manufactured. Pulp pumps are seldom used to transport pulp containing particles coarser than half a centimetre, although some designs may cope with boulders up to 25 cm size or so in a copious stream of water. The effective in-plant efficiency of centrifugal pumps may be as low as 30%, with the resistance of the attached piping taken into account, as compared with the 50 to 70% attained under optimum conditions. The housings and impellers of the pumps used to transport coarser sands are often rubber-lined to reduce wear. The inner bearing(s) of the impeller shaft must be sealed off from direct contact with the pulp.

Diaphragm pumps are often used to transport thick pulps. The pulp sucked into the housing through a bottom valve when the diaphragm rises passes upward through a valve in the diaphragm as it descends. These pumps are used more or less exclusively in the suction mode: if so used, their effective head is limited by the height of the pulp column corrected for the vapour pressure of the water and for the friction head.

Airlifts ("mammoth pumps") serve well in the lifting of pulps or sandy slurries. Their main advantage over all other pulp-lifting machinery is that they have no moving parts, and pipe wear in them is moderate. Their drawback is that they require compressed air for their operation and a deep suction sump to hold the fluid to be moved. Compressed air injected at the bottom of the airlift pipe reaching down into the sump reduces the bulk density of the fluid column in the pipe. The condition of hydrostatic equilibrium then requires the height of the column to increase. The fundamental airlift formula,

$$\frac{V}{Q} = \frac{H\gamma}{23\eta \log{(1 + 0.1h\gamma)}},$$

is based on the equality of lifting work $QH\gamma$ and the isothermal expansion of air,

$$P_0 V \ln{\left(\frac{p}{p_0}\right)},$$

corrected for efficiency η, where V is the volume at ambient conditions of the air required to transport the pulp volume Q (both given in the same units, e.g. m³/min), H is lifting head in m, h is depth of immersion into the sump in m, γ is pulp density in t/m³, and η is the efficiency of the airlift ($\eta \simeq 0.3$ to 0.4, greater for greater h/H ratios). A fair approximation is provided by the formula

$$\frac{V}{Q} \simeq \frac{K}{\left(\dfrac{h}{H}\right)^n},$$

where $K \simeq 4$ and $n \simeq 2$ if $h/H < 1$ and $K \simeq 5$ and $n \simeq 1$ if $h/H > 1$ (Nicklin 1963).

11.4. SAMPLING

A sample will represent the aggregate from which it has been taken to a fair enough approximation if the sample is made up of a large enough number of particles and sample-taking procedure has been correctly executed. The minimum number of particles needed in the sample is

$$N = \frac{v(1-v)z^2}{h^2} = \frac{(1-v)z^2}{vr^2},$$

where v is the volume fraction of the mineral containing the element to be assayed for, h is the admissible error of sampling, likewise in volume fraction terms, $r = h/v$ is the admissible relative error and

$$z^2 \simeq 4 \log\left(\frac{1}{1-w}\right) - 1.4.$$

The expression

$$w = \frac{1}{\sqrt{2\pi}} \int\limits_{t=-z}^{+z} e^{\frac{-t^2}{2}} dt$$

states the probability of $100w$ samples out of 100 having an error less than $\pm h$ or $\pm r$, respectively. For example,

	$w =$	0.80	0.85	0.90	0.95	0.99
if	$z =$	1.18	1.38	1.62	1.95	2.58,
or	$100w\% =$	68.3	86.6	95.5	98.8	99.7
if	$z =$	1.0	1.5	2.0	2.5	3.0 .

The number of particles in a unit volume of sample is

$$N' = \frac{c}{x_{avg}^3},$$

where c is a form factor which equals e.g. $6/\pi$ for spheres, unity for cubes and ab for a prism of side lengths $ax > x > bx$; it is $c > ab$ for an irregular shape that can be inscribed into such a prism. x_{avg} the volume-average particle size (cf. Vol. 1, p. 78) is established by replotting the data of the granulometry curve $s = f(x)$ into a coordinate system whose abscissa axis is linear in x^3 to obtain the curve $s = f(x^3)$; the area under the curve,

$$\int\limits_{x_{min}}^{x_{max}} f(x)^3 \, dx,$$

is converted into a rectangle of height $s = 100\%$: the base of the rectangle furnishes x_{avg}^3, and its cube root furnishes x_{avg}. The procedure can be performed

693

numerically also: one first forms the cubes of the particles sizes x_i, x_{i+1} limiting the weight percentage $\Delta s = s_{i+1} - s_i\%$ and forms the arithmetic average of the cubes obtained. The result is multiplied by the corresponding Δs value:

$$\Delta s \, \frac{x_i^3 + x_{i+1}^3}{2} \, .$$

The products are added together and divided by $\Sigma \Delta s = 100\%$, giving

$$x_{\text{avg}}^3 = \frac{\Sigma \left(\Delta s \, \dfrac{x_i^3 + x_{i+1}^3}{2} \right)}{100} \, .$$

The cube root of this expression is the average particle size x_{avg} to be introduced into the formula of N'. (A more accurate value of x is obtained using e.g. the Simpson rule rather than the arithmetic average of the x^3 values.)

For practical purposes, it is satisfactory as a rule to calculate $\Sigma(\Delta s \cdot x^3)$ for the particles coarser than x_{80} only; neglecting the finer particles hardly affects the result, so abruptly do the third powers of small numbers decrease and those of large ones increase.

If the granulometry of the aggregate is of the Schuhmann–Gaudin type, then a distribution

$$s_F = 100 \left(\frac{x}{a} \right)^m$$

entails a volume function

$$s = 100 \left(\frac{x}{a} \right)^{3m} \, .$$

Now

$$\int_0^{100} s \, \mathrm{d}s = 100 \int_{x_{\min} = s}^{x_{\max} = s} \left(\frac{x}{a} \right)^{3m} \mathrm{d}x = \frac{100 x^{3m+1}}{(3m+1) a^{3m}} \Big|_0^a = \frac{100 a}{3m+1} \, ;$$

hence, the particle size to be introduced into the N' formula will be

$$x_{\text{avg}} = \frac{a}{3m+1} \, .$$

At $\quad m = \quad 0.7 \quad 1.0 \quad 1.3,$

$\quad 3m + 1 = \quad 3.1 \quad 4.0 \quad 4.9;$

hence, at a fair approximation,

$$x_{\text{avg}} \cong \frac{a}{4} = \frac{x_{\max}}{4} \, .$$

Table 11.2. Finding the volume average particle size of an aggregate of given granulometry

$s_F\%$	x mm $(\cdot 10^{-1})$	x^3 $(\cdot 10^{-2})$	$\Delta s\%$	$\bar{x}^3(\cdot 10^{-2})$	$\bar{x}^3 \cdot \Delta s$ $(\cdot 10^{-2})$	$\%$
0	0	0	0	—	—	—
30	0.6	0.22	30	0.11	3	0
50	1.2	1.72	20	0.97	19	0
60	2.0	8	10	4.86	49	0.1
70	3.7	51	10	29.5	29.5	0.7
80	6.2	239	10	145	1,450	3.3
90	10.0	1,000	10	620	6,200	14.0
95	14.2	2,810	5	1,905	9,525	21.5
98	18.0	5,840	3	4,325	12,975	29.2
100	20.0	8,000	2	6,920	13,840	31.2
			100		44,356	100.0

If the granulometry is as stated in the numerical example of Table 11.2, then

$$x_{\mathrm{avg}}^3 = 444 \cdot 10^{-3} = 0.444 \ \mathrm{mm}^3,$$

$$x_{\mathrm{avg}} = \sqrt[3]{0.444} = 0.76 \ \mathrm{mm},$$

and

$$\varphi = \frac{x_{\max}}{x_{\mathrm{avg}}} = \frac{2.0}{0.76} = 2.6.$$

Neglecting the particles finer than

$$x_{80} \qquad x_{90} \qquad x_{95},$$

one obtains instead of 0.444 mm

$$0.425 \qquad 0.363 \qquad 0.268 \ \ \mathrm{mm}^3 \ \text{for} \ x_{\mathrm{avg}}^3$$

and $\quad$ 0.75 $\qquad$ 0.71 $\qquad$ 0.64 $\quad$ mm for x_{avg},

that is, 99 $\qquad$ 93 $\qquad$ 84% of the original.

If

$$x_{\max} = 2.2 \ (1.8) \ \mathrm{mm} \ \text{instead of} \ 2.0 \ \mathrm{mm},$$

then the average particle size of the last $\Delta s = 2$ weight percent will be

$$x_{98} = 2.1 \quad (1.8) \ \mathrm{mm} \ \text{instead of} \ 1.9 \ \mathrm{mm}; \ \text{hence,}$$

$$x_{\mathrm{avg}}^3 = 0.502 \ (0.422) \ \mathrm{mm}^3 \ \text{instead of} \ 0.444 \ \mathrm{mm}^3$$

and $\qquad x_{\mathrm{avg}} = 0.80 \ \ (0.75) \ \mathrm{mm} \ \text{instead of} \ 0.76 \ \mathrm{mm}.$

The corresponding

$$\varphi = x_{max}/x_{avg} = 3.0 \quad (2.4) \text{ mm instead of 2.6 mm,}$$

and the minimum sample weights required become

$$\left(\frac{0.80}{0.76}\right)^3 = 1.17 \quad \left(\frac{0.75}{0.76}\right)^3 = 0.96$$

times that belonging to 0.76 mm.

The minimum sample volume required is

$$V = \frac{N}{N'} = \left[(1-v)\frac{x_{avg}^3}{cvr^2}\right]\left[4\log\left(\frac{1}{1-w}\right) - 1.4\right] =$$
$$= z^2(1-v)\frac{x_{avg}^3}{cvr^2} = z^2(1-v)\frac{x_{max}^3}{\varphi^3 cvr^2} = Kz^2(1-v)\frac{x_{max}^3}{vr^2};$$

the corresponding sample weight is

$$S = V\delta,$$

where δ is the average s.g. of the aggregate to be sampled. If x is in cm, then V is in cm^3 and S in grams (or ponds). The variation vs. w of z^2 (the dot-dash curve) and of Kz^2 (the other curves) is presented in Fig. 11.6, with φ and c as the parameters.

$$K = \frac{1}{\varphi^3 c};$$

of the two c values shown, $c = 1$ refers to cubes; $c = 6/\pi$ refers to spheres.

For the r.o.m. ores of base metals and the corresponding tailings, v tends to be fairly small $(1 - v \to 1)$, so that formulae of the form

$$V = Kz^2\frac{x_{max}^3}{vr^2}$$

or

$$V = Kz^2\frac{vx_{max}^3}{h^2}$$

may be used. Under average conditions, K may be put at 0.075. Simplified and generalized, the formula may be written to read

$$S = C\frac{x_{max}^3}{\left(\dfrac{r}{z}\right)^2}, \text{ or } S = C_1\frac{x_{avg}^3}{\left(\dfrac{h}{z}\right)^2}$$

where

$$C = K(1-v)\frac{\delta}{v}$$

696

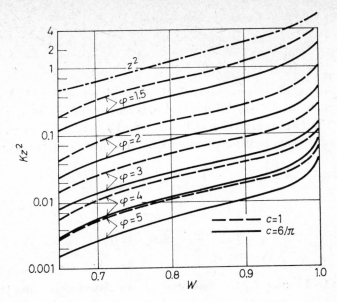

Fig. 11.6. Variation of Kz^2 and z^2 vs. w, with c and φ as the parameters

and

$$C_1 = v(1 - v)\frac{\delta}{c} = Cv^2\varphi^3.$$

According to a method proposed by Gy (1955), C can be obtained as a product of four factors, $C = ijkl$. Here, $i = 1/c$, the form factor, is in the 0.3 to 0.7 range as a rule and averages about 0.5 (except for gold ores, for which it is 0.2); $j = 1/\varphi^3$ is the particle size deviation factor, which is in the 0.1 to 0.4 range as a rule and 0.25 on average (but between 0.5 and 0.8 for close-sized materials); k is a heterogeneity (liberation) factor, which equals zero for totally homogeneous materials and unity for totally inhomogeneous ones. The usual ranges of k are 0.4 to 0.8 for heterogeneous concentrates, 0.2 to 0.4 for homogeneous concentrates, heterogeneous tailings and the waste in coal washing and 0.05 to 0.2 for homogeneous tailings and for washed coal in coal washing. The k value of r.o.m. material and middlings can be calculated using the formula

$$k = \frac{0.8}{\left(\dfrac{x}{L}\right)^{0.6}},$$

where L is the grain size of dissemination or liberation. For example,

$k =$	0.8	0.4	0.2	0.1	0.05
if $x/L =$	1	4	10	40	100.

The l factor or factor of mineral composition is

$$l = \frac{1-v}{v}[(1-v)\delta_1 + v\delta_2] = \frac{1-v}{v}[\delta_1 - (\delta_1 - \delta_2)v] = (1-v)^2\frac{\delta_1}{v} + (1-v)\delta_2,$$

where δ_1 is the s.g. of the pay mineral, of volume fraction v, which contains the chemical element to be assayed for, and δ_2 is the s.g. of the gangue mineral(s). One may as a fair approximation put $\delta_1 \cong 5$ and $\delta_2 \cong 2.6$ for ores and $\delta_1 \cong 2.2$ and $\delta_2 \cong 1.4$ for coals (letting v denote ash): in other words, at a fair approximation,

$$l \cong \frac{1-v}{v}(5 - 2.4v)$$

for ores and

$$l \cong \frac{1-v}{v}(2.2 - 0.8v)$$

for coals.

According to Visman, C_1 for coals can be calculated also using the formula

$$C_1 = (v_1 - v_2)^2 s(1 - s)\frac{\delta_1\delta_2}{\delta},$$

where v is ash content and δ is s.g., and the subscript 1 refers to the heavy and subscript 2 to the light fraction obtained on separation at s.g. 1.6. s and $1 - s$ are the weight fractions of the two. The ash content v and s.g. δ of the entire sample may be established in separate tests or calculated using the formulae

$$v = sv_1 + (1 - s)v_2$$

and

$$\frac{1}{\delta} = \frac{s}{\delta_1} + \frac{1-s}{\delta_2}.$$

The errors of sampling, which comprise h, dependent upon the nature of the sampled aggregate (its granulometry, heterogeneity, etc.), h_1, the error of sample reduction, h_2, the error of segregation on the taking of the part-samples making up the whole sample and h_3, the error of chemical analysis, add up as

$$\left(\Sigma\frac{\bar{h}}{z}\right)^2 = h^2 + h_1^2 + h_2^2 + h_3^2,$$

where

$$h^2 = C_1\frac{x_{avg}^3}{S},$$

as presented above.

One also has

$$h_1^2 = \Sigma h_1'',$$

698

where h_1' is the mean error of each step of comminution in the process of sample reduction:

$$h_1'^2 = aC_1 \frac{x_{avg}'^3}{S'}, \tag{1}$$

where S' is the ultimate minimum sample quantity in a given step of reduction, and x_{avg}' is the volume average particle size of the comminuted material. (The average particle size of a material passed by a screen of aperture size x_{max}', comminuted in several steps, will be approximately

$$x_{avg}' \cong 0.6 x_{max}',$$

so that,

$$\varphi \cong \frac{1}{0.6} = 1.66.$$

On a single halving ($m = 1$) of a comminuted sample, a in (1) equals unity; on the second and any further halving ($m > 1$), $1.5 < a < 2$. The argument is that if a sample weight S' is obtained on the last halving, then the preceding halvings have yielded $2S'$, $2^2 S'$, etc., and the first halving after comminution has yielded $2^{m-1} S'$; hence,

$$h'^2 = h_m^2 = C_1 \frac{x_{avg}'^3}{S'\left[1 + \dfrac{1}{2} + \dfrac{1}{4} + \dfrac{1}{8} + \cdots \dfrac{1}{2^{m-1}}\right]} = aC_1 \frac{x_{avg}'^3}{S'}.$$

$a =$	1	1.5	1.75	1.875	1.9375	1.96875...2.0
if $m =$	1	2	3	4	5	6 ...∞.

For a sample reduction operation, the minimum necessary sample weights S_{min}' kg, given a maximum particle size x_{max}' cm in the comminuted material, can be calculated also by means of the formulae

$$S_{min}' = c_1 z^2 x_{max}'^3$$

or

$$S_{min}' = c_1' z^2 x_{avg}'^3.$$

Table 11.3. Parameters c and C figuring in the sampling formulae for as-mined coals and the products of their washing

Product	c_1	c_1'	c_2	$C_{1\,avg}(\pm 50\%)$	C_1
Clean coal	0.6	2.6	4	0.024	0.01—0.04
Middlings	1.2	5.5	5	0.06	0.03—0.09
Waste	2.6	12.0	10	0.12	0.05—0.18
As-mined coal	5.5	24.6	6.7	0.24	0.15—0.30

Approximate values of c_1 and c_1' for the different products of coal washing are found in Table 11.3.

$$h_2^2 = \frac{C_2}{n},$$

where n is the number of part-samples, of weight S_2 each $[S_2 = S/n]$, and C_2 may, at a fair approximation, be equated with $h_2'^2$, the square of the mean ash-content error h_2' calculated from the individual ash analyses of the n part-samples, of weight S_2 each, of the material sampled. At a rough approximation,

$$h_2' = \frac{v}{c_2},$$

where v refers to ash. Approximate c_2 values are also listed in Table 11.3.

The error of ash analysis, h_3, may be assumed to equal 0.1%; that is, $h_3 \simeq 10^{-3}$ and $h_3^2 \simeq 10^{-6}$, which is negligible.

The average values and the extremes encountered in practice of C_1 in the formulae for h^2 and h_1' are also given in Table 11.3. For coal samples of unknown origin, the $C_{1\text{avg}}$, c_1 and c_2 values of the table may be used. More accurate values

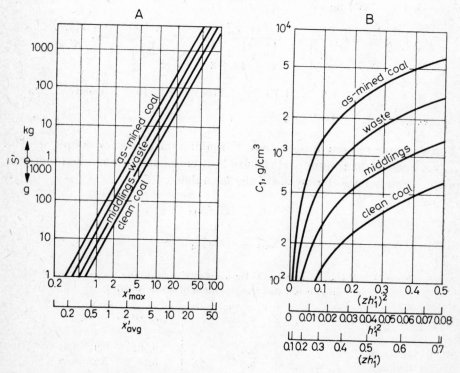

Fig. 11.7. A and B — The S' and C_1 parameters of as-mined coal and its washing products, the first vs. $x_{\max}$ and the second vs. h_1' and zh_1', at $z = 2.5$

may be obtained using the nomograms in Fig. 11.7. Part A permits to read off the minimum sample weights S' corresponding to the particle size x'_{max} (or x'_{avg}) of the individual steps of reduction (putting $z = 2.5$), both for as-mined coal and the washing products. (The figure is not to be used to find the weights S_1 of the part-samples or the weight S of the combined sample!) Part B of the figure presents the relationship between the C_1 values (g/cm³) and the mean ash errors h'_1 and maximum possible ash errors zh'_1 of the successive steps of reduction corresponding to the x'_{max} and S' values of Part A, for $z = 2.5$ (that is, $w = 0.99$).

The parameters C_1 and C_2 may be obtained by testing several samples of the coal to be sampled for granulometry (or x_{avg}), ash content v, s.g. δ, the relative weights s and $1 - s$ of the fractions separated at a s.g. of 1.6 and their ash contents v_1 and v_2 and s.g.'s δ_1 and δ_2. (Instead of direct testing, v and δ can be calculated out of the fractions' data also.) The granulometries of the individual samples permit to establish x^3_{avg}; the $(v_1 - v_2)^2$, $s(1 - s)$ and $\delta_1\delta_2/\delta$ values permit to calculate C_1; averages, mean and maximum deviations for all these and for the ash content v of the sample can then be determined. The mean ash error of the individual samples approximately equals the square root of C_2. A more accurate value of C_2 can be obtained using the formula

$$h^2 = C_1 \frac{x^3_{avg}}{S_1} + \frac{C_2}{n} + \Sigma h'^2_1 + h^2_3,$$

where h is the mean ash error of the single sample, $n = 1$, and $h^2_3 = 0.01$ and $\Sigma h'^2_1$ can be read off Part B of Fig. 11.7 (Badger 1950; Gy 1955, 1967; Hancock 1950; Keller 1965; Sommer 1955; 1965; Stange 1957; Tarján 1970; Visman 1947; Wenzel 1966).

Table 11.4 presents a worked example of the calculation for minus-50 mm as-mined coal and plus-0.5, minus-8 mm clean coal.

If the 20-g sample of raw coal and the 500-g samples of clean coal are reduced in two steps each, according to the "as-mined coal" and "clean coal" curves of Part B of Fig. 11.6, then

$$\Sigma h'^2_1 = 0.035 + 0.035 = 0.7$$

for as-mined coal and

$$\Sigma h'^2_1 = 0.08 + 0.08 = 0.16$$

for clean coal. Hence,

$$h^2 = 4.31^2 = 19.47 = \frac{24,100}{20,000} + \frac{C_2}{1} + 0.07 + 0.01$$

for the as-mined coal, implying

$$C_2 = 18.19.$$

Table 11.4. Finding refined sampling parameters of an as-mined and a clean coal

	$(v_1 - v_2)^2$	$s(1-s)$	$\dfrac{\delta_1 \delta_2}{\delta}$	x^2_{avg} cm	C_1 g/cm³	$r\%$	$C_1 x^2_{avg}$ g
As-mined coal, minus-50 mm	5,991	0.233	2.02	8.96	2,820	31.32	25,270
$S_1 = 20$ kg	6,037	0.232	2.01	10.27	2,809	31.67	28,950
$n = 52$	5,837	0.240	1.99	9.08	2,793	34.25	25,345
Averages	5,682	0.230	1.99	9.16	2,630	32.27	24,100
Variance of individual samples, h $\{$	441	0.019	0.044	2.09	758	4.41	—
	8%	8%	2%	23%	29%	—	—
Max. variance of the mean, $2.5h/\sqrt{52}$	2.8%	2.8%	0.7%	8%	10%	—	—
Clean coal, minus-8	2,884	0.053	1.90	0.071	290	7.1	20.5
Plus-0.5 mm	2,894	0.062	1.88	0.002	399	8.8	31.0
$S_1 = 500$ g	2,460	0.044	1.79	0.094	192	9.0	18.0
$n = 25$	....	....	....	....	....	....	....
Averages	2,958	0.065	1.89	0.091	365	10.01	33.2
Variance of individual samples, h $\{$	338	0.022	0.063	0.012	140	2.94	—
	11%	34%	3%	14%	38%	—	—
Max. variance of the mean, $2.5h/\sqrt{52}$	5.5%	17%	1.5%	7%	19%	—	—

In other terms, putting $z = 2.5$, the sampling equation for this coal becomes

$$(\Delta v)^2 = 2.5^2 \left[\frac{24,100}{S} + \frac{18.19}{n} + 0.08 \right].$$

It furnishes total sample weight, S grams, and the number n of the part-samples, on the assumption that Δv is the maximum admissible ash error (the actual error being less than that in 99 cases out of a hundred). The equation of the clean coal in the example is

$$h^2 = 2.94^2 = 8.65 = \frac{33.2}{500} + C_2 + 0.16 + 0.01,$$

whence

$$C_2 = 8.41$$

and

$$(\Delta v)^2 = 2.5^2 \left[\frac{33.2}{S} + \frac{8.41}{n} + 0.17 \right].$$

One sometimes encounters in literature or in draft standards prescriptions for sampling or sample reduction in which sample weights do not vary as the cube of particle size. Any such approach is wrong.

For example, for average conditions, the prescriptions

$$p\sqrt{T} = 250$$

and

$$S \simeq 2.5\sqrt{T}$$

have been proposed for relating the weight T (or particle number) of the bulk material to be sampled and the weight S (or particle number) of the sample, where $p = 100\,S/T$ is sample weight as a percentage of bulk weight. Others have proposed relationships

$$S \simeq 0.1T$$

plus or minus 50%, depending on the nature of the material, for the starting sample weight to be taken from a r.o.m. ore or

$$S = 0.005T$$

from fine-grained concentrates. The relationship

$$S' \simeq Ax_{max}^n$$

for determining the minimum weight, S' kg, necessary at a given limiting particle size x_{max} cm, is also fairly widespread; it is wrong in principle if $n < 3$. (In fact, however, values of $A = 250$ and $n = 1.2$ have been proposed for average conditions. According to Soviet authors (e.g. Chechott), assuming an

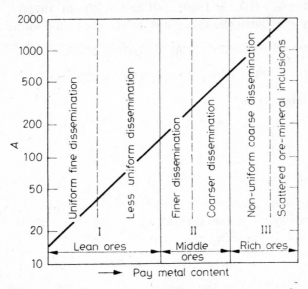

Fig. 11.8. Coefficient A of Chechott's sample weight formula $S = Ax_{max}^2$ for various ore grades (S in kg; x_{max} in cm)

exponent $n = 2$ for the types of ores shown in Fig. 11.8, the A values can be read off the diagonal of the diagram. Another Soviet method is used for

Group	I	II	III	materials
(ore:	poor	middle	rich	
or material:	homogeneous	middle	inhomogeneous)	
the values $A =$	4	10	32,	
$n =$	1.8	2.0	2.25.	

These parameters furnish, e.g. in Category II, S values less by a factor of 15 to 60 than those proposed in Fig. 11.8.

The average of the A and n parameters in the sample weight formula

$$S = A x_{max}^n$$

proposed by different authors for the x_{max} range between 0.1 and 25 cm was found to be $A = 12$ and $n = 1.3$ (with a correlation coefficient of 0.9). Total sample weight S may be obtained as the sum of

$$n' = \left(\frac{zs}{h} \right)^2$$

samples of weight $S_2 = S/n'$ each. (At $w = 95\%$, $z = 2$; s is the error of the individual samples and h is their maximum admissible deviation from the arithmetic average) (Bintig 1960; Göll and Helfricht 1972.)

US practice stipulates the minimum weight of the individual samples to be

S_{2min}	= 20	40	75	90	180	270 kg
at x_{max}	$\lesssim$ 10	25	50	100	150	250 mm,

and their number to be

$n'_{min} =$ 70	35	20

for materials

	of great	medium	small

quality fluctuation. (Any raw material is to be considered to be of greatly fluctuating quality.) For example, at $x_{max} = 100$ mm, these rules prescribe $S_{2min} = 90$ kg and (assuming $n'_{min} = 70$)

$$S_{min} = 70 \cdot 90 = 6{,}300 \text{ kg,}$$

whereas at $x_{max} = 200$ mm they prescribe $S_{2min} = 270$ kg and

$$S_{min} = 70 \cdot 270 = 18{,}900 \text{ kg.}$$

According to one German standard (TGL 7641, Blatt 6, 1967), the total sample weight S_{10} kg to be taken from coal of weight T tons, ash $v < 10\%$ and upper limiting particle size x cm is to be

$$S_{10} = a \log (T - 5),$$

where

$$\log a = 1.06 + \frac{x}{20}.$$

If ash content v is between 10 and 25%, the minimum sample weight required is furnished by the formula

$$S_v = S_{10} + (S_{10} + 67) \frac{v - 10}{30}.$$

The number of part-samples is furnished by

$$n = b\sqrt{T},$$

where b equals about 3 for inhomogeneous materials and 2.5 for materials of middling quality fluctuation; it is 1.5 for homogeneous materials at $x \lesssim 1.5$ cm and 2 at $x \gtrsim 1.5$ cm.

The Czechoslovak standard prescribes for sampling out of a coal stream in coal washeries the taking of part-samples of weight

$$S_2 = 0.4x_{max} \text{ kg};$$

the minimum number of part-samples required is

$$n' \cong 10 + v$$

for sized coal and

$$n'' \cong 20 + 1.5v$$

for as-mined coal ($v\%$ is ash content on a dry basis).

Examples. (1A) What is the probable error of sampling a sphalerite-quartz ore of 4% Zn content whose granulometry is given in Table 11.1 ($x_{max} = 0.2$ cm; $x_{avg} = 0.076$ cm), if the form factor, $c = 1.5$, overall s.g., $\delta = 2.8$ and $S = 250$ g?

$$v = \frac{0.04}{0.67} = 0.06;$$

$$\left(\frac{r}{z}\right)^2 = x_{avg}^3 \delta \frac{1 - v}{vcS} = \frac{0.94 \cdot 2.8 \cdot 0.076^3}{0.06 \cdot 1.5 \cdot 250} = 5.66 \cdot 10^{-6};$$

$$\frac{r}{z} = 2.38 \cdot 10^{-3};$$

$$h = vr = 0.06r;$$

hence,

$$\frac{h}{z} = 1.43 \cdot 10^{-4}.$$

At $z = 1$,

$$h = 1.43 \cdot 10^{-4} = 0.0143\% \text{ ZnS},$$

tantamount to 0.0096% Zn. In other words, if a sample of weight $S = 250$ g is taken, the Zn metal content of 68 samples out of 100 will be in the 4 ± 0.0096 % range, that is, between 3.99 and 4.01%.

If

$z =$	2	2.6,
then the error is	± 0.0192	$\pm 0.025\%$ Zn,
meaning that the Zn content of	95	99 samples
out of a hundred will be in the	3.98 to 4.02	3.975 to 4.025 range.

(1B) Find the error if $S = 25$ g rather than 250 g. The hypothesis increases $(r/z)^2$ by a factor of $250/25 = 10$ and r/z or h/z by a factor of $\sqrt{10} = 3.16$ against the foregoing case: hence,

$$\frac{h}{z} = 0.0096 \cdot \sqrt{10} = \pm 0.0304\% \text{ Zn}.$$

The Zn content ranges for different values of $z(w)$ are stated in Table 11.5.

(1C) Find the error if $x_{max} = 2$ cm and $S = 10$ kg. The hypothesis increases the value of $(r/z)^2$ by a factor of

$$\left(\frac{x_{max, 1}}{x_{max\ 2}}\right)^3 \frac{S_2}{S_1} = \left(\frac{2}{0.2}\right)^3 \frac{250}{10,000} = 25$$

and the value of r/z or h/z by a factor of $\sqrt{25} = 5$ against the case (1A), implying

$$\frac{h}{z} = 5 \cdot 0.0096 = \pm 0.048\% \text{ Zn}.$$

The results are compiled in Table 11.6.

(1D) To what fineness x_{max} should the ore of Example (1C) be comminuted in order that the deviation in Zn content should be within $\pm 0.05\%$ in 99 cases out of a hundred ($z = 2.6$)?

In Example (1C), we had $h = \pm 0.048$; here,

$$h = \frac{0.05}{2.6} = 0.0192.$$

Hence,

$$\frac{2^3}{0.048^2} = \frac{x_{max}^3}{0.0192^2},$$

706

Table 11.5. Example (1B): Zinc content ranges Zn% and errors h% corresponding to different values of z (w)

	z = 1, w = 68%	z = 2, w = 95%	z = 2.6, w = 99%
h% =	±0.0304	±0.0608	±0.079
Zn% =	3.97—4.03	3.94—4.06	3.92—4.08

Table 11.6. Example (1C): Zinc content ranges Zn% and errors h% corresponding to different values of z (w)

	z = 1	z = 2	z = 2.6
h% =	±0.048	±0.096	±0.125
Zn% =	3.95—4.05	3.90—4.10	3.875—4.125

whence the x_{max} sought for is

$$2 \left(\frac{0.0192}{0.048} \right)^{2/3} = 1.084 \text{ cm.}$$

(1E) What is the least sample weight S needed if the ore is ground to minus-0.5 mm rather than minus-1.084 cm prior to sampling, and the limitations on the error of the Zn content are as in (1D)?

Sample weights are to vary as the cube of the upper limiting particle size: that is,

$$\frac{S}{10,000} = \left(\frac{0.05}{1.084} \right)^3 = 0.0461^3 = 9.8 \cdot 10^{-4}.$$

Hence, $S = 9.8$ g.

(1F) What sample weight S is required if the maximum particle size of the ore is 10 cm?

$$\frac{S}{10^4} = \left(\frac{10}{1.084} \right)^3 = 9.22^3 = 785;$$

$$S = 785 \cdot 10^4 \text{ g} = 7,850 \text{ kg.}$$

(1G) Out of a sphalerite-quartz ore of 4% Zn content, of maximum particle size $x_{max} = 2$ cm and average particle size $x_{avg} = 1$ cm ($\varphi = 2$), with $v = 4/67 = 0.06$, $c = 1.5$ and $\delta = 2.8$, one takes n part-samples of $S_2 = 40$ kg each, adding up to a total of $S = nS_2$. These are reduced by repeated comminution and halving to the ultimate sample weight. Let the maximum particle sizes obtained on the successive steps of comminution be

$$x'_{max} = 5.0 \quad 1.0 \quad 0.2 \text{ mm};$$

and let the corresponding average particle sizes be

$$x'_{avg} = 0.6 \ x'_{max} = 3.0 \quad 0.6 \quad 0.12 \text{ mm.}$$

What should S and n be and what sample weights S' should be taken in the successive stages if, in the final sample, the prescribed deviation should not exceed

$$\frac{\Sigma r}{z} = 5 \cdot 10^{-3} \tag{1}$$

or $\pm 0.03\%$ ZnS and

$$\frac{\Sigma h}{z} = \frac{vr}{z} = 3 \cdot 10^{-4} \tag{2}$$

or $\pm 0.02\%$ Zn?

The C_1 parameter of the sample is

$$C_1 = v(1-v)\frac{\delta}{c} = 0.06 \cdot 0.94\frac{2.8}{1.5} = 0.1052.$$

The ultimate sample is attained in four successive steps of reduction, giving average particle sizes of 10, 3, 0.6 and 0.12 mm, respectively. Assuming the error to be about the same in each step, the final deviation is to be divided up equally among the four steps:

$$\left(\frac{h}{z}\right)^2 = \frac{(3 \cdot 10^{-4})^2}{4} = 2.25 \cdot 10^{-8}.$$

The reduction ratios of the successive steps are

$$R = \frac{10}{3} = 3.33; \quad \frac{3}{0.6} = 5; \quad \frac{0.6}{0.12} = 5.$$

Sample weights decrease proportionally to R^3/a. Putting e.g. $a = 2$,

$$\frac{3.33^3}{2} = \frac{37}{2} = 18.5;$$

$$\frac{5^3}{2} = 62.5.$$

The number m of halvings is given by the relationship

$$\frac{R^3}{a} = 2^m$$

as

$$m = \frac{\log\left(\frac{R^3}{a}\right)}{\log 2},$$

that is,

$$m = \frac{\log 18.5}{\log 2} = \frac{1.267}{0.3} = 4.2$$

for the first step of reduction (to be rounded to $m = 4$), and

$$m = \frac{\log 62.5}{\log 2} = \frac{1.795}{0.3} = 6.0$$

for each of the other two steps. The accurate a values are obtained, by a reverse calculation using these formulae, as 1.97 for $m = 6$ and 1.875 for $m = 4$.

The total sample weight S needed is

$$S = C_1 \frac{x_{avg}^3}{\left(\frac{h}{z}\right)^2} = 0.1052 \frac{1^3}{2.25 \cdot 10^{-8}} = 4.68 \cdot 10^6 \text{ g} = 4,680 \text{ kg,}$$

and the number of part samples is to be

$$n = \frac{S}{S_2} = \frac{4,680}{40} = 117.$$

The sample is comminuted to minus-5 mm and halved $m = 4$ times; it is then comminuted to minus-1 mm and halved $m = 6$ times; again comminuted, this time to minus-0.2 mm, and again halved $m = 6$ times. The resulting reduced sample weights are

$$S_5' = \frac{S}{2^4} = \frac{4,680}{16} = 292 \text{ kg;}$$

$$S_1' = \frac{S_5'}{2^6} = 4.56 \text{ kg;}$$

and

$$S_{0.2}' = \frac{S_1'}{2^6} = \frac{4,560}{64} = 71 \text{ g.}$$

The variance of the ultimate sample

$$\left(\sum_1^2 \frac{h}{z}\right)^2 = C_1 \frac{x_{avg}^3}{S} + \Sigma \left(a C_1 \frac{x_{avg}'^3}{S'}\right) =$$

$$= C_1 x_{avg}^3 \left[\frac{1}{S} + \frac{1.875}{3.33^3 \cdot S_5'} + \frac{1.97}{3.33^3 \cdot 5^3 S_1'} + \frac{1.97}{3.33^3 \cdot 5^3 \cdot 5^3 S_{0.2}'}\right] =$$

$$= 0.1052 \cdot 1 \left[\frac{1}{4.68 \cdot 10^6} + \frac{1.875}{37 \cdot 2.92 \cdot 10^5} + \frac{1.97}{37 \cdot 125 \cdot 4.56 \cdot 10^3} + \right.$$

$$\left. + \frac{1.97}{37 \cdot 125 \cdot 125 \cdot 71}\right] = 0.1052[2.14 \cdot 10^{-7} + 1.735 \cdot 10^{-7} + 0.933 \cdot 10^{-7} +$$

$$+ 0.48 \cdot 10^{-7}] = (2.255 + 1.828 + 0.983 + 0.505) \cdot 10^{-8} =$$

$$= 5.571 \cdot 10^{-8}.$$

The variance of the reduced samples is less than

$$\frac{\left(\sum \dfrac{h}{z}\right)^2}{4} = 2.25 \cdot 10^{-8},$$

because the weights S' are greater than that which corresponds to

$$\left(\frac{h_1'}{z}\right)^2 = 2.25 \cdot 10^{-8}.$$

For example, if the minus-5 mm sample is halved five rather than four times, one obtains a sample weight

$$S_5' = \frac{4{,}680}{2^5} = 146 \text{ kg}$$

and a variance

$$\left(\frac{h_1'}{z}\right)^2 = \frac{1.94 \cdot 0.1052 \cdot 0.3^3}{1.46 \cdot 10^5} = 3.78 \cdot 10^{-8}.$$

The difference of $3.43 \cdot 10^{-8}$ between the aggregate variance of $5.571 \cdot 10^{-8}$ and the admissible one, $9 \cdot 10^{-8}$, is sufficient to accommodate any other errors that may arise. Let e.g. the mean error of the Zn assays of the part-samples of weight $S_2 = 40$ kg, as established by assaying many part-samples one by one, be $\pm 0.12\%$ Zn $= \pm 0.18\%$ ZnS, giving

$$h_2' = 1.8 \cdot 10^{-3}$$

and

$$C_2 = h_2'^2 = 3.24 \cdot 10^{-6},$$

and let the segregation error of the part-samples be

$$h_2^2 = \frac{C_2}{n} = \frac{3.24 \cdot 10^{-6}}{117} = 2.77 \cdot 10^{-8}.$$

If the deviation of the Zn assays is e.g. 0.01% Zn $= 0.015\%$ ZnS, then

$$h_3 = 1.5 \cdot 10^{-4}$$

and

$$h_3^2 = 2.25 \cdot 10^{-8};$$

hence,

$$h_2^2 + h_3^2 = 5.02 \cdot 10^{-8},$$

giving

$$\left(\sum_1^4 \frac{h}{z}\right)^2 = (5.57 + 5.02) \cdot 10^{-8} = 10.59 \cdot 10^{-8}$$

710

instead of the admissible $9 \cdot 10^{-8}$. Also,

$$\left(\sum \frac{h}{z}\right) = 3.25 \cdot 10^{-4}.$$

The total error for various hypotheses is listed in Table 11.7.

(2A) Find the Cu content and s.g. of a chalcopyritic r.o.m. ore and of the flotation concentrate and tailings in the first two columns of Table 11.8. What sample weights S are to be taken if the desired accuracy is 0.01% Cu, provided that $x_{max} = 0.15$ mm, $\varphi = 2.5$ and $c = 1.6$? (Assume all the chalcopyrite to be liberated and intergrowths to be absent.)

$$x_{avg} = \frac{0.15}{2.5} = 0.06 \text{ mm} = 6 \cdot 10^{-3} \text{ cm};$$

$$x_{avg}^3 = 2.16 \cdot 10^{-7};$$

$$0.01\% \text{ Cu} = 0.029\% \text{ CuFeS}_2;$$

$$\frac{h}{z} = 2.9 \cdot 10^{-4},$$

$$\left(\frac{h}{z}\right)^2 = 8.4 \cdot 10^{-8}.$$

The values

$$v = \text{Cu}\% \cdot \frac{\delta}{34.5 \cdot 4.2},$$

Table 11.7. Example (1G): Total errors and error ranges of Zn and ZnS content in a sphalerite ore, corresponding to different values of z (w)

$z =$	1	2	2.6
$w\% =$	68	95	99
$\pm$ZnS% $=$	0.0325	0.065	0.0845
$\pm$Zn% $=$	0.0218	0.0435	0.0566
Zn% $=$	3.98—4.02	3.96—4.04	3.94—4.06

Table 11.8. Example (2A): Test data and worked results

Product	Cu%	δ	v	C_1	S (g)		
					$z = 1$	$z = 2$	$z = 2.6$
R. o. m. ore	1.5	2.9	0.030	0.0527	0.135	0.54	0.91
Concentrate	25.0	3.9	0.673	0.5360	1.37	5.50	9.26
Tailings	0.3	2.8	0.0058	0.0101	0.026	0.102	0.173
Chalcopyrite	34.5	4.2					

$$C_1 = v(1 - v)\frac{\delta}{c}$$

and

$$S = C_1 \frac{x_{avg}^3}{\left(\dfrac{h}{z}\right)^2}$$

are listed in further columns of Table 11.8.

(2B) If the r.o.m. sample is taken from an aggregate of average particle size 5 mm rather than from material comminuted to minus-0.15 mm, then the sample required is greater by a factor of

$$\left(\frac{0.5}{6 \cdot 10^{-3}}\right)^3 = 83.3^3 = 5.8 \cdot 10^5,$$

that is, the desired accuracy of ± 0.01 Cu can be obtained by taking

$$S = 78 \qquad 313 \qquad 528 \text{ kg,}$$

assuming $\qquad z = 1 \qquad\qquad 2 \qquad\qquad 2.6.$

(3) It is intended to assay an ore of s.g. 3, containing 3 g/t of free gold, at a gold assay accuracy of 0.15 g/t. What sample weights are to be taken, if the average particle size of the comminuted ore and of the gold grains in it is (a) 0.1 mm, (b) 1 mm, and (c) if the ore is comminuted to 0.1 mm average, and the average grain size of the gold is 10 μm?

The weight fraction of the gold in the ore is $3/10^6$; its volume fraction is

$$v = \left(\frac{3}{18}\right)\left(\frac{3}{10^6}\right) = 5 \cdot 10^{-7}.$$

Hence,

$$C_1 = \frac{v\delta}{c} = \frac{5 \cdot 10^{-7} \cdot 3}{1.5} = 10^{-6},$$

that is,

$$S = C_1 \frac{x_{avg}^3}{\left(\dfrac{h}{z}\right)^2} = 10^{-6} x_{avg}^3 \frac{z^2}{6.25 \cdot 10^{-16}} = 1.6 \cdot 10^9 \, x_{avg}^3 \, z^2.$$

S is in grams if x is in cm. The results are presented in Table 11.9.

Table 11.9. Example (3): Worked results

	x_{avg}, cm	x_{avg}^3	S, kg		
			$z = 1$	$z = 2$	$z = 2.6$
a)	0.01	10^{-6}	1.6	6.4	10.8
b)	0.1	10^{-3}	1,600	6,400	10,8000
c)	0.001	10^{-9}	0.0016	0.0064	0.018

712

Table 11.10. Example (4A): Test data and worked results of a coal sampling operation

	Ash%	m	δ	c	φ	v	C_1	x_{avg}	S (kg) $z=1$	S (kg) $z=2$	S (kg) $z=2.6$	S_r (kg) $z=2.6$	S_r (kg) $z=2$
a	25	0—80	1.6	1.5	2.2	0.25	0.20	3.64	385	1,540	2,600		246
b		0—40						1.82	48.2	193	326		31
c		0—20						0.91	6.0	24	41		3.84
d		0—10						0.455	0.75	3	5		0.48
e	25	40—80	1.6	1.2	1.5	0.25	0.25	5.333	1,520	6,085	10,260		947
f		20—40						2.666	190	760	1,280		122
g		10—20						1.333	23.6	95	160		15.2
h	10	40—80	1.45	1.2	1.5	0.10	0.109	5.333	661	2,645	4,460		2,645
i		0—10			2.2			0.455	0.41	1.64	2.8		1.64
j	75	0—80	2.1	1.6	2.2	0.75	0.246	3.64	474	1,900	3,200		57
k		40—80			1.5			5.333	1,500	6,000	10,100		180
l		0—10			2.2			0.455	9.3	37	63		1.1

713

(4A) What sample weight S is to be taken from the coal grades characterized in the left-hand columns of Table 11.10 in terms of ash, granulometry, s.g. δ and factors c and φ, if the error in ash content may be $\pm 0.5\%$ ($h = 5 \cdot 10^{-3}$; $h^2 = 2.5 \cdot 10^{-5}$) everywhere?

The parameters v,

$$C_1 = v(1 - v)\frac{\delta}{c},$$

x_{avg} and

$$S = C_1 \frac{x_{avg}^3}{\left(\dfrac{h}{z}\right)^2}$$

are listed in further columns of the table.

If the admissible ash error is doubled to $\pm 1\%$ (halved to $\pm 0.25\%$), the S stated in the table is to be divided (multiplied) by four.

The last column, headed S_r kg, lists the sample weights corresponding to the admissible relative error

$$r = \frac{h}{z} = 0.05$$

at $z = 2$. The resulting correspondences are

ash content:	25	10	75%,
admissible error: $\pm h =$	0.0125	0.005	0.0375,
implying ash errors	± 1.25	± 0.5	$\pm 3.75\%$
and S_r/S ratios	$\dfrac{1}{2.5^2}$	1	$\dfrac{1}{7.5^2}$
that is,	0.16	1	0.0178.

(4B) Putting $r = 0.05$ and $z = 2$, $[r/z = 0.025$, $(r/z)^2 = 6.25 \cdot 10^{-4}]$ and suitably choosing the parameters i, j, k and l, Gy's method furnishes the values listed in Table 11.11.

On comparing the S_r values of Table 11.11 with those of Table 11.10, one finds sample weights to be about equal for as-mined coal but less by about 25% for clean coal and less by about 50% for waste. (Different assumptions concerning i, j, k and l will of course modify the values of C and S_r also.)

For an approximate calculation, one may use the formula $C = c_3 l$, where $c_3 = ijk$. Fair assumptions for c_3 include

> 0.08 for as-mined coal,
> 0.04 for sized coal,
> 0.02 for washed coal,
> 0.03 for middlings and
> 0.06 for washery waste.

Table 11.11. Example (4B): Values of the Gy parameters and worked results

	$i = 1/c$	$j = 1/\varphi^3$	k	l	C	x_{max}	x^3_{max}	S_r kg	(C)	(S_r)
a	0.66	0.1	0.8	6.0	0.32	8	512	262	0.48	394
b						4	64	33		49
c						2	8	4.1		6.2
d						1	1	0.51		0.8
e	0.8	0.4	0.6	6.0	1.15	8	512	943	0.24	197
f						4	64	118		25
g						2	8	14.7		3
h	0.8	0.4	0.4	19.1	2.44	8	512	2,000	0.38	312
i		0.1			0.61	1	1	0.98		0.6
j	0.8	0.1	0.8	0.5	0.03	8	512	24.6	0.03	24.6
k		0.4			0.12	8	512	98		24.6
l		0.1			0.03	1	1	0.48		0.5

This gives with the l values 6, 6, 19.1 and 0.5 of Table 11.11 the C and S_r valuet listed in the last two columns of the table, the latter on the assumption thas

$$\left(\frac{r}{z}\right)^2 = 6.25 \cdot 10^{-4}.$$

(4C) Using the Visman method and choosing v_1, v_2, δ_1, δ_2 and $\dfrac{\delta}{\gamma}$ values rough-ly according to Table 11.10, the

$$C_1 = (v_1 - v_2)^2 s(1 - s)\frac{\delta_1 \delta_2}{\delta}$$

values listed in Table 11.12 are obtained. These C_1 values and the corresponding S_r values amount to about 76, 61, 29 and 10% only, in that order, of the values in Table 11.10. The $C_{1,avg}$ values of Table 11.3 roughly coincide with those of Table 11.10 for as-mined coal (0.24), but give only 22% as much (0.024) for washed clean coal and about 50% (0.12) for waste.

(5A) Let a minus-60 mm coal containing 25% ash have a primary dissemina-tion of waste of size $L = 1$ mm, and let the upper limiting particle sizes of the individual steps in the comminution and reduction of the sample be 20, 5, 1 and 0.15 mm, respectively. What sample weights are to be taken in each step if the deviation may be $r = 5 \cdot 10^{-3}$ in the ultimate sample, implying

$$h = rv = 5 \cdot 10^{-3} \cdot 0.25 = 1.25 \cdot 10^{-3}$$

or, e.g. at $z = 2$, an ash content deviation of $\pm 0.25\%$?

The final sample is obtained after five samplings; let us assume that the variance of the final sample is the sum of the variances of the individual samples. Assuming the error to split about evenly among samplings, the variance of one sampling is

$$h_1^2 = \frac{h^2}{5} = \frac{(1.25 \cdot 10^{-3})^2}{5} = \frac{1.56 \cdot 10^{-6}}{5} = 0.312 \cdot 10^{-6}$$

or

$$r_1^2 = \frac{r^2}{5} = \frac{(5 \cdot 10^{-3})^2}{5} = \frac{25 \cdot 10^{-6}}{5} = 5 \cdot 10^{-6},$$

Table 11.12. Example (4C): Visman's C_1 parameter and the data making it up

	v_1	v_2	δ_1	δ_2	s	v	δ	C_1
a—b—c—d	0.10	0.75	1.45	2.1	0.77	0.25	1.56	0.1525
e—f—g	0.10	0.75	1.45	2.1	0.77	0.25	1.56	0.1525
h—i	0.09	0.29	1.4	1.7	0.95	0.10	1.41	0.0321
j—k—l	0.20	0.80	1.5	2.2	0.05	0.77	2.16	0.0262

giving an admissible deviation of

$$h_1 = 5.62 \cdot 10^{-4}$$

or

$$r_1 = 2.24 \cdot 10^{-3}.$$

The C_1 parameter of the coal sample is

$$C_1 = \frac{v(1-v)\delta}{c} = 0.25 \cdot 0.75 \cdot \frac{1.6}{1.5} = 0.20.$$

Let us put $\varphi = 2.2$; then,

$$x_{avg} = \frac{x_{max}}{\varphi} = \frac{6}{2.2} = 2.73 \text{ cm.}$$

At $z = 1$, the required aggregate sample weight is

$$S = C_1 \frac{x_{avg}^3}{\left(\dfrac{h_1}{z}\right)^2} = 0.2 \frac{2.73^3}{3.12 \cdot 10^{-7}} = 1.3 \cdot 10^7 \text{ g} = 1,300 \text{ kg;}$$

it is 5,200 kg at $z = 2$ or 8,800 kg at $z = 2.6$. If the part-samples are taken from an uninterrupted stream of coal e.g. at five-minute intervals over eight hours, the number of samples is obtained as

$$n = \frac{8 \cdot 60}{5} = 96,$$

and the weight of one part-sample is to be

$$S_L = \frac{1,300}{96} = 13.5 \text{ kg} \qquad \frac{5,200}{96} = 54.1 \text{ kg} \qquad \frac{8,800}{96} = 91.6 \text{ kg}$$

at $z =$ 1   2   2.6.

Reduction ratio per step is

$$R = \frac{60}{20} = 3 \qquad \frac{20}{5} = 4 \qquad \frac{5}{1} = 5 \qquad \frac{1}{0.15} = 6.66.$$

Sample weight decreases as R^3/a. Putting $a = 2$, this implies

$$R^3/a = 13.5 \quad 32.0 \quad 62.5 \quad 148.0,$$

and the number of halvings is furnished by

$$m = \frac{\log (R^3/a)}{\log 2}$$

as

$$3.78 \quad 5.0 \quad 5.96 \quad 7.21,$$

rounding to

$$4 \quad 5 \quad 6 \quad 7$$

whence $R^3/a =$

$$13.8 \quad 31.8 \quad 63.9 \quad 127.7,$$

giving $S'_{20} = S/13.8$, $S'_5 = S'_{20}/31.8$, etc. (cf. Table 11.13).

The approximate formula

$$S'_{min} = c_1 z^2 x'^3_{max}$$

provides, on the insertion of $c_1 = 5.5$ for as-mined coal as given in Table 11.3, and e.g. of $z = 2$, the minimum reduced sample weights S'_{min} given in Table 11.13 for the different maximum particle sizes x_{max} assumed there. The corresponding variances are in the same ratio to the variance

$$h_1^2 = 0.312 \cdot 10^{-6}$$

admissible by hypothesis as the sample weights S' are to the minimum sample weights S'_{min}. In other terms,

$$h'_1 = h_1 \sqrt{\frac{S'}{S'_{min}}} = 5.62 \cdot 10^{-4} \sqrt{\frac{S'}{S'_{min}}}.$$

The last columns of Table 11.13 list the S'/S'_{min} ratios, the h'_1 values corresponding to the sample weights S'_{min} and the ash deviations $\pm h'$ for $z = 1$. (The ash deviation is $\pm 0.0562\%$ if $h_1 = 5.62 \cdot 10^{-4}$.)

(5B) Gy's method — on the assumptions $i = 0.5$, $j = 0.15$, and

$$l = (2.2 - 0.8 \cdot 0.25)\frac{0.75}{0.25} = 6.0$$

furnishes $r_1^2 = 5 \cdot 10^{-6}$ and the $C = ijkl$ and

$$S = Cx^3_{max}\frac{z^2}{r_1^2}$$

values listed in Table 11.14.

Table 11.13. Example (5A): Minimum reduced sample weights furnished by an approximate formula and other parameters

x_{max} cm	R^3/a	S'				S'_{min} (z = 2)	S'/S'_{min}	h'_1 ($\cdot 10^3$)	$\pm$ ash %
		$z = 1$	$z = 2$	$z = 2.6$					
6	—	1,300	5,200	8,800	kg	—	—	—	—
2	13.8	94.2	327	638	kg	176	2.113	0.82	0.082
0.5	31.8	3.0	11.7	20.1	kg	2.75	2.35	0.86	0.086
0.1	63.9	47	183	315	g	22	8.32	1.62	0.162
0.015	127.7	0.37	1.43	2.47	g	0.075	19.06	2.46	0.246

Sampling proper can be performed by hand or — if the material moves in a continuous stream — by means of a mechanical sampling device. Sample quality is most vulnerable to the occasional systematic error. These may be due to the improper performance of sampling procedure or to segregation by s.g. and/or particle size in the stream or in the dump.

Dry dumps are usually sampled by hand. Shovel sampling is the most frequent method if the dump is big enough: the dump is shovelled from one place

Table 11.14. Example (5B): Example (5A) worked by the Gy method

	x mm x/L	k	C	x_{max}^3	S, that is S'		
					$z-1$	$z-2$	$z-2.6$
1	60	0.07	0.031	216	1,350	5,400	9,100 kg
2	20	0.13	0.060	8	95	380	640 kg
3	5	0.30	0.131	0.125	3.45	13.8	23.3 kg
4	1	0.80	0.360	0.001	72	290	486 g
5	0.15	1.00	0.450	$3.38 \cdot 10^{-6}$	0.3	1.2	2.0 g

to another; in the process, every 5th, 10th or 15th shovelful is deposited in the sample container. The sample is reduced after comminution of the greatest lumps by another reshovelling during which, say, every other shovelful is rejected. The procedure is repeated until the desired sample weight is obtained. Smaller sample heaps should be moved with smaller shovels, as far as this is feasible.

In the sampling of smaller heaps of material, the procedure of coning and quartering is often employed. The material is shovelled into a conical heap, with every shovelful poured onto the tip of the cone; the cone is then spread out into a circular cake of uniform height, and quartered by two perpendicular diameters. Two opposite quarters are rejected. The retained mass is similarly treated, possibly after comminution. The method is fraught with a number of systematic errors, some of which may be intentional.

For the manual halving of a small quantity of material, the Jones riffle is recommended. It is made up of an even number of parallel chutes installed side by side, adjacent chutes discharging in opposite directions. If material is fed to the riffle from a scoop or shovel of width equal to its own, then the sample will be exactly halved. Chute width should be greater than the length of the largest lumps in the material to be halved and at least three times the maximum thickness of those.

The basic idea of sampling a stream of dry material or pulp is to make a narrowish trough (a cutter) perpendicularly sweep at regular intervals the stream free-falling in air. The material caught in the cutter is the sample. The cutter is moved manually or mechanically: in the latter case, the sampling interval

719

may be pre-set on a suitable timer. The interval is to be the shorter, the greater the quantitative or qualitative fluctuation of the stream in time. If the cutter revolves or swings to and fro about an axis, its sides should flare out radially from the axis, to ensure proportional sampling from every part of the stream.

11.5. MONITORING AND AUTOMATION

Monitoring is required to verify the successive operations for performance and to adjust them to their respective optima. Monitors establish the through-put rates of solids and pulps and their quality parameters (metal content, ash content, granulometry, etc.) as well as the operating parameters of the machin-ery and equipment (power draft, wear, downtimes, etc.). For general operation control, water, steam, power and reagent meters and/or recorders should be installed.

Feed rate is usually established by means of an automatic weightometer installed into the feed conveyor. Samples to be assayed for feed quality (metal content, ash content, moisture, granulometry, etc.) are usually taken by means of mechanical samplers. The approximate mineralogical composition of fine-grained products is determined in operation by rapid tests such as hand win-nowing, s.g. measurements, separation in heavy liquids and microscopy. More recently, physical assaying methods such as X-ray spectrometry, etc., have been introduced for the purpose.

In a modern beneficiation plant, one will encounter instruments monitoring, recording and regulating the flow of solids, water and pulp, levels in the tanks/bins/hoppers containing those, and many other parameters affecting the technological and economic performance of beneficiation (throughput rates, pulp density, product s.g., grade, moisture, granulometry, reagent dosage, pH, residual ion concentrations, etc.) in addition to automatic balances, weightom-eters and samplers, some or all of which may have their telemeter recorders and/or indicators at the dispatcher console. With the help of these, it is possible to stabilize to a considerable extent the individual cycles (comminution, grind-ing, concentration, filtration, water and waste handling, etc.) as well as the operation of the machinery and equipment performing those cycles and that of the plant at large. This results first and foremost in an improvement of the technological parameters: pay component recovery, pay mineral content in the concentrate and output will increase; specific energy and material consump-tion (of reagents, water, steel, etc. will decrease); downtimes and the necessary manning will be reduced. In the normal run of things, about 40 to 50% of operating costs is spent on materials (reagents, balls and other steel, filter cloth, auxiliary materials, etc.); 15 to 20% is spent on electric power and 6 to 10% on labour. Grinding usually takes about 30% of the total; flotation takes 50 to 55% more often than not.

In the comminution cycle, instruments monitoring ore levels in bins and hoppers, feed rates to or blinding of the comminuting machinery, the state of their bearings (overheating, the temperature of overflowing lubricant), the presence or otherwise of feed on the feeders and conveyors, devices detecting tramp metal and removing it from the feed stream and, more recently, instruments continuously monitoring the granulometry of the comminuted material are encountered. In grinding, the aim of automation is to increase the output of finished-size material of the desired granulometry, in order to optimize the conditions of concentration (flotation). Uniform granulometry (grain size) can be ensured by adjusting ore and water feed rates to feed grade (granulometry, hardness, etc.), whenever the latter changes. To this end, instruments are installed to monitor ore and water feeding, to regulate pulp density at the outflow of the mill and of the classifier or sizer, to regulate reagent dosage into the mill (proportionately to solids throughput or to reagent-ion concentration), to control the lubrication of mill bearings, to verify the feeding of ore to the mill (by monitoring the noise level, the flow rate of material in the recycle stream or output granulometry), to monitor granulometry and pay mineral concentration in the finished-size product, to control the closed grinding cycle and ball-load makeup, to monitor and regulate pulp level and density in the suction sump of the cyclones, etc.

The automation of flotation ensures a better metal recovery from a given grade of concentrate at lower reagent consumptions. The system monitors and regulates feed pulp temperature and density, reagent dosage, the mineral composition of the flotation products (their metal contents), pulp levels in the cells (by means of piezometric, float or electrode transducers which activate e.g. a valve on the discharge pipe), height of froth (e.g. using electrode transducers) and the dosage of the different reagents (xanthate, CN^-, CaO, etc.), e.g. by verifying residual concentrations.

The automation of the dewatering operation monitors overloading in the thickeners, the pulp density of the thickened product, slimes concentration (turbidity) in the overflow, vacuum in the filters, pulp levels in the filter tank and in the surge tank before it, the automatic discharge of filtrate out of the tank containing it, and regulates the blow-through of the filter cloth, cake weight and moisture, etc.

The (residual) concentrations of various reagents may be measured e.g. by polarographic, photometric or colorimetric means. Radioactive isotopes are being encountered in the monitoring and recording of levels in bins, tanks and hoppers and in the rapid determination of ash or moisture content (by the measurement of the reflected or transmitted intensity of beta [electron] or gamma [X-ray] or neutron radiation). Pulp density (and s.g.) can be measured by radioactive means or by balance-type or piezometric s.g. meters. Polarography or X-ray fluorescence spectrometry or atomic-absorption measuring devices and recording and regulating equipment based on them for the continuous qualitative and quantitative monitoring of metal contents in concentrates are also available (e.g. for monitoring 12 different chemical elements in 20 different pulp streams or 7 different elements in 42 different pulp streams, all to within the desired accuracy).

Regulating systems are often controlled in today's modern large-scale beneficiation plants and adjusted to give the technologically or economically optimal performance by hooking them all up to a central digital computer (say, in the real-time on-line mode). At the Kidd Creek plant of Texasgulf Inc., for example, the Pb, Cu, Zn, Fe and Ag contents and pulp density of 15 pulp streams are continuously monitored by X-ray means: optimum reagent dosage is adjusted by a Honeywell 21 or 4K-316 type computer. At the Clarabelle plant of the International Nickel Co., an IBM 1800 type computer regulates the dosage of xanthate, copper sulphate and water glass on the basis of information obtained by monitoring Cu, Ni, Fe, S and Si concentrations in the feed, the concentrates and the tailings. At the Fox Lake plant of Sherritt Gordon, an ARL make on-stream analyser and an X-ray spectrometer (the portable Portaspec type) serve for the automatic regulation of comminution and flotation, etc., etc. According to recent special literature, control computers pay for themselves in a very brief span of time even in flotation plants of very modest output if hooked up to the appropriate automatic monitoring and control equipment to give economically optimum performance.

In the US, the minerals industry has since the mid-1960s been spending 6 to 7% of total investment in plant on regulation and automation, but in some facilities this item atteined as much as 15 to 20%. By 1975, the US average had risen to 15% or so. In the 1960s, automation in the mineral industry of the US brought more cost saving and incremental profits than any other invention or measure (Armstrong and Durfec 1969; Atkinson 1966; Bartelt 1967, 1973; Behrend 1971; Brookes and Whitmore 1966; Cahalan and Wolski 1960; Carr-Brion 1967; Cooper and Vaughn 1973; Dijkstra and Sieswerda 1959; Faulkner 1966; Giessler 1965; Görtz 1968; Hall et al. 1967; Horst 1965; Koryakov-Savoisky 1969; Lewis 1971; Lynch 1971; Manula 1969; Mular 1970; Pataraia and Koch 1968; Rotter 1968; Schäfer 1965; Smallbone and Lathe 1969; Stewart et al. 1970; Thies 1969; Thornton 1971; Vuchot et al. 1964; Wisskirchen 1970; Woodcock 1970).

11.6. LITERATURE ON AUXILIARY OPERATIONS

ARMSTRONG, C. W.—F. L. DURFEC: Role of process control in the design of modern ore beneficiation plants. *Min. Congr. J.* 1969 March 18—21.
ATKINSON, P.: An introduction to the theory of automatic control. *Coal Prep.* 1966, 219—224.

AULIO, O.: Control computers process at Outokumpu. *Canad. Min. J.* June 1973, 44—45. (Cf. also ANONYMUS: Outokumpu Oy installing Courier on stream analyzer in five mills. *World Mining* 1971, May, 30—34.)

BADGER, E. H. H.: The modern theory of coal sampling. *Colliery Engng* 1950, 223—228.

BARBERY, G.: Deviation of a formula to estimate the mass of a sample for size analysis. *Trans. IMM* 1972, C49—C51.

BARTELT, D.: Bisheriger Stand der Automation in der Steinkohlenaufbereitung, Möglichkeiten und Grenzen. *AT* 1967, 21—30.

BARTELT, D.: Prozesssteuerung von Aufbereitungsanlagen. *Glückauf* 1973, 212—219.

BATTAGLIA, A.: Some problems of designing closed washery circuits. *J. of mines, metals and fuels (India)* 1964, 6/2, 97—100.

BATTAGLIA, A.: Some aspects of the closed circuit theory. *Coal Preparation* 1966, 142—147.

BEHREND, G. M.: The evolution of process control in the mining industry. *CIM Bull.* 1971, 42—45.

BINTING, K.-H.: Die Bestimmung der Optimalwerte für die Anzahl und das Gewicht der Einzelproblem bei der Haufwerksprobenahme. *Bergakademie* 1960, 149—157.

BRANSBY, P. L.—P. M. BLAIR-FISH—R. G. JAMES: An investigation of the flow of granular materials. *Powder Tech.* 1973, 197—206.

BROOKES, G. F.—R. L. WHITMORE: An application of the digital computer to coal preparation. *Coal Preparation* 1966, 95—101.

BUSSIAN, G.—R. BOARD: Feeding the feeder — an approach to bin design. *Rock Products* 1975 May, 121—124, 131—132.

CAHALAN, M. J.—R. WOLSKI: Automatic control in mineral processing. *IMPC*, London 1960, 983—997.

CAMPBELL, D. G.—P. D. FARM—C. V. GLADISZ: Grade control using neutron activation analyses at the Sherman mine. *CIM Bull.* 1974 June, 90—96.

CARR-BRION, K. G.: Performance of an on-stream radioisotope X-ray fluorescence analyzer. *Trans. IMM* 1967, C94—C100.

CIBULKA, J.—J. KASPAR—J. MICHAL: Möglichkeiten der automatischen Regelung des Flotationsprozesses nach der Restkonzentration von Flotationsmitteln. *Erzmetall* 1973, 322—326.

COLIJN, H.—P. J. CONNERS: Belt conveyor transfer points. *Trans. AIME* 1972, 204—210.

CONDOLIOS, E.—E. E. CHAPUS: Transporting solid materials in pipe lines. *Chem. Engng* 1963 June, 24, July 8, 22.

COOK, H. L. Jr.: Industrial measurement and control of slurries using radioisotope gauges. *Canad. Min. J.* 1964 Dec., 62—65.

COOPER, H. R.—R. L. VAUGHN: Computer automated X-ray fluorescence assaying. *Trans. AIME* 1969 Sep., (Cf. also: ANONYMUS: Computer applications and process control. *CIM Bull.* 1973 Sep. 61—117.)

DAHLSTROM, C. D.: Cloasing coal preparation plant water circuits with clarifiers, thickeners and continuous vacuum filters. *2nd Symp. Coal Prep.*, Leads 1957, 151—189.

DALE, L. A.—D. A. DAHLSTROM: Design and operation of thickening equipment for closed water circuits in coal preparation plants. *Trans. AIME* 1965, 141—149.

DENBURG, J. F. VAN—W. C. BAUER: Segregation of particles in the storage of materials. *Chem. Engng* 1964, No. 20, 135—140, 142.

DIJKSTRA, H.—B. S. SIESWERDA: Cendrex apparatus for the continuous determination of the ash of coal. *Coll. Engng* 1959, 430—434.

DOEKSEN, G.: Eliminating rat holes in base metal concentrate bins. *CIM Bull.* 1970 1049—1058.

FAULKNER, B. P.: Computer control improves metallurgy at Tennessee Copper's flotation plant. *Min. Engng* 1966 Nov. 53—57.

FOWLER, R. T.—J. R. GLASTONBURY: The flow of granular solids through orifices. *Chem. Eng. Sci.* 1959, 154—160.

FOWLER, H. B.—K. R. KAY—L. KILPINEN: Process instrumentation and control at Frood-Stobie mill. *Canad. Min. J.* 1971 June, 49—56.

GATHEN, R. VON DER: Grenzen der Automatisierung in Förder- und Aufbereitungsanlagen. *Glückauf* 1963, 1458—1464.

GIESSLER, H.: Über die Anwendung digitaler Prozessrechner in der Zementherstellung. *AT* 1965, 527—535.

GÖLL, G.—R. HELFRICHT: Probenahme an körnigen Stoffen. *Baustoffindustrie* 1972, No. 1, 23—28.

GÖRTZ, W.: Einsatz von Röntgenfluoreszenz-Geräten für die automatische Prozesskontrolle. *Erzmetall* 1968, 160—166.

GY, P.: Die Probenahme von Erzen. *Erzmetall* 1955, Beiheft (Glossar), 199—222.

GY, P.: Probenahme fein- und feinstkörniger Erze. *Freib. Fh. A415* 1967, 7—14.

GY, P.: Les différents types d'erreurs rencontrées dans l'échantillonage des minerais en vrac. *9. IMPC*, Praha 1970, 365—371.

GY, P.: Die Probenahme bei stückigen Erzen. *AT* 1972, 687—697.

HALL, D. A. et al.: Automatic measurement of ash and moisture in coal, methods and their application. *Coal Prep.* 1967, 154—159.

HAMPEL, M.: Kontinuierliche Schnellbestimmung des Wassergehaltes von Schüttgütern. *Glückauf* 1973, 524—528.

HANCOCK, R.: The sampling of blended coals. *Colliery Engng* 1950, 268—271, 291.

HELFRICHT, R.: Die Festlegung der Mindestprobemasse mit Hilfe des Probenahmemodells von Gy. *Neue Bergbautechnik* 1971, 858—863.

HILBIG, M.: Probenahme und Probenaufbereitung von fein- und grobkörnigen Gütern. *AT* 1972, 705—712.

HORST, W. E.: On-stream continuous X-ray units are gaining wider acceptance. *E/MJ* 1965 June, 173—175.

HUNTINGTON, F. R.: Sampling systems — a design approach. *Rock Products* 1975 May, 118—120, 130—131.

INGLES, J. C.: Atomic absorption and on-stream analysis. *Canad. Min. J.* 1966, 62—65.

INGLES, J. C. et al.: Panel discussion on instrumental analysis. *Canad. Min. J.* 1968 Jan., 28—35.

JENIKE, A. W.: Entwicklung eines Verfahrens zur Verbesserung des Fliessverhaltens von gebunkerten Schüttgütern. *Bergbauwiss.* 1964, 443—447.

JENIKE, A. W.—J. R. JOHANSON: Review of the principles of flow of bulk solids. *CIM Bull.* 1970, 677—682.

JENIKE, A. W.—J. R. JOHANSON: Fliessgerechte Siloformen für Schüttgüter. *AT* 1971, 309—317.

KELLER, G. E.: Determination of quantities needed in coal sample preparation and analysis. *Trans. AIME* 1965, 218—225.

KENNEDY, G. H.—H. E. CRINER: Application of the cyclone thickeners to preparation plant water circuits. *Min. Engng* 1951, 259—261.

KNESCHKE, G.: Verringerung der Brückenbildung bei gebunkerten feinstkörnigen Schüttgütern. *AT* 1968, 603—608.

KÖHLING, R.: Entwicklungstendenzen bei der Probenahme und Probevorbereitung fester mineralischer Rohstoffe. *AT* 1972, 698—704.

KORYAKOV-SAVOISKY, B. A.: Die Entwicklung von lokalen Systemen der automatischen Steuerung von technologischen Prozessen in den Betrieben des sowjetischen Erzbergbaus. *Bergakademie* 1969, 504—514.

KOTT, A.—F. B. KRAMER: Influence of wall material on bulk solids flow. *Chem. Engng Progr.* 1966 Nov., 73—78.

KRIEGEL, E.—H. BAUER: Gesetzmässigkeiten beim hydraulischen Transport körniger Feststoffe in Rohrleitungen. *Chem. Ing. Tech.* 1965, 264—265.

LEE, C. A.: Hopper design up to date. *Chem. Engng* 1963 Apr., 75—78.

LESKINEN, T. et al.: Performance of on-stream analyzers at Outokumpu concentrators, Finland. *CIM Bull.* 1973 Feb., 37—47.

LEWIS, C. L.: Application of a computer to a flotation process. *CIM Bull.* 1971, 47—50.

LINDKVIST, L.: Froth pumping. *Australian Mining* 1973 Oct., 92—94.

LYNCH, A. J.—G. G. STANLEY: Automatic control in Australian mineral processing plants. *World Mining* 1971 May, 24—29.

MANULA, C. B.: Operations research and computers in the mineral industries. *Min. Engng* 1969 Feb., 69—73.

MIRANI, A.I Verfahren zum Berechnen der wirtschaftlichsten Bunkergrösse im Grubenbetrieb des Steinkohlenbergbaus. *Glückauf-Fh.* 1968, 23—34.

MULAR, A. L.: The future of computers in the mining and metallurgical industries. *CIM Bull.* 1970, 1191—1195.

NICKLIN, D. J.: The air-lift pump. Theory and optimisation. *Trans. ICE* 1963, 29—39.

NOWAK, Z. A.—H. ALESKA: Matematisches Modell eines Wasser- und Schlammkreislaufs. 6. *ICPC*, Paris 1973, 24D.

OSBORNE, B. F.: Continuous in-line sampler for slurry systems developed in Canada. *E/MJ* 1971 Sep., 146.

OSBORNE, B. F.: A complete system for on-stream particle size analysis. *CIM Bull.* 1972 Sep., 97—107.

OSZTER, Z. F.: Improving material flow in plug-flow type fine ore bins — Case studies. *CIM Bull.* 1970, 333—338.

PAAKKINEN, U. et al.: Computer control of Outokumpu Oy concentrators. 10. *IMPC*, London 1973, P. 32.

PATARAIA, D.—P. KOCH: Über die optimale Steuerung von Aufbereitungsvorgängen mit Hilfe eines Prozessrechners, erläutert am Beispiel der Flotation. *Bergakademie* 1968, 418—422.

PAUL, H.: Der Wasserkreislauf mit den Einrichtungen für Klärung und Eindickung. *Der deutsche Steinkohlenbergbau. Bd. 5:* Aufbereitung der Steinkohle. Verlag Glückauf, Essen 1966, 109—277.

PLANK, F. W.: Bunkergestaltung. *Z—K—G* 1974, 271—277.

PRICE, J. D.—W. M. BERTHOLZ: Modernisierung der Schlämmaufbereitung und Wasserklärung in einer Wäsche. 3. *ICPC*, Liège 1958, E-11.

ROBERTS, O. S.: Belt conveyor drive selection. *Trans. AIME/SME* 1972 Sep., 239—249.

ROTTER, R.: Multi-channel X-ray fluorescent analyser for automatic control of elementary composition of beneficiation products. 8. *IMPC*, Leningrad 1968, F5.

SCHÄFER, W.: Aufbereitungs- und Förderanlagen unter der Steuerung von analogen und digitalen Rechenanlagen. *AT* 1965, 522—526.

SCHRANZ, H.—W. BERGHOLZ: Die Ermittlung des Erfolges von Entwässerungseinrichtungen und die rechnerische Erfassung von Wasserkreislaufen. *Bergbauwiss.* 1954, 242—250.

SCHWEDES, J.: Dimensionierung von Bunkern. *AT* 1969, 535—541.

SHAHEEN, E. J.: Rheological study of viscosities and pipeline flow of concentrated slurries. *Powder Tech.* 1972 Oct., 49—56.

SIEMES, W.—W. RAHMEL—E. THRUN: Zur Darstellung der Leistungsaufnahme von Rührern. *Chem. Ing. Tech.* 1957, 791—797.

SMALLBONE, A. H.—R. LATHE: On-stream X-ray analyser and digital computer simplify ore analysis. *Min. Engng* 1969 Aug.

SMIRNOV, S.: Beitrag zur Frage der Rationalisierung von Aufbereitungsanlagen. *AT* 1973, 125—129.

SMITH, R. A.: Experiments on the flow of sand-water slurries in horizontal pipes. *Trans. ICE* 1955, 85—92.

SOMMER, O.: Probenahme, Probemenge, Probeverarbeitung. *Staub* 1955, 644—677.

SOMMER, O.: Beitrag zur Bestimmung der Anzahl von Proben. *Schlägel und Eisen* 1965, 491—493.

STANGE, K.: Genauigkeit der Probenahme bei mischungen körniger Stoffe. *Chem. Ing. Tech.* 1957, 585—592.

STEWART, R. F. et al.: Plant tests for a neutron moisture meter for coal. *Min. Congr. J.* 1970 Nov., 60—66.

STRUBE, H. L.: Conveyors and elevators. *Chem. Engng* 1954, 195—210.

TANILA, J.—U. PAAKKINEN—T. HUHTELIN: Computer control pays off at Finnish copper flotation mill. *E/MJ* 1973 Apr., 112—117.

TARJÁN, G.: A helyes mintavételről. (On correct sampling.) *BKL-Bányászat* 1970, 433—442.

THIES, G.: Beispiele für Regelungen und Prozeßsteuerungen in Aufbereitungsanlagen. *Erzmetall* 1969, 488—492.

THOMPSON, T. L. et al.: Slurry pump — a survey. *CIM Bull.* 1973, 102—108.

THORNTON, N. R.: Process control in the mineral industry. *CIM Bull.* 1971 Sep., 69—71.

TONJES, E.—E. J. WASP: Designing a slurry pipeline. *Rock Prod.* 1970 Feb., 66—67.

TRAWINSKI, H.: Die unvollständige Klärung von Kreislauf-Waschwasser unter Gleichgewichtsbedingungen. *Glückauf* 1961, 991—996.

ULLRICH, H.: Zur Typisierung von Rühreinrichtungen. *AT* 1970, 281—285.

ULLRICH, H.: Probleme beim Rühren zäher Substanzen. *AT* 1971, 699—704.

VANKOVÁ, J.—M. BOLEK: Neue Ergebnisse auf dem Gebiet der mechanischen und automatischen Probenahme von körnigen Haufwerken. *Baustoffind.* A. 1973 May, 18—21.

VANNINEN, P.: Operating experience with on-stream analyzer in five Finnish mills. *World Mining* 1973 March, 56—58. (Cf. also ANONYMUS: Outokumpu Oy installing Courier on-stream analyzer in five mills. *World Mining* 1971 May, 30—34.)

VIERLING, A.: Gestaltung der Förderbandanlagen für den Massenguttransport. *Z-VDI* 1965, 1389—1393, 1446—1450.

VISMAN, J.: *Sampling of coal and washery products.* Fuel Economy Conference, Hague 1947, A2/4.

VUCHOT, L.—B. BAVOUX—J. C. ZEGERS: Some examples of the use of control and regulation in uranium ore dressing and hydrometallurgy. 7. *IMPC*, New York 1964, 493—501.

WALVOORD, O. W.: Chosing ore feeders for beneficiation plants. *Min. Engng* 1955, 131—134.

WEHMEIER, K. H.: Bandförderer in der Aufbereitungstechnik. *AT* 1967, 538—548.

WENZEL, H.: Der Einfluss der Stichprobenahme und Stichprobenumfanges auf die Aussagekraft von Messungen. *VDI-Z* 1966, 1717—1720.

WILLIAMS, J. C.: Design of storage hoppers for bulk solid. *CPE* 1965, 173—179.

WILSON, G.: The design aspects of centrifugal pumps for abrasive slurries. *CIM Bull.* 1973 May, 91—102.

WISSKIRCHEN, T.: Regler und Prozeßsteuergeräte. *Chem. Ing. Tech.* 1970, 1547—1555. (ACHEMA 1970).

WÖHLBIER, H.—W. REINERS: Problems in bunker storage of medium and fine-grained solids. *Chem. Ing. Tech.* 1962, 603—609.

WOODCOCK, J. T.: Is chemical control of flotation pulps possible? *Australian Mining* 1970 Feb., 50—56.

WOODHEAD, R. C.: The capital and operating coast of typical closed water circuits. 5. *ICPC*, Pittsburgh 1966, F3.

SUBJECT INDEX

affinity
—, selective 448
—, specific 150
afterdrying 564, 565, 633
afterpressing of refractory bricks 639
ageing 625, 632, 633
agent
—, dispersing 414
—, flocculating 414
agglomeration 315, 581
aggregate 355
—, fine 436
—, fine-grained 676
—, granular 676
—, monodisperse 476, 479, 480
—, monomineralic 392
—, particulate 487
—, polydisperse 480
— storage capacity 675
Agitair
— cell 286, 293
— machine 282
agitation 299, 437, 455
—, combined pneumatic-mechanical 437
— intensity 300
—, mechanical 315
ahydration 565
— autoclave 565
air 339, 347, 407, 505, 553, 559, 562
—, ambient 545
— bubble 458
—, classifying 606
—, clean 590
—, cold 547
—, compressed 500, 530—533, 619, 692
— —, blast 533
— —, requirement 532
— deflector 597
— flushing 529
— gap 395
—, hot 545, 547
—, humid 547
— isothermal expansion 692
— requirement 75, 532
—, saturated 547
— supply 553
— velocity 572
— viscosity 572
airlift 277, 437, 442, 469, 684, 692
— formula 692

Ajka, Hungary 627
Albert emulsion process 636
albite 123, 395
albumin 322
alcane 160, 194, 444, 445
alcohol 124, 129, 133, 160, 193, 194, 250,
624
—, amyl 177, 178
—, butyl 177
—, ethyl 177
—, fenchyl 178
—, higher 177
— —, aliphatic 529
—, long-chain 128
—, lower 177
—, methyl 177
—, primary 320
—, propyl 177
—, secondary 320
—, standardized synthetic 178
—, terpene 178
aldehydes 177
alkali
— acrylate 542
— cyanide 299, 312, 322
— dichromate 226
— earths 314
— sulphates 251
— sulphides 309, 312
— sulphites 312
— sulphonates 251, 317
alkalinity 114
alkane 447
alkyl
— amine 226
— — salts 169
— carboxylate 187
— compounds 147
— hydrocarbon 624
— hydroxy benzophenonoxime (LIX—
64N) 447
—, long-chain 156
— phosphate 197
— sulphate 157, 166, 169, 179, 182,
183
— sulphonate 182, 316
— triophosphate 458
allotrope 424
alloy 359
alni 359

730

bubbling 248
bucket 488
buffer 115
buffering effect 680
bulk 303, 317
— concentrate 313, 469
— flotation 226, 291
buoyancy 305, 408, 523
buoyant force 245, 303
burden
—, all-sinter 664
—, no-sinter 664
—, sinterless 665
— weight, total 663
burnt fireclay 586

Ca carboxylate 206
CaCl₂ 495, 634
cadmium sulphide 466
cake 479, 498, 518, 520
—, compressible 520
—, deformable 518
—, dewatered 528
—, finished 531
—, inhomogenous 518
— moisture 499
— — content 533
— output 523
— production 522
— resistance 527, 528
— —, specific 520, 535
—, rigid 518
— thickness 525
— volume per revolution (wet) 521
calamine 314
calcite 142, 159, 199, 203, 234, 237, 238, 240, 303, 316, 381, 386, 414, 417, 423
calcium 294
— chloride 12, 322
— feldspar 423
— humate 625, 630, 632—634
— lignosulphate 617
— metahumate 320
— peroxide 233
calgon 414
camphor 178
— oil 178
cancer 618
canvas 277, 530, 531
— filter 531

capacitance 382, 385, 390
— of a sphere 382
capacitor 382, 383
capillary 245, 305, 476, 519, 548, 549, 564, 625
— action 476, 478, 606
— condensation 610
— force 548, 549, 551, 606, 611, 613, 657
— orifice 247, 308
— porosity 625
— pressure 305, 476
— —, differential 482
— radius, equivalent 483
— ring 484
— rise 476, 479—481, 484
— state 606
— suction 478, 609
caprylic acid 317
car
—, mine 420
—, rail 420
carbamate 185
carbon 340, 586
—, activated 535
— dioxide 113, 114, 633
— — gas 632
— disulphide 184
— monoxide 132
— number, effective 147
— tetrachloride 124
carbonate 161, 233, 314, 379, 469
carbonic acid 185
carboxy methyl cellulose 417
carboxyl 441, 458
— acid 160, 161, 188
— methyl cellulose 541
— radical 177
carboxylate 182, 235, 317, 414, 544
carnotite 423
cascade 95, 437
— arrangement 405
— method 276
cascadyne
— launder 103
— sluice 94
cassiterite 109, 223, 375, 395, 403, 423
cathode 407, 472
cation 441
caustic soda 184, 206, 240, 322, 434, 470—472, 624

colloidal
- liogel 625
- particle 506
- phenomeny 187
colophonium 636
colorimetry 309
colour 421
columbita 395, 403
column
-, drying 637
-, fluid-bed 442
combustion
- gas 545, 553, 559, 626, 633, 635, 636, 660
- - drier 555, 631
comminuting
- circuit 295, 690
- machinery 721
comminution 363, 425, 436, 561, 606, 618, 720, 721
- coefficient 497
- equipment 376
-, impact 425
compacted
- sediment 506
- zone 506
compaction 613, 625
- modulus 616
compartmentation 563
complex metal cyanide anions 224
complexon 227
compounds
-, amphoteric 228
-, complex 226, 444
-, heteropolar 119
-, micromolecular 541
-, monocarboxyl 183
compressed air 289, 421
- blast 422
compressibility 625
compression
-, dry 617
-, irreversible 616
- zone 506, 514
computer
-, central digital 722
-, Honeywell 21 722
-, IBM 1800-type 722
-, 4K-316 type 722
concentrate 240, 303, 317, 356, 368, 373,

374, 391, 392, 401, 403, 523, 533, 537
-, chalcopyrite 467
-, first-pass 391
-, heterogeneous 697
-, homogeneous 697
- yield 368
concentrating 690
concentration 148, 424, 507, 510, 720, 721
-, collector 309
-, critical 220, 234, 251, 507
- -, anion 220
- degree 264, 267
-, D. M. 70
- gradient 133, 549
-, graphs of critical 221
- of fine slimes 242
- of solids 259
- organic solvent 445
-, reagent 250, 721
-, threshold 154, 156
concentrator
-, Cannon 96
-, spiral 429
concrete 106, 553
- texture 621, 622
condensate 563
condensation 124, 441, 546, 593
- front 529
- nucleus 548
condenser 382
condition attachment 174, 203
conditioning 275, 302, 312, 315, 318, 394, 587
-, dry 211
- temperature 238
conduction 384, 387
- band 118
conductivity 211, 384, 390, 391, 394, 404, 408, 409
-, electric 407
-, equivalent 158
- into p-type 211
- of minerals 381
-, volume 381, 404
conductor 118, 380, 384, 387, 388, 390, 391, 394, 395, 403, 584
-, fair 389, 395, 401, 405
-, grounded 384, 389
-, ideal 389
-, ion 394

dilution 505, 506, 508, 510, 515
—, average 510, 511
—, conjugate 511
—, critical 514
—, final 509
—, initial 515
— interface 511
—, ultimate 516
dimensionless numbers 245
dimers 147, 227
dimethyl glyoxime 446
diopside 395
dipole 114
— effect 544
— molecules 132
— moment 538, 611
discharge 513, 586
— aperture 677
— density 513
— rate 513
— velocity 513
disengagement 458
disintegrator 598, 602, 618, 619, 637
—, blending 619
—, dynamic 595
disodium phosphate 317
dispatcher console 720
dispersant 244, 623, 625
dispersed phase 623, 625
dispersing agent 414
dispersion 299, 414, 416, 417, 455
— effect 234
—, stable 539
disposal 468
dissaturation 548
dissemination 697, 716
dissociation 441
— constant 216, 239
dissolution 433—435, 460
—, physical 434
disthene (or kyanite) 143
distillation 419
distilling oven 635
dithiocarbamate 165, 315
—, monoalkyl 185
dithiophosphate 165, 186
dithiophosphoric acid 186
—, dicresyl 186
—, esters of 445
dixanthogen 184, 212, 226

D. M.
— concentration 70
— hydrocyclone 70
— separation technology 33
dodecyl
— amine 151—154, 166, 190, 200, 267, 316, 318
— — acetate 168, 200
— — chloride 189
— ammonium acetate 235, 240
— ammonium chloride 160, 169, 193, 195, 200, 242
dolomite 142, 234, 415, 416, 422—424
doming 677
donor 118
doping 118
durain 319, 322, 425
Dorog—Tatabánya region, Hungary 627
Dorr
—, biggest 502
—, single-compartment 500
—, thickener 501, 502
— —, multi-compartment 500, 502
dosage 300
double
— decomposition reaction 434
— film 169
Dowfroth 178, 275
downtime 720
draft 561
drag
— chain 690
— coefficient 574, 577, 580, 598, 603
drainage 488
draining
— tank 487
— tower 487
drag
— belt 25
— coefficient 246, 481
— factor 576
draw
—, gate 63
—, hutch 38, 63
— mechanism 73
drier 555, 629
—, Bütter type 558
—, combined counter- and concurrent 556
—, combustion-gas fan 633

743

drier

electron
 — mobility 380
 — volt 118
electronic conduction 117
electroosmosis 145, 407
electrophoresis 145, 255, 407
electro-precipitation 587
electro-precipitator 560, 581–584, 588, 589
 —, pipe 583
 —, plate-type 583, 587
electrostatic
 — attraction 596
 — forces 148, 384
 — repulsion 268, 416
 — separation performance 384
elevator 25, 485, 488, 684, 688, 690
 —, bucket 690
 — —, continuous 690
 —, centrifugal-discharge 690
 —, waste discharge 488
eluant 442
elution 434
elutriation 399, 400
emission
 —, critical current density of 586
 — intensity 423
empty space 379
emulsifier 314
 —, non-frothing 320
emulsion 244, 308, 309, 315, 320, 455, 457
 —, oil-in-water 244
 —, water-in-oil 244
Emulsol X-1 183
enargite 423, 466
encounter
 — likelihood 252
 — probability 254, 257, 265, 267
energy 688
 — bands 117
 — consumption 296
 — — per unit of cell volume 284
 — cost 419
 — demand 678
 —, Fermi 238
 —, free 125, 172, 256, 594
 — input 296
 —, kinetic 539, 547, 595
 —, least 121
 — — free 170
 —, relative 329

—, specific 720
—, surface 117
—, ultrasonic 539
enstatite 395
enthalpy 146
—, free 147
environmental pollution 467
epidote 318
equilibrium 546, 550
 —, hydrostatic 514
 — isotherm 443
 — of evaporation-condensation 548
 —, once 546
equipment 690
 —, recording 722
 —, regulating 722
erosion 572
error of
 — ash analysis 700
 — chemical analysis 698
 — mean ash content 700
 — sample reduction 698
 — sampling 698
 — segregation 698, 710
erythroamylose 543
ester 177, 529
 —, alkoxy 178
 —, alkyl 178
 —, di of fatty acid 316
 —, mono of fatty acid 316
ethanol 127
ethers 177
ethyl
 — acetate 262
 — alcohol 127
 — ether 181
 — xanthate 167
ethylene
 — bromide 12
 — diamine tetraacetate 227
 — imine 542
 — oxide 542
eucalyptus oil 178
evaporation 124, 133, 262, 460, 545–547,
  562, 612
 — heat 124, 546, 549, 552, 627
 — performance 557
 — — of screen driers 560
 — rate 547, 559, 561, 564
 —, smoulder 635

filtrate
- discharge 522
- output 523
- volume 517, 525

filtration 433, 469, 525, 572, 573, 720
- aid 528
-, coal slurry 535, 536
-, effective time of 526
- equation 516, 519, 525, 526
- -, fundamental 519, 527
- formula, general 526
-, intermittent 526, 527
- needed 528
- of dilute suspension 525
-, optimum duration of 527
- rate 519
- -, constant 525
- time, useful 531
- velocity 494, 517

fire
- hazard 593
- strength 628

first filling-up 458

first-order reaction equation 269

flash
- drying 561
-, pneumatic 560
- treatment, high-temperature 635

Fleissner
- ahydration 564, 633
- method 562, 565

flintstone 425

floatability 113, 117, 159, 176, 200, 208, 226, 300, 327
-, corrected 273
-, measure of 320
-, native 133, 138, 165, 179, 181, 212, 216, 228, 312, 318, 320
- of clean coal 327
- of coal particles 322
-, poor 267
- ratio 273
-, relative 264, 274
-, specific 264, 265, 267, 269, 326

floc 516, 544, 545

flocculant 417, 418, 506, 528, 529, 544, 545, 683
- as thickening accelerator 545
-, organic 540
- -, artificial 540

- overdose 544

flocculate 417

flocculated
- cluster 507
- feed filtration 545
- pulp volume 545
- suspension 506

flocculating 433
- agent 414, 515
- effect 417, 540, 543
- -, specific 542

flocculation 242, 244, 414, 433, 523, 539, 543, 544
-, selective 414, 418

flotation 70, 109, 113, 138, 226, 234, 324, 412, 413, 418, 419, 433, 467, 469, 523, 720, 721
-, agglomerating 244, 314, 414
-, amine 159, 302
-, anionic 242
- apparatus 291
-, bulk 291
-, cationic 242, 315
-, cleaning 289, 296, 297, 313
-, coal 292, 325
- collector 545
- concentrate 556, 559, 681, 711
- depressing agent 419
- differential 238, 291, 312, 313
-, electrostatic 154
- equipment 275
-, film 413
-, froth 413
-, ionic 155
-, industrial 270
- intensity 284
-, laboratory test 289
-, liquid phase in 114
- machine 263, 267, 274, 295
- - airlift-type 276
- middling 291
- of cell 254, 286, 289
- of fine slimes 242
- of non-sulphide minerals 314
- of oxides 226
- of polar non-ores 316
- of soluble salts 203
- operation 300
- performance 168, 202, 234, 255, 289, 302, 314

head
 − −, Plat-0 108
 − −, Wilfley 107
 − sprocket 690
heat
 − consumption 561
 − −, total 565
 − drying 627
 −, radiant 424
 − transfer 563
 − treatment 211, 360, 424, 632, 634
 −, specific 553, 622
 − − of the gas 553
heating 394, 547
hemimicellae 153, 154, 200, 201, 237
hemimorphite 124
henry 339
heptylic acid 170
Hercules CMC 417
heterogeneity factor 697
heteropolar molecules 124
hexadecane 195
hexadecyl
 − ammonium chloride 168
 − sulphate 169
hexagonite 395
hexanethiol 199
Heyl & Patterson 559
Hidas (Hungary) 629, 630, 634
Hock & Jeckel process 635
hodograph 645, 646
Hofmeister's ion sequences 148, 149
hole 211, 381
homogenization 669, 672, 673
hood 572
hockup 289, 300
 −, concurrent 437
 −, countercurrent 437
hopper 308, 373, 675, 690, 691, 720, 721
 − products 391
host rock 435
HS− ion 216, 223, 225, 233
 −, critical concentration of 224
humate 625
Humboldt WEDAG & Ferro-Magnetics Ltd.
 Montreal, Canada 374, 375
humic acid 294, 318, 322, 564, 624, 625,
 631−633
 −, free 630, 634
 − molecular weight 625

humidity 405, 622
 − of ambient air 393, 405
 −, relative 584, 587, 626, 627, 635
humin 318, 322, 564, 633
humoligninic acid 624
hutch 38, 73
 − draw 38, 63
hydration 434
 − heat 204
 −, negative 205
 −, positive 205
hydraulic radius 479, 519, 588, 676, 685
hydrocarbon 128, 133, 413
 −, aliphatic 131
 −, aromatic 624
 −, cyclic 193
 −, halogenated 12
 −, heteropolar 177, 179, 251
 −, non-polar oleaginous 181, 320
 − solvent 315
 −, terpene 178
hydrochloric acid 115, 451, 463, 632, 634,
 635
hydrochlorite 313
hydrocyclone 35, 98, 312, 500, 682
 − as a D. M. separating device 29
 −, D. M. 70, 376
hydrocycloning 318, 324
hydrogen 306
 − cyanide (HCN) 216
 − fluoride 318, 405
 − ion concentration 113, 114
 − ion exponent 114
 − sulphide 113, 216
hydrolysis 115, 179, 414, 439, 441
 −, fluid-bed 463
hydrometallurgical process 468
hydrometallurgy 109, 469, 532
 −, conventional 469
 − − of gold ores 470
hydrophilia 157, 622
hydrophilic nature 593
hydrophobia 113, 157
hydrophobic
 − dust particle 594
 − nature 593
 − particle 523
 − protective coating 632
hydroquinoline 460
hydrostatic equilibrium 514, 692

mechanism
— , interparticle bonding 616
Mechanobr (USSR)
 — cell 288
 — machines 281
medium
 — , fluidizimg 561
 — friction 593
 — gravity 687
 — , heating 559
 — solid 8
melting point 657
meniscus 477, 478, 548, 606, 609, 610
mercaptan 165, 182, 184, 199
mercaptid 184
mercury 113, 419
 — vapour 406
mesomerism 121
metabolism 440
metal 381, 443, 611
 — content 720, 721
 — — in concentrate 722
 — cost 458
 — ion, base 299
 — , native 380
 — output, daily 458
 — oxide 380, 381, 434
 — , polyvalent 544
 — , precious 468
 — price 297
 — product of shipping purity 441
 — recovery 263, 296, 297, 300, 451, 721
 — salt 434
 — sulphide 135, 381
metallic bond 380
metallurgical
 — furnace 542, 587
 — operation 419
metallurgy 439, 468
 — , igneous 469
metathesis 434
methacrylate 418
methacrylic acid 418
methanol 127
method
 — , agitation-froth 276
 — , cascade 276
 — , Coe & Clevenger 508
 — , cyclone (injector) 276
 — , Fleissner 562, 565

 — , pneumatic 276
 — , pressure 276
 — proposed by Gy 697, 714, 718
 — , subaeration (bottom-impeller) 276
 — , vacuum 276
 — , Visman 716
methyl
 — alcohol 127
 — isobutyl carbinol (MIBC) 178, 179, 320, 329
methylated spirit 184
MgCO₃ 615
Miami Copper Co., Arizona, U.S.A. 436, 462
mica 88, 124, 187, 317, 318, 381, 386, 398, 400
micelle 147, 150, 151, 154, 155, 160, 166, 192, 251, 315, 543, 564, 623, 625, 629
 — formation, threshold concentration of 156, 158, 160
 — , lamellar 564
microbubble 277
microcline 395, 414
micromolecular compound 541
microorganism 439
Micum-drum cohesion 657
middling 289, 300, 367, 368, 374, 376, 391, 401, 403, 697, 714
 — , fine-grained 58
migrine 395
milk 250
mill 299, 721
 — , ball 312
 — , fan 636
 — , grinding 299, 312, 561
 — , hammer 619, 636
 — , impact 425
 — , impact-blade fan 561
 — , paper 621
 — , sugar 637, 640, 651
 — , tumbling 419
mimetesite 314
mine 293
 — , Canadian 439
 — , coal 440, 680
 — , ore 440
 — sulphide ore 680
 — water 436, 438
mineral 383
 — , aerophobic 163
 — , alkali earth 183

monohydrate 471
— —, mixed 471
— type 471
monomolecular lining, full 307
monopoles 379
montmorillonite 138, 535
mortar 621, 623
Mörtsell 364, 366
motor spirit 190
MS cell 281
— machines 282
— subaeration cell (Minerals Separation
Ltd.) 280
mud 499
— box 650
— — of alumina refineries 535
—, red 472
mullite 144
multiclone 579—581
muscovite 138, 139
myristic acid 129, 183

n-alcane 195
n-alcohols 127
n-alkyl
— amine 203
— amine chloride 156
— ammonium 195
— radicals 165
— sulphonates 160
n-octyl alcohols 128
NaCl 414, 418, 634
NaCN 216
NaF 414, 418
Na-hexametaphosphate 414
Na humate 634
NaOH 414
Na-pyrophosphate 414
Na_2S 414
$Na_2S \cdot 9H_2O$ 216
Nalco 600 417
naphthalene 620
naphthenic acid 183, 451
naphthoic acid 183
nascent 467
natrolite 472
Nchanga Consolidated, Zambia 462, 468
neutralization 299
neutralizing the activating ions 226
Newton number 283

Ni—Co ore 463
nickel 341, 451
— ore 463
Niederlausitz (GRD) 629, 630, 632
Niro 562
niroing 562
nitrate 203
nitric acid 322, 405, 451, 470
nitrogen 211
nodoid 549
— droplet 549
Nógrád County, Hungary 627
noise level 721
non-conductor 385, 387, 403
nozzle 562
—, rotary 597
number m of halvings 708
number of part-samples 705
—, minimum 705
nutsch 529
—, tiltable 530
nylon 535

oblique leaf springs 108
octyl alcohol 181
oersted (Oe) 338, 339
oil 113, 308, 412, 413, 617, 634, 635
—, aliphatic 620
—, aromatic 620
—, bunker C 620
—, camphor 178
—, fuel 317, 318, 620
—, heavy tar 618
—, lubricating 412
—, non-polar 244, 315, 413
—, pine 178, 312, 318, 320, 405
—, sulphonated castor 183
—, tall 183
—, Turkey-red 183
—, viscin 602
oleaginous liquid 308
oleate 159, 161
—, sodium 316
oleic acid 131, 159, 181, 183, 202, 226, 235,
237, 238, 302, 309, 312, 316, 317
oleophilic surface 179
olivine 124, 395
onium 186
— compound 440
open multipole system 349

operation
—, continuous 104
— — downstream 672
—, steady-state 682
optical space 421
optimum
— duration of filtration 527
— productivity in intermittant filtration 527
ore 721
—, chlorinating 433
—, complex 433
—, leaching 433
—, low-grade r.o.m. 433
—, oxidizing 433
—, reducing 433
— stock 436
—, sulphatizing 433
organic
— acids 124
— carrier 458
— electrolyte 538
— liquids 125
— matter 471
— non-electrolyte 538, 543
— solvent 650
— substance, heteropolar 176
orifice 649
orlon 535
oronite 315
orthoclase 124
orthohydroxy aryl oxime 447
orthosilicates 124
orthotoluidine 185
oscillation 121
osmosis
—, reverse 434
other anions 226
outflow velocity 677
output 36, 491, 492, 639, 642, 649, 664, 665
—, cyclone 38
— of the machine 641
—, specific 69
overdosage 212
overground particle 299
overoxidation 293
overpressure 560
oxalic acid 317
oxidation 434
— under pressure 438

oxide 117, 198
—, activating metallic and non-metallic 234
— coating 611
oxidized lead 184
oxidizer 322
oxidizing 435
— agent 469
oxygen 113, 211, 306
— concentration 309
oxyhydryl 182
ozokerite 636

palmitate 161
palmitic acid 131, 183, 302
paper 636
paraffins 130, 133, 160
— oil 320
paramagnetic 338, 340, 343, 347
— materials 341
— — of high susceptibility 355
parameter
—, average operating 592
—, dimensionless 483
par-interstitial particles 12
particle
—, acicular 400
—, bridged 590
— charge 393
—, colloidal 506
—, conducting 404
— —, poorly 404
—, crystalline 525
—, dendritic 612
—, electric model of the 385
—, electrically neutral 407
—, elongate 388, 390
—, fibrous 612
—, flattish 388, 390
—, hydrophobic 523
—, isometric 519
—, liberated 433
—, maximum limiting feed 400
—, misrouted 391, 392
—, near-cubic 400
—, non-conducting 404
—, non-polar 413
—, polarized 384
— radiation 422
—, rounded 388

power
  — input 315
Power Plate process 467, 468
PPA 541
Praestol 541
precious stone 426
precipitate 457
precipitation 433, 439
  —, chemical 433, 434, 460, 470
precipitator
  — length 587
  —, pipe type 588
  —, plate type 588
pre-concrete 376
pre-drying 620
  — operation 487
preferred orientation 124, 131, 154, 155,
    165, 176, 519
pre-flotation 440
pregs 436, 437
pre-heating 658, 662
pre-pelletizing 658
press 614, 633, 637, 639
  —, air-cured 621
  —, angle-lever 638
  —, Apfelbeck 648
  —, band 649
  —, belt 639
  —, brick 637
  —, briquetting 619
  —, Couffinhal 640, 642
  —, dual-action 638, 639
  —, electric 645
  —, excenter 638, 639
  — —, moving-feeder 639
  —, Exter-type rod 637, 642, 644, 649
  —, extrusion 649
  —, hand 638
  —, hydraulic 638, 649
  — —, stationary-table 639
  —, impact 638
  —, moving-feeder 638
  —, pill 639
  —, piston 637, 638
  —, rapid 642
  —, revolver 642
  —, revolving-table 639, 642
  —, ring 648
  —, roll 647, 648, 651
  —, semy-dry 638

—, spiral 650, 651
—, steam 645
—, Tigler 638
—, Toggle 638
—, twin 648
—, vacuum 651
—, Yeadon 642
—, Zeitz 642
pressing 651
  — time, effective 645
pressure 408, 649
  — acting on the bottom 676
  — acting on the wall 676
  — buildup 645
  — differential 516, 518, 520, 523, 525,
    527, 528
  — —available for filtration 494
  — overcoming the filter resistance 494
  — drop 573, 580, 581, 597
  — gradient 529
  —, partial 545—547
  — — gas 438
  — — of vapour 547
  — — of water vapour 547
  — vessel 433
pre-treatment with suitable reagents 405
prism 652
process
  —, adiabatic 125
  —, direct-reduction 375
  —, isothermal 125
probability 391, 392
probable error 705
product
  —, activity 139
  —, finished-size 721
  — hopper 391
  — s.g. grade 720
  —, solubility 139
  — takeoff 364
  —, thrown 391
profit 298
propylene
  — glycol 178
  — oxide 178
protein 228, 250
proton
  — deficit 114
  — surplus 114
proustite 423

radiation
— , alpha 422
— , beta 422
— , electromagnetic 422
— , gamma 66, 721
— , infra-red 422
— , neutron 721
— , nuclear 66
— , particle 422
— , ultraviolet 422, 438
— , X-ray 422, 721
radical
— , amide 540
— , anionic 544
— , carboxyl 415, 540, 541
— , complex 414
— , polar 611
— sulfonate 414
radii
— , atomic 119
— , ionic 116, 119
radioactive isotope 721
radioactivity
— , induced 422
— , natural 422
radiation
— , gamma 423
— , infra-red 423
— reflected 422
radius
— of action 596
— — , maximum 596
ragging 55, 63
rake 437, 559
— , high-lift 501
Ranchers Bluebird mine of Miami Copper
   Co. 462
rapid determination 721
rapidity 370
rare earth 458, 460
Raschig ring 603
rate of
— adhesion 134
— air feed 254, 283—285, 327
— air flow 303
— air input 307
— circulation 458
— — , aqueous-liquor 458
— — , leach 458
— clarification 507

— critical throughput 245
— diffusion 550
— discharge 502, 511
— — , clear liquor 502
— dissolution 134
— feed 421, 497, 516
— — , solids 503
— gas feed 250
— handling 421
— inflow 286
— passage of the filtrate 524
— reaction 134, 303
— removal 264
— — , water 268
— slurry feed 499
— throughput 264, 328
ratio
— , distribution 443—445 451, 454
— — , equilibrium 445, 446
— , free-settling 71
— , H/D 437
— , hindered-settling 7, 57, 71
— , hutchwork-discharge 68
— of floatability 273
— of mineral concentration 269
— of relative gravities 98
— , phase 448, 450
— , volume 449
ray
— , alfa 211, 422
— , beta 211, 422
— , gamma 211, 422
— , light 211
— , ultraviolet 211
— , visible 211
— , X 211, 422
rayon 535
raw ore 264
reaction
— , complex-forming 434
— , double-decomposition 434
— equation 273
— — , second order 273—275
— , extraction-and-stripping 448
— , extraction-reextraction 448
— , general, equation 272
— mechanism 444
— order 272
— — , first 272, 274
— — , second 272

sample
 − − error 698
 − − operation 699
 −, required aggregate 717
 − taking procedure 693
 −, ultimate 716
 − weight 696, 707
 − − formula 704
 − −, total 705
sampler 720
 −, mechanical 720
sampling 675, 693, 719
 − by a mechanical device 719
 − by hand 719
 − error 698
 −, shovel 719
sand 317, 442, 480, 534
 −, monodisperse 549
 −, placer 685
 −, rubber-lined 692
sandstone 343
sapinol 178
saponine 176, 250
saturated-steam temperature 547
saturation 134, 443, 482, 484, 546
 −, average 482
 − concentration 546
 − degree 555
 −, effective 484
 −, fixed 484
 − maximum 450
 − pressure 305
 −, residual 484
 − −, effective formula of 484
 − temperature 553, 555
sawdust 613
scapolite 395
scavening 300
scheelite 142, 227, 240, 303, 375, 395, 423
schwelen 627
schwelgase 634
scintillation
 − counter 422
 − detector 422
scoop 719
scraper 492, 532, 533, 535, 680
 −, cable 500
screen 429, 476, 490, 561, 699
 −, centrifuge 413, 490, 491
 − cloth 531

−, dewatering 485, 490
 − −, shaking 485, 489
 −, impact 488
 −, shaking 74, 108
 −, stationary 485
 − surface 531
 −, swinging 559
 −, trommel 318
 − − aperture 57, 68
 −, vibrating 413, 488−490, 559
screening 425, 500, 602, 606
 −, wet 420
scrubber 426
 −, concurrent 426
 − cyclone 598
 −, drum 426
 −, static 595, 596
 −, Venturi 598
scrubbing 318
 − efficiency 596
 − tower 587
sea water 460
second law of thermodynamics 125
section
 −, constant-velocity 510
 −, slowing-velocity 510
Sedipur 541
Sedosan 541
seep 435
segregation 523, 672
 − error 698, 710
selectivity 138, 261, 308, 441, 442, 445, 446, 458
 − index (S. I.) 265, 273
 − of flotation 273
selenides 117
selenium 406, 471
self-activation 293
semi-coking 623
semiconductors 117, 118, 211, 380, 381, 394, 610
 −, n-type 118, 238
 −, p-type 118, 238
semi-dry stamping 640
semi-plasticity 651
sendust 359
Separan NP 10 417, 541
separating surface 364
separation 391
 − by shape 429

sulphide
— mineral 198
— — oxidation 440
— ore 289, 293, 299, 463, 466, 658
— — mine 680
— oxidation 300
—, polymetallic complex lead-zinc 312
—, sodium 440
— with oxidized surface 312
—, zinc 226, 314
sulphidization 234, 314
— of carbonates, polyacrilates 234
— of Pb, Cu and Zn oxides 234
sulphidryl 215
sulphite
—, alkali 226
— —, hydro 226
— route 621
sulphonate 179, 182, 183, 204, 318, 529, 544
— soap 318
sulphonation 309
sulphonic acid 441
sulphonium 186, 187, 441, 466
sulphoxy compounds 226
sulphur 133, 324, 386, 439, 463, 467, 469,
    587, 665
— contents 323, 324
— dioxide 226
— gas 635
sulphuric acid 240, 317, 318, 434, 436,
    439, 451, 463, 538, 632, 635, 680
— by-product 468
— leach 470
sulphurous acid 226, 240, 313, 315, 587, 635
sulphydryl (thiol) 182
sump 439, 692, 721
sunlight 438
Superfloc 541
superphosphate 656
surface
— active ions 154
— activity 177
— adsorption density 146
—, aero 320
— area 595
— — diameter 598
— average grain size 532
— charge 136, 147, 148, 240, 384, 538
— conductivity 393
— contamination 405

—, dynamic 255
— energy 117, 163, 419, 593
— —, latent 125
—, hydrophilic 413
—, oleophilic 320
—, oleophilic-aerophilic 413
—, non-polar 132
—, polar 132
— pressure 129
— — equilibrium 131
— — function 129
— sealing 630
—, specific 320, 416, 480
—, static 255
— sulphidization 309, 312, 314
— tension 125, 158, 163, 176, 177, 245,
    246, 249, 250, 262, 283, 304, 305, 372,
    476, 484, 485, 528, 529, 532, 593, 606,
    608, 609
— — equilibrium 128, 255
— — steady-state 128
— treatment 632
— viscosity 250
— water 547
surface-active
— agents 113
— ions 154
surfactant 12, 113, 117, 127, 129, 131, 155,
    176, 255, 307, 458, 485
susceptibility 337, 343, 363, 364, 369
—, dielectric 383
—, low 374
—, magnetic 383
—, specific 341, 343, 348, 353, 355, 358, 368
—, volume 341, 343, 347
— —, of the medium 347
suspension 442, 560
—, aerated 436
—, flocculated 506
—, heterogenous 686, 687
—, homodisperse 13
—, homogenous 686
—, non-flocculated 506
—, quasi-homogeneous 686
— zone 506
swarf 470
Swedish patent 657
swelling
— coal 635
—, phase-1 629, 632

transition
— point 405
— zone 246, 506
transportation 485, 606, 675
—, downward 688
—, horizontal 688
— —, belt speed of 688
—, mechanical 688
—, upward 688
trap door 421
Traube's rule 128
travel time 588
travelling trippe 672, 688
tray 515
— pelletizer 655
—, revolving 660
—, rotary 691
triboelectric charge 211
tributyl phosphate (TBP) 444, 470
trichlorethylene 12
trihydrate 471, 472
trimethyl
— amine ion 204
— ammonium chloride 156
trithiocarbonate 165
trommel 425, 426
Tromp
— curve 38, 56, 70, 103, 597
— percentage 578
— value 578
troughs 105
truck tire 426
trunnion 563
T–T mixture 185
tungstate 161, 187, 434
turbidity 721
turbulence 304, 436, 455, 679
turbulency 573
turmoil 561
turpentine 178, 405

ultimate strength 620
ultraflotation 242
ultrasonic
— dust precipitation 593
— energy 539
ultraviolet light 420
Ultrawet 183
undecyclic acid 238
Union Carbide Bulletin 455

unit resistance 494
uraninite 374
uranium 443—445, 460, 469, 470
— concentrate 470
— extraction 445, 457
— flocculation 542
—, four-valent 469
— leaching 443
— mineral 315, 374
— —, sorting of 422
— ore 434
— —, pyritic 439
— recovery 438, 439
—, secondary 315
—, six-valent 469
urano-hydrate 470
uranothorite 374
uranyl 435
— anion 470
— disulphate 470
— nitrate 444, 470
— trisulphate 470
uric acid 185
Úrkút, Hungary 428
US practice 704, 722
utilization range 492

vacuum 339, 533, 534, 536, 546, 564
— degassing 471
— filter 533, 535
— — throughput 534
—, high 534
—, low 534
— pump, water-jet 529
—, uncompartmented (cell-less) 533
— tube 406
— valve 532, 533
valence band 117, 118
valve 531
—, butterfly 590
—, rotary airlock 561
—, rotating 532, 533
—, vacuum 532, 533
vanadate 161, 187, 315
van der Waal's
— correction 129
— force 138, 156, 244, 249, 255, 610, 611, 613, 616, 623, 625
— —, dipole 611
vanner 105